TEXTILE FIBERS, YARNS, AND FABRICS

A COMPARATIVE SURVEY OF THEIR BEHAVIOR WITH SPECIAL REFERENCE TO WOOL

By

ERNEST R. KASWELL

Associate Director
Fabric Research Laboratories, Inc.
Boston, Massachusetts

BOOK DIVISION

REINHOLD PUBLISHING CORPORATION

330 West Forty-Second Street, New York 36, N.Y.

1953

PRINTED IN THE U.S.A. BY THE MAPLE PRESS COMPANY, YORK, PA.

To

WALTER J. HAMBURGER

FOREWORD

The Wool Bureau is proud to have initiated and sponsored this compilation and interpretation of the scientific literature on the properties of wool. We have lived with wool and its products so long that its many valuable properties have been accepted as a part of our daily lives. Few have questioned just which inherent exclusive properties of wool are responsible for its superior performance under many types of service.

More recently, as new fibers appear on the market and their performance is estimated in advance from laboratory examination of their properties, there has been a growing interest in two types of information. The first is information about the intrinsic properties of the fiber itself, and the second is the way these properties are utilized in providing fabric service.

Research on the properties of wool has been in progress for some thirty-five years and the published results have been widely dispersed through the literature of that period. The average technical man has scant familiarity with many of these sources, and even the specialists are only vaguely familiar with the data available in fields outside of their own particular interests. Therefore, it appeared to us that it would be a public service of considerable importance if we could commission a disinterested group to compile a selection of the available data and to interpret these data in terms of ultimate performance. In order to provide orientation it has also been necessary to present comparative values for other fibers, where they are available. Values for one fiber alone are meaningless unless they are presented with similar values for other fibers to enable us to appreciate the significance of the data presented.

The study has involved a volume of work far beyond our original expectations, even though we were well aware that the very magnitude of the undertaking had discouraged previous efforts in this direction. To make the work as complete as possible, the Fabric Research Laboratories has voluntarily extended its search considerably beyond the limitations of the original agreement. Obviously it is a type of work which is never complete since each day the research laboratories of the world are adding to our knowledge. As experience is gained in the actual performance of each new fiber, our understanding of fiber-fabric relationships will improve. We therefore have encouraged the presentation of the material as it stands today and look forward to an ever-increasing expansion of our knowledge and understanding through the coming years.

F. Eugene Ackerman
President,
The Wool Bureau, Inc.

February 1, 1953

v

PREFACE

In January, 1950, the Wool Bureau, Inc. requested Fabric Research Laboratories, Inc. to survey the literature relative to the properties of the wool fiber, the relationship of these fiber properties to the functional characteristics of wool textiles, and to ascertain wool's relative position in the field of textile fibers. It is frankly admitted that the initial motivation behind this study included a need on the part of those representing the interests of wool in the competitive textile market to have an accurate comprehensive compilation of the comparative properties of all commercial fibers. Only from such a source could spring honest and intelligent promotional campaigns, and a rational imaginative design for necessary wool research.

To survey the literature of wool and the other better known fibers of commerce proved to be a more formidable assignment than was initially recognized, because of the enormous amount of information on all fibers and textile structures reported in the journals. Ideally, the literature survey would be made sweeping and all-inclusive. This defined a demand for completeness which was impossible of attainment, and the writer freely acknowledges the inevitability of many oversights and omissions.

It became necessary very early in the work to define as targets for analysis those inherent fiber properties, and those yarn and fabric structural geometry or "form" effects, which have an influence, solely or in interaction, upon functional properties. It is recognized that the relationships which exist between specific engineering properties and functional requirements are complex. No implication is intended that such relationships are completely and quantitatively known. However, every functional requirement, to a degree, can be broken down into basic chemical, physical, or engineering parameters which are measurable. Employment of such an approach, certainly not new or novel, has permitted some conclusions as to the relative merit of textile fibers and textile structures in specific functional or end-use requirements. However, this difficult goal is by no means wholly achieved in this book.

Preparation of the survey proceeded for almost three years and gradually the accumulated data took on a seemingly useful form—a form that seemed basic enough in outline to lend itself easily to additions and corrections in future revisions, and complete enough for those who have become concerned with the possibilities of applying basic chemical, physical, and engineering concepts to the design of textile products. Hence, the decision was made, and permission was granted by the Wool Bureau, Inc., to publish the survey as a book.

The book is actually an annotated and interpretive bibliography describing and discussing the research results of some 400 investigators. The writer's own comments and interpretations are interspersed among the verbatim quotations of many authors. This technique is employed because it is felt that the authors' original statements state the case more precisely than would be so were the writer to paraphrase such remarks merely in order to eliminate such quotations.

The book is written for the scientifically or technically trained individual who does not have fluent knowledge of the particular field which is being discussed. The chapter on "Dyeing," for example, should be of little interest to the dye-application chemist or the dyer who is acquainted with dyestuff nomenclature, methods of application and resulting properties. Similarly, the chapter on "Microbiology" may appear elementary and unnecessarily long to the biologist. However, the biologist should find the chapter on Dyeing a ready source of fundamental information, and the dyer likewise may find use for the microbiological portion.

Two important definitions must be made at this point since references to them will be made throughout the book. They are the concepts which Hamburger and Schwarz[1] have entitled "Inherent Fiber Property" and "Form Factor or Geometric Effect." The inherent properties of a fiber are those physical and chemical properties which characterize it per se, such as: density, refractive index, tenacity, rupture elongation, elastic modulus, resistance to chemicals. Form factors are those effects resulting from the conversion of the fiber into a textile structure: yarn denier, density, twist, diameter; fabric weight, thickness, thread count, weave. Both inherent and form factors will influence functional properties such as fabric luster, crease retention, abrasion resistance, resilience, and the like.

Thus the book is divided into two sections. Part A discusses the inherent properties, and Part B discusses the geometric factors.

I am grateful to the many authors and publishers who, without exception, have given me permission to quote text and to reproduce tables, figures, and graphs. In each case, acknowledgment has been duly made. It will be noted that all quotations are in a different format so that the reader should have little difficulty in differentiating between the remarks of a quoted author and my own remarks, herein after referred to as "the writer."

In taking the words of other authors and compiling them with my own words into what I hope is a logical and interpretive story, the danger always exists that the context of an author's remarks may be changed. I have been most meticulous in my attempts to preclude such occurrences, and if any changes in context do occur, they are unintentional.

A word of caution concerning the voluminous data listed is probably in order. I have attempted to give, where possible, the most authentic and reliable values available. Of course no guarantee can be made as to their validity.

Synthetic fiber properties are ever changing—sometimes without formal announcement by the manufacturer. One should keep in mind, therefore, that as progress in synthetic fiber manufacture is made, some or much of the data included here may be obsolete.

In spite of the lengthy time spent in preparing this book, a number of subjects are freely acknowledged to be either omitted or abridged. It will be recognized that a physical and engineering approach predominates; the chemistry of the fibers is outside the scope of the book, and has been deliberately omitted from consideration, except as noted in the text. Time did not permit thorough preparation of sections on static electricity, pilling, and wicking—subjects which are assuming greater significance with synthetic fiber development. Also, neither fiber crimp, tear resistance nor the entire field of fiber blending is discussed. It was hoped that a report on blending, presently being intensively studied at the Fabric Research Laboratories, Inc., would be available for inclusion. Unfortunately, this was not the case, and a review of this significant area of textile research must await a future revision.

Because this book inherently is an annotated bibliography, it is presumed that revisions will be necessary from time to time in order that it be kept up-to-date and thus maintain its usefulness as a reference book. Recognizing the problem of keeping pace with the voluminous publication of textile science literature, I hope ultimately to have the opportunity of preparing sections on the above-mentioned omissions, and to catalog additional information as it becomes available.

ERNEST R. KASWELL

BOSTON, MASS.
January 19, 1953

ACKNOWLEDGMENTS

It will be apparent from the nature of this book, that the cooperation of a large number of persons, companies, and organizations was required, in its preparation. The writer acknowledges their contributions with sincere appreciation, and extends his thanks to:

Mr. F. Eugene Ackerman, Mr. Giles E. Hopkins, and The Wool Bureau, Inc., sponsors of the survey out of which this book has grown.

To Dr. Leta H. Webber, who wrote Sections 29 and 30 of Chapter 8 on the microbiological properties of fibers.

To the more than one hundred authors whose works have been quoted verbatim. Without exception they extended their permission to publish. Among these were the following who wrote personal messages giving added information and interpretations:

Dr. Peter Alexander, Mr. Richard Armour, Miss Ruth R. Bien, Dr. Stanley Backer, Mr. George S. Buck, Jr., Dr. Percival W. Carlene, Dr. Arnold B. D. Cassie, Dr. Donald Finlayson, Dr. L. P. Herrington, Dr. Marianne Karrholm, Dr. D. J. Lehmicke, Dr. M. C. Marsh, Mr. Reginald Meredith, Dr. John M. Preston, Dr. W. Howard Rees, Mr. George H. Slowinske, Dr. John B. Speakman, Mr. Charles Stock, Dr. C. M. van Wyk, Dr. Charles S. Whewell, and Mr. J. Guilfoyle Williams.

To persons, organizations and companies who submitted factual data on fiber, yarn, and fabric properties:

Mr. Clare W. Bendigo, Mr. George Hotte, Dr. Linton G. Ray, Jr., Dr. E. W. Rugely, Mr. Edmund A. Leonard, Mr. Claude S. Clutz, Mr. Werner von Bergen, Mr. B. S. Sprague, Dr. George Susich.

American Cyanamid Company, Carbide and Carbon Chemicals Corp., Celanese Corporation of America, E. I. du Pont de Nemours & Co., Inc., Forstmann Woolen Company, Imperial Chemical Industries, Ltd., Sears Roebuck and Co., Alexander Smith Carpet Company, Virginia-Carolina Chemical Company, and Philadelphia Quartermaster Depot.

To those persons, proficient in various phases of textile sciences, who critically reviewed portions of the text:

Dr. Stanley Backer, Mr. Ladislav Boor, Dr. Alfred C. Goodings, Mr. Giles Hopkins, Dr. F. G. Lennox, Dr. Milton M. Platt, Mr. Hyman P. Selya, Mr. Henry G. Simonds, Dr. Ralph G. H. Siu, Dr. George Susich, Dr. J. R. H. Van Nouhuys, Dr. Simon Williams, Dr. Harold Webber.

To publishers who extended permission to publish copyrighted material:

American Dyestuff Reporter, Journal of The Society of Dyers and

Colourists, Journal of the Textile Institute, Modern Plastics Encyclopedia, Textile Research Journal, Textile World.   Bailliere, Tyndall & Cox, Ltd., Emmott & Co., Ltd., The MacMillan Company, McGraw-Hill Book Company, Inc., Reinhold Publishing Company, W. B. Saunders Company, The Textile Institute, D. Van Nostrand Company, Inc., John Wiley and Sons, Inc.

To Mr. Julian Jacobs, Editor of the Textile Research Journal, for supplying "cuts" of many graphs which originally were printed in the Textile Research Journal.   To Miss Beulah Adkins of The Wool Bureau, who checked much of the copy in the original Wool Bureau report.   To Mr. Gesmer Hawley and Miss Alberta W. Gordon of the Reinhold Publishing Company for their efforts in converting the manuscript into a book.

To the following members of the staff of Fabric Research Laboratories, Inc.:

Mr. Horace N. Lee who did much of the original abstracting of the literature.

Miss Jeannette Rea who assisted in the writing of several chapters.

Mr. Myron J. Coplan, Mr. Chauncey C. Chu, Mr. Henry M. Morgan, Dr. Milton M. Platt, Dr. Walter J. Hamburger, Dr. Simon Williams for their continued contributions in the form of suggestions and discussion of many topics.

Mrs. Celia B. Conrad, Mr. Joseph Curran, Mr. Robert Evans for the preparation of figures and graphs.

Miss Nancy Blanchard, Miss Joan Chatterton, Miss Marie Daley, Mrs. Ilse Entenmann, Miss Marijane Hamilton, Mrs. Alfred N. Hamilton, and Miss Barbara Shwartz for their painstaking care in typing and proofreading the manuscript.

Mrs. Ilse Entenmann, Mr. Robert Evans, and Mr. Eric Singer for their assistance in preparing the index.

The writer expresses a special word of thanks to Mr. F. Eugene Ackerman who envisaged the need and first proposed this survey.   He had the enduring patience to put up with continued extensions of time necessary to complete a task which originally was designed to be a six-months' survey, but which ultimately developed into a three-year program.

Finally, a special word of love and acknowledgment is given to my wife for her help in proofreading, and for her forebearance and encouragement while this book was in preparation.

ERNEST R. KASWELL

BOSTON, MASS.
January 19, 1953

CONTENTS

Part A—The Inherent Properties of Textile Fibers

xiii

Part B—The Properties of Textile Structures which are Dependent Upon Fabric Geometry as Well as Upon Inherent Fiber Characteristics

PART A

THE INHERENT PROPERTIES OF TEXTILE FIBERS

Chapter 1

THE TENSILE PROPERTIES OF FIBERS

(1) Trade and Commercial Names of Fibers

Throughout this book we shall be discussing the various fibers, and shall be quoting from various authors, many of whom use trade names of fibers. At the outset it is deemed advisable to list these trade names, their chemical type, and the manufacturer's name. With respect to nomenclature, conforming to current practice, the term *rayon* connotes viscose rayon only. Cuprammonium rayon will be so designated. Cellulose acetate will be called "acetate"—no longer "acetate rayon." Nylon is a generic name, and unless otherwise specified the type 66 (polyhexamethylene adipamide) is meant. In using the term "Vinyon" the type will be designated wherever possible. Contrary to Loasby's classification in Table 1[2] the word "Terylene" is not used generically, but specifies Imperial Chemical Industries' polyethylene glycol tereph-thalate fiber. Fiber V, or "Amilar," ultimately called "Dacron," refers specifically to the duPont terephthalate fiber. Similarly "Orlon" is not a generic classification but refers specifically to the duPont acryloni-trile fiber. "Acrilan" is specifically Chemstrand's acrylonitrile fiber.

TABLE 1. TRADE NAMES, CHEMICAL TYPE, AND MANUFACTURERS OF SYNTHETIC
FIBERS
Part I
(From Loasby[2] "The Development of The Synthetic Fibers")

Fiber	Chemical Type	Manufacturer
nylon		
nylon	(polyhexamethylene adipamide)	duPont
		Canadian Industries, Ltd.
		Ducilo, Argentine
		British Nylon Spinners, Ltd.
		Imperial Chemical Industries, Ltd.
		Societe Rhodiaceta, France
		Del Toce, Italy
		La Viscose Suisse, Switzerland
nylon 66	(polyhexamethylene adipamide)	duPont
Perlon T	(polyhexamethylene adipamide)	I. G. Farben
Amilan		Toyo Rayon Co., Japan

3

TABLE 1.   TRADE NAMES, CHEMICAL TYPE, AND MANUFACTURERS OF SYNTHETIC
FIBERS—(*Continued*)

Fiber	Chemical Type	Manufacturer
nylon type 6	(66/610/6 interpolymer)	duPont
nylon type 8	(methoxy methylated 66)	duPont
Perlon		
Bayer-Perlon		Farben Fabriken Bayer
Bobina-Perlon		Kunstseide Fabrik Bobingen
Dorlon		Farbenfabrik Bayer Leverkusen
Enkalon		Algemeene Kunstzijde Unie, Arnhem
Perluran		I. G. Farben
Grilon		Fibron S.A. Switzerland
Kapron		Klin, Russia
Mirlon		Plabag A.G. Romanshorn, Switzerland
Nefa Perlon		Vereinigte Glanstoff Fabriken, Wuppertal, Elberfeld
Perlon L	(caprolactam)	Vereinigte Glanstoff Fabriken, Wuppertal, Elberfeld
Phrilon		Phrix A.G., Neumunster, Schleswig Holstein
Silon		Batizovec-Pobrad, Czechoslovakia
Steelon		Hirschberg, Poland
Rhodia-Perlon		Deutsche Rhodiaceta A.G.
polyamide with 11 carbon atoms		
Rilsan		Organico S.A. Paris
Polymer R		Rehoboth Research Laboratories, Israel
polyurethanes		
Perlon U		Farbenfabrik Bayer
Fiber 32		U.S. Celanese Corporation
"Vinyons"		
"Vinyon"	(vinyl-chloride/vinyl-acetate)	American Viscose Corporation
"Vinyon E"	(elastic Vinyon)	American Viscose Corporation
"Vinyon HH"	(85% vinyl-chloride/15% vinyl-acetate)	American Viscose Corporation
"Vinyon" HST	(high stretched "Vinyon" yarn)	American Viscose Corporation
"Vinyon" N	(60% vinyl-chloride/40% acrylonitrile)	Carbide & Carbon Chem. Corp.
"Vinyon" ST	(medium stretched "Vinyon")	American Viscose Corporation
"Vinyon" VST	(unstretched "Vinyon")	American Viscose Corporation
"Vinyon" NEXX		Carbide & Carbon Chem. Corp.
"Vinyon" NEZZ		Carbide & Carbon Chem. Corp.
"Vinyon" NEHT		Carbide & Carbon Chem. Corp.
"Vinyon" NOZZ		Carbide & Carbon Chem. Corp.
"Vinyon" NOHU		Carbide & Carbon Chem. Corp.

TABLE 1. TRADE NAMES, CHEMICAL TYPE, AND MANUFACTURERS OF SYNTHETIC FIBERS—(*Continued*)

Fiber	Chemical Type	Manufacturer
"Vinyon" NORU		Carbide & Carbon Chem. Corp.
"Vinyon" NORT		Carbide & Carbon Chem. Corp.
"Dynel"	(vinyl-chloride/acrylonitrile)	Carbide & Carbon Chem. Corp.
vinylidene chloride		
"Lumite"	(vinylidene chloride)	Chicopee Mfg. Corporation
"Permalon"	(vinylidene chloride)	Pierce Plastics Inc.
saran	(vinylidene chloride/vinyl-chloride)	Dow Chemical Company
"Velon"	(vinylidene chloride)	Firestone Plastics Corp.
polyvinyl chloride		
Fibravyl		Societe Rhovyl, France
Isovyl		Societe Rhovyl, France
Pe-Ce		Badische Anilin und Soda Fabrik
Rhovyl		Societe Rhovyl, France
Thermovyl		Societe Rhovyl, France
P.C.U.		I. G. Farben
regenerated proteins		
"Aralac" (lactic casein)		National Dairy Products Corp.
"Ardil" (peanut protein)		Imperial Chemical Industries
Lanital		Snia Viscosa, Milan
Silkoon (soybean protein)		Japan
Soybean (soybean protein)		Drackett Corporation, U.S.A.
Vandura		
"Vicara" (zein ex maize)		Virginia Carolina Products Co.
Casolana		
Fibrolane		Courtaulds
Caslen (lactic casein)		U.S.A.
Lactofil (lactic casein)		Holland
Cargan (lactic casein)		Belgium
Tiolan (lactic casein)		Germany
"Sarelon" (peanut protein)		U.S.A.
"Terylene"		
Fibre V	(polyethylene glycol terephthalate)	duPont
"Dacron"	(terephthalate)	duPont
"Amilar"	(terephthalate)	duPont
"Terylene"	(terephthalate)	Imperial Chemical Industries
glass		
"Fiberglas"		Owens-Corning Fiberglas Corp.
"Orlon"		
A3		duPont
"Acrilan"	(acrylonitrile)	Chemstrand, U.S.A.
Fiber A	(acrylonitrile)	duPont
"Orlon"	(acrylonitrile)	duPont
"Orlon E"		duPont
polyvinyl alcohol		
Kanebiyan		Kanegafuchi Spinning Co., Japan
Kanebin (probably P.V.A.)		Kanegafuchi Spinning Co., Japan

TABLE 1.   TRADE NAMES, CHEMICAL TYPE, AND MANUFACTURERS OF SYNTHETIC
FIBERS—(*Continued*)

Fiber	Chemical Type	Manufacturer
Vinylon		Japanese Synthetic Textiles Association
polyethylene		
polyethylene		American Viscose Corp.
polystyrene		
"Polyfiber"		Dow Chemical Company
"Algil"		Polymers Incorporated

Part II
(From Sherman and Sherman[5] "The New Fibers")

"Acele"	cellulose acetate yarn and staple	duPont
"Avisco"	high strength viscose rayon staple	American Viscose Corp.
"Bemberg"	cuprammonium rayon	American Bemberg Corp.
"Briglo"	bright viscose rayon	American Enka Corporation
Celafibre	acetate staple	British Celanese Ltd.
"Celafil"	acetate worsted-like yarn	Celanese Corporation
"Celanese"	cellulose acetate yarn	Celanese Corporation
"Cordura"	high tenacity viscose tire yarn	duPont
"Fibro"	viscose staple	American Viscose Corp.
"Fortisan"	saponified cellulose acetate	Celanese Corporation
"High-Narco"	medium high tenacity viscose	North American Rayon
"Narco"	regular tenacity viscose	North American Rayon
"Seraceta"	acetate yarn and staple	American Viscose Corp.
"Spun-Lo"	viscose rayon yarn and circular knitted fabrics	Industrial Rayon Corp.
"Teca"	crimped acetate staple	Tennessee Eastman Corp.
"Tenasco"	high tenacity viscose rayon	

Note: This is an abridged list; for the complete table see Sherman and Sherman[5] "The New Fibers," p. 347.

Part III
(From Miscellaneous Sources)

"Rayolanda"	basified viscose	
"X-51"[413]	copolymer composed principally of acrylonitrile	American Cyanamid Co.

(2) Tensile Strength

One hesitates to start a catalog of fiber information with the topic of tensile strength or tenacity for fear that more importance will be attached to this parameter than it deserves. Strength undoubtedly is an overworked criterion. For purposes of quality control, that is, as a yardstick for the confirmation of specified standards, it is a useful measure. For specific requirements it may properly be employed. But the prevailing custom of employing it as a general measure of value is not valid. Because a textile is strong does not mean that it is good; because it is weak does not mean that it is bad. Tenacity should be considered as only one of a number of properties to be included in the evaluation of fiber, yarn, or fabric.

Several editors have compiled lists of the tensile properties of fibers; they are listed below.

TABLE 2. TENSILE STRENGTH OF TEXTILE FIBERS
(From Sherman and Sherman[5] "The New Fibers")

Fibers	Tenacity (g/den.) Dry (g/den.)	Wet (% of dry)	Strength (lbs/inch²) Dry (× 1000)
acetate rayon, regular	1.3–1.7	60–70	22–29
casein	0.6–0.8	40–50	10–13
cotton, American Egyptian	4.2–5.5	110–130	59–124
cotton, American Upland	3.0–4.9	110–130	59–124
cotton, Sea Island	4.4–6.3	110–130	59–124
cuprammonium rayon	1.7–2.3	55	33–45
glass	6.5–	92	213
nylon, high tenacity	6.0–8.0	84–90	117
nylon, regular	4.5–5.7	84–90	65–117
peanut protein ("Ardil")			14
ramie	6.7	130–160	130
saponified acetate ("Fortisan")	5.0–7.0	86	96–135
saran	1.1–1.7	100	
silk, degummed	2.8–5.0	75–90	45–80
soybean protein	0.6–0.7	35–50	10–12
vinylidene chloride	1.8–2.5	100	40–55
vinyl resin, "Vinyon," high tenacity	3.5–4.0	100	35–69
vinyl resin, "Vinyon," regular	2.0–2.8	100	35–69
"Vinyon" E	0.2		
viscose rayon, high tenacity	3.4–4.6	61–65	35–90
viscose rayon, medium tenacity	2.5–2.9	62	35–90
viscose rayon, regular	1.8–2.4	45–55	35–90
wool	1.2–1.7	80–90	20–29

Note: It is presumed that "dry" indicates equilibrium at standard conditions of 65 per cent relative humidity and 70°F.

Newell[3] has tabulated a host of data on fiber properties, and includes the following for tensile strength:

TABLE 3. DRY AND WET TENACITIES OF TEXTILE FIBERS
(From Newell[3] "Synthetic Fiber Table")

	Tenacity (g/den.) Dry	Wet
acetate	1.3–1.5	0.8–1.2
"Acrilan" (acrylonitrile, staple)	3.0	3.0
"Azlon" (corn protein)	1.1–1.2	0.5
cotton (American Upland)	3.0–4.9	3.3–6.4
cuprammonium rayon	1.7–2.3	0.95–1.25
"Dacron" (polyester)	4.0–5.0	4.0–5.0
"Dynel" (vinyl chloride, acrylonitrile, staple)	3.0	3.0
"Fortisan" (saponified acetate)	7.0	6.0
glass	6.3–6.9	5.4–5.8
nylon		
regular tenacity	4.7–5.6	4.2–5.0
high tenacity	6.4–7.5	5.7–6.6

TABLE 3. DRY AND WET TENACITIES OF TEXTILE FIBERS.—*(Continued)*

	Tenacity (g/den.)	
	Dry	Wet
"Orlon" (acrylonitrile, continuous filament)	4.4–5.2	3.8–4.8
polyethylene	1.0–2.5	1.0–2.5
saran (vinylidene chloride)	1.4–2.3	1.4–2.3
"Vinyon" N (vinyl chloride-acrylonitrile)	2.8–3.5	2.8–3.5
viscose rayon		
high tenacity	3.0–4.6	1.9–3.0
medium tenacity	2.4–3.0	1.2–1.7
regular tenacity	1.5–2.4	0.7–1.2
wool	1.0–1.7	0.8–1.6

An outstanding compilation of textile fiber properties which has surely become a classical work is H. DeWitt Smith's paper on "Textile Fibers: An Engineering Approach to Their Properties and Utilization."[13]

TABLE 4. TENACITIES OF TEXTILE FIBERS
(From Smith[13] "Textile Fibers")

	Tenacity (g/gx)	Tensile Stress (psi × 10³)
abaca (manila "hemp")	4.6	
acetate	1.2–1.5	22–28
acetate (high impact)	1.3	
casein	0.7	
cotton	2.0–5.0	44–109
cuprammonium R.T.	1.9	
flax	2.4–7.0	50–150
glass	6–30	217–1,100
hemp	5.3–6.2	112–132
jute	2.7–5.3	57–112
nylon (regular)	4.5	
nylon (strong)	4.0–6.3	55–102
ramie	5.0	
saponified acetate	4.5–6.3	97–136
silk (boiled off)	2.2–4.6	42–88
silk (Tussah)	3.8	
sisal	3.7	
steel (structural)	0.4–1.1	50–125
vinyl	1.8–3.6	35–69
vinyl-l	2.0	
vinylidine	3.6–5.4	88–132
"Vinyon" E	0.15	
viscose	1.8–4.5	39–97
viscose-G	4.5	
viscose HT	3.0	
viscose MT	2.4	
wool	1.1–1.5	21–28

Note: If 9,000 meters of yarn weighs 1 gram, it is a 1-denier yarn. If 10,000 meters of yarn weighs 1 gram, it is a 1-grex yarn. To convert g/gx to g/den. multiply by 1.11.

TABLE 5. TENSILE PROPERTIES OF FILAMENTS AND YARNS
(From Susich and Backer[233] "Tensile Recovery Behavior of Textile Fibers")

Sample No.	Material	Characteristic and Designation	Actual Fineness (gx)	Breaking Tenacity (g/gx) Dry	Wet	Source*	Remarks†
1	"Fiberglas" ECD	multifilament 900-1/2	114	5.81		1	
2	cotton	staple yarn 50/1	118	1.56	1.94	2	1
3	"Ethocel"	multifilament 500/100/0	642	0.66	0.43	3	2
4	high ten. "Fortisan"	multifilament 90/120/3	100	6.68	5.28	4	
5	cotton	staple yarn 12/1	585	1.37	1.58		3
6	saran	monofilament 5 mils diam.	209	2.32		5	4
7	regular viscose	multifilament 100/40	111	1.89	0.80	6	
8	saran	multifilament 200/12/5z	222	1.91	1.86	5	4
9	"Vinyon" NOZZ	multifilament 80/40/5z	89	3.60		7	5, 6
10	high ten. viscose	multifilament 100/40	111	2.51		6	
11	viscose	staple yarn 20/1	296	1.61			7
12	"Orlon" acrylic fiber	multifilament 100/40/z	111	4.19	4.11	8	2, 8
13	Fiber V	multifilament 100/40	111	5.17	5.21	8	2, 9
14	silk	multifilament 100/132	117	4.39	3.21	9	
15	"Vinyon" CF-HST	multifilament 80/108/3.5	89	2.90		6	10
16	acetate	multifilament 100/40/2.5	111	1.23	0.66	8	
17	acetate	staple yarn 20/1	296	0.85			11
18	nylon, type 300	multifilament 100/40/2.5s	111	5.52	4.42	8	
19	"Vinyon" N	staple yarn 20/1	296	1.14			5, 12
20	"Vinyon" NORU	multifilament 100/60	111	2.85	2.79	7	5, 13
21	wool	worsted staple yarn 28.4/1	314	0.81	0.48	10	14
22	casein, raw	multifilament 300/40	333	0.91	0.28	11	2
23	casein, stabilized	multifilament 300/40	333	0.83		11	2, 15
24	polyethylene, type B	monofilament 12 mils diam.	684	1.17		6	2, 16
25	polyethylene, type A	monofilament 12 mils diam.	684	1.08		6	2, 17

*Source 1. Owens-Corning Fiberglas Corp., Toledo, Ohio
2. Standard Coosa-Thatcher Co., Chattanooga, Tenn.
3. The Dow Chemical Co., Midland, Mich.
4. Celanese Corp. of America, New York, N.Y.
5. The Saran Yarns Co., Odenton, Md.
6. American Viscose Corp., Marcus Hook, Pa.
7. Carbide & Carbon Chemicals Corp., S. Charleston, W.Va.
8. E. I. duPont de Nemours & Co., Inc., Wilmington, Del.
9. Belding Heminway Co., Inc., New York, N.Y.
10. Forstmann Woolen Co., Passaic, N.J.
11. Eastern Regional Research Laboratory, Philadelphia, Pa.

† Remarks 1. Staple: 1⅛ in. (2.86 cm), 22.7 t.p.i. (8.9 t.p.cm)
2. Experimental sample
3. Staple: 1¹⁄₁₆ in. (2.72 cm), 11.6 t.p.i. (4.6 t.p.cm)
4. Polyvinylidene chloride
5. Copolymer of vinyl chloride and acrylonitrile (40%)
6. Oriented stretched 1300%
7. Staple: 2 in. (5.08 cm), 3.3 gx
8. Polyacrylonitrile
9. Polyethylene glycol terephthalate
10. Copolymer of vinyl chloride and vinyl acetate (10%)
11. Staple: 1½ in. (3.81 cm) 3.3 gx
12. Staple: 1½ in. (3.81 cm), 3.5 gx
13. Oriented stretched 1300%, reacted without tension 135°C
14. Staple: 2.9 in. (7.37 cm), U.S. 64's, 4.2 t.p.i. (1.7 t.p.cm)
15. Formaldehyde-treated
16. Cold-drawn not relaxed—highly oriented
17. Cold-drawn and relaxed—medium oriented

Susich and Backer[233] report in Table 5 data resulting from their own research—not a compilation from various sources.

Table 6 is a miscellaneous list of tenacities obtained from various sources.

TABLE 6. MISCELLANEOUS LIST OF FIBER TENACITIES

	Tenacity (g.p.d.)		Strength (psi $\times 10^3$)	
	Dry	Wet	Dry	Wet
"Dacron"[414] (type 5400)	3.0–3.9			
"Dacron"[414] (type 5600)	4.4–5.0			
"Dynel"[415] (3 denier staple)	3.0–3.5			
"Fortisan"[421]	6.0			
henequen[416]	3.0–3.5	2.5–3.0		
manila abaca[416]	6.0–7.5	6.0–8.5		
nylon[414] (staple)	3.8–4.5			
"Orlon"[412]	4.7–5.2	4.6–5.0	71–79	69–75
"Orlon"[414] (type 41)	2.0–2.5			
"Orlon"[414] (type 81)	4.7–5.2			
sansevieria[416]	4.0–5.0	4.0–5.0		
sisal[416]	4.0–5.0	4.0–4.6		
steel[6]			50–150	
"Vicara"[420]	1.1–1.2		17.6–19.2	
"X-51"[413] (continuous filament)*	3.4–3.9	2.9–3.6		
"X-51"[413] (staple)*	2.0–3.0			

* Tested at 73°F and 50% R.H.; Instron Tester, elongation rate 100% per minute.

In the above tables, strengths are compared on a basis of tenacity (strength per unit weight) and tensile strength (strength per unit cross sectional area). Sherman and Sherman[5] show the relationship between the two to be:

Tensile strength (psi) = tenacity (g.p.d.) $\times$ 12,800 $\times$ specific gravity

Specific gravity values are given in Table 7.

Sherman and Sherman[5] state:

> "On the basis of tenacity, the strongest fibers are nylon, saponified acetate, ramie, and glass. It is noteworthy that the two fibers at the top of the list are manufactured rather than natural. Wool is far down on the list for tenacity, but has many other desirable properties which account for its widespread use."

Manila abaca, improperly called "manila hemp" should be added to the four mentioned above. It is of course an extremely useful fiber employed for cordage purposes.

It becomes obvious that the attributes of wool do not lie in that area where high strength alone is the governing criterion. There have been superficial statements made to the effect that the wool fiber is as strong as steel. On a psi basis, wool is only one-fourth to one-fifth as strong as steel. On a denier basis, because of the high specific gravity of steel, its tenacity becomes 1.00 to 1.5 g.p.d. (based on a strength of steel of from 100,000 to 150,000 psi) so that wool is as strong as steel on a weight per unit length basis. In spite of this fact it still is evident that fibers other than wool are preferred for such industrial end use items as conveyor belts, tow ropes, and cordage.

TABLE 7. SPECIFIC GRAVITY OF THE COMMON FIBERS
(From References Cited Below)

	Sieminski[417]	Sherman and Sherman[5]	Preston[418]	Textile Institute[419]	Miscellaneous
acetate	1.33	1.32	....	1.31	....
acetate (delustered soap)	....	....	....	1.18	....
acetate (delustered TiO₂)	....	....	....	1.33	....
"Acrilan"	....	....	....	....	1.135[3]
alginate rayon	.........,	....	1.78	1.72	....
angora rabbit fur	....	....	....	1.15–1.16	....
"Aralac"	1.29	....	....	....	....
"Ardil"	....	....	....	1.29–1.30	....
asbestos	2.10–2.80	....	....	2.5	....
camel hair	1.32	....	....	....	....
casein	....	1.29	1.29	1.29–1.30	....
cotton	1.50	1.54	1.56	1.55	....
cotton, acetylated	....	....	....	1.43	....
cuprammonium	1.52	1.52	....	1.52	....
"Dacron"	....	....	....	....	1.38[3]
"Dynel"	....	....	....	1.28	1.31[415]
"Fiberglas"	2.56	2.54	....	2.5	....
"Fortisan"	1.52	1.50	....	....	....
hemp	1.48	....	....	....	....
Isovyl (polyvinyl chloride)	....	....	....	1.38	....
jute	1.48	....	....	....	....
linen	1.50	1.50	....	....	....
mohair	1.32	....	....	....	....
nitrate rayon	1.54	....	....	....	....
nylon	1.14	1.14	1.14	1.14	....
"Orlon" (filament)	....	....	1.18	1.19	....
"Orlon" (staple)	....	....	....	1.39	1.17[3]
Permalon (vinylidene chloride)	1.72	....	....	....	....
PeCe	....	....	....	1.54	....
polyethylene	....	0.92	....	....	....
ramie	1.51	1.52	....	1.55	....
Rhovyl (polyvinyl chloride)	....	....	....	1.40	....
saran	1.72	1.72	1.72	1.72	....
silk boiled off	1.25	1.25	....	....	....
silk raw	1.33	....	1.34	1.34	....
silk Tussah	1.27	....	....	1.32–1.33	....

TABLE 7. SPECIFIC GRAVITY OF THE COMMON FIBERS.—(*Continued*)

	Sieminski[417]	Sherman and Sherman[5]	Preston[418]	Textile Institute[419]	Miscellaneous
silk (weighted)				1.6+	
soybean		1.31			
steel		7.8			
"Terylene"			1.39	1.38	
Thermovyl (polyvinyl chloride)				1.38	
"Velon"	1.72			1.72	
"Vicara"				1.25	1.25[420]
"Vinyon"	1.35	1.35		1.35–1.37	
"Vinyon" E	1.19				
"Vinyon" N		1.2	1.27–1.33	1.27–1.32	
viscose	1.52	1.52	1.52	1.52	
wool	1.32	1.32	1.30	1.30	
"X-51"					1.17[413]

Ref: 5 Sherman and Sherman, "The New Fibers"
   417 Sieminski, M. A., "Relation of Tensile Strength Units"
   418 Preston, J. M., "Identification of Textile Fibers"
   419 British Textile Institute, General Technical Committee "C" "Identification of Textile Materials"

Cotton and ramie are outstanding in that they are stronger when wet than dry. Abaca shows no significant change in strength when wet.[416] The hydrophobic fibers (water resistant with zero moisture regain) maintain substantially the same strength when wet as when dry. Wool, when wet, retains 75 to 95 per cent of its dry strength—a percentage considerably higher than for viscose rayon or regenerated protein fibers.

(3) Elongation to Rupture

The values reported in Table 7A are concomitant with the tenacity and tensile strength values given in Tables 2, 3, 5, and 6.

Some of the elongation-to-rupture data appearing in the literature and in technical bulletins appear excessively high. Newell reports the elongation of regular nylon as 25 to 28 per cent. A fiber producer reports elongation values of staple fiber in the order of magnitude of 45 per cent, states that this value is too high, and attributes the inaccuracy to the short specimen length. Hamburger and Kaswell[422] investigated the sources of error in ascertaining true elongation to rupture. They found that with capstan jaws and nominal free gage lengths (i.e., length between capstan tangent points) of 6 to 10 inches, errors of as much as 200 per cent could develop because of the progressive deformation of the specimen around the capstan where the snubbing action takes place. This progressive deformation must be taken into account in calculating true elongation. Similarly, with flat jaws the test specimen will exhibit inhibited elongation within the jaw.   If the original gage length is sufficiently great, for example with a standard 3-inch ravel strip test specimen, the error is negligible and the jaw separation depicts the true elongation.   If the gage length is short, e.g., ½ inch for staple testing, the "jaw penetration" effect becomes appreciable and large errors can develop.   Hamburger and Kaswell propose an "effective gage length" calculation to compensate for such errors.

TABLE 7A.   PER CENT ELONGATION TO RUPTURE
(From References Cited Below)

	Sherman and Sherman[5] Dry (65% R.H.) (70°F.)	Wet	Newell[3] Dry (65% R.H.) (70°F.)	Wet	Miscellaneous Dry	Wet
acetate	23–30	30–38	23–30	30–40		
"Acrilan"			16	16		
casein	30–50	85–120				
cotton	3–7		3–7			
cuprammonium			10–17	17–33		
"Dacron"			20–30	20–30		
"Dacron" type 5400					25–40[414]	
"Dacron" type 5600					18–22[414]	
"Dynel"			31	31	31	
"Fortisan"	6–6.5	6–6.5	6–6.5		6.0[421]	
glass	2–3	1–2	3–4	2.5–3.5		
henequen[416]					3.5–4.5	5.5–7
manila abaca[416]					2–3	2.5–3.5
nylon high tenacity					14–20[414]	
nylon regular tenacity	12–20	13–26			18–25[414]	
"Orlon" (type 41)					20–45[414]	
"Orlon" (type 81)			15–17	15–17	15–17[412]	15–17[412]
ramie	3–7					
sansevieria[416]					2–2.5	2.5–3
saran	20–30	20–30				
silk	13–20				10–25[414]	
sisal[416]					2–2.5	2–3
soybean	30–40	60–70				
"Vicara"[420]					30–35	30–40
vinylidene chloride	20–30	20–30				
"Vinyon"	18–35	18–35				
"Vinyon" E	400					
"Vinyon" N	30	30	25–35	25–35		
viscose						
(regular tenacity)			15–30	20–35		
(medium tenacity)	9–20	14–35	12–20	17–30		
(high tenacity)			9–17	14–20		
wool	30–50	30–60	25–35	25–50		
"X-51" continuous filament					20–24[413]	20–23[413]
"X-51" staple (3 denier)					20–30[413]	
zein			30–35	30–40		

TABLE 8.   PER CENT ELONGATION TO RUPTURE OF FILAMENTS AND YARNS
(From Susich and Backer[233] "Tensile Recovery Behavior of Textile Fibers")

Sample No.	Material*	Characteristic and Designation	Dry 65% R.H.–70°F	Wet
1	"Fiberglas" ECD	multifilament 900-1/2	2.3	
2	cotton	staple yarn 50/1	4.6	9.6
3	"Ethocel"	multifilament 500/100/0	5.0	3.6
4	high ten. "Fortisan"	multifilament 90/120/3	5.8	6.7
5	cotton	staple yarn 12/1	7.9	12.8
6	saran	monofilament 5 mils diam.	13.4	
7	regular viscose	multifilament 100/40	14.7	22.1
8	saran	multifilament 200/12/5z	15.5	15.4
9	"Vinyon" NOZZ	multifilament 80/40/5z	15.7	
10	high ten. viscose	multifilament 100/40	15.8	
11	viscose	staple yarn 20/1	16.0	
12	"Orlon" acrylic fiber	multifilament 100/40/z	16.6	16.5
13	Fiber V	multifilament 100/40	18.2	19.0
14	silk	multifilament 100/132	19.9	33.0
15	"Vinyon" CF-HST	multifilament 80/108/3.5	20.0	
16	acetate	multifilament 100/40/2.5	20.5	29.8
17	acetate	staple yarn 20/1	22.8	
18	nylon, type 300	multifilament 100/40/2.5s	23.3	24.7
19	"Vinyon" N	staple yarn 20/1	26.8	
20	"Vinyon" NORU	multifilament 100/60	31.1	31.0
21	wool	worsted staple yarn 28.4/1	31.9	49.0
22	casein, raw	multifilament 300/40	34.4	44.2
23	casein, stabilized	multifilament 300/40	40.8	
24	polyethylene, type B	monofilament 12 mils diam.	41.3	
25	polyethylene, type A	monofilament 12 mils diam.	50.5	

* See Table 5 for source of samples.

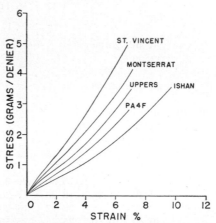

Graph 1.   Stress-strain curves for cotton.   (*From Meredith,*[8] *"Tensile Behavior of Cotton."*)

Note: Stress is based upon the original cross sectional area.

As a general rule, for any particular type of polymeric material, it can be stated that the higher the strength, the less the extensibility. Again it is emphasized that high strength is not the sole fiber property worthy of attainment. Glass is a classical example of outstandingly

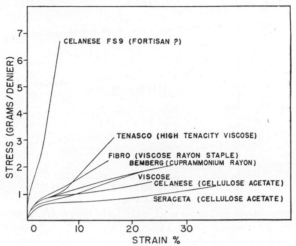

Graph 2.　Stress-strain curves for rayons.*　(*From Meredith*,[8] "*Tensile Behavior of Cotton*.")

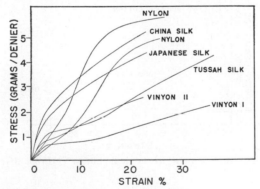

Graph 3.　Stress-strain curves for silks and synthetics.*　(*From Meredith*,[8] "*Tensile Behavior of Cotton*.")

high strength, but it is so inextensible (brittle) that there are severe limitations to its use. Nylon is outstanding because it exhibits high tenacity as well as high extension; hence it has a large capacity to absorb energy or do work. Such energy absorption, represented by the area

---

* Stress is based upon the original cross-sectional area.

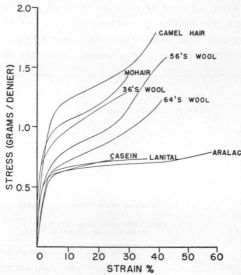

Graph 4.   Stress-strain curves for wool, hair, and casein fibers.*   (*From Meredith,*[8] *"Tensile Behavior of Cotton."*)

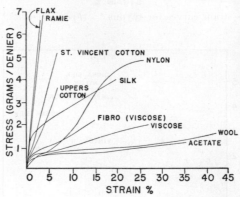

Graph 5.   Stress-strain curves of typical fibers.*   (*From Meredith,*[8] *"Tensile Behavior of Cotton."*)

under the load elongation diagram (Section 5), is important in such non-apparel usages as parachute suspension lines, tow ropes, etc.   Of greater importance is its use, when combined with cyclical repeated stress (below rupture) diagrams, in evaluating materials for abrasion resistance, crease resistance, and resilience.   Here it becomes important to differentiate between the properties of wool and other fibers under such repeated stress conditions.

* Stress is based upon the original cross-sectional area.

(4) Load-Elongation Diagrams

Meredith[8] lists the load-elongation diagrams of many of the well-known fibers. Fifty seven references to the subject of tensile properties of fibers are given in his paper entitled "Tensile Behavior of Raw Cotton and Other Textile Fibers." Graphs 1, 2, 3, 4, and 5, taken from Meredith's[8] article, show diagrams for cottons, rayons, silks and synthetics, wools and caseins, and a comparison of the generally accepted commercial fibers, respectively. He makes the following remarks concerning the various fibers:

"Cotton: there is a tendency for coarser fibers to have a higher breaking load but not in proportion to their area of cross section. The specific strength shows a large increase with increasing fineness so that the long fine cottons are considerably stronger for the same weight than short coarse cottons. Extension at break has a mean value of 7.3 per cent and shows no correlation with fineness.

"Bast Fibers: Line flax has a higher specific strength than tow flax. Jute has an average tenacity of 3.5 g.p.d. Hemp has a value of 5.2 g.p.d. Kapok and Akund are weak compared with other fibers. Owing to the low extensibility of the bast fibers, their work of rupture is comparatively low in spite of their high strength.

"Rayons: When considering the elastic properties of rayons, it must be realized that they are determined to a large extent by the manufacturing process. Generally, the stretched rayons have fine filaments, are strong, and relatively inextensible.

"Wool and Hair: Three samples of combed wool show no significant change of specific strength (tenacity) with fineness, although the coarse wool has nearly seven times the breaking load of the fine wool. This conclusion is confirmed by results scattered through the literature for thirty-one samples of wool ranging in fineness from 2 to 41 denier. These same samples indicate that the extension at break increases slightly with decreasing fineness. Camel hair has a very similar extension at break to wool, but is appreciably stronger.

"Casein: The three samples of casein fiber, i.e., Casein (English), Lanital (Italian), and 'Aralac' (American), show very similar strengths which are, however, only just more than half the average value for wool. Their mean extensions at break vary from 25 to 60 per cent, but most of it is not recoverable, and this fact should be realized when comparing these fibers with natural wool."

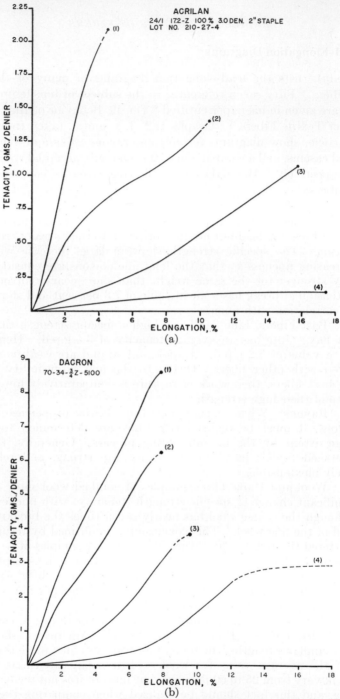

Graph 6. Load-elongation diagrams of producers' yarns (all filament except "Acrilan"). (*From* Coplan,[424] "*The Effect of Temperature on Textile Materials.*")

Note: Elongation values are based upon an original gage length measured at 65% R.H., 70°F.

Code: Curve 1 − 70°F, 100% R.H.   Curve 3 + 210°F, < 2% R.H.
        Curve 2 + 70°F, 65% R.H.   Curve 4 + 350°F, < 2% R.H.

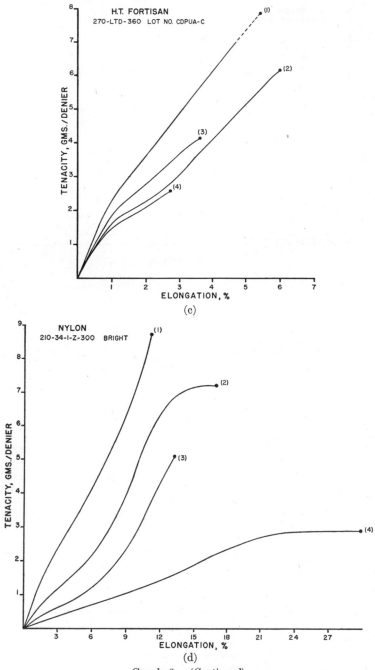

(c)

(d)

Graph 6.—(*Continued*)
(See page 18 for identifying code.)

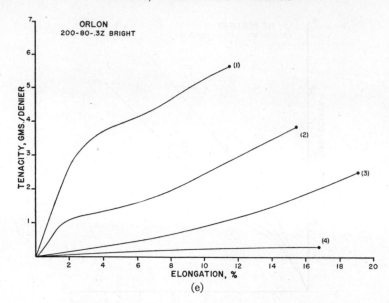

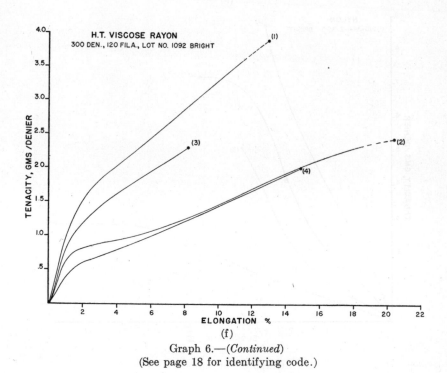

Graph 6.—(*Continued*)
(See page 18 for identifying code.)

The following additional sources of load-elongation diagrams are taken from Coplan,[424] Newell,[3] Carbide and Carbon Chemicals Company,[415] American Cyanamid Company,[413] Kaswell and Platt,[416] and Susich and Backer.[233]

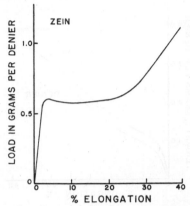

Graph 7. Load-elongation diagram of zein protein fiber. (*From Newell,[3] "Synthetic Fiber Table."*)

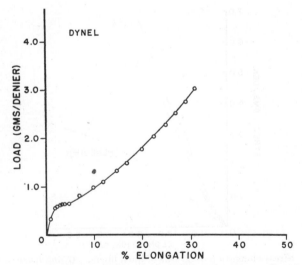

Graph 8. Load-elongation diagram of "Dynel." (*From Carbide and Carbon Chemicals Co.,[415] "Private Communication."*)

(5) Energy Absorption

The load-extension diagrams of the fibers having been discussed, it immediately becomes obvious that the load is a force, the extension is a distance, and the area under the load-extension diagram is the product of force and distance, or work (energy).　The area thus is a depiction of the fiber's ability to have work done upon itself, i.e., to absorb energy. Some investigators use the term "toughness."　This ability of the fiber

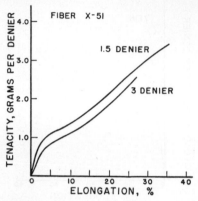

Graph 9.　Load-elongation diagram of "X-51."　(*From American Cyanamid Co.,*[413] "*A Summary of Facts About X-51 Acrylic Fiber.*")

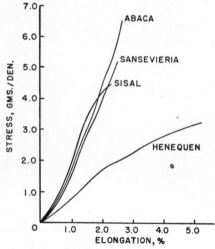

Graph 10.　Stress-elongation diagrams of hard fibers.　(*From Kaswell and Platt,*[416] "*Mechanical Properties of Hard Fibers.*")

to absorb energy when extended, and to return to its original dimensional configuration when the load is removed, are two parameters of extreme importance in considering such end use requirements as crease resistance, abrasion and wear resistance, shape retention and resilience.　For exam-

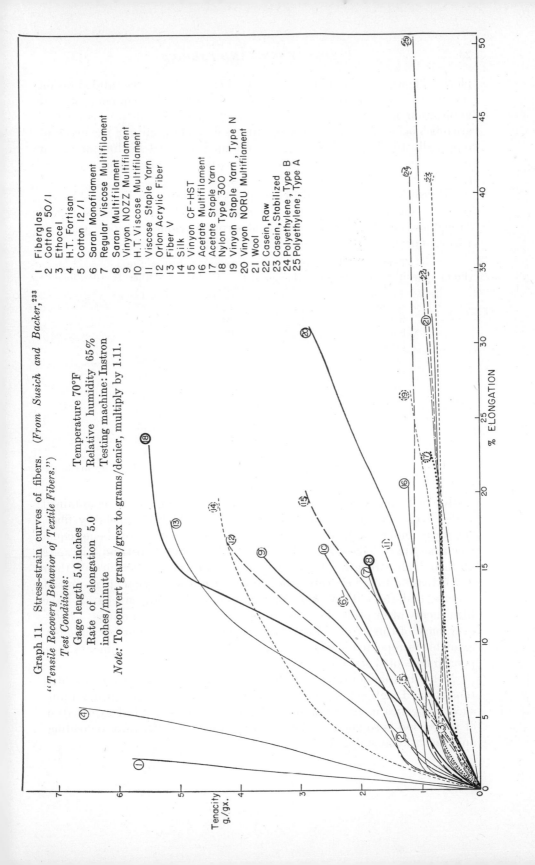

Graph 11. Stress-strain curves of fibers. *(From Susich and Backer,*[233]
"Tensile Recovery Behavior of Textile Fibers.")

Test Conditions:

Gage length 5.0 inches   Temperature 70°F
Rate of elongation 5.0   Relative humidity 65%
inches/minute   Testing machine: Instron

Note: To convert grams/grex to grams/denier, multiply by 1.11.

1   Fiberglas
2   Cotton 50/1
3   Ethocel
4   H.T. Fortisan
5   Cotton 12/1
6   Saran Monofilament
7   Regular Viscose Multifilament
8   Saran Multifilament
9   Vinyon NOZZ Multifilament
10   H.T. Viscose Multifilament
11   Viscose Staple Yarn
12   Orlon Acrylic Fiber
13   Fiber V
14   Silk
15   Vinyon CF-HST
16   Acetate Multifilament
17   Acetate Staple Yarn
18   Nylon Type 300
19   Vinyon Staple Yarn, Type N
20   Vinyon NORU Multifilament
21   Wool
22   Casein, Raw
23   Casein, Stabilized
24   Polyethylene, Type B
25   Polyethylene, Type A

Tenacity g./gx.

% ELONGATION

ple, it will be pointed out later[9] that the phenomenon of wear and abrasion resistance is in part one of low magnitude and high frequency of load application, i.e., the textile fabric is *repeatedly* subjected to forces which are much below those necessary to rupture it.   The ability of the material repeatedly to absorb this energy input upon cyclical loading and load removal, in part governs the inherent abrasion resistance property of the material.

Meredith[8] in Tables 9 and 10 lists Work of Rupture, or Energy Absorption, or Toughness of the various fibers.   Smith,[13] and Coplan[424] report "toughness indices" and energy absorption values, respectively, of various fibers.

TABLE 9.   WORK OF RUPTURE OF THE COMMON FIBERS
(From Meredith[8] "The Tensile Behavior of Raw Cotton and Other Textile Fibers")

Fibers	Work g cm/cm den.	Work Factor*
cotton	.11	.47
flax	.09	.50
hemp	.07	.49
jute	.03	.50
ramie	.12	.47
viscose	.26	.62
stretched viscose	.17	.51
acetate	.25	.70
silk	.82	.63
nylon	.86	.61
wool	.36	.68
casein	.26	.86

* The "work factor" is defined as the ratio of the measured work of rupture to the product of load at break and extension at break.

Kaswell[10] has shown that equal energy absorptions may be obtained with a strong-low extensibility fiber, or a weak-high extensibility fiber, the areas under the load-elongation diagrams in both cases being equal (see page 318).   Glass, flax, the "hard" fibers, and "Fortisan," in spite of their high strengths, have low energy absorptions because of their low extensibilities, i.e., they are brittle.   Undrawn nylon, high-impact acetate, and the old "Vinyon" E, in spite of their low strengths, have high energy absorptions because of their very high extensibilities.   However, most of this extensibility is nonrecoverable, and is not continuously available in repeated stressing.   Fabrics made from such filaments have poor dimensional stability.

Nylon has outstandingly high energy-absorption because of its high tenacity and high extensibility.   Add to these the fact that it maintains such properties in repeated stressing, and we have a valid explanation of why nylon is so good in abrasion resistance, flex life, impact loading, and dimensional stability.

TABLE 10. INITIAL YOUNG'S MODULUS AND TORSIONAL RIGIDITY MODULUS
(From Meredith[11] "The Elastic Properties of Textile Fibers")

Fibers	Specific Strength* (kms wt)	Extension At Break† (%)	Toughness‡ (kms wt)	Elastic Recovery§ (%)	Initial Young's Modulus‖ (kms wt)	Torsional Rigidity Modulus¶ (kms wt)
glass	76	2.5	1.0	100	3000	1520
"Fortisan"	60	6	1.8	69	1650	75
flax	55	3	0.9	59	1800	95
nylon	48	26	7.7	91	250	42
silk	44	26	7.4	51	780	200
saran	36	20	4.0	85	180	37
cotton	32	8	1.2	36	500	135
"Tenasco"	28	17	2.3	39	620	22
steel wire	27	8	1.8	...	2900	1050
"Vinyon"	21	29	3.5	43	300	107
viscose rayon	19	21	2.3	36	600	73
coir	18	16	1.6	...	430	....
cupra rayon	17	23	2.5	37	610	112
kapok	16	1.2	0.1	...	1300	400
beryllium alginate rayon	14	5	0.5	...	700	120
wool	13	38	3.3	75	250	78
acetate rayon	12	29	2.2	27	300	37
casein	7	40	2.3	26	200	90
copper wire	4	20	0.6	...	1250	490

* Specific strength (kms wt) = breaking load (g wt)/fineness (micrograms/cm) for 1-cm test length loaded at $1\frac{1}{2}$ km wt per second.

† Extension at break, % = 100 × extension at break/original length. Same conditions as for strength.

‡ Toughness (kms wt.) = energy per unit mass to rupture the fiber = area under the stress-strain curve.

§ Elastic recovery, % = 100 × recovered extension/total extension after an imposed energy per unit mass of 1 km wt.

‖ Initial Young's Modulus (kms wt) = resistance to extension = load ÷ fineness/ extension/unit length.

¶ Torsional rigidity modulus (kms wt.) = resistance to twist ~ torque × density^2/fineness^2/twist per unit length.

In the case of wool, we know that its nominally high energy absorption is attributable to its high extension and not because of its high strength. Wool's ability to deform under low loads, and to return to its original dimension upon load removal are some of the reasons for its excellent wear resistance.

The subject of repeated stressing will be discussed at length in ensuing chapters.

Table 11. Stiffness and Toughness of Textile Fibers
(From Smith[13] "Textile Fibers")

Fiber Material	Average Stiffness g/gx	Toughness Index*
glass	290	6
flax	270	6
hemp	200	4
jute	185	2
abaca (manila "hemp")	175	7
ramie	167	8
sisal	127	5
saponified acetate ("Fortisan")	105	19
viscose rayon (Fiber G)	75	14
cotton	57	14
nylon, high tenacity	41	41
silk (Tussah)	24	30
viscose rayon, high tenacity	23	20
nylon, regular	22	45
vinyl resin ("Vinyon"), high tenacity	22	25
vinylidene chloride	18	56
silk, degummed	15	40
viscose rayon, medium tenacity	15	19
cuprammonium rayon, regular tenacity	14	13
viscose rayon, regular tenacity	10	17
vinyl resin ("Vinyon"), regular tenacity	7	30
acetate rayon, regular tenacity	5	16
wool	4	20
acetate, high-impact	3	32
casein	2	14

* Smith defines toughness as one half the product of load and elongation, the premise being that the area of such a triangle is a good approximation of the true area under a load-elongation diagram.

Table 12. Energy Absorption Values of Yarns at Rupture
(From Coplan[424] "The Effect of Temperature on Textile Materials")

Fiber	Energy (in. lbs/in/den. $\times 10^{-5}$)	At Rupture Tenacity of (g/den.)
"Dacron" (210 den.)	76	6.7
"Fiberglas" (202 den.)	20.5	6.5
nylon type 300 (210 den.)	97.5	7.3
"Orlon" (200 den.)	76	4.2
saponified acetate (270 den.)	44	6.4
staple yarns		
"Acrilan" (24/1 ≈ 222 den.)	22.0	1.6
cotton (20/4 ≈ 1064 den.)		
greige	19.0	1.8
mercerized	17.5	1.9
"Dynel" (20-1 ≈ 266 den.)	35.5	1.2
"Vinyon" NOHU (270 den.)	111	3.5
"Vinyon" NORU (250 den.)	60.5	2.8
viscose high tenacity (300 den.)	71.5	2.5

(6) Modulus of Elasticity in Tension

In light of the condition wherein two fibers may have different load-elongation properties and the same energy absorption, it becomes necessary to define a term which will relate these two parameters. Young's modulus in tension is defined as the ratio of stress (load) to strain (elongation) at loads below the elastic limit. In addition to the tensional Young's modulus, similar moduli exist for compression, bending, and torsion loadings. In some engineering materials (e.g., steel) certain quantitative relationships exist between these four values.

Textile fibers are not Hookian in nature, i.e., they do not obey Hooke's Law which states that strain (elongation) is proportional to stress (load), thus producing a straight line load-elongation diagram. Instead, textile fibers are said to be visco-elastic. Part of the deformation is Hookian or "elastic"; part of the deformation is non-Hookian, "viscous flow" taking place. Stress is not proportional to strain throughout the entire diagram, deviations therefrom depending upon the amounts of the elastic and visco-elastic components.

Because the load-elongation diagram is normally not linear, the ratio of load to elongation (Young's Modulus) is not a constant. It must be defined and listed for the particular portion of the diagram under discussion. Otherwise the term is meaningless.

Meredith[8,11] in two articles in the *Journal of the Textile Institute* reports moduli data for the common fibers (Table 10) and discusses this property in relation to molecular structure. He states:

"Well oriented fibers such as flax and 'Fortisan' have a high Young's modulus and low extension at break. Fibers with low orientation such as wool and acetate rayon are easily extended, and have a high extension at break. In general, strong fibers have relatively low breaking extensions. Exceptions are silk and nylon which have a high work of rupture due to their strength and extension at break both being high.

"Below the yield point, stress is proportional to strain (Hooke's Law). The energy of elastic deformation may be stored in a fiber by two mechanisms: (1) the atoms may be displaced from potential troughs, and after removal of the tension fall back again as in glass, asbestos; or (2) primary valence chains may be straightened by tension and may return to their original shape as a consequence of thermal agitation as in nylon. Cellulose corresponds to the first case, but the second case may occur in cellulose acetate where the secondary bonds are much weaker, owing to the acetylation of the hydroxyl groups.

"Beyond the yield point where the fibers have begun to extend easily there are several interesting molecular re-arrangements taking place, depending upon the nature of the particular molecules involved. In wool, there is an intramolecular transformation from alpha to beta keratin, i.e., the chain molecules unfold. Moreover, the primary valence side bonds remain unbroken so that suitable encouragement, such as immersion in water, will bring the fiber back completely to its initial length. In an artificial protein fiber such as casein, the polypeptide grid is much less well developed so the molecules slip under tension and very little extension can be recovered."[11]

Cassie[4] lists Young's tensional and torsional rigidity moduli in Table 13.

TABLE 13. TENSION AND TORSION MODULI
(From Cassie[4] "Natural vs. Man-Made Fibers")
Young's Tensional Modulus Y

	Y kg/mm²		Y kg/mm²
cotton	745	silk	1000
flax	2750	nylon	310
viscose	880	wool	325
stretched rayon	2300	casein	270
acetate	380	phenol formaldehyde*	500
vinyl acetate*	300	nylon*	310
methyl methacrylate*	350	cellulose nitrate*	150
casein*	350	cellulose acetate*	150
horn*	500		

Torsional Rigidity Modulus

	kg/mm²		kg/mm²
cotton	0.21	acetate	0.07
mercerized cotton	0.20	raw Silk	0.27
viscose	0.08	wool	0.25

* plastics

Smith[13] lists average tensional stiffness values in Table 11. Table 14 lists average tensional stiffness values, and stiffness values at 1 per cent elongation.

TABLE 14. STIFFNESS VALUES OF FIBERS
(From References Cited Below)

| | Average Stiffness | | Stiffness at 1 % Extension | |
	Newell[3] (g.p.d.)	Miscellaneous (g.p.d.)	Sherman and Sherman[5] (g.p.d.)	Miscellaneous (g.p.d.)
acetate	5.5		.40	
"Acrilan" (staple)	30			
cotton	57–60		.50	
cuprammonium rayon	15.5		.90	
"Dacron"	13–25			
"Dynel"	9.7	9.7[415]		
glass	322		2.75	
nylon (high tenacity)	39			
nylon (regular tenacity)	20		0.25	
nylon (shrunk)			.10–.15	
"Orlon" (continuous fil.)	28			0.8[412]
polyethylene	2–15			
saponified acetate	116.6	120[421]		
silk			.75–1.16	
"Vicara"				0.32[420]
vinylidene chloride	20			
"Vinyon" N	10.5			
viscose				
(high tenacity)	25.5			
(medium tenacity)	16.6			
(regular tenacity)	11.1		.70	
wool	3.9		.32	
"X-51" (continuous fil.)				0.6[413]
"X-51" staple				0.3[413]
zein	2.8–3.4			

Ref.:   3 Newell, W. A., "Synthetic Fiber Table"
     5 Sherman and Sherman, "The New Fibers"
     412 DuPont, E. I., "Orlon Technical Bulletin"
     413 American Cyanamid Co., "A Summary of Facts About X-51 Acrylic Fiber"
     415 Carbide & Carbon Chemicals Corp., "Private Communication"
     420 Virginia-Carolina Chemical Co., "Vicara Staple Fiber"
     421 Sprague, B. S., "Private Communication"

The significance of the parameter "elastic modulus" can only be demonstrated and emphasized after additional information is presented and several important concepts are discussed. To the present, we have been concerned with the stress-strain diagram in "one-time loading to rupture." The ability of the fiber, yarn, or fabric to have and to maintain a proper modulus under repeated load or strain, will control its performance for such end-use requirements as fabric hand, abrasion resistance, crease retention, wrinkle resistance, deformations other than tension, dimensional stability, etc.

It should also be pointed out here that fiber stiffness need not necessarily reflect fabric stiffness. For example, the presence of crimp in the fiber as it lies in the yarn, or crimp in the yarn as it lies in the fabric all contribute to a reduction in modulus of the textile structure via geometric design. Equally important with inherent fiber property, is yarn and fabric geometry.

TABLE 15. MODULUS OF ELASTICITY

(From "Modern Plastics Encyclopedia"[7])

Fibers	Static Method 10^{10} dynes/cm	Static Method g/den.	Velocity of Sound Method 10^{10}dynes/cm	Velocity of Sound Method g/den.
acetate rayon ("Estron"), regular	3.0–4.8	26–41	6.1	52
acetate rayon ("Estron"), high elongation	3.0–4.8	26–41	6.1	52
saponified acetate rayon	20.4–24.5	152–183	....	....
cuprammonium rayon	9.2	68	....	....
viscose rayon, regular	6.4–9.1	48–68	11.5–13	86–96
viscose rayon, medium tenacity	12.5	93	20	147
viscose rayon, high tenacity	9.9–23.6	74–176	20–33.8	150–252
nylon regular	2.3–3.8	23–38	....	....
nylon, high tenacity	2.3–3.8	23–38	....	....
protein, zein	2.7–4.0	25–37	....	....
protein, soybean	2.6–4.6	23–40	....	....
glass	68.9	307	74	331
vinyl resin, regular	3.3–4.5	28–38	....	....
vinyl resin, high tenacity	3.3–4.5	28–38	....	....
vinyl resin, staple	3.3–4.5	28–38	....	....
vinylidene chloride resin (saran)	0.3–1.7	2–11	....	....
polyacrylonitrile ("Orlon")	5.7–6.2	55–60	10.4–12.5	100–120
acrylonitrile-vinyl chloride ("Vinyon" N)				
NOZZ	10.5	95	13	120
NORU	4.3–6.4	37–56	....	....
NORT	10	85	....	....
cotton	5.7–11.2	42–82	....	....
silk	8.4–12.9	76–117	14.4	130
wool	2.7–3.9	24–34	5.1	44

(7) Additional Tensile Data on Various Qualities of Animal and Synthetic Protein Fibers

Meredith[8] in Table 16, lists the various tensile properties of animal and synthetic protein fibers discussed in this chapter.

TABLE 16. INHERENT PHYSICAL PROPERTIES OF WOOL AND CASEIN
(From Meredith[8] "The Tensile Behavior of Raw Cotton and Other Textile Fibers")

	Wool			Mohair	Camel Hair	Casein	Lanital	"Aralac"
	64's	56's	36's					
fineness (denier)	3.94	12.0	26.8	10.9	9.55	3.30	3.67	5.34
breaking load, (g.)	5.14	18.8	35.1	14.2	16.1	2.35	2.60	4.13
tenacity, (g./den.)	1.28	1.59	1.29	1.44	1.79	0.72	0.72	0.79
breaking extension (%)	42.5	42.9	29.8	30.0	39.4	25.6	36.5	59.3
initial Young's Modulus (g./den.)	26.1	24.1	33.9	39.4	33.3	24.1	25.7	19.5
yield point (stress g.p.d.)	0.64	0.70	0.83	0.88	1.06	0.55	0.61	0.62
yield point (strain %)	5.0	5.1	3.6	3.4	4.0	3.8	4.6	6.3
work of rupture (g. cm/den.)	0.350	0.424	0.301	0.301	0.520	0.161	0.235	0.391
work factor	0.64	0.62	0.78	0.70	0.74	0.86	0.89	0.84

Chapter 2

THE TENSIONAL REPEATED STRESS
PROPERTIES OF FIBERS

(8) Recovery from Strains below Rupture

Smith[13] broadly discusses the properties of strength, stiffness, and toughness (energy absorption) in the following nontechnical language:

> "Just as the adjectives hot and cold describe opposite ends of a temperature scale, so we can describe the range of each of these three mechanical qualities on numerical or percentage scales thus:
>
> "Strength or tenacity ranges from 'strong' to 'weak.' Stiffness ranges from 'stiff' to 'pliant.' Toughness ranges from 'tough' to 'yielding.'
>
> "The data show that silk substance is several times stiffer than wool substance, and that cotton substance is several times stiffer than silk substance; while glass substance, at the top of the stiffness scale, is some seventy-five times stiffer than wool. Acetate is about as pliant as wool, viscose is comparable to silk. Some of the strongest fibers (glass, flax, ramie) are very stiff, but very low on the toughness scale, i.e., very yielding. This combination spells brittleness. The combination of low toughness and low strength means excessive softness and makes a poor fiber. Some fibers, such as wool and acetate rayon, are approximately equal in strength but differ in toughness. The personalities of the four material fibers are:
>
> "Wool: very pliant, weak, but tough. Silk: pliant, moderately strong, very tough. Cotton: moderately stiff, moderately strong, moderately tough. Flax: very stiff, very strong, but very yielding (brittle)."

Note: The writer disagrees with Smith's connotation that flax is very yielding and therefore brittle. The writer visualizes "yielding" to mean highly deformable at low loads, e.g., molasses candy. Flax is brittle because it is non-yielding. This disagreement with Smith is one of definition of terms, and does not reflect a dispute in fundamental philosophy.

Smith's[13] data on stiffness and toughness are given in Table 11. Continuing to quote Smith:[13]

"The above three quality indices provide a guide to the mechanical nature of a fiber substance which is far more enlightening than breaking strength alone, on which we have all been inclined to lean too heavily in the past. They are an answer to the question, 'Can a fiber material take it?' They do not, however, tell us anything about the elasticity or resilience of the fiber. These criteria do not answer the question, 'Can a fiber material take it and hand it right back?' For this we can have some sort of stress-strain curve, and when we turn to the traditional type of curve we find it inadequate because most textile fiber materials exhibit complex plastic-elastic behavior, characteristic of high polymeric materials in general, rather than the simpler behavior of crystalline materials, such as metals.

"The typical stress-strain curve for many metals at room temperatures has a rather sharply defined *yield point* below which the metal is essentially elastic, and above which it is essentially plastic. Therefore the location of the yield point in the curve permits the ready determination of elastic limit, elastic stiffness, and resilience. The elastic limit is read directly from the yield point. The elastic stiffness is computed from the slope of the curve between the origin and the yield point. Resilience is computed from the area under that portion of the curve between the origin and yield point. In the case of fibers, the very structure which makes them useful for textiles, results in a much more complex behavior under stress. Elastic and plastic phenomena are concurrent rather than consecutive. Furthermore, the elastic reaction itself is not wholly instantaneous, as in the case of a metal, but exhibits 'laziness'; i.e., if a given load *which is within the elastic limit* is applied to a fiber material, the material does not stretch *instantly* to the corresponding elongation, but stretches part way rapidly, and then creeps, slower and slower until finally it reaches its equilibrium elongation. When the load is removed, the fiber material contracts rapidly at first, and then creeps, slower and slower until it reaches its original length."

In the above analysis, Smith has carefully pointed out that the applied load is below the elastic limit. Therefore the total deformation is completely recoverable.

Hamburger[14] and Leaderman[15] identify the immediate deformation which results when a fiber is loaded as "instantaneous elastic deflection," and the delayed portion as "creep deflection." If, upon unloading, the

TABLE 17. REPEATED-STRESS PROPERTIES OF TEXTILE FILAMENTS AND YARNS

(Samples were cyclically loaded for 5 cycles to designated per cents of ultimate rupture loads, and were then broken on the 6th cycle)

	Nylon[10] (673 den.)	"Orlon"[10] Fiber A (190 den.)	Silk[10] Parachute Line (4900 den.)	Acetate[14] Rayon (300 den.)	Viscose Rayon (150 den.)	Cotton 8s/10 ply (6800 den.)	Cotton 3.4 Twist Multiplier (90 den.)	Cotton 4.1 Twist Multiplier (105 den.)	Wool (300 den.)	Victoria Henequen[416] (456 den.)	Java Sisal[416]	Manila Abaca[416]
Single Load to Rupture												
breaking load (lbs.)	9.8	1.7	450	0.96	0.51	30.8	128	180	0.38	3.17	4.94	7.61
tenacity (g/den.)	6.61	4.1	4.15	1.45	1.54	2.05	1.42	1.72	0.57	5.12	2.28	2.38
elongation (%)	23.4	18.9	18.3	25.9	9.9	12.3	6.6	7.9	16.0			
energy absorption (in. lbs/in.)	1.09	0.17	36.6	0.18	0.051	1.35			0.046			
energy/denier (in. lbs/in/den. $\times 10^{-6}$)	162	89	74.6	59	34	198			15.2			
After 25% Stress												
breaking load (lbs)	9.3	1.7	442	0.96	0.50	31.0			0.40			
tenacity (g/den.)	6.27	4.1	4.08	1.45	1.51	2.06			0.60			
corrected residual elong. (%)	20.4	18.7	14.6	26.4	10.3	8.8			18.6			
energy absorption (in. lbs/in.)	0.96	0.17	33.8	0.18	0.037	1.17			0.053			
secondary creep (%)	1.7	0.7	2.1	0.0	0.0	3.15			0.0			
E.P.C.	0.49	0.78	0.33	0.91	0.99	0.232			0.88			
After 50% Stress												
breaking load (lbs.)	9.7	1.7	420	0.96	0.50	31.0			0.42	3.44		
tenacity (g/den.)	6.54	4.1	3.88	1.45	1.51	2.06			0.63	4.4		
corrected residual elong. (%)	18.3	13.3	11.8	26.3	10.4	7.5			17.0	0.78	0.22	
energy absorption (in. lbs/in.)	0.83	0.13	23.3	0.17	0.038	1.00			0.044			
secondary creep (%)	3.7	5.3	6.1	0.1	0.11	5.43	2.6	3.5	0.17	0.52	0.63	
E.P.C.	0.47	0.32	0.20	0.85	0.79	0.206	0.24	0.19	0.86	0.095	0.061	
energy/denier (g cm/cm den.)												
After 90% Stress												
breaking load (lbs.)	9.8	1.6	386*	1.10	0.53	30.6			0.45	3.75	5.06	
tenacity (g/den.)	6.61	3.8	3.57*	1.66	1.59	2.03			0.68	3.31	2.32	
corrected residual elong. (%)	15.5	8.5	6.8*	6.9	5.0	4.3			16.8	1.91	0.57	0.62
energy absorption (in. lbs/in.)	0.70	0.07	12.4*	0.06	0.021	0.48			0.051			
secondary creep (%)	6.8	11.3	9.1*	17.6	5.5	8.03			1.6	0.39	0.54	0.53
E.P.C.	0.49	0.32	0.19*	0.14	0.23	0.187			0.67	0.074	0.064	0.089
energy/denier (g cm/cm den.)												

* At 76% of rupture load.

Note: The data on nylon 210/1/3, silk, and cotton 8s/10 ply are not directly comparable with the other fibers since the values given do not indicate inherent properties alone, but rather inherent plus "geometric" factors. Tenacity and energy/denier are based upon the original denier before stressing.

fiber returns to its original length, the creep recovery is 100 per cent and it is stated that the specimen has primary creep only, being *completely*, but not *perfectly*, elastic. If the specimen has not been loaded beyond the yield point, the creep in all probability is primary creep only. If the specimen has been loaded (or extended) beyond the yield point, in all probability it cannot return to its original length. That portion of the creep deflection which is recoverable is still called "primary creep." That portion which is non-recoverable is called "secondary creep."

The following diagrams depict perfect elasticity, complete elasticity and imperfect elasticity.

Hamburger[14] states:

> "Textiles are seldom designed to withstand a single stress application of high magnitude. Conventional structures are likely to be subjected to long usage, and, during their lifetime, to experience a series of repeated-stress applications and removals. To resist destruction, the specimen must be capable of absorbing energy imparted to it upon stress application, and of releasing this energy upon removal of the stress without the occurrence of failure.
>
> "The fundamental physical properties of materials govern their ability to absorb and return energy. Energy absorption properties are a function of the load-deflection characteristics of the material. If the energy absorbed by a specimen upon load application is to be returned without appreciable loss upon load removal, then the basic requirement is one of elasticity in the classical sense."

Hamburger states that the absorption and return of energy is a criterion of repeated-stress performance and uses the term "elastic performance coefficient" to define such a property. It reflects the effect of immediate elastic, primary, and secondary creep deflections. The elastic performance coefficient (E.P.C.) is a normalized index which expresses degree of perfect elasticity. A material which exhibits identical elastic properties after repeated stressing with those which it had originally (one-time loading) is called perfectly elastic and has an E.P.C. of 1.0. Similarly, a perfectly viscous material (no recoverability) will have an E.P.C. of zero. The reader is referred to Hamburger's original paper[14] for the details of the E.P.C. calculation.

The data in Table 17 are taken from articles by Kaswell,[10] Hamburger,[14] Kaswell and Platt,[4,16] and Fabric Research Laboratories[16] unpublished reports.

All data are not directly comparable for three reasons: First, the cotton and wool yarns are composed of staple fibers, and in testing them

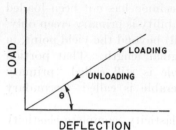

we are not measuring solely inherent fiber properties. On the other hand, such fibers are normally used in textile yarns and fabrics and in this sense we must accept their yarn properties as being inherent. At optimum construction, yarn tenacity and elastic performance values must necessarily be less than corresponding fiber properties. Energy absorption could be greater. Secondly, the silk parachute line and the cotton 8's/10 ply are not basic structures. Both "inherent" and "geometric" form factors are contributing to the determined values. Thirdly, even for the continuous filament nylon, "Orlon," acetate, and viscose, different twists might modify inherent properties. The data are useful, however, in drawing broad conclusions.

Graph 12. Load-deflection diagram for perfect elasticity. (*From Hamburger,*[14] *"Development of An Elastic Performance Coefficient in Tension."*)

Hookian material wherein strain is proportional to stress, producing a straight line in both the loading and unloading portions of the diagram. For perfect elasticity, they must superimpose.

Breaking Load after Repeated Stressing. With the exception of the silk line, none of the yarns lose any appreciable amounts of strength.

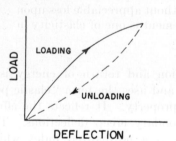

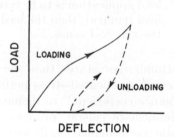

Graph 13. Load-deflection diagram for complete elasticity. (*From Hamburger,*[14] *"Development of An Elastic Performance Coefficient in Tension."*)

Visco-elastic material with primary creep (completely recoverable), but with no secondary creep. The material is considered to be completely elastic, but not perfectly elastic since its recovery is not instantaneous but requires time.

Graph 14. Load deflection diagram for imperfect elasticity. (*From Hamburger,*[14] *"Development of An Elastic Performance Coefficient in Tension."*)

Visco-elastic material with both primary and secondary creep. That deformation beyond the yield point may be considered to be approximately the amount of secondary creep. The material never recovers to its original dimension, but contains permanent set.

Residual Elongation after Repeated Stress. After 25 per cent cyclical loading and unloading for five cycles, none of the basic yarn structures (i.e., those uncomplicated by fabric geometry) show any reduction in elongation. The nylon 3-ply yarn (a component of a parachute suspension line) with 8 T.P.I. S-twist in the single and 6 T.P.I. Z-twist in the ply does lose what is probably some irrevocable geometric elongation. A similar condition exists for the silk line and the cotton cord.

After 50 per cent loading, the structures complicated by geometry lose additional elongation. The only "basic" yarn which has lost elongation is "Orlon." Here it is apparent that the yield point of this fiber was reached somewhere between 25 and 50 per cent of rupture tenacity.

After 90 per cent stressing, the "Orlon" has lost over half of its elongation; so has the silk; the acetate has lost three-fourths, indicating that the yield point was reached between 50 and 90 per cent of rupture; the viscose has lost half; the cotton cord has lost two-thirds; the nylon has lost about one-third. The wool has lost none at all. This is particularly remarkable for wool, since it is a staple fiber wherein fibers are prone to slide by each other (geometric elongation) as well as to be extended inherently. It is regrettable that no silk-filament data are available; the value for the silk suspension line should not lead one to conclude that silk loses either inherent strength or elongation upon repeated stressing. Similarly with nylon, based on the data shown one should not conclude that it suffers elongation losses when stressed to 90 per cent. Preliminary study of Type 311 high-tenacity producer's nylon shows no loss in strength or elongation after stressing up to 90 per cent of rupture.

Energy Absorption after Repeated Stressing. Since strengths have remained substantially constant, losses in energy follow losses in elongation. After 25 per cent stressing, the viscose yarn is the sole loser of inherent energy. The silk, nylon and cotton structures all lose "geometric" energy. After 50 per cent stressing, the acetate and wool retain their original energy; the "Orlon," viscose, nylon, silk, and cotton cord all lose energy. After 90 per cent stressing, all lose from one-half to two-thirds, with the exception of the wool yarn. Type 311 nylon appears to retain all of its energy, and one would expect regular-tenacity filament nylon to retain more of its energy than exists for the 210/3 structure discussed here.

Per Cent Secondary Creep after Repeated Stressing. After 25 per cent loading, only the silk, nylon, and cotton show secondary creep, and this is probably geometric. After 50 per cent loading, the "Orlon" has considerable secondary creep, the cotton singles begin to show evidences of it, and again the nylon yarn, the silk line, and cotton cord show appreciable amounts of it. Acetate, viscose and wool have very little secondary creep. After 90 per cent loading, all materials exhibit high secondary creep, with the exception of wool. The same remarks made above hold for Type 311 and regular-tenacity nylon.

Elastic Performance Coefficient after Repeated Stressing. After 25 per cent stressing, only viscose has an E.P.C. of 1. Acetate and wool have about the same; "Orlon" is poorer; the silk line, the nylon yarn, and the cotton cord have low E.P.C.'s. After 50 per cent loading, acetate and wool again are the highest; the other structures suffer progressive losses in E.P.C. Preliminary evidence shows nylon Type 311 to have an E.P.C. approaching 1, and it would be anticipated that regular nylon would have an E.P.C. lying somewhere between 0.75 and 0.9. This would be reflected in its reputation for being a strong, extensible, tough, and elastic fiber, good in abrasion resistance, crease resistance, and all around serviceability. Wool, of course, is not available as a continuous filament material but the fact is that even in staple form, it far excels many of the other fibers. Its high E.P.C. is one reason for its good wear resistance, crease resistance, and compressional resilience. It is an extensible fiber, and it yields when subjected to force or deformation. Because it does not resist deformation, excessive tensile loads cannot be built up in it and hence it does not fail (rupture). Its value lies in its ability to spring back when the force or deformation is removed. Nylon

TABLE 18. ELASTIC RECOVERY OF TEXTILE FIBERS

(From Meredith[17] "A Comparison of the Tensile Elasticity of Some Textile Fibers")

Elastic Recovery at

	Stress (g/den.)					Strain (%)				
	0.5	1	2	3	4	2	5	10	15	20
cotton	0.79	0.60	0.41	0.34	....	0.74	0.45	....	....	....
flax	....	0.78	0.71	0.66	0.60	0.65	....	....	....	....
ramie	....	0.76	0.58	0.48	0.43	0.52	....	....	....	....
viscose rayon	0.87	0.45	0.32	....	....	0.82	0.52	0.40	0.34	0.30
stretched rayon	....	0.94	0.80	0.72	0.68	0.81	0.66	....	....	....
acetate rayon	0.92	0.21	....	....	....	0.94	0.73	0.39	0.27	0.23
silk	1.0	0.96	0.66	0.46	0.34	0.92	0.70	0.51	0.40	0.33
nylon	1.0	0.97	0.91	0.87	0.80	1.0	0.98	0.90	0.82	0.75
wool and hair	0.92	0.63	....	....	....	0.99	0.89	0.74	0.67	0.63
casein	0.48	....	....	....	....	0.86	0.60	0.47	0.41	0.36
"Vinyon" I	0.85	0.42	0.38	....	....	0.99	0.82	0.57	0.46	0.42
"Vinyon" II	0.98	0.80	0.63	....	....	0.98	0.85	0.71	0.65	0.63
"Bemberg" (cupra- ammonium rayon)	0.93	0.40	....	....	....	....	0.48	0.38	0.32	....
"Rayolanda" I	0.98	0.56	0.40	....	....	....	0.54	0.43	....	....
jute	....	0.72	0.74	0.75	....	(0.74) at 1% strain				
ramie	....	0.76	0.56	0.48	0.43	0.52	(0.44) at 3% strain			

is the only other fiber so far studied which appears to exceed wool's ability in this attribute. It is regrettable that no comparable data are available for the newer fibers "Acrilan," "Dacron," "Dynel," "Vicara," "Vinyon," "X-51," etc.

Section 9 will further compare wool and nylon, as well as other fibers, to show that at low loads, wool is more *perfectly* elastic than even nylon, in that it has a greater ratio of instantaneous elastic deflection (see page 44, Reference 21) to primary creep than any other fiber.

Additional Data on Elastic Recovery Properties of Fibers. Meredith[17] discusses the tensional elasticity of textile fibers, defining the term according to A.S.T.M. Standards, namely: "that property of a body by virtue of which it tends to recover its original size and shape after deformation." He defines "elastic recovery" as the ratio of elastic extension to total extension.

Meredith[17] discusses his data as follows:

"Nylon is the most elastic fiber and shows an excellent recovery from strain (elongation) up to near rupture. Stretched rayon and flax show high elastic recovery at high stresses (loads), but owing to their high Young's moduli, their elasticities decrease relatively rapidly as strain increases. Silk shows a high degree of elasticity for large stresses and strains although it is not as good as nylon. Wool and hair show excellent recovery from large strains, but they are inherently weak fibers and show only the same elastic recovery as cotton for comparable stresses. Of course, wool is much more elastic than cotton for any given strain. Casein fiber shows a large degree of plasticity, and its elastic recovery falls rapidly when the yield stress is exceeded. This test clearly shows the higher elasticity of wool compared with casein fibers, a fact which is not so clearly indicated by the normal stress-strain curves."

TABLE 19. ELASTIC RECOVERY OF WOOL AND CASEIN FIBERS
(From Meredith[17] "A Comparison of the Tensile Elasticity of Some Textile Fibers")

	Approx. Den.	Stress (g/den.)					Elastic Recovery at Strain (%)				
		0.5	0.75	1	1.25	1.5	5	10	15	20	30
wool 64s	3.9	.80	.63	.49	.40	...	.87	.72	.64	.59	.52
wool 56s	12.0	.94	.80	.67	.59	...	.95	.84	.76	.71	.62
wool 36s	26.8	.95	.80	.66	.52	...	.85	.71	.62	.57	...
mohair	10.9	.94	.77	.61	.51	...	.78	.66	.59	.54	.50
camel hair	9.6	.98	.92	.75	.64	.57	.89	.78	.71	.67	.59
casein	3.3	.48	...	...	...	...	.60	.47	.41	.36	...

Table 20, by Beste and Hoffman,[236] gives an excellent summary of both strain recovery and energy recovery at two relative humidities.

TABLE 20. TENSILE AND WORK RECOVERY

(From Beste and Hoffman[236] "A Quantitative Study of Resilience")

	Tensile Recovery (%)								Work Recovery (%)							
	60% R.H.				90% R.H.				60% R.H.				90% R.H.			
% Elongation →	1	3	5	10	1	3	5	10	1	3	5	10	1	3	5	10
Japan silk	84	60	52	34	78	65	58	45	57	32	23	17	47	30	24	23
wool 50/56's	99	84	69	51	94	89	82	56	83	58	37	21	67	54	45	25
wool top 64's	100	81	65	49	98	94	84	62	79	58	41	21	65	59	39	24
zein	100	74	47	..	85	59	43	28	90	36	22	..	48	31	21	15
nylon 66	90	90	89	86	92	92	90	..	66	57	55	52	68	68	64	..
casein	90	65	47	30	76	58	43	25	74	45	23	11	53	34	18	9
polyethylene terephthalate C.F.	98	79	65	51	92	75	60	47	82	49	35	24	76	46	30	21
polyethylene terephthalate staple	95	75	70	..	92	73	69	..	85	44	37	..	83	43	34	..
polyacrylonitrile C.F.	92	56	50	43	90	55	48	39	64	27	23	21	66	24	21	16
polyacrylonitrile staple	89	66	51	..	84	62	48	..	63	33	20	..	62	30	19	..
polyvinylidene chloride	89	86	83	70	..	..	..	..	62	60	56	43	..	..	..	..
polyethylene	80	81	80	78	80	83	83	80	55	52	50	47	63	57	55	51
"Cordura" textile rayon	72	40	31	25	54	35	30	26	49	14	14	10	27	13	13	13
du Pont viscose rayon	67	38	32	23	60	33	28	27	50	14	11	9	27	12	10	11
cotton II	91	69	52	..	83	68	59	..	50	37	31	..	42	38	33	..
"Acele" acetate rayon	96	65	46	24	75	50	37	22	80	33	18	9	70	24	14	8
glass fiber	..	..	..	..	..	..	..	..	97	..	..	..	..	..	..	..

Test Details: Samples tested at constant rate of elongation of 1% per minute, with the sample held for 30 seconds at the maximum elongation before it was allowed to retract. Each specimen was elongated successively to the 3 elongations specified above, with only enough pause between cycles to enable the operator to take up slack in the samples.

Their investigation pertains particularly to the relationships between fiber tensional resilience and crease recovery. As such, it will be discussed in Chapter 16. Some general comments may be made here, however:

Tensile Recovery. At both 60 and 90 per cent R.H., nylon exhibits outstandingly high recovery. Polyethylene and polyvinylidene chloride also exhibit high recovery, but are not normally considered to be textile fibers. Wool thus may be considered second only to nylon, closely followed by polyethylene terephthalate ("Dacron" or "Terylene").

Apparel textiles are used under ever-changing ambient conditions. In the summertime, the relative humidity rises appreciably higher than the 65 per cent textile standard. Furthermore, the R.H. in close proximity to the human body is apt to approach the saturation point, and often times reaches it. Perspiration under the arms, at the back, crotch, etc. adds to this high humidity and wet effect. Hence, erroneous conclusions as to fiber and fabric performance may result if high R.H. or wet properties are omitted from consideration. Chapter 5 on Moisture Properties and Chapter 16 on Crease Retention and Relative Humidity discuss the many involved factors in detail.

The wool shows higher recovery at 90 per cent R.H. than it does at 60 per cent R.H., while the polyesters remain unchanged or possibly lose a slight amount. Page 108 shows a dry and a wet load-elongation

TABLE 21. MISCELLANEOUS STRAIN RECOVERY VALUES
(From Various Sources)

Fiber	% Strain	% Recovery	Remarks
"Dynel"[415]	2	97	
"Orlon"[412]	2	97	instantaneous release*
	4	84	instantaneous release
	8	75	instantaneous release
	2	85	delayed release†
	4	66	delayed release
	8	57	delayed release
"X-51"[413] (continuous filament)	2	95	instantaneous release
	8	69	instantaneous release
	2	71	delayed release
	8	43	delayed release
"X-51"[413] (staple)	2	92	instantaneous release
	8	70	instantaneous release
	2	53	delayed release
	8	35	delayed release

  * Instantaneous release: Strained to the designated level and released instantaneously.

  † Delayed release: Strained to the designated level and released after 100 seconds.

repeated-stress diagram for wool, and demonstrates that the wet wool fiber exhibits 100 per cent recovery when strained to the 20 per cent level.

Polyacrylonitrile ("Orlon?") exhibits poor tensile recovery when strained to 3 per cent extension. The regenerated celluloses, casein and acetate are even poorer and lose additional ability to recover from strain when wet out.

Work Recovery. The same general comments made for strain recovery apply here. Nylon is outstanding, followed by wool and the terephthalates. Again, wool exhibits slightly increased work recovery at high relative humidity.

(9) Instantaneous Elastic Recovery, Primary Creep, Secondary Creep

On page 36 definitions were given for perfect, complete and imperfect elasticity. Reviewing them here, we obtain:

Perfect elasticity: Total deflection = instantaneous elastic deflection.

Complete elasticity: Total deflection = instantaneous elastic deflection + primary creep.

Imperfect elasticity: Total deflection = instantaneous elastic deflection + primary creep + secondary creep.

The secondary creep component of the load-elongation diagram has been given considerable attention in the past ten years. It is generally accepted that all other things being equal, the lower the secondary creep, the better is the fiber in terms of wear, shape retention, and crease resistance. This does not mean that glass, which has no secondary creep, is better in abrasion resistance than high-tenacity viscose rayon which has secondary creep, for their respective energy absorption capacities, exclusive of secondary creep, are not equal. It also does not mean that fibers which contain secondary creep are of no value. For the above-mentioned requirements of wear and crease resistance and shape retention, care must be taken to insure that the load and extension yield points of such fibers are not exceeded in use. For certain end-use and (particularly) processing requirements, secondary creep may be necessary in order that the fiber be permanently deformed to fit a given state of aggregation in the textile structure. For most end-use items, however, even if a flow region in the stress-strain diagram is required, it is advantageous to obtain this flow region by primary rather than secondary creep.

Presuming that no secondary creep is present in a material, either because it is completely elastic to the rupture point or because it is being utilized at a deformation below the yield point, we must give consideration in differentiating among the various fibers, to the amounts of I.E.D. and primary creep which go to make up the total deflection. Reference to Table 20 will show that nylon (under the test conditions employed) is the most nearly completely elastic fiber up to 10 per cent strains. Wool is the only other fiber (under test conditions employed) which approaches it. Does this mean that the elastic properties of wool at low loads are identical with those of nylon, and approach nylon at high loads? Not necessarily, since the amounts of instantaneous elastic deflection and primary creep, and their sum, may be entirely different in the two materials.

When a mass of wool fibers is crumpled and compressed in the hand, it springs back to its original shape when released. In other words, wool is accepted as being soft, springy and resilient. Time is an important factor in this springback; wool has the reputation of returning extremely quickly. It will be shown here that such a reputation is deserved. Chapter 3 shows that when a fiber is subjected to a bending force, the ability to resist bending and to return to its original dimension is a function, for the most part, of its *tensional* elastic properties (page 60). A similar situation exists for crease resistance[18] wherein it is proposed that tensional modulus is a governing factor.

The *instantaneous elastic deflection* component of the load-elongation diagram is a measure of a fiber's ability to return instantly to its original dimension, and in the case of wool is the property which gives wool its unique and outstanding resilience. Referring to Graph 12 (page 36), a linear stress-strain diagram is shown depicting perfect elasticity (100% I.E.D.). Hamburger[19] points out that such

> "materials manifesting *perfect elasticity* may vary from one another elastic-wise only as do their stiffness or softness, i.e., their modulus of elasticity which is represented as tan θ. (Graph 12.)"

This means that a material may be perfectly elastic and stiff (high tan θ) or perfectly elastic and soft (low tan θ); the shape of the load-deflection diagram always remaining a straight line.

Steel, up to its yield point, is a classical example of a perfectly elastic *high-modulus* material. It has no secondary creep and no primary creep; its I.E.D. equals 100 per cent of its total deflection. Wool, up to its yield point, is a good example of a completely but not perfectly elastic *low-modulus* material. It contains no secondary creep but does contain some primary creep. Its I.E.D. is somewhat less than 100 per cent.

Hamburger, Morgan and Platt,[21] in a recently printed paper, have separated the instantaneous elastic and primary deflections of various fibers, and show that wool more nearly approaches perfect elasticity than any of the commercial fibers investigated. Its I.E.D. as a percentage of its total deflection is greater than for any other fiber shown, and thus account for wool's outstanding ability in quickly recovering from deformations.

The methods of separating and measuring I.E.D. from primary creep are not easy, since by definition I.E.D.[19] is

> "that deformation occurring at (a time approaching) zero time, measured in (a time approaching) zero time."

By means of sonic techniques,[19,20] wherein the speed of sound through the material is ascertained, the instantaneous elastic modulus and deflection are calculated.

Table 22 lists instantaneous elastic deflection, total deflection, and the ratio of the former to the latter.[21]

Up to strains of 5 per cent, silk is the most nearly perfectly elastic fiber, followed by wool and mohair. At the 5 per cent strain level, "Terylene" has the greatest amount of I.E.D. and the greatest ratio of I.E.D. to total elongation, while wool and nylon have almost identical values. Acetate is good until its yield point is exceeded and then, of course, its I.E.D/total ratio drops appreciably. Viscose, Fiber A, Fiber G (high-tenacity viscose), and "Orlon" deviate most from perfect elasticity, i.e., one would expect them to be poorest in crease resistance, resilience and shape retention.

TABLE 22.   INSTANTANEOUS ELASTIC DEFLECTION VS. TOTAL DEFLECTION OF VARIOUS FIBERS WHEN SUBJECTED TO LOW STRAINS
(From Hamburger, Morgan and Platt[21] "Elastic Behavior at Low Strains")

	Total Deflection				
	1%		3%		5%
Fibers	I.E.D.	$\frac{\text{I.E.D.}}{\text{Total}}$	I.E.D.	$\frac{\text{I.E.D.}}{\text{Total}}$	I.E.D.	$\frac{\text{I.E.D.}}{\text{Total}}$
silk (in the gum), 15 den.	.96	.96	1.79	.60	2.12	.42
wool (Uruguay 6's), 17 den.	.83	.83	1.83	.61	1.90	.38
mohair (B.A. 6's), 25 den.	.71	.71	1.49	.50	1.71	.34
"Terylene" (Fiber V), 200 den., cont. fil.	.73	.73	1.42	.47	2.19	.44
nylon (type 300), 210 den., cont. fil.	.59	.59	1.23	.41	1.91	.38
acetate, 300 den., cont. fil.	.73	.73	1.41	.47	1.45	.29
viscose, 150 den., cont. fil.	.50	.50	.60	.20	.70	.14
Fiber A,* 190 den., cont. fil.	.50	.50	.90	.30	1.10	.22
"Orlon," 385 den., cont. fil.	.48	.48	.83	.27	1.00	.20
Fiber G (high ten. viscose), 1100 den., continuous filament	.30	.30	1.00	.33	1.60	.32

* Fiber A is an experimental sample of polyacrylonitrile fiber which ultimately has been produced as "Orlon."

Graph 15 shows plots of I.E.D. vs. total deflection for these fibers. A perfectly elastic material is depicted by the straight line wherein the I.E.D. equals the total deflection at each point. A material which exhibits any degree of visco-elasticity (primary and/or secondary creep) will fall below this line, the deviation being a measure of the degree of imperfect elasticity.

The integrated closeness to the straight line may be employed as a numerical index of perfect elasticity, calculated as follows: at any total

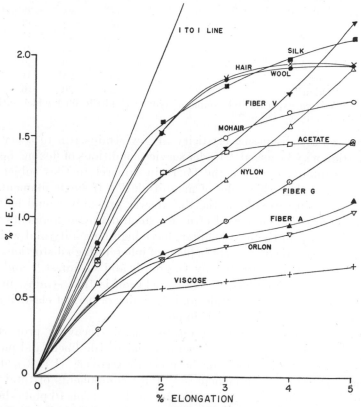

Graph 15. *Per cent instantaneous elastic deflection vs. per cent total deflection of textile fibers. (From Hamburger, Platt, and Morgan,*[21] *"Some Aspects of Elastic Behavior at Low Strains.")*

strain, the area under the curve for the material is divided by the area under the theoretical straight line and reported as a percentage, viz:

$$\text{Elasticity index*} = \frac{\text{area under fiber curve}}{\text{area under theoretical curve}} \times 100$$

Elasticity Indices are given in Table 23 and confirm the finding that up to strains of 5 per cent, wool and silk have a greater amount of perfect elasticity.

* This term has been selected by the writer; not by the authors.[21]

TABLE 23.   ELASTICITY INDEX

(From Hamburger, Morgan and Platt[21] "Elastic Behavior of Fibers at Low Strains")

| | Total Deflection | | |
	1%	3%	5%
silk (in the gum), 15 den.	.96	.77	.59
wool (Uruguay 6's), 17 den.	.83	.73	.57
mohair (B.A. 6's), 25 den.	.71	.61	.48
"Terylene" (Fiber V)	.73	.57	.49
nylon (type 300)	.59	.49	.42
acetate	.73	.56	.44
viscose	.50	.30	.21
Fiber A*	.50	.39	.29
Fiber G	.30	.34	.31
"Orlon"	.25	.20	.16

* Fiber A is an experimental sample of polyacrylonitrile fiber which ultimately has been produced as "Orlon."

Since we are discussing elasticity at low strains (up to 5 per cent), the question may be asked, "Under service conditions of flexing, bending, creasing, rubbing, etc., are the fibers in apparel textiles subjected to strains greater than this order of magnitude?"   If single filaments were used as yarns in a textile fabric, the answer probably would be "yes." However, yarns are composed of many small-diameter filaments which, as will be shown in the next chapter, have high flexibility and which are capable of geometric movement in place of inherent high distortion.   This subject has been investigated by Gagliardi and Grunfest,[18] and Hamburger, Morgan, and Platt.[21]   The conclusion is that strains, in many end-usages are low in magnitude, and the index of perfect elasticity when measured at such strain levels is important.

Susich and Backer[233] report on the elastic recovery properties of substantially all of the presently commercial textile fibers and monofils. Tables 24 and 25 list the immediate elastic recovery (I.E.R.), delayed recovery (D.R.), and permanent set (P.S.) components of total strain, measured at various levels of strain and load.   Graph 16 plots the same data over the entire range of elongations and tenacities.

TABLE 24. PER CENT IMMEDIATE ELASTIC RECOVERY, PER CENT DELAYED RECOVERY, AND PER CENT PERMANENT SET COMPONENTS, OF DESIGNATED TOTAL STRAIN†

(From Susich and Backer[233] "Tensile Recovery Behavior of Textile Fibers")

No.	Materials	At 5% Strain			At 10% Strain			% Strain at Which Permanent Set Appears
		I.E.R. (%)	D.R. (%)	P.S. (%)	I.E.R. (%)	D.R. (%)	P.S. (%)	
1	"Fiberglas"	..	..	..	..	..	..	1
2	cotton 50/1	44*	33*	23*	..	..	..	2
3	"Ethocel"	50	36	14	..	..	..	2
4	H. T. "Fortisan"	46	30	24	..	..	..	1
5	cotton 12/1	32	40	28	..	..	..	2
6	saran, monofilament	60	40	0	48	52	0	13 (rupture)
7	reg. viscose, multifil.	37	32	31	22	24	54	2
8	saran, multifil.	65	35	0	48	48	4	9
9	"Vinyon" NOZZ	61	34	5	30	50	20	4
10	H. T. viscose multifil.	32	37	31	22	24	54	2
11	viscose staple yarn	34	36	30	22	24	54	2
12	"Orlon" acrylic fiber	42	30	8	27	43	30	4
13	Fiber V	38	52	10	27	46	27	3
14	silk	41	41	18	25	33	42	2
15	"Vinyon" CF-HST	42	48	10	30	48	22	3
16	acetate, multifil.	54	35	11	27	32	41	2
17	acetate staple yarn	48	42	10	26	26	48	4
18	nylon 300	38	59	3	28	67	5	5
19	"Vinyon" N staple yarn	42	51	7	27	45	28	4
20	"Vinyon" NORU	58	38	4	28	52	20	4
21	wool	56	44	0	40	48	12	6
22	casein, raw	71	23	6	36	42	22	4
23	casein, stabilized	66	28	6	32	36	32	4
24	polyethylene B	82	18	0	48	52	0	11
25	polyethylene A	76	24	0	52	44	4	6

* Data taken at approximately 4.5% strain.

† For example, when "Ethocel" (No. 3) is strained 5%, 50% of that strain (namely 2.5%) is recovered instantaneously (immediate elastic recovery).

See Table 5 for a description of the samples.

TABLE 25. TENSILE RECOVERY PROPERTIES OF TEXTILE FIBERS

(From Susich and Backer[23] "Tensile Recovery Behavior of Textile Fibers")

Elongation Components in Per Cent of Actual Total Elongation

No.	Material	At 50% of Breaking Tenacity			At 50% of Elongation at Break			At the Breaking Point		
		Immed. Elastic Recovery	Delayed Recovery	Perma-nent Set	Immed. Elastic Recovery	Delayed Recovery	Perma-nent Set	Immed. Elastic Recovery	Delayed Recovery	Perma-nent Set
1	"Fiberglas"	78	19	3	78	19	3	72	22	6
2	cotton 50/1	63	35	2	60	34	6	44	32	24
3	"ethocel"	71	29	0	80	18	2	50	36	14
4	H. T. "Fortisan"	50	34	16	48	37	15	44	28	28
5	cotton 12/1	34	44	22	36	46	18	26	30	44
6	saran monofil.	53	47	0	53	47	0	42	58	0
7	reg. viscose multifil.	50	42	8	26	27	47	19	20	61
8	saran multifil.	56	44	0	54	46	0	33	54	13
9	"Vinyon" NOZZ	39	49	12	40	48	12	26	44	32
10	H. T. viscose multifil.	28	38	34	23	32	45	18	21	61
11	viscose staple yarn	28	32	40	24	40	46	16	22	62
12	"Orlon" acrylic fiber	30	47	23	30	45	25	21	37	42
13	Fiber V	33	52	15	28	50	22	18	37	45
14	silk	47	42	11	25	33	42	16	37	64
15	"Vinyon" CF-HST	27	51	22	30	48	22	25	46	29
16	acetate multifil.	74	26	0	26	32	42	14	16	70
17	acetate staple yarn	58	42	0	23	25	52	12	18	70
18	nylon 300	29	67	4	27	67	6	18	54	28
19	"Vinyon" N staple yarn	32	68	0	22	40	38	12	30	58
20	"Vinyon" NORU	17	39	44	21	41	38	12	28	60
21	wool yarn	64	34	2	28	50	22	16	44	60
22	raw casein	88	12	0	22	40	38	13	29	57
23	stabilized casein	77	24	0	20	30	50	12	28	60
24	polyethylene B	76	24	0	22	58	20	10	30	60
25	polyethylene A	35	58	7	20	64	16	10	49	41

See Table 5 for the description of the samples.

Chapter 3

FIBER STRESSES AND DEFORMATIONS OTHER THAN TENSILE

(10) Bending and Bending Fatigue

Textiles are called upon to withstand deformations other than tensile, and it is regrettable that little data are found in the literature on the topics of bending, torsion, and shear, in one-time loading to rupture or in repeated stress. It appears unnecessary to comment upon the importance of the relationship of such deformations to fiber, yarn, or fabric performance.

The terms employed to describe non-tensional deformations are used in loose fashion by many textile people. However, the physicist has classical definitions of these terms and it is well to review them here. Frank's "Introduction to Mechanics and Heat"[22] defines the terms for elastic bodies as follows:

"There are five typically simple types of elastic deformation:
"(a) Simple Tension (Figure 1): Equal and opposite forces acting on opposite ends of the rod increase its length from L_0 to L_1, and decrease the width (and breadth) from D_0 to D_1. The whole-line figure indicates the rod before deformation and the dotted-line figure after deformation.
"(b) Simple Compression: The forces act as in case (a), but are of opposite sign and decrease the length of the rod from L_0 to L_1 therebye increasing the width from D_0 to D_1.
"(c) Simple Shear: The forces act almost along the same straight line perpendicular to the length of the rod and move the cross section cd relative to the section ab into the position $c'd'$.
"(d) Simple Torsion: The forces act as torques about the long axis AA: they rotate two neighboring cross sections relative to each other about their common axis and turn the straight fibers parallel to AA into screw lines such as indicated by the dotted curve in Figure 1-d.

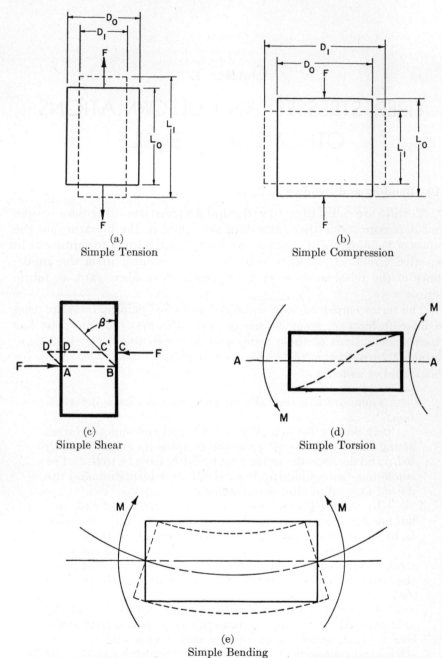

(a)
Simple Tension

(b)
Simple Compression

(c)
Simple Shear

(d)
Simple Torsion

(e)
Simple Bending

Figure 1.   Five simple types of elastic deformation.   (*From Frank,*[22] *"Introduction to Mechanics and Heat."*)

"(e) Simple Bending: Here the forces act as torques about axes perpendicular to the length of the rod at its ends so that they produce bending, compression in the fibers above the long axis of the rod, and tension in the fibers below it."

In order for textile fibers to function in the manner required by man, they must be flexible. To that end, certain values of bending, shear and torsion moduli are requisite; otherwise the "fibers" will not be useful as textiles, particularly apparel textiles. Glass, to the present, cannot be used for clothing because it is too stiff (brittle). It is poor in abrasion resistance, is easily cut, and of course because it is so stiff and sharp, causes irritation to the wearer. From the figures in Frank's book, it is evident that the larger the fiber diameter, the more force is required to bend the fiber through a given angle; e.g., it is much easier to bend a thin wood rod than a heavy beam, although the *inherent* stiffness (modulus) of the wood is the same. Thus the geometric aspects of the problem of flexibility of textile fabrics must not be forgotten. Smith[13] shows that the stiffness of an ideal cylindrical rod is proportional to the square of the denier. Since the denier, in turn, is proportional to the square of the diameter, it is seen that stiffness increases as the fourth power of the filament diameter. This explains why the finer the diameter of a glass filament, the more flexible and serviceable it becomes. The shape of the filament cross section also must be considered as is demonstrated by the fact that I beams are so made because they exhibit high rigidity per unit weight.

Bending Modulus. Finlayson[23] discusses the relationship between inherent filament stiffness and the effect of yarn geometry:

"The most obvious influence of filament size on textile properties is its effect on yarn or fabric flexibility. Drape, handle, ease of creasing, recovery from creasing, softness, and limpness are effects which spring readily to the mind. Consider the fundamental connection between filament size and flexibility. The manner in which fabrics vary in handle, drape, crease recovery, etc., depends in a complicated manner on the way in which the yarns and fabrics are constructed, but when all effects due to yarn and fabric construction are eliminated, there remain factors which are inherent in the filaments themselves, in their size, and in the physical properties of the material of which they are formed. Such factors can most conveniently be studied by considering the bending of a filament, supported as a cantilever, and caused to bend either under its own weight, or that of a suitably chosen minute applied weight.

TABLE 26.　THE SIZE OF NATURAL FIBERS

(From Finlayson[23] "Effect of Filament Size on Yarn Properties")

Fibers	Range of Widths microns	Av. Fiber Width microns	Av. Fiber Den.
Canton silk	5– 18	11	0.9
China tram silk	3– 21	12	1.1
Japanese organzine	3– 23	13	1.3
Fur hairs	12– 15	13	1.3
Vicuna	6– 25	13	1.3
goat wool hair	8– 20	14	1.5
flax cells	15– 17	16	1.9
American and Egyptian cotton	6– 26	16	1.9
cashmere	5– 30	17	2.2
jute cells	15– 20	17	2.2
fine American Upland cotton	8– 27	17	2.2
camel hair	9– 40	18	2.4
Manila hemp	10– 30	19	2.7
coarse American Upland cotton	8– 30	19	2.7
sisal	10– 30	19	2.7
fine wool	17– 23	20	3.0
hemp fibers	18– 23	20	3.0
Indian cotton	10– 33	21	3.3
Llama hair	20– 27	23	4.0
alpaca	10– 60	27	5.5
medium wool	23– 33	28	5.9
Tussore silk (China)	9– 51	29	6.3
carpet wools	20– 50	35	9.2
coarse wool	33– 42	37	10.3
pony hair	17– 75	43	13.9
ramie fibers	24– 70	47	16.6
goat kid beard	15– 90	52	20.3
mohair	14– 90	57	24.4
goat beard	50–200	72	38.9
human hair	15–110	83	51.7
Kuriwata silk (Japan)	50–126	87	56.8
horse hair (body)	80–110	90	60.8
horse hair (mane)	50–150	110	90.8
cow hair	15–230	111	92.4
kempy fibers for carpet wools	70–200	135	136.7
horse hair (tail)	75–280	140	147.0
hog bristles (tip)	98–250	180	243.0
hog bristles (base)	148–326	256	491.6

"The deflection of the end of a cantilever of uniform section under its own weight is

$$(1) \quad f = \frac{mgl^4}{8EI}$$

"The deflection under an applied weight is

$$(2) \quad f = \frac{Fl^3}{3EI}$$

where

f = deflection
m = mass of fiber/unit length
g = gravitational constant
I = moment of inertia

l = length of cantilever
E = Young's modulus
F = applied load modulus."

While the foregoing formulas are rigorous and precise only when (in engineering terminology) small Hookian deflections exist, they nevertheless show in a general manner the dependency of deflections upon: the rigidity EI (deflection functionally inverse with rigidity); the force mg or F (deflection functionally direct with force); and length e (deflection functionally direct with length).

Finlayson cites the importance of filament cross-sectional shape, assuming that most fibers can be considered to be elliptical or round. A simplified equation which he uses is

$$\frac{f}{F} = (f) \frac{l^3 R}{EW^4}$$

where R = eccentricity of the elliptical cross section, and W is the average diameter. This states that the deflection of a fiber under load increases as the cube of the unsupported length. Inherent filament flexibility is defined as

$$\frac{f}{Fl^3} = (f) \frac{R}{EW^4}$$

and demonstrates that

"the flexibility of a filament is directly proportional to its flatness, as measured by the ratio of major to minor axis of the elliptical cross section, and is inversely proportional to its modulus of elasticity and the fourth power of its width or diameter."

Finlayson lists data on the average width and denier of the various natural fibers (Table 26) and comments:

"The fact that the table begins with Canton silk is consistent with the supremacy which natural silk enjoyed over all other textile materials for many years, a supremacy largely associated with the fineness of its filaments and thus of the fineness of the yarns and fabrics which could be prepared from it. However, it is incorrect to list natural silk as the finest fiber in nature, since the filaments of the spider's web have a filament denier of approximately 0.1, corresponding to a filament width of 3.6 microns."

Data are also reported on the deniers required to give equal filament flexibility (Table 27).

TABLE 27. FILAMENT DENIERS REQUIRED TO GIVE EQUAL FILAMENT FLEXIBILITY
(From Finlayson[23] "Effect of Filament Size")

	S Density (g/cc)	R Flatness Ratio	N Yarn or Filament Stiffness (g.p.d.)	E Young's Modulus (kg/mm²)	D Filament Den.
silk	1.33	1.7	59.6	713	0.97
"Celanese"	1.33	1.5	23.0	275	1.47
viscose	1.56	1.35	57.0	800	0.96
nylon	1.14	1.1	25.0	256	1.11
"Fortisan"	1.56	1.2	116.6	1637	0.63
glass	2.54	1.0	322.0	7362	0.44
wool[24]	1.33	1.25	46.0	550	0.97

The implications of the above data in terms of applied properties are worth quoting from Finlayson:[23]

"Textile men have known for many years that in order to obtain a required level of drape and handle, much finer filament deniers have had to be used in viscose than in cellulose acetate. The table shows that the required ratio of filament denier is 1.47 for 'Celanese' to 0.96 for viscose, i.e., to get the equivalent of 2.5 filament denier cellulose acetate, 1.6 denier viscose had to be used. To attain the flexibility of silk, 'Fortisan' must have a denier of 0.63 and glass 0.44."

Carlene[25] discusses bending modulus and its importance in evaluating bristles wherein resistance to bending and ability to recover are used as criteria of value. His method consists of considering the fiber to be a beam supported at the center while the ends are deflected under a known load. For isotropic* materials, Carlene's formula is:

$$`` E = \frac{W l^3}{48 y I}$$

* Isotropic: equivalent properties in all directions of test.

where E = Young's modulus of elasticity
W = load on the center of the beam
l = length of beam
I = moment of inertia of the cross section of the beam
y = deflection of the beam at its center.

"For a beam of circular cross section

$$I = \frac{d^4}{64}$$

where d = diameter of the beam."

The term $Wl^3/48yI$ is defined as the bending modulus. Unfortunately, the author records values only for polyamide and polyurethane monofils. The values are in the order of 31 to 50 thousand kg/cm² for monofils of 0.325 to 0.473 mm mean diameters. Meredith[8,11] reports a value of 30,800 kg/cm² for nylon yarn.

Attention is called to a paper by Carlene[425] concerning the relationship between fiber and yarn flexural rigidity in continuous filament viscose. It will not be discussed here, however.

Bending Fatigue. Thomson and Traill[26] discuss the importance of the resistance of fibers to repetitive bending. They state:

"It may well be that a spuriously high value is set on fibers possessing high tensile strength. Some modern rayons with tensile strengths of 60 to 120 kg/mm² break with great ease at knots and creases, while other fibers with lower strengths do not show such brittleness. Fibers which, though of very high tensile strength, break very easily on bending, may be less serviceable in use in twisted cord or woven fabric, than weaker, more flexible fibers."

The authors present data on the following topics relating to the bending problem:

"(a) Number of 180° bends required to fracture fibres held under a 1-gram tension."

The outstanding ability of wool and nylon to flex and bend is obvious. Since bending consists of compressive forces on the inside of the bend[18,22] and tension forces on the outside, it follows that the reason that wool is so excellent in repetitive bending lies in its compressional and tensional repeated-stress properties. We have not yet discussed compression. Indeed, it is difficult, if not impossible, to ascertain true axial compressional properties of single textile filaments, since they are so flexible that they buckle before any appreciable compressional strain can be applied.

TABLE 28. THE NUMBER OF 180° BENDS REQUIRED TO FRACTURE FIBERS HELD UNDER 1-GRAM TENSION
(From Thomson and Traill[26] "The Bending Fracture of Fibres")

	Breaking Load (g)	Diameter (microns)	Average Number of Bends
wool	4	24	some unbroken at 20,000
nylon	6	14	some unbroken at 20,000
Sea Island cotton	4.5	17	3200
natural silk	6	15	1800
"Tenasco"	6	16	950
"Delustra"	4	21	660
boiled-off silk	4	11	370
soya bean fiber	3	21	150
cellulose acetate	4	19	100
viscose	4	13	75
casein	3	25	23
deacetylated cellulose acetate, e.g., "Fortisan"	3	7	1
glass	...	8	1

But in light of the excellent tensional repeated-stress properties of wool already discussed in detail in the previous sections, it is not surprising that the repeated-bending properties of the fiber have been found to be excellent.

(b) Photomicrographs[26] at the point of bending for wool and cotton are shown. After 10,000 bends, the wool fiber shows partial fracture and a fibrillar structure.

"Cotton[26] at a similar stage shows flattening prior to partial fracture but no distinct fibrils as in wool."

(c) Bending fracture[26] properties of fibers under various tensions are given in the following table:

TABLE 29. NUMBER OF 180° ANGLE BENDS REQUIRED TO FRACTURE A FIBER
(From Thomson and Traill[26] "The Bending Fracture of Fibres")

Tension (g)	Viscose	Number of Bends Sea Island Cotton	Wool
0.5	450	5100	....
1.0	75	3200	some unbroken at 20,000
1.5	3	720	some unbroken at 19,700
2.0	...	752	....
5.0	...	....	1040

Again the superiority of the wool fiber is obvious.

(d) Bending fracture[26] at various angles of bend are given in the following table:

TABLE 30. BENDING FRACTURE OF FIBERS AT VARIOUS ANGLES OF BEND (UNDER
1-GRAM TENSION)

(From Thomson and Traill[26] "The Bending Fracture of Fibres")

| Angle | % Unbroken at 20,000 Bends | |
	Sea Island Cotton	Wool
90°	36%	80%
135°	33%	40%
180°	all broken	all broken

"For wool and cotton, the number of bends to break increases as the bending angle decreases. The wool here was not the same as that shown in Tables 28 and 29 above, and was slightly less resistant to bending fracture."[26]

Table 31 shows flex life data taken from two du Pont Bulletins.[141,426]

TABLE 31. FLEX LIFE OF FIBERS

(From du Pont[426] "This Is Orlon")

Fiber	Flex Cycles to Failure*
nylon	380,000
"Orlon"	316,000
wool	44,000
silk	5,000
viscose	2,500
acetate	200

(From du Pont[141] "Fiber V Continuous Filament Yarn")

Fiber	Flex Cycles to Failure (Masland Tester)
nylon, type 300	212,000
nylon, type 100	200,000 (approx.)
Fiber A	200,000
Fiber V	55,000 to 140,000
"Cordura" viscose rayon	29,000

* The type of test is not designated.

(11) Shear Properties

There appears to be a dearth of information on this topic. Finlayson[27] confirms this by saying:

"It is surprising that little has been published on the subject of the shear strengths of textile materials. Most stresses which occur in nature are compound; that is why they are made up of stresses in tension and compression combined with stresses in shear. When, for example, pressure is applied to the face of a woven fabric, the warp imposes shear stresses on the weft, while the weft imposes shear stresses on the warp. Similarly, shear stresses are set up whenever threads or fibers are twisted or knotted."

Finlayson[27] reports shear properties of fibers tested in an apparatus consisting of three closely fitting rectangular steel bars, the center one of which is movable with respect to the other two. A $\frac{3}{32}$ inch hole runs through the bars and carries the clamped group of fibers. The middle portion is moved, and the force required to shear the fibers is measured. Data are reported as shear tenacities (g/den).

TABLE 32. SHEAR TENACITIES OF TEXTILE FIBERS
(From Finlayson[27] "The Shear Strength of Filaments and Fibres")

Fiber	Shear Tenacity (g/den.)		Tensile Tenacity (g/den.)		Extension at Break (%)		"Corrected" Tensile Tenacity (g/den.)		Ratio: Corr. Tensile Tenacity / Shear Tenacity		Wet Strength / Dry Strength (%)	
	Dry	Wet	Dry	Wet	Dry	Wet	Dry	Wet	Dry	Wet	Tension	Shear
"Fortisan"	1.17	1.06	8.00	6.70	7.9	7.9	8.63	7.23	7.39	6.82	83.8	90.9
nylon	1.27	1.08	4.45	4.00	24.0	27.2	5.52	5.09	4.35	4.70	92.5	85
linen	0.92	0.83	2.93	3.21	5.5	8.0	3.09	3.47	3.36	4.18	110	90.3
"Vinyon"	1.10	1.07	3.08	2.82	16.7	17.2	3.58	3.30	3.26	3.09	92.2	97.2
viscose	0.72	0.35	1.98	0.79	14.4	15.5	2.27	0.91	3.16	2.60	40	48.5
cupram.	0.72	0.52	2.00	0.93	12.4	12.0	2.24	1.12	3.14	2.16	50	68.1
silk	1.31	1.00	3.50	2.80	17.0	28.0	4.10	3.60	3.14	3.60	87.6	76.3
cotton	0.96	0.87	2.63	2.49	6.4	4.1	2.80	2.59	2.92	2.98	92.5	91
"Celanese"	0.65	0.56	1.32	0.84	24.0	30.0	1.64	1.09	2.52	1.95	66.5	86

The author[27] comments on Table 32 as follows:

"The range of variation of shear tenacity among the different fibres is much less than the corresponding variation in tensile tenacity. For example, the dry shear tenacities range between 0.5 and 1.31 grams per denier, while the corresponding tensile tenacities range from 0.94 to 8.27.

"The textile material with the highest dry shear tenacity is real silk, 1.31 grams per denier; followed by nylon, 1.27; and 'Fortisan,' 1.17. In the wet state, the position is slightly altered: nylon, 'Vinyon' and 'Fortisan' having almost identical values of 1.08, 1.07, and 1.06 respectively, while real silk falls back to fourth place with 1.00 grams per denier.

"Though linen has a higher tensile strength wet than dry, this does not apply to the shear strength, which is higher dry than wet. Similarly, in cotton, the dry shear strength is appreciably above the wet shear strength.

"Another point of interest is the ratio of tensile tenacity to shear tenacity dry and wet. According to the theory of the strength of materials, in a perfectly isotropic material, i.e., a material of which the physical properties are the same in all directions, the tensile strength should have twice the value of the shear strength. Textile fibres, however, are not isotropic, since their method of production usually involves a certain amount of orientation in the direction of the length of the filament or fibre. This, of course, causes the well-known effect of increased tenacity in the longitudinal direction.

"Contrary to what is sometimes suggested, orientation causes an increase in the shear strength also, though to a much smaller extent than the increase in tensile strength. This being so, the ratio of the ordinary tenacity to the shear tenacity may be used to indicate the degree of orientation of different types of fibre. For this reason, the order in which the different materials have been arranged in the table is that of decreasing ratio of tensile tenacity to shear tenacity. It will be seen that the order of the different fibres is roughly in agreement with the order of orientation of the same materials as disclosed by X-ray methods."

It is regrettable that Finlayson gives no values for wool. Based on the data and discussion presented, one would predict that the absolute shear tenacity of wool would be low. However, the ratio of shear to tensile strength would probably be high. This is because wool's extensibility would result (in Finlayson's apparatus) in the conversion of the shear force to a tensile force, i.e., the specimen would extend and would then be in longitudinal tension for the most part. Previous discussions have shown wool's attributes do not result from its high strength and orientation, but rather in its ability to deform and recover.

The problem of shear usually is of much greater significance in brittle, high modulus materials, where, although absolute shear strengths are higher (than for low modulus materials), the inability of the material to deform causes extremely high stress concentrations to develop at certain points (e.g., at the cross-over of a warp and filling yarn) and the failure results. This is a disadvantage of glass.

For textile purposes wherein flexibility is requisite, Platt[28] demonstrates that shear, bending, and torsional stresses are relatively minor factors when compared with tensional stresses.

"The application of an external tensile load, P, along the axis of a yarn results in forces being applied to the various fibers. In general, the only stresses which can possibly act on the cross section of a fiber are: (1) tensile force, p_r, direction along the fiber axis and normal to the fiber cross section; (2) a shear force, v, acting tangential to the fiber cross section; (3) a bending moment, m; (4) a torsional moment, t. These stresses are illustrated in Figure 2.

"It is now assumed that the fibers are perfectly flexible members, incapable of resisting any axial compressive forces. Because of the extremely low modulus of elasticity of textile fibers, in addition to the extremely large ratio of fiber length to fiber diameter, this is a reasonable assumption. As a result of this assumption, the stresses m, v, and t vanish, and the only fiber force acting as a direct tension is p_r. The concept of perfect flexibility is not an uncommon one in engineering. The classical design of the long cables of a suspension bridge

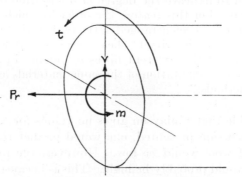

Figure 2. General stresses in fibers.   (v, t, and m assumed $= 0$.)   (*From Platt,*[28] *"Some Aspects of Stress Analysis of Textile Structures."*)

depends upon the assumption that only tensile forces are acting, as is the case for many other structures."[28]

The predominance of tensile forces in flexible fibers is sometimes beclouded by other factors erroneously attributed to shear. For example, in the conventional loop-strength test wherein two filaments or yarns are looped through each other and the ends pulled so that one loop ruptures the other, the forces are predominantly tensional—not shear. Figure 3 depicts a typical loop test.

Platt,[427] in a private communication, points out that before tension is applied at A and B, a distribution of stress is already induced in the filament ACB as a result of the bend. The strain distribution at a cross section C is depicted in the right-hand portion of Figure 3. Maximum tension is developed at the outer periphery of the filament. It becomes progressively less until a neutral axis of zero stress is reached. The inner portion of the filament is placed in compression, attaining a maximum value at the inner periphery.

Upon the application of tension at points A and B, Platt further shows that the stress distribution at cross section C remains non-uniform. Failure occurs at a total stress level which is inevitably less than that developed in a straight tension-to-rupture test. The mechanism of failure is primarily tensile, however.

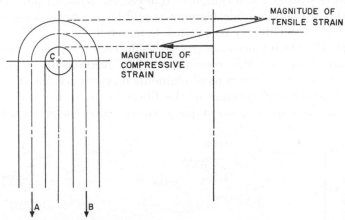

Figure 3. The distribution of tensile stress produced in a loop test. (*From Platt,*[427] *"Private Communication."*)

(12) Loop Strength and Knot Strength

Quantitative data reported in the literature are limited and some are repetitious.

Loop Strength. Coplan[424] has recently reported loop strengths and per cent efficiencies (based on tensile strengths).

TABLE 33. LOOP STRENGTH AND EFFICIENCY OF CONTINUOUS FILAMENT YARNS
(From Coplan[424] "The Effect of Temperature on Textile Materials")

	Den.	Loop Strength (g/den.)	Loop Strength Efficiency (% of tenacity)	Tensile Elongation (%)
nylon (type 300)	210	5.94	82.5	13.1
"Orlon"	200	3.13	80.9	15.3
"Dacron"	210	4.66	72.8	8.85
viscose (H.T.)	300	2.34	96.5	20.0
saponified acetate	270	3.19	51.0	5.8
"Vinyon" NOHU	270	2.47	71.2	29.9
"Vinyon" NORU	250	2.41	88.0	30.8
"Fiberglas"	202	0.42	8.4	2.99
"Fiberglas"	101	0.42	8.4	2.39
staple yarns				
cotton 20/4				
greige	1064	1.85	100.0	9.4
mercerized	1064	2.06	97.1	7.7
"Dynel" 20-1	266	1.35	94.1	27.8
"Acrilan"	222	1.33	92.4	11.21

Based partially on the analysis given in the previous section, plus the fact that brittle, low-extensible materials are more prone to build up excessive stresses which cannot be relieved via deformation, one would expect that a low-extensible filament would have a lower loop strength efficiency than would a highly extensible material.

Graph 17, which plots loop strength efficiency vs. tensile elongation to rupture, bears out this conclusion. The relationship is not linear since all stress-strain diagrams of filaments or yarns are not of the same shape. Furthermore, slippage of the fibers in the staple yarns, or the presence of weak spots in the staple yarns can alter the relationship.

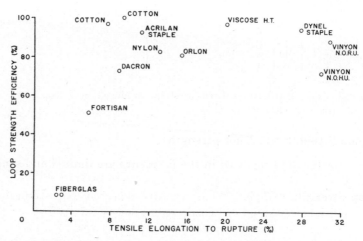

Graph 17. Loop strength efficiency vs. tensile elongation to rupture. (*Data Taken From Coplan,*[424] *Table 33.*)

It is unfortunate, since wool is of specific interest here, that no data are available concerning it. Because of its high extension, it can be presumed that it would have a high loop strength efficiency but a low absolute loop strength. The fact that wool deforms rather than ruptures in bending is of obvious advantage both in fabric manufacture and in use. On the other hand, in end-use applications where complete rigidity and high shear strength is necessary, for example, in reinforced rigid plastic laminates, the advantages of glass, "Fortisan" and flax, and the disadvantages of low strength and low modulus fibers become obvious.

Knot Strength. Maillard,[35] and Schiefer, Fourt, and Kropf,[36] report data originally listed in an article by Bohringer and Schieber.[37] Schiefer, Fourt, and Kropf discuss the article from the broad point of view of fabric serviceability:

"This work involved extensive measurements on many fibers for the following properties: breaking strength, unevenness, elasticity, elongation, knot and loop strength, wet strength, fatigue, flexural endurance, degree of polymerization, swelling, fiber splintering, abrasion, ageing and internal fiber stresses. Correlations of the results among these properties for the different kinds of fibers were studied. On the basis of these correlations, the mutual interdependence among eight of these properties which affect serviceability was arrived at. These are tensile strength, elasticity or specific elastic work, knot strength, elongation, relative wet strength, tensile fatigue resistance, flexural endurance, and degree of polymerization. Table 34, Part a, gives numerical values for these properties. Since the units for these properties are different, it is necessary to convert them to some common basis before they can be combined into a quality index. For this purpose, the values of the properties of rayon are arbitrarily taken as 100 and the values of the properties for the other fibers are expressed as percentages of the corresponding values for rayon. The average value for each fiber is taken as the quality index. (Table 34, Part b, shows the normalized values.) Judgment must be exercised in using this quality index of fibers intended for radically different uses. Indiscriminate use would, of course, lead to erroneous conclusions."

TABLE 34. PHYSICAL PROPERTIES OF FIVE KINDS OF FIBERS
(From Schiefer, Fourt and Kropf[36] "Serviceability Evaluation of Textiles" from an original article by Bohringer and Shieber[37])

Part a—Absolute Values of Physical Properties

	Tensile Strength (kg/mm²)	Specific Elastic Work (kg/cm²)	Relative Knot Strength (%)	Elonga- tion at Break (%)	Relative Wet Strength (%)	Tensile Fatigue Resist- ance (%)	Flexural Endur- ance (cycles)	Average Degree of Polymeri- zation	Fineness Nm
nylon	54.5	2.81	86	25	87	94	244,000	....	2790
wool	17.8	1.94	85	34	82	100	156,000	....	2600
silk	65.1	2.92	88	31	79	93	76,300	....	9450
cotton	43.5	0.427	91	11	98	64	64,750	3130	5770
rayon	29.0	0.661	58	17	61	88	6,800	330	5800

Part b—Relative Values of Physical Properties of Above Fibers

									Average Quality Index
nylon	188	422	149	148	143	106	3,590	....	678
wool	61	287	147	202	135	114	2,295	....	463
silk	224	439	151	182	130	106	1,123	....	336
cotton	150	64	157	65	161	73	952	950	232
rayon	100	100	100	100	100	100	100	100	100

The above data indicate no outstanding advantages in the knot strength of wool compared to nylon, silk, or cotton. Since relative knot strength is recorded as a per cent of tensile strength and since the tensile strength of wool is by no means high, it follows that the absolute knot strength of a wool yarn on a per denier basis would not be high. Tensile fatigue resistance and flexural endurance are striking examples of the superiority of wool. No fiber is comparable with wool in tensile fatigue resistance; only nylon is comparable in flexural endurance.

(13) Torsional Properties

Morton and Permanyer,[29] Meredith,[30] Steinberger,[31] and Peirce[32] discuss the torsional properties of textile yarns and textile structures. Morton and Permanyer[29] cite the importance of torsion stresses and strains, as well as the relaxation of such stresses: distribution of twist in ring-spun yarns, the snarling of single yarns, twist balance in ply yarns, fabric curl, crêping power of highly twisted yarns. Again there is a lack of information of inherent torsional fiber properties.

Lochner[33] describes a method and gives data on the damping capacity for torsion of fibers:

> "The damping capacity is obtained from the decay of torsional oscillations of a small disc suspended from a fiber. A method for the determination of Young's modulus for bending of short fibers is also described. Results obtained by two sonic methods of measuring damping capacity by means of resonance techniques are in good agreement for homogenous fibers. For fibers with a heterogeneous structure such as wool, the damping capacity for bending is not necessarily the same as the value for torsion."

Lochner discusses the importance of damping capacity and bending and torsion in the following remarks:

> "Most materials exhibit appreciable plastic strain under cyclic stresses well within the 'elastic limit.' This plastic strain, which accompanies the elastic strain, is responsible for the so-called mechanical hysteresis loop, the area of which represents the energy converted into heat during one cycle. It is this conversion into heat or absorption of kinetic energy that damps out the resonant vibrations of elastic bodies.
>
> "The 'damping capacity,' defined by O. Foppl[34] as the non-dimensional ratio ψ, obtained by dividing the area of the hysteresis loop by the strain energy stored in the extreme position of the cycle, depends on the ratio of the plastic to the elastic strain, and is an important physical property of materials to be used under alternating stresses. Damping in any material depends on the amplitude of swing, the temperature of the

specimen and on the number of stress cycles completed; but it does not become exhausted in time and is no indication of impending fatigue failure.

"Thus, damping capacity is a property of genuine practical importance in judging materials and can be relied on to the same extent as can the breaking point of the steel of a machine part.

"According to Foppl a material of high damping capacity is superior to one of low damping capacity for the following reasons:

"(a) According to elastic theory, there are severe local concentrations of stress at certain spots such as flaws, surface scratches, etc., which may reach values from twice to five times the surrounding stress. Consequently fatigue cracks are particularly prone to start from surface blemishes. The effect of plastic strain is to lessen the intensity of a peak stress by spreading it over a wide area. On this account, the danger of starting a fatigue crack is diminished.

"(b) When a machine part is thrown into resonant vibration by a periodic exciting force, the amplitude of swing is held in check by damping resulting from the conversion of kinetic energy into heat. This means that if a material possesses high damping capacity it will not be so severely stressed. Resistance to fatigue failure depends essentially on the area of the hysteresis loop, i.e., on the damping capacity of the material.

"Overhead cables stretched by a given force may fail by fatigue due to resonant vibrations excited by cross winds. It is found that copper possessing strong damping properties is less likely to fail than light-metal alloys possessing greater tensile and fatigue strengths than copper.

"For the same reason mine cables should be made of steel with a high damping capacity to absorb standing and shock waves. Similar conditions apply to the wings of aeroplanes, propellers of aeroplanes, crankshafts of internal combustion engines, blading of steam turbines, etc.

"Very often ropes and belts are made of organic fibrous materials. The useful life of such ropes and belts will depend on the damping capacity of the fibres of which they are made. Similarly the strength and resistance to fatigue of fabrics depend on the damping capacity of its fibres. The superiority as regards resistance to bending fracture of wool and nylon[26] over most of the artificial fibres may be due to the fact that their damping capacity is high compared with the damping capacity of the other fibres. It is, therefore, of the utmost importance to be able to measure the damping capacity of fibres."

TABLE 35. DAMPING CAPACITY IN TORSION AND BENDING

(From Lochner[33] "Damping Capacity of Wool and Other Fibres")

Fiber	Fiber Diameter (cm $\times 10^{-5}$)	Damping Capacity Torsion	Bending
quartz	321	0.030	0.035
human hair	721	0.231	0.228
wool	254	0.329	0.479
wool	354	0.258	0.342
nylon	204	0.600	0.625
acetate	260	0.393	0.552

The damping capacity of wool is far above such classically brittle materials as quartz, glass, etc., but is inferior to nylon.

It should be pointed out that the forces applied are below the elastic limit of the same type described in Section 9, page 44. Lochner agrees that

"to the present, attention has been paid only to hysteresis losses occurring during the extension of textile fibres, and for this purpose fibres have been stretched far beyond the elastic limit. In the case of bending, it is doubtful whether in practice the elastic limit is ever exceeded and a study of the internal friction giving rise to hysteresis losses within the elastic limit seems to be imperative. Apart from the structural (geometric) properties of a fabric, it is possible that the resistance against fatigue of a fabric may depend very largely on the damping capacity or internal friction of the fibres, and may be greater the higher the damping capacity, but whether this is the case or otherwise has still to be investigated."

The writer agrees with this last sentence in that Lochner's premise has not been proved. Depending upon the amount of secondary creep in a material, the fiber might exhibit high damping capacity, and yet be poor in abrasion and wear resistance. This probably explains why acetate, with a high damping capacity, exhibits poor bending fatigue properties (Table 28). High secondary creep contributes little or nothing to the material's ability to absorb energy in repeated bending stress.

Chapter 4
FRICTION

Fabric properties which are governed in part by frictional effects are fabric "hand," strength, elongation, abrasion resistance, dimensional stability, and seam slippage. The conversion of staple fibers into yarns is dependent upon friction, as are many of the subsequent manufacturing operations, particularly those procedures employed in the wet finishing of wool: felting, fulling, milling, and shrinkage. Particular emphasis is given, in the literature, to wool and animal hairs since they are probably the only fibers which exhibit two frictional effects, depending upon whether the relative motion is with or against the scales. This chapter will contain friction data as they pertain to the dry properties of fibers and yarns. The frictional properties of fabrics will be discussed in Chapter 20 on "Fabric Hand." Wet frictional properties will be found in Chapter 18 on Felting and Shrinkage.

Employing classical definitions and terminology, Fuller and Johnson[330] state:

> "When one body slides, or tends to slide, over the surface of another, the resistance to the motion which is developed is called the *force of friction* or simply *friction*. This is a force which always acts opposite to the motion and depends on the nature and condition of the surfaces in contact. . . . *Static* friction is that which opposes a tendency to move due to the forces acting on a body at rest, and its limiting value occurs when the body is at the point of transition from rest to motion. *Kinetic* friction is that which continually opposes the motion. . . .

> "If a weight, W, is moved along a horizontal plane by a horizontal force, P, (Figure 4), a force of friction will be developed at the surface between the weight and the plane. If we let F = the friction and N = the normal pressure between the plane and the weight, the ratio of F to N is called the coefficient of friction.

> "Denoting[330] this coefficient by f, we have

$$f = \frac{F}{N}."$$

67

(Most authors use the letter μ to connote friction coefficient.)

"If we let R equal the resultant of F and N, and ϕ the angle which R makes with N, we shall have

$$R = \sqrt{F^2 + N^2}$$
$$f = \frac{F}{N} = \tan \phi$$

that is, *the coefficient of sliding friction* is equal to the tangent of the angle ϕ between the resultant force exerted by the plane on the weight and its normal component. The angle ϕ is called the *angle* of friction . . . it is evident that N is equal

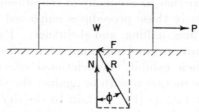

Figure 4. Coefficient of friction. (*From Fuller and Johnson,*[330] *"Applied Mechanics."*)

to W and, if the weight moves with a uniform velocity, P is equal to F and $f = \dfrac{F}{N} = \dfrac{P}{W}$ is the coefficient of kinetic friction. If the weight is at rest and the force P is the force required to start it in motion, $f = \dfrac{P}{W}$ is the coefficient of static friction. Generally the latter coefficient is larger than the former."

Backer[294] states that Coulomb in 1781 confirmed the results of Leonardo da Vinci in the 15th century, that

"the force which resists relative motion between two bodies in contact depends only upon the normal load at the interface between the bodies, and is independent of the apparent area of contact. . . . Coulomb was the first to differentiate between static and kinetic friction, and he showed that the latter was the smaller (of the order of one-third of the static frictional resistance) and, further, was nearly independent of speed."

Backer[294] cites three mechanisms of friction: the surface roughness hypothesis, the adhesion hypothesis, and the plowing hypothesis. The first suggests that

"surface roughness and the mechanical interlocking of surface
protuberances (are) considered . . . to cause frictional resistance. . . . The second mechanism . . . has been more generally accepted by students of friction and wear. . . . The
theory proposes that when . . . two bodies are rubbed
together, the atoms of the protuberances of upper and lower
surfaces are moved into each other's electrostatic field of
attraction and thus form minute welds or adhesions. Continued movement of the surfaces requires additional force to
rupture these adhesions."

The third mechanism involves the ploughing of a soft surface by a hard
one. Backer suggests that all three mechanisms probably contribute to
the total force of friction.

(14) Techniques for Measuring Friction

Speakman and Stott[331] use a "violin-bow" technique wherein a
series of parallel fibers are clamped across a small bridge (Figure 5).

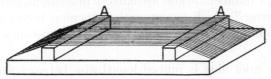

Figure 5. The "Bow" method for measuring friction. (*From Speakman and
Stott,*[331] *"A Contribution to the Theory of Milling."*)

In testing wool fibers, care is taken to insure that each fiber has its scales
pointing in the same direction.

In any friction measurement, the material against which the test
specimen is to be rubbed is of obvious importance. Speakman and
Stott[331] are particularly interested in milling shrinkage and comment:

"Milling shrinkage takes place by the migration of fibers
in contact with their own kind, and the ideal surface on which
friction measurements should be made would be one composed
of fibers of the same kind as those constituting the bow, the
fibres being arranged parallel to one another with the scales all
pointing in one direction. Using such a surface, measurements
could be made with the scales of both bow- and surface-fibres
opposing motion and with the scales in each case favoring
motion. The difference between the two determinations of
friction would then be the maximum possible in the case of any
one wool, and would give a perfect measure of scaliness.
Unfortunately the diameter of wool fibres is so very small that
the labour involved in constructing the surface is such as alto-

gether to prohibit its use. Even if no attempt were made to arrange the fibres with their scales all pointing in one direction, the tedium of constructing surfaces of this type would still be prohibitive. At the same time it is clearly necessary . . . that the surface used in friction measurements (Writer's note: here) should be one composed of wool. Ultimately a face cloth having a trail-pile finish was chosen as the best possible compromise."

In making the test, the surface pad is placed on an inclined plane, the bow placed upon it, and the plane is rotated to the angle where slippage of the bow occurs. Friction in the direction of root and tip can be measured in turn.

Morrow[332] describes an apparatus for measuring the friction of fibers in bundle form by preparing two pads of fibers and enclosing a tuft of similar or different material between them. A spring mechanism holds the assembly under constant pressure, and the force necessary to pull out the tuft is ascertained.

Speakman, Chamberlain and Menkart[333] describe an instrument called the "Lepidometer" which measures the creeping power (tendency for the fibers to move relative to each other). The principle evolves from the fact that

"when a wool fibre is rubbed lengthwise between finger and thumb, it migrates in the direction of the root-end, because the surface is composed of a series of overlapping scales which function like a ratchet. . . . The fibre, with its root-end downwards, is placed between two surfaces which are caused to reciprocate under standard pressure. Fibre travel proceeds until the tension developed in a measuring device, to which the tip-end of the fibre is attached, is sufficient to arrest motion, and the maximum tension developed is taken as a measure of scaliness. . . . Fibre migration of this type is responsible for the felting of loose wool and the shrinkage of wool fabrics under suitable mechanical conditions in the presence of aqueous media."

Several investigators, among them Morrow,[332] Martin and Mittelmann,[334] Buckle and Pollitt,[335] Lipson and Howard,[336] and Breazeale,[340] employ the well-known belt friction formula wherein a belt (or yarn or fiber) slips over a cylindrical surface:

$$\frac{T_1}{T_2} = e^{\mu\theta}$$

where T_1 and T_2 are the forces applied to the two ends of the belt, θ is the angle of surface contact, and μ = the friction coefficient.

The pulley surface is of obvious importance, and Lindberg and Gralen[337] comment:

"Lipson and Howard[336] used a keratin rod as a cylinder in order to get a surface of the same chemical composition as the wool fibre. They treated the keratin rod in the same way as the fibre in order to obtain changes in friction, and they claimed to get results that could be consistent for wool-wool friction. Mercer and Makinson[338] have pointed out that the interior keratin layer of horn is not likely to give the same effect as the surface layer of wool when treated according to some non-felting process. Martin and Mittlemann[334] have used different materials for the cylinder surface, and have also used a piece of cloth of the same wool as the single fibre attached to the rod. . . . It must be of only minor interest, however, to know the friction between a wool fibre and another material like horn, glass, rubber, and so on. . . . "

Lindberg and Gralen[337] then go on to discuss the more important problems of measuring the friction between single fibres.

Mercer and Makinson[338] describe an apparatus originally designed by Bowden and Leben[339] for the study of friction between metals. It is called a stick-slip apparatus, and

"depends on the fact that the relative motion between rubbing surfaces at low average velocities is not usually uniform, but is a series of alternate sticks and slips."[338]

An individual fiber is mounted on a glass bow and is pressed against a surface which may be another fiber . . .

"but in our experiments on wool was usually a cylindrical piece of polished horn, which is chemically very similar to wool and, as a rubbing surface, is much more convenient than a second fiber."[338]

(Writer's note: This point can be debated.)

The platform which holds the fiber is moved at constant velocity such that the fiber is brought into contact with the test surface. Ultimately the fiber sticks to the test surface, causing the surface to deflect a spring . . .

"until its elastic-restoring force becomes equal to the maximum force of static friction. If the kinetic friction is less than the static friction, which is usually the case at low velocities, the test surface then slips rapidly back over the fiber, coming to rest relative to the fiber at some position which is determined by the dynamics of the system. The cycle is then repeated."[338]

The motion of the fiber relative to the test surface is a series of "slips" and "sticks." Photographic traces of the slip deflections are made.

> " . . . Consecutive sticks are joined by a light trace . . . in general, the slip will be longer the greater the difference between the static and kinetic coefficients of friction. . . . In one traverse of the fiber, from 50 to 100 separate determinations are made of the coefficient of static friction."[338]

Gralen and Olofsson[341] describe a torsion wire apparatus for measuring the static and dynamic friction between two fibers placed at selected angles. A mechanical-optical recording system produces a saw-tooth trace of a series of dynamic and static friction values as the fibers "stick" and then "slip."

In a later paper, Lindberg and Gralen[337] discuss disadvantages of this apparatus as follows:

> "The measurements of wool fibre in this apparatus showed considerable dispersion especially in the anti-scale direction. This is considered to be due to the small area of contact between the two fibres which allows only a few scales to hook in each other. The nature and the shape of the scales are obviously very different at different parts of the fibre and consequently the values are varying. In order to obtain a good average it is necessary to measure a large number of points along the fibre.
>
> "Therefore it was desired to have an apparatus for friction measurement with an increased area of contact. The principle used consists in twisting two fibres a certain number of turns, and applying loads at the fibre ends. By increasing the load at one of the four ends, slippage can be obtained, and the sizes of the loads give the frictional forces."

Figure 6 shows the two fibers positioned at the start of the test.

> "The main parts of the apparatus are two torsion balances and two ordinary balances . . . (to which) . . . the four ends of the fibre twist are fixed . . . one fibre runs from the right-hand upper balance to the right-hand lower and the other from the left to the left."[337]

The technique consists, essentially, of loading two opposite fiber ends and noting the force required to induce slippage. The total force necessary is given by the general equation:

$$N_{\text{Total}} = 2P\pi n \sin \frac{\beta}{2}$$

where N_{Total} = total normal force between the two fibers

P = tension in the fiber

n = number of turns in the twist

β = angle between the two fibers

Then
$$N_{\text{Total}} = \frac{P_2 - P_1}{\mu}$$

where P_1 and P_2 are the tensions on the two fibers, and μ is the coefficient of friction. Figure 7 shows the position of the fibers after slippage has occurred. Both static and kinetic friction values are obtainable.

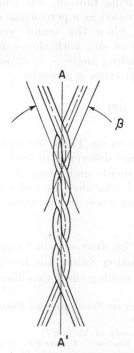

Figure 6. Original fiber twist with two turns. (*From Lindberg and Gralen,*[337] "*The Frictional Properties of Wool Fibres.*")

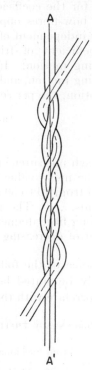

Figure 7. Distorted fiber twist. (*From Lindberg and Gralen,*[337] "*The Frictional Properties of Wool Fibres.*")

(15) Frictional Properties of Fibers and Yarns

Frictional Data on Fibers. Speakman and Stott,[331] using the violin-bow method (see page 69) report on differences in friction of wool fibers when measured root-to-tip and tip-to-root. The authors are particularly concerned with differential friction as it pertains to fulling and milling; this subject will be discussed in Chapter 18. They[331] comment:

> "The various wools differ considerably in fiber diameter, and although the load applied (by the bow) to the sets of 50 fibres during friction measurements may in all cases be identical, the effective load (per fibre) will vary as some inverse function of the mean fibre diameter. The exact nature of this function is difficult to determine and absolute measurements of friction are correspondingly difficult to interpret. It was, however, found that the difference between the two values for the coefficient of friction, obtained with the scales of the bow-fibres opposing and favouring motion, was completely independent of load when expressed as a percentage of the coefficient of friction observed when the scales were favouring motion. If θ_1 is the angle of slip with the scales favouring motion, and θ_2 the corresponding angle . . . opposing motion, the per cent difference in friction is given by . . .

$$\frac{\tan \theta_2 - \tan \theta_1}{\tan \theta_1} \times 100$$

> "Each measurement of scaliness given (in Table 36) represents the mean value for the percentage difference in friction derived from 40 to 50 pairs of measurements under four different loads. . . . The merino wools are classified in order of increasing fibre diameter, the remaining wools being arranged in order of decreasing scaliness."

The significance of the following data will be discussed in Chapter 18. It can briefly be stated here that the limiting values for merino and mohair do correlate with the known ease of milling these two fiber types.

TABLE 36. PERCENTAGE DIFFERENCE IN FRICTION OF WOOL FIBERS, ROOT-TO-TIP AND TIP-TO-ROOT
(From Speakman and Stott[331] "Theory of Milling")

Wool	% Difference in Friction	Average Fiber Diameter (μ)
Tasmanian super quality Merino	50.9	16.1
90's Australian Merino	42.9	17.4
80's Australian Merino	60.4	17.7
80's Cape Merino	52.0	18.3
70's Cape Merino	59.4	19.0
70's Cape Merino	60.0	19.4
64's Cape Merino	52.0	20.8
64's Cape Merino	44.3	21.4
70's Australian Merino	39.8	22.0
64's Australian Merino	44.0	23.0
60's Australian Merino	33.7	24.8

TABLE 36. PERCENTAGE DIFFERENCE IN FRICTION OF WOOL FIBER, ROOT-TO-TIP
AND TIP-TO-ROOT—(*Continued*)

Wool	% Difference in Friction	Average Fiber Diameter (μ)
60's Australian Merino	35.0	27.4
Australian Merino	22.6	33 2
Southdown	28.3	32.8
Romney Marsh	27.5	34.3
56's Southdown	25.7	31.7
Corriedale	25.2	23.8
Exmoor	23.5	40.9
Oxford Down	21.3	41.7
Wensleydale	16.3	36.8
Leicester	13.5	38.0
mohair	5.0	31.7

Morrow,[332] using the tuft pull-out test described on page 70, shows a straight-line graph of friction force vs. pressure on a cotton tuft.   He lists the following coefficients of friction.

TABLE 37. COEFFICIENTS OF FRICTION, HAIRS UPON HAIRS
(From Morrow,[332] "The Frictional Properties of Cotton Materials")

Material	Coefficient of Friction (μ)
Sakel cotton (air dry 70% R.H.)	0.24
Sakel cotton (wet)	0.32
Sea Island cotton (raw)	0.22
Sea Island cotton (soda boiled)	0.27
Texas cotton (raw)	0.24
Texas cotton (soda boiled)	0.26
Vistra staple fiber	0.30

Morrow[332] comments:

"Rayon staple fibre has about the same coefficient as cotton under a high pressure, but is far more slippery under zero pressure, probably because of the absence of convolutions.   Scouring of cotton increases the coefficient, probably by removing some of the wax, which may act as a lubricant at high pressures, although at low pressures it may have a gumming effect. A wet (cotton) sample gives a higher value than the same material dry, which is doubtless one of the reasons for the temporary increase of yarn strength at high humidities."

Mercer and Makinson,[338] using their stick-slip apparatus, report the following presumably static friction values.   Fibers were mounted at right angles; from 50 to 100 stick-slips were obtained with each pair of fibers.

TABLE 38.   COEFFICIENTS OF FRICTION OF VARIOUS AIR DRY TEXTILE FIBERS AND
FILAMENTS IN COMMERCIAL CONDITION
(From Mercer and Makinson[338] "The Frictional Properties of Wool and Other
Textile Fibers")
(Load 0.17–0.18 g wt.)

Rubbing Surfaces	Friction Coefficient (μ)	Fiber Diameter (microns)
nylon/nylon		
very fine	.14	18
6 denier	.15	28
27 denier	.23	62
bristle	.6 (.5–.8)	500 approx.
silk/silk	.26	
viscose rayon/viscose rayon	.19	30 (variable)
acetate rayon/acetate rayon	.29	41 (variable)
cotton/cotton		
from sewing thread	.29	
from cotton wool	.57	18 (variable)
sylko/sylko (treated cotton)	.19	
Pe Ce/Pe Ce*	.19	19.5
glass/glass	.13	5.25
lanital/lanital	.21	21
soya bean/soya bean	.16	18
Lanusa/Lanusa†	.14–.35	19
Vistra/Vistra (XT matt)†	.17	20
wool/wool‡		
from tops	$\begin{cases} \mu_2 = .38 \\ \mu_1 = .24 \end{cases}$	20
commercially scoured	$\begin{cases} \mu_2 = .49 \\ \mu_1 = .20 \end{cases}$	18
coarse, "clean"	$\begin{cases} \mu_2 = .42 \\ \mu_1 = .25 \end{cases}$	26
wool/horn, coarse "clean"	$\begin{cases} \mu_2 = .50 \\ \mu_1 = .34 \end{cases}$	26

   * Chlorinated polyvinyl chloride.
   † I. G. Farbenindustrie wood fibres.
   ‡ The variety of results obtainable with commercial wool reflects differences in treatment during scouring and manufacture rather than original difference between the wools.

Mercer and Makinson[338] show that the coefficient of friction, under their test conditions, is not a constant, but varies with load as shown in Graph 18.

In recent years, an outstanding series of papers have been published by Gralen, Olofsson, and Lindberg.[337,341,342,343,344] The first of the series,

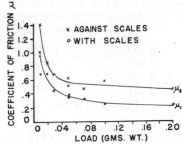

Graph 18. The variation of μ with load for air dry wool on horn. (*From Mercer and Makinson,*[338] *"The Frictional Properties of Wool and other Textile Fibres."*)

by Gralen and Olofsson[341] used the stick-slip technique in obtaining the following data:

TABLE 39. STATIC FRICTION BETWEEN TWO WOOL FIBERS
(From Gralen and Oloffson[341] "Measurement of Friction between Single Fibers")

	Fibers Untreated		Fibers Halogenated
	μ_s	σ	μ_s
fibers placed in opposite directions			
movement against scales	0.73	0.25	0.41
movement with scales	0.15	0.04	0.27
fibers placed in same direction			
movement against scales for the lower fiber	0.26	0.07	0.32
movement with scales for the lower fiber	0.24	0.05	0.31

μ_s = static frictional coefficient, σ = standard deviation of μ_s; load = 47 mg (58's South American crossbred wool).

"If the fibres are placed in opposite directions and the lower one is moved in the tip direction, the tips of the fibre scales will hook into each other and the frictional forces will be very high. . . . There is a great dispersion of the values due to the unevenness of the scales and variations in the distances between them. If the lower fibre is moved in the root direction, no hooking can occur and we obtain the real friction between the surfaces of the scales, which is very much smaller. If the fibres are put in the same direction, the direction of movement is of no great importance. . . . A strong halogenation of the fibres (by treatment with a saturated solution of bromine in distilled water at room temperature for 15 minutes) does diminish the anti-scale friction and increase the with-scale friction but there is still a pronounced difference. It is obvious that the decrease of felting properties on halogenation cannot be explained only by friction measurements in the dry state. The friction must be measured in the liquid used for milling."[341]

TABLE 40.   FRICTION BETWEEN TWO VISCOSE RAYON FIBERS
(From Gralen and Olofsson[341] "Measurement of Friction")

Static Friction

N	μ_s	σ	m
17	0.302	0.035	82
47	0.282	0.018	62
67	0.276	0.018	67
97	0.271	0.019	75

Dynamic Friction

N	μ_d	σ	m
17	0.180	0.026	82
47	0.156	0.011	62
67	0.144	0.010	67
97	0.140	0.006	75

N = Normal pressure; μ = Coefficient of friction; σ = Standard deviation; m = Number of measurements.

These investigations[341] show that graphs of frictional force (F) vs. normal pressure (N) for wool fibers, under both static and dynamic conditions, are substantially straight lines.   They state:[341]

"As a first approximation we have $\mu = F/N$ = constant for both static and dynamic friction.   However there is a small increase of μ with decreasing N.   This can be interpreted by assuming that small adhesion forces act between the fibers and give $F > 0$ even for $N = 0$."

In ascertaining the coefficient of friction of both nylon and wool, Lindberg and Gralen[337] show linear relationships between μ and $1/N$, thus confirming the hyperbolic function of μ vs. N shown in Graph 18.

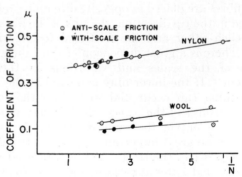

Graph 19.   Frictional coefficients of nylon and wool fibers.   (*From Lindberg and Gralen,*[337] "*Friction Between Single Fibers.*")

It may appear surprising that the coefficient of friction of the nylon, a supposedly "smooth" fiber is higher than for wool.   It must be kept in mind that the actual surface areas in contact are different.   Lindberg and Gralen call this value S and state that it might be dependent on the normal pressure. Gralen[344] adds

"The low friction of animal fibres is not surprising, perhaps, when the smooth feel of fur is considered. The smoothness of the wool surface is probably hidden by the crimp in the loose fibres and by the interlacing of fibres in the woven or knitted cloth. The friction in the dry state of wool fibres is of the same order of magnitude as that of well-lubricated metallic surfaces, and this low friction gives the impression of a very hard and smooth surface."

TABLE 41. STATIC COËFFICIENTS OF FRICTION OF FIBERS
(From Gralen and Olofsson[344] "Measurement of Friction Between Single Fibers")

Fiber	Friction Coefficient
wool	
with scale	0.11
anti-scale	0.14
wool in water	
with scale	0.15
anti-scale	0.32
cotton	0.22
jute	0.46
silk	0.52
viscose rayon	0.43
acetate rayon	0.56
casein	0.46
nylon	0.47
saran	0.55
"Terylene"	0.58
steel	0.29

Frictional Data on Yarns. Morrow,[332] using the belt-pulley formula, reports on the frictional properties of running yarns as they pass through machinery guides, etc.:

TABLE 42. MISCELLANEOUS YARN FRICTIONS
(From Morrow[332] "The Frictional Properties of Cotton Materials")
Initial tension, weight of two hanks, wherever possible

Yarn	Surface	Speed	Friction μ
20's American twist	steel	60 yds/min.	0.25–0.35*
20's American twist	steel	60 yds/min.	0.26†
20's American twist	steel	Static	0.06, approx.
20's American twist	duralumin	140 yds/min.	0.26
20's American twist	polished boxwood	140 yds/min.	0.16
20's American twist	polished boxwood	Static	0.20
20's–70's American	ring traveller (steel)	15 yds/min.	0.27‡
38's American twist	glass, 0.47-cm diam.	150 yds/min.	0.20§
38's American twist	glass, 0.62-cm diam.	150 yds/min.	0.22§

TABLE 42.   MICELLANEOUS YARN FRICTIONS—(*Continued*)

Yarn	Surface	Speed	Friction μ
36's sakel	duralumin, 0.8-cm diam.	150 yds/min.	0.28§
36's sakel	duralumin, 1.4-cm diam.	150 yds/min.	0.27§
2/50 mercerised knitting	glass, 0.62-cm diam.	150 yds/min.	0.21§
2/50 mercerised knitting	glass, 0.47-cm diam.	150 yds/min.	0.17§
2/50 mercerised knitting	steel	150 yds/min.	0.30
rayon	duralumin	150 yds/min.	0.45
sized rayon	wood	2–3 in./min.	0.21
sized rayon	wood	Static	0.31
rayon staple fiber			
ungassed	steel	140 yds/min.	0.34
gassed	steel	140 yds/min.	0.39
sewing thread			
3/50 unwaxed	steel	65 yds/min.	0.28
3/50 waxed	steel	65 yds/min.	0.16

* Values vary with regain and temperature.

† At 70°F and 70% R.H. conditions, under which all experiments were conducted unless otherwise noted.

‡ Measured on Krumme's apparatus.

§ These were obtained by the four-roller method.

Morrow lists data showing the effect of moisture regain, humidity, and temperature on friction.

TABLE 43.   EFFECT OF MOISTURE REGAIN, HUMIDITY, AND TEMPERATURE ON
COTTON YARN FRICTION

(From Morrow[332] "The Frictional Properties of Cotton Materials")

Effect of Moisture on the Friction of Yarn

Yarn 20's American Twist, against steel

Speed approx. 65 yds/min.

Temp. between 20 and 21°C

Regain	Friction	Regain	Friction	Regain	Friction
1.6	.242	5.1	.262	9.6	.297
1.8	.240	6.2	.270	10.0	.300
3.3	.250	7.2	.282	10.5	.317
4.0	.255	8.0	.289	10.5	.325
4.2	.252	8.6	.297	12.3	.342

Effect of Relative Humidity on Friction

Relative Humidity (%)	Friction (μ)	Relative Humidity (%)	Friction (μ)	Relative Humidity (%)	Friction (μ)
0	.265	52	.321	86	.409
34	.289	70	.334	100	.436

Effect of Temperature on Yarn Friction

Yarn 20's American Twist

Speed approx. 140 yds/min., Krumme's apparatus

Yarn Dry		Yarn Moist	
Temp. (°C)	Friction (μ)	Temp. (°C)	Friction (μ)
20	0.34	19	0.43
55	0.31	50	0.44
86	0.29	87	0.33
		91	0.28
		100	0.25

" . . . the coefficient of friction (for cotton) increases considerably with increase in regain. This conclusion is supported by the results of another experiment (wherein the humidity was controlled) . . . a pronounced increase in the coefficient of friction with increase of humidity and hence of regain (is noted). . . . Temperature has a much greater effect on damp than on dry yarn. . . . (However) since the arrangement adopted for keeping the yarn moist was necessarily crude and unlikely to keep the yarn from drying considerably at high temperatures, it seems probably that the effect of temperature in reducing the coefficient of friction can be attributed mainly to its effect in drying the yarn, though . . . there may be an additional small effect due possibly to the softening of the wax. . . . In actual mill conditions, the relative humidity usually decreases as the temperature is raised, so that the yarn friction will decrease. This might tend to cause a slight reduction in the number of weaving breaks, though the effect would probably be masked by the reduction in yarn strength consequent on the lessened regain."[332]

Buckle and Pollitt[335] report friction values of yarns wound at selected speeds and also when passed over various types of pulley surfaces:

TABLE 44. COEFFICIENT OF FRICTION AND SPEED OF WINDING
(From Buckle and Pollitt[335] "Coefficient of Friction of Yarns")
Stainless steel friction object, radius 0.75 in.; initial tension, approx. 25 g; room temperature 70 ± 2°F; relative humidity 65 ± 2%

Yarn Description	Coefficient of Friction at Winding Speed in Yds/Min. of:									
	1.9	3.4	10	18	32	53	67	79	120	140
grey cotton, 32s/5	0.159	.166	.202	.210	.237	.261	.268	.275	.279	....
acetate rayon "dull" 300-den.	0.221	.226	.249	.271	.298	.321	.339	.345	.357	.363
spun silk, 5/2	0.129	.151	.226	.245	.292	.313	.330	.336	....	.357
viscose rayon "dull" 300-den.	0.131	....	.242	.272	.315	.344	.354	.365	....	....
viscose rayon "bright" 300-den.	0.138	.162	.227	.272	.305	.339	.363	.380	....	.408

TABLE 45. EFFECT OF YARN/MATERIAL COMBINATION
(From Buckle and Pollitt,[335] "Coefficient of Friction of Yarns")
Winding speed, 79 yd/min; initial tension, approx, 25 g.; room temperature 70 ± 2°F; relative humidity, 65 ± 2%

Yarn Description	Coefficient of Friction			
	Hard Steel Radius 0.5 in.	Porcelain Guide Radius 0.37 in.	Fiber Pulley Radius 0.2 in.	Ceramic Insul. Radius 0.1 in.
viscose rayon "bright" 300-den.	0.39	0.43	0.36	0.30
viscose rayon "bright" 200-den.	0.37	0.43	0.40	0.31
viscose rayon "bright" 150-den.	0.37	0.46	0.32	0.30
acetate rayon "bright" 250-den.	0.38	0.38	0.19	0.20
acetate rayon "dull" 300-den.	0.30	0.29	0.20	0.22
grey cotton, 32s/5	0.29	0.32	0.23	0.24
nylon (untreated) 70-den.	0.32	0.43	0.20	0.19
linen thread	0.27	0.29	0.19	....

Platt, Klein, and Hamburger,[346] in work currently in progress for the Office of Naval Research, have studied the extent to which fiber slippage occurs in cordage yarns under tensile loads. This has been done by pulling fibers out of yarns while the yarns are loaded to various tensile stresses, and continuously measuring the pull-out force. Materials studied were manila abaca, henequen, and sansevieria yarns of varying twists. Fiber lengths for these materials are of the order of 24–50 inches. In all cases it was found that the fibers in general break rather than slip. Forces of friction per unit length of fiber, as the fiber lies in the yarn, have been determined by selecting lengths of fiber imbeddment sufficiently short such that slippage does occur. The results indicate that the length of fiber available to transmit tension by friction is far in excess of that required for all loads from zero to maximum yarn load. In other words, under normal conditions of cordage yarn manufacture, the staple length of the fiber is sufficiently long and sufficiently completely imbedded in the yarn structure that the total friction force capable of development is greater than the inherent fiber strength, and therefore the fiber will break before it pulls out.

The frictional properties of fabrics are discussed in conjunction with Fabric Hand in Chapter 20.

Chapter 5

MOISTURE ABSORPTION PROPERTIES OF FIBERS

(16) Moisture Regain

If a bone-dry fiber is allowed to come to moisture equilibrium in atmospheres of successively increasing relative humidities until 100 per cent R.H. is attained, a moisture regain vs. relative humidity curve may be plotted. Graph 20 (full line) is a typical plot for wool,[30] the curve being sigmoid or S shaped.

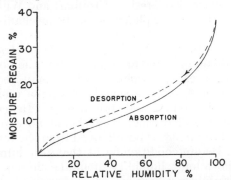

Graph 20. Per cent moisture regain vs. relative humidity for wool (at constant temperature). (*From Meredith,*[30] *"Properties Depending on the Amorphous Regions of Fibers."*)

If the fiber, containing its maximum moisture regain at 100 per cent R.H., is allowed to "decondition" by attainment of separate equilibria in progressively decreasing humidities until zero R.H. is reached, the resulting desorption curve can be plotted as shown by the dotted line on Graph 20. The absorption and desorption curves at any selected constant temperature are called isotherms. The two curves fail to superimpose and the area so encased is called the hysteresis area.

Carlene[38] has surveyed the literature on the subject and has prepared a review which will be heavily drawn upon on the following pages. He states that "prior to 1924, when Urquhart and Williams[39] began their researches on the absorption of cotton, the only comprehensive work was due to Schloesing[40] and Hartshorne.[41] Both investigators, by plotting water absorbed against relative humidity, obtained a sigmoid type of curve characteristic of the absorption of fibers by many colloidal gels. Some indications that textiles in common with other gels exhibited hysteresis effects were obtained from the work of Hartshorne[41] and others. It was Rakovski[42] who demonstrated the existence of a real hysteresis in cotton, flax and hemp . . .

"The Absorption and Desorption of Water:[38]

"A-Cotton

Urquhart and Williams[39,43] demonstrated in preliminary experiments that the absorption-desorption isotherms of raw and purified cotton were sigmoid in shape and that a hysteresis effect did in fact exist. Cotton, which attains equilibrium regain by desorption, has a higher regain than if it approaches equilibrium by absorption. Drying at a high temperature reduces its absorptive capacity. Removal of non-cellulosic impurities increases hysteresis. Urquhart and Williams[43] give a lengthy and detailed explanation of the mechanism of water absorption.

"A further study of hysteresis[44] made it clear that the absorption and desorption curves are merely the boundaries in an equilibrium area, any point in which may be capable of representing the regain of a sample of cotton under suitable conditions of humidity and pre-history. In conditioning samples for physical testing, they should be exposed to an atmosphere of humidity as far removed from the test humidity as possible. Before conditioning at that test humidity, it is preferable that a lower humidity should be chosen, since by so doing the variability at high humidity is avoided and the final regain will lie on the boundary absorption curve of the material.

"Peirce[45] thought it possible to divide the effects of absorbed water into two classes: (a) That in which water influences physical properties (strength, elasticity, rigidity, swelling and evolution of heat); and (b) That in which it provides the necessary moisture for chemical reactions and maintains a vapor pressure. Thus one portion of the absorption is connected intimately with molecular structure of the cellulose (one molecule of water per hexose unit) and produces effects of class (a) above, while the remaining water is held more loosely and fills the spaces available under attracting forces like those of a liquid, accounting for the effects of class (b).

"B—Rayon[38]

Work by Urquhart and Eckersoll[46] demonstrated that the

absorption-desorption isotherms of the regenerated cellulose have the same form as those for cotton, but that the actual values for the regain for any particular humidity are all appreciably higher, the highest hygroscopicity being shown by cellulose nitrate rayon. The rayons exhibit the phenomenon of hysteresis, and the absorption-desorption curves enclose an equilibrium area as in the case of cotton. Cellulose acetate rayons differ from regenerated cellulose in that their isotherms do not exhibit rapid rise at low humidity, an effect obviously related to the esterification of the hydroxyl groups.

"C—Wool[38]

According to Speakman,[47] the absorption-desorption isotherms of different varieties of wool show their absorptive capacities to be very similar and that differences between varieties appear to be related to relative fineness. A marked hysteresis was observed in all cases. Speakman and Stott[48] observed that wool dried from regains lower than saturation become less absorptive as the temperature of drying increases. Partial as well as complete drying causes this effect, but drying from saturation or heating wool dried at a low temperature has no such influence. The normal affinity of wool for water may be restored by allowing it to reach saturation with water vapor, but the reduced affinity of wool heated over water at a high temperature is irreversible.

"Cassie[49] studied the variation of regain of wool with changes in humidity and temperature and showed that the slow rate of change in regain during conditioning is due less to the slow sorption of water vapor by the fibers than to the diffusion of water vapor through the layers of air surrounding the fibers and to the difficulty experienced by fibers in losing or gaining heat generated or absorbed when regain increases or decreases.

"The importance of these findings is discussed in Cassie's paper in relation to the time of conditioning and their application to the hygiene of clothing.

"D—Silk[38]

The curves of silk regain are sigmoid in shape so that the behavior of silk is analogous to that of wool and cotton. . . .

"F—Nylon

The hygroscopicity of nylon is very low compared with that of the natural textile fibers. At 65% relative humidity, nylon absorbs only 4.2% water, whereas wool takes up 14% to 19%, depending upon its form; silk 11%, and cotton 8½%. Nylon, in fact, resembles cellulose acetate (regain 6%) in low water absorbency. Again, when nylon[50] is thoroughly wet out and hydroextracted only 20% to 25% of moisture is retained, whereas under identical conditions cotton retains 50%. It should also be noted that, in light of available data, there is no evidence to suggest that nylon exhibits a hysteresis effect. The low absorbency of nylon is responsible in part for the special difficulties experienced in its dyeing and finishing."

The following table[38] gives the standard regain at 65 per cent R.H. and 22°C, and the saturation regain at 100 per cent R.H. and 22°C.

TABLE 46. STANDARD AND SATURATION REGAIN VALUES FOR TEXTILE FIBERS
(From Carlene[38] "Moisture Relations of Textiles")

Material	Standard Regain (%)	Saturation Regain (%)
cotton	8.5	about 40
silk	11	35.8
flax and hemp	12	. . . . . .
jute	13.8	about 33
wool	16.0	34
wool (tops combed with oil)	19.0	. . . . . .
wool (tops combed without oil)	18.25	. . . . . .
worsted yarns	18.25	. . . . . .
carded woolen yarns	17.0	. . . . . .
wool noils (ordinary)	14.0	. . . . . .
wool noils (scoured and carbonized)	16.0	. . . . . .
woolen and worsted cloths	16.0	. . . . . .
viscose rayon	11	about 45
cuprammonium rayon	11	31–36
cellulose acetate rayon	6	17–19
nylon	4.2	about 10
casein fiber	13.0	. . . . . .
"Vinyon"	0	. . . . . .

Standard regain: That measured under equilibrium conditions at 65% R.H. and 22°C.

Saturation regain: That measured under equilibrium conditions at 100% R.H. and 22°C.

Saturation regain values given in Tables 46 and 47 should be employed with caution. Varying states of aggregation of bulk fibers, or fibers in yarns and fabrics may result in the mechanical entrapment of free water. Hydrophobic fiber fabrics, for example, can hold much larger amounts of water than is connoted by the saturation regain of the fiber per se. Such fabrics can be just as wet to the touch as the hydrophilics. The technique employed in measuring saturation regain is also important. Hotte[428] states that acetate has a saturation regain of 18 per cent when immersed in water at room temperature and centrifuged to constant weight in a 100 per cent R.H. atmosphere. The total amount of water which a textile can hold will be discussed further under Section 20.

TABLE 47.   MOISTURE REGAIN AND SATURATION REGAIN VALUES FOR TEXTILE FIBERS
(From Newell[3] "Synthetic Fiber Table")

	Regain (or Adsorption) (at 65% R.H.) (and 70°F)	(at 95% R.H.)	% Saturation Regain
viscose rayon	13	27	100–125
cuprammonium rayon	12.5	27	100–125
acetate	6	14	
saponified acetate	10.5	20	
nylon	3.8	6.1	
glass	0		up to 0.3
vinylidene chloride	0		less than 0.1
polyethylene	0		less than .01
"Orlon"	0.9	2 (78°F)	
"Acrilan"	1.7 (58% R.H.)		17 (after centrifuging)
"Dynel"	0.3 (60% R.H., 78°F)	1 (78°F)	
"Dacron"	0.4	0.5	
"Vinyon" N	0.3 (60% R.H., 78°F)	1	
protein	10	25	
cotton	7.0		24 to 27
wool	16	21.9 (90% R.H., 77°F)	
Additional Sources:			
acetate[428]			18
"Vicara"[420]	10	16–18 (75°F)	40 (approx.)

(17) Relative Humidity vs. Moisture Regain

Hailwood and Horrobin[51] discuss the mechanism of water absorption, and are in essential agreement with Peirce:[45]

> "In the case of proteins, fibrous and otherwise, attempts have been made to account for the shape of the experimental isotherms by postulating two kinds of combined water, attached respectively to the polar side chains and to the polar groups in the polypeptide chains, as well as a final condensation of liquid water in the pores of the fibers.
>
> "In this paper a different model is chosen.   The adsorbed water is assumed to exist in two states; first, water in simple solution, and second, water combined to form a hydrate with a definite unit of the fiber molecule.   It is then assumed that the three species present in the solid phase—dissolved water, unhydrated molecules, and hydrated molecules—form an ideal

solid solution. This assumption of ideality in the solid phase allows the absorption isotherm, and also the equation connecting volume and amount of adsorbed water to be explicitly derived and tested by comparison with experimental data.

"In all those cases in which both adsorption and desorption isotherms have been experimentally determined, with the exception of nylon, there is a marked hysteresis effect which appears to be real. The simple model adopted does not

TABLE 48. RELATIVE HUMIDITY VS. MOISTURE REGAIN VALUES
(OBSERVED AND CALCULATED)
(From Hailwood and Horrobin,[51] "Absorption of Water")

Wool[52] at 25°C

R.H.	% Regain Observed	Calculated
10	4.08	4.03
25	6.96	7.13
34.7	8.68	8.73
49.5	11.50	11.30
64.5	14.83	14.58
74.5	17.37	17.56
89.7	23.73	24.57
100.0	33.90	32.98

Human Hair[53] at 22.2°C

R.H.	% Regain Observed	Calculated
8.5	3.93	3.85
24.2	7.32	7.44
40.4	10.20	10.22
63.0	14.84	14.73
85.8	22.55	22.34
100.0	31.18	31.44

Silk[54] at 25°C

R.H.	% Regain Observed	Calculated
3.5	1.1	1.2
9.9	2.4	2.5
19.5	3.8	3.8
34.5	5.7	5.4
64.5	9.5	9.4
74.5	11.6	11.8
89.8	17.2	18.2
97.5	25.4	24.7
99.4	30.5	27.1

Cotton[43] at 25°C

R.H.	% Regain Observed	Calculated
1.1	0.59	0.51
4.6	1.37	1.54
8.6	1.84	2.11
13.6	2.32	2.62
27.9	3.48	3.62
46.4	5.06	4.90
68.9	7.31	7.35
79.6	9.20	9.43
92.0	13.27	13.80
97.7	18.04	17.64
100.0	22.97	19.54

Wool[55]

R.H.	25°C % Regain Observed	Calculated	40°C % Regain Observed	Calculated
5	2.97	2.64	2.50	2.05
10	4.25	4.29	3.88	3.60
20	6.25	6.46	5.65	5.86
30	8.22	8.14	7.50	7.76
40	9.90	9.72	9.36	9.39
50	11.43	11.43	10.90	11.15
60	13.47	13.42	12.66	13.10
70	15.61	15.91	14.70	15.37
80	18.05	19.21	17.16	18.26
90	22.54	23.91	20.97	22.10
95	29.15	27.14	25.75	24.40

Nylon

R.H.	25°C % Regain Observed	Calculated	40°C % Regain Observed	Calculated
5	0.58	0.50	0.49	0.43
10	0.83	0.88	0.68	0.78
20	1.36	1.49	1.16	1.35
30	1.92	1.99	1.71	1.85
40	2.48	2.48	2.24	2.34
50	3.10	3.00	2.80	2.86
60	3.72	3.60	3.36	3.45
70	4.48	4.33	4.06	4.16
80	5.28	5.29	4.88	5.09
90	6.57	6.64	6.03	6.38
95	7.70	7.55	6.65	7.24

account for the hysteresis; hence a possible modification is suggested, but has not been developed or proved."[51]

The authors[51] present theoretically calculated and observed data as given in Table 48.

(18) Heat of Water Absorption

The physiological aspect of clothing is not a major topic in this book. However, certain fiber and fabric properties have a direct influence on body comfort, and as such they should be discussed. One of these is the heat of water absorption exhibited by those textile fibers which are partially soluble in, or reactable with water.

Meredith[30] states

"When textile fibers absorb moisture they evolve heat. This produces a thermostatic action in clothing; for example,[56] in passing from a room at 18°C and 45% R.H. into an outside atmosphere at 5°C and 95% R.H., a man's woolen jacket weighing one kilogram will produce 100,000 calories of heat, i.e., as much heat as normal body metabolism will produce in one hour.

"From the theoretical and practical point of view we are interested in the heat of absorption (w) which is defined as the heat evolved when one gram of water is absorbed in a large mass of fiber. This quantity can be calculated from two absorption isotherms at different temperatures, but the accuracy is not high.[57] It is better obtained by measuring experimentally the heat of wetting (W), which is the heat evolved per gram of fiber when completely wetted. The relation between these two quantities is:

$$W_a = \int_a^{a'} w \cdot da$$

where a = initial moisture regain
a' = saturation moisture regain.

"Graph 21 shows the relationship between heat of wetting and moisture regain for several fibers where it will be seen that wool evolves more heat than any of the other fibers, that evolved by nylon being the smallest."

In interpreting this graph, the above formula must be kept in mind; the value given at each per cent regain is that amount of heat evolved in taking the fiber from the designated regain, to saturation.

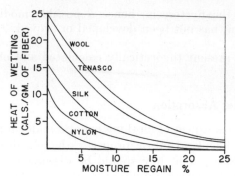

Graph 21.   Heat of wetting vs. moisture regain.   (*From Meredith,*[30] *"Properties Depending on The Amorphous Regions of Fibres."*)

Traill gives the following heats of wetting of fibers.   The presumption is that the values listed are the heats evolved in bringing the fiber from the bone dry condition to complete wetting out.

TABLE 49.   HEAT OF WETTING OF FIBERS
(From Traill[436] Clothing an Expanding Population)

Fiber	Heat of Wetting (cals/g of textile)
"Ardil"	27.41
wool 64's Merino	27.00
viscose	25.00
Japanese regenerated silk	19.83
"Fortisan"	18.00
cotton	11.00
bright nylon	7.6
"Terylene"	1.36

Continuing to quote Meredith:[30]

"Both Hermans[58] and Rees[57] have shown that the slope of the heat of wetting-moisture regain curve, i.e., the heat of absorption, has the same value at zero moisture regain for both viscose and cotton and this means that the mechanism of moisture absorption is the same for both.   Now the ratio of the heat of wetting for dry viscose rayon to that for dry cotton is about two, so we conclude that there must be twice as much amorphous cellulose in ordinary viscose rayon as in cotton, a result in agreement with the relative moisture regains of the two fibers.

"A similar argument may be extended to cover most fibers, for the slope of the heat of wetting-regain curves at zero moisture regain is almost constant for all the fibers, or in other words, the heat of absorption lies between 200 and 300 calories per gram of water absorbed for all fibers; this is about the same as the heat of hydration of hydroxyl groups or carboxyl ions. Since the heat evolved per gram of water absorbed is of the same order for all fibers, it would be expected that the heat of wetting per gram of fiber would be proportional to the moisture regain of the fiber. This is illustrated in Graph 22 which shows that the difference between the heat of wetting from dryness and that from 65% R.H., i.e., that heat evolved from 0% to 65% R.H. is proportional to the moisture regain at 65% R.H. for a wide variety of textile fibers. Differences in heats of wetting have been taken in preference to the heat of wetting from dryness, to avoid the effect of loosely held water near saturation which contributes little to the heat of wetting and is not chemically bound."

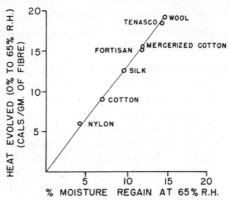

Graph 22. Heat of absorption vs. moisture regain of textile fibers. (*From Meredith*,[30] "*Properties Depending on Amorphous Regions of Fibers.*")

Examination of Graph 22 shows that the heat of absorption of wool from 0 to 65 per cent R.H. is over three times that of nylon, over twice that of cotton, and appreciably more than silk, "Fortisan," and mercerized cotton. The only fiber which approaches wool is "Tenasco," (viscose rayon). Hotte[428] reports the heat of wetting of acetate to be 6.01 cals/g. Again referring to Carlene's survey:[38]

"Shorter[59] obtained an expression for the heat of absorption of water by textiles, which is a form of the Kirchoff equation for the heat of dilution of a solid. Hedges[60] tested these conclusions and found that the heats of absorption given by the form of the Kirchoff equation and those deduced from the heats of wetting were in full agreement. The process of water absorption by wool was considered by Hedges to fall into three stages with no sharp line of demarcation between them: first, water entering the wool (up to 5%) is absorbed at the large surface presented by the capillary structure and is accompanied by a large heat of absorption; second, during the second stage of the absorption, i.e., when the true absorption is complete, there is a filling up of the pores (5-25% regain). The third stage (25–33% regain) is an osmotic absorption and the heat of absorption becomes very small as saturation is approached."

Speakman[52] confirms the above mechanism. The first amounts of moisture taken up have little influence on fiber rigidity, but are accompanied by large evolution of heat, and this water is probably absorbed within the micelles without seriously distorting the crystal structure. Subsequent absorption causes a linear fall in rigidity. The last portion of water absorbed occurs with no change in rigidity and little evolution of heat. This water is considered to flood the gross pores of the fiber.

Cassie[4] in a debate with Rose on "Natural vs. Man-Made Fibers" cites the importance of heat of moisture:

"We all know that the relative humidity of air indoors is less, particularly in winter than it is outdoors: 40–45% R.H., indoors and 90–100% outdoors are typical for Britain in all but the summer months. The position is then, that clothing worn indoors will have a low regain, and when taken outside it will absorb water vapor from the air; the greater the access of fibers to the air, the more rapid will be the pickup of water vapor. The absorption and condensation of water vapor is accompanied by a large evolution of heat, and this heat is available to counteract the decrease in air temperature on proceeding from indoors to outdoors. This amount of heat is of significant practical amount. For example, if indoor conditions are 65°F. and 45% R.H., with outdoor conditions of 40°F. and 95% R.H., corresponding wool regains are 10% and 27%. Thus on proceeding outdoors wool clothing ultimately absorbs 15% of its weight of water from the atmosphere. A man's greatcoat weighs roughly five pounds; it will thus absorb as much as three-quarters of a pound or two-thirds of a pint of water on going from indoors to outdoors in winter. The heat evolved is that required to evaporate this amount of water by boiling; or as much heat as the average man's body loses in three to four hours when he is awake. The wool thus takes water vapor from the air and uses it to generate heat which in turn opposes a drop in air temperature. The heat is not liberated rapidly but as it is required, thus opposing temperature change for several hours duration. Ultimately, of course, the fibers become conditioned to the outside air, but by then the body is prepared for the temperature change, and any feeling of chill is greatly reduced. Wool is the outstanding fiber in offering this protection."

Hailwood and Horrobin[51] have a highly technical article on water absorption properties of fibers. It is abstracted below for general reference.

The authors report the "standard free energy" changes governing the solution of water in the polymer, and the combination of dissolved water with unhydrated polymer to form the hydrate.

$\Delta G°$ sol = free energy change corresponding to the transfer at temperature $T°_k$ of one mol of water from the external ordinary liquid form, or from the saturated vapor, to that hypothetical state implied in equating the activity a' in the solid solution to the mol fraction of water present. It is therefore the state in which the water, in the solid solution, has a mol fraction of unity.

$\Delta G°$ chem = free energy change when one mol of dissolved water in its standard state in solution combines with the polymer to form one mol of monohydrate—also in its standard state when its mol fraction is unity.

Finally $\Delta G°$ total = $\Delta G°$ sol + $\Delta G°$ chem = change in free energy when one mol of ordinary liquid water or of saturated vapor reacts with dry polymer to form one mol of monohydrate.

TABLE 50. FREE ENERGY CHANGES ACCOMPANYING THE SOLUTION OF WATER IN POLYMER AT 25°C

(From Hailwood and Horrobin[51] "Absorption of Water by Polymers")

	Monomer Wt	$+\Delta G°$ sol	$-\Delta G°$ chem	$-\Delta G°$ total
wool[52]	218.9	164	1307	1143
wool 80's Merino[47]	233.9	162	1444	1282
wool oxford down[47]	218.2	166	1325	1159
wool[55]	219.2	174	1400	1225
human hair	202.4	187	1313	1126
silk[54]	383.1	107	1344	1237
silk[55]	395.3	107	1574	1467
nylon[62]	751.6	184	1484	1300
stretched nylon[55]	755.0	178	1012	834
unstretched nylon[55]	805.0	110	932	822
cotton[43]	566.3	106	1736	1630

TABLE 51. HEAT OF ABSORPTION AND ENTROPY OF ABSORPTION OF WATER INTO POLYMER

(From Hailwood and Horrobin[51] "Absorption of Water by Polymers")

	Heat of Absorption (Cals/mol)			Entropy of Absorption (E.U./mol)		
	$-\Delta H$ sol	$-\Delta H$ chem	$-\Delta H$ total	$-\Delta S$ sol	$-\Delta S$ chem	$-\Delta S$ total
wool	1056	5416	6473	4.13	13.48	17.61
silk	498	2960	3457	2.03	4.65	6.69
stretched nylon	147	2570	2717	1.09	5.23	6.33
unstretched nylon	525	7315	7840	2.13	21.42	23.55

The Rate of Gain or Loss of Moisture as It Pertains to Heat of Absorption and Body Comfort. The rate at which water vapor can be absorbed or released by a textile structure has a bearing on the heat of absorption or desorption, which in turn may affect the skin temperature and comfort of a person. Carlene[197] cites a paper by Fisher[209] which gives the following equation of moisture evaporation

$$\text{``}\frac{-dW}{dt} = R(P_0 - P_1)$$

where P_0 = vapor pressure of the evaporating water
$\quad P_1$ = pressure of water in the air
$\quad dW$ = water evaporated in time dt
$\quad R$ = function of air velocity."

Carlene[197] points out that

"a very rapid evaporation would, of course, cause undue chilling of the body surface and a very slow rate would result in injury to the skin. . . . The body requires time to adjust its thermal conductivity after a temperature change occurs, and if this change is sudden, then the adjustment made by the body will be temporarily too small, resulting in discomfort. Clothing helps greatly in avoiding such effects, since it mitigates and delays the change of temperature of the skin."

Thus the rate of water vapor absorption or evaporation should be relatively slow to enable the body to make the necessary adjustments.

King and Cassie[210] have given the problem considerable analysis in terms of the rate of moisture absorption of wool. The same principles hold for desorption, of course.

" . . . Despite absence of diffusion, wool fibers absorb water vapor slowly; this slowness is not, however, due to a slow diffusion of water into the fibers themselves, but is due to the high temperature attained by the fibers because of the large heat of absorption of water vapor. . . . The effect of this increase in temperature on regain of the fibers can be determined from Kirchoff's relation. . . . It states that if regain is to remain unchanged, the temperature and pressure must be varied according to the relation

(1) $$\log \frac{P}{P_0} = \frac{Q}{R}\left(\frac{1}{T_0} - \frac{1}{T}\right)$$

where Q equals heat of absorption per mol, R is the gas constant per mol, and T and T_0 are the absolute temperatures at P and P_0.

"Suppose a mass of wool is contained in an evacuated chamber and water vapor at a pressure p is suddenly introduced. If a fractional regain M is instantly acquired by the wool, the rise in temperature of the wool is given by

$$(2) \qquad\qquad T = q/c \frac{M}{100}$$

where q equals the heat of absorption per gram of water vapor and c is the specific heat per gram of wool.

"Now q is large, being roughly 750 cals per g for dry wool, and $c = 0.3$ cal/g/°C. An increase in regain from 0 to 2 per cent, therefore, gives an increase in temperature of 50°C; and according to equation (1) a large water vapor pressure will be required to give the sudden increase of regain to 2 per cent even when the fibers reach equilibrium with the water vapor instantaneously. Take the conditions of the experiment just described. Here the wool was originally at 25°C and water vapor at 23.5 mm was suddenly introduced. If the temperature of the wool remained at 25°C, its regain would be more than 30 per cent. But rise of temperature because of heat of absorption makes the regain immediately acquired much less."[211]

Paraphrasing the above, we can say: Wool has a high heat of moisture absorption. When dry wool is exposed in a relative humidity such that it absorbs moisture, the initial increment of moisture which is absorbed, evolves heat. This tends to increase the vapor pressure of the water in the fiber with a concomitant tendency on the part of the water to leave the fiber. Thus the absorption reaction is opposed by a desorption process and the over-all absorption rate is thus slowed down. The effect is not exclusive with wool, but exists with other fibers as a function of their heats of absorption.

With respect to the chilling effect mentioned above, the reverse mechanism on evaporation occurs. When a wet wool or high-regain fiber starts to dry, the evaporation causes heat to be absorbed (endothermic reaction) by the fiber. This causes a lowering of the temperature and of the vapor pressure, with a concomitant reduction in evaporation rate. The chilling effect is diminished.

Thus, on both absorption and desorption, the hydrophilic fibers, wool and viscose particularly, act as a damping mechanism in protecting the body from environmental changes. The higher the moisture regain, the greater will be the damping action.

Cassie[211] further comments on the subject as follows:

"Hygroscopic textiles can give a large measure of protection against sudden temperature changes at the skin. A temperature change in the surrounding atmosphere begins to be propagated through textiles as if they had no hygroscopic property; but once the initial temperature is attained, the rate of change of textile temperature becomes very slow. (Graph 23) . . . shows a curve obtained experimentally for wool: air with a constant water vapor pressure and at 15°C was blown through a cylinder of wool until this was fully conditioned; the temperature of the air entering the wool was then raised to 31°C, and curve B shows the rise in temperature with

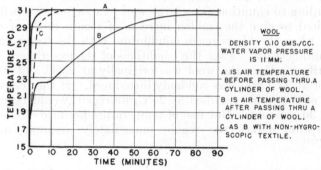

Graph 23. Time vs. temperature of air which has passed through a cylinder of wool. (*From Cassie,*[211] *"Regain of Textiles and Humid Atmosphere Changes."*)

time at the center of the cylinder. Rapid establishment of an initial temperature of 22.5°C is clearly shown and this is followed by the slow change to 31°C. If the wool was non-hygroscopic, its temperature would have increased according to curve C. The ratio of the times required to reach say 27°C by following curves B and C is roughly 20:1. Theory and experiment thus both agree that hygroscopic textiles prevent sudden atmospheric temperature changes from reaching the skin suddenly. The degree of protection increases . . . proportional to the rate of increase of regain with relative humidity; or very roughly, the greater the regain of a textile the greater is its protective power; provided of course the absorbed water does not give surface wetting of the fibers. Animal fibers are superior to all others in these respects: they absorb more water than other textiles without losing their physical properties; in particular they show no surface wetting. They have long been recognized as supreme in avoiding sudden temperature changes at the skin, and there can be little doubt from the preceding discussion that this is due, in a large measure to their high regains."

(19) Fiber Swelling

When fibers absorb water, they swell.   As a general qualitative rule, it can be stated that the greater the ability of the fiber to swell, the greater the moisture regain.   Meredith,[30] in Preston's "Fiber Science," states:

"Water molecules penetrate the amorphous regions of fibers readily, but very little water goes into the crystalline regions. Since in all fibers the molecules show a preferred orientation in the direction of the fiber axis, and since the crystallites are much longer than they are wide, the same thickness of amorphous fiber-water phase surrounding a crystalline region will produce a greater swelling laterally than longitudinally.   The following longitudinal and diameter changes take place:

TABLE 52.   SWELLING PROPERTIES OF TEXTILE FIBERS
(From Meredith[30] in Preston's "Fiber Science")

Fibers	Increase in Length (%)	Increase in Diameter (%)
nylon	1.2	5
cotton	1.2	14
wool	1.2	16
silk	1.7	18.7
viscose rayon	3–5	26

"The amount of swelling in different fibers depends upon the amount of amorphous material, on the size of the crystallites, and on the presence of polar groups.   Although silk and nylon have about the same amount of amorphous material, there are more polar groups in silk and its swelling is much greater than that of nylon.

"When fibers absorb water there is initially a small contraction in total volume compared with that of the fiber and water separately."

In other words, when a fiber absorbs water, the total volume of the wet fiber is less than that of the sum of the dry fiber and the added water. This is because the water occupies some of the voids within the fiber. Meredith[30] employs Hermans'[62] explanation of this phenomenon, taking the analogy of a mixture of billiard balls and marbles.   When they are mixed together, some of the marbles may occupy the spaces between the billiard balls.

Preston[63] in Table 53, and Preston and Nimkar[430] in Table 54 list the swelling properties of various fibers.

TABLE 53. SWELLING PROPERTIES OF TEXTILE FIBERS (IN WATER)
(From Preston[63] "Modern Textile Microscopy")

Fibers	Swelling in Water % Change in		
	Diameter	Cross Sectional Area	Length
silk	16–20	....	....
wool	16.5	36	0
cotton	7.0	....	....
viscose rayon	25–52	....	....
	41.0	65.9	4.8
cuprammonium rayon	41–53	....	....
	35.2	61.8	3.65
acetate rayon	9,14	....	....

TABLE 54. SWELLING PROPERTIES OF TEXTILE FIBERS (IN WATER)
(From Preston and Nimkar[430] "The Swelling of Fibers in Water")

	Transverse Swelling		Axial Swelling	Vol. Swelling
	Diameter	Area		
cotton	20–30	40–42		42–44
linen		47	0.1–0.2	
jute	20–21	40		
mercerized cotton	17	24*, 46*	0.1	
mercerized linen			5.6	
viscose	25, 35, 52	50, 65–67, 113	3.7–4.8	74, 109–127
cuprammonium rayon	32, 41, 53	56–62	2–6	68, 103–107
"Fortisan"		22		
acetate	0.6, 9–14	6–8	0.1–0.3	
wool	15–17	25–26		36–41
silk	16.3–18.7	19	1.3–1.6	30–32
nylon	1.9–2.6	1.6–3.2	2.7–6.9	8.1–11.0

* Various investigators have reported various values. The reader is referred to the original paper for a detailed list of references.

Carlene's[38] review of moisture properties lists the following swelling data:

"Collins[64] found that the lateral swelling of cotton fibers is much greater than longitudinal swelling at the same relative humidity. For example, in water, the longitudinal swelling is 1.2%, the lateral swelling (change in diameter) is 20%. Speakman[47] observed that the increase in length of wool fibers in water is 1.19% and that of the diameter is 17.5% corresponding to an increase in cross-sectional area of 38%. Since X-ray data have shown that the dimensions of the unit cell remain unchanged when the wool fiber is immersed in water, the lateral swelling must be due to separation of the micelles. The lateral swelling of silk increases gradually with increasing humidity. Japanese silk at 100% relative humidity showed a swelling of 18.7%. Lawrie[65] states that the increase in diameter of viscose rayon in water is 35%, cuprammonium rayon 41–53%, cellulose acetate 9–14%."

Sprague[421] states that the increase in cross sectional area of "Fortisan" is 32 per cent. "Modern Plastics Encyclopedia[7]" reports an area increase of 4.3 per cent for the "Vinyon" N's. Ott[431] reports for cellulose acetate values of 0.14 per cent, 5.7 per cent and 6.0 per cent, for length, area, and volume, respectively.

The importance of fiber swelling as it pertains to fabric dimensional stability and shrinkage is discussed in Chapters 16 and 18.

(20) The Maximum Amount of Water Which Textiles Can Hold

Carlene[197] has surveyed the literature on the subject and reports:

"There are few experimental data for the amounts of water held by different fabrics. Rouget de Lisle[207] soaked materials in water and determined the amount held (after removing the excess by hand wringing, machine wringing, or centrifuging). Flannel was found to hold the greatest amount of water, with cotton-wool next, followed by silk and finally linen with the lowest capacity. The following percentage absorptions of materials wrung out by hand were found by Roaf.[208]

	(%)
mosquito net	133
Japanese crepe	140
China silk	101
cotton	132
flannel	141
drill	93
light serge	102

"Preston and Matthews investigated the absorption of water by linen fabrics. . . . In plain woven laundered linen the effect of yarn twist on completeness of wetting is negligible, as is the effect of closeness of weave. However, the percentage of water held after dipping depends upon the completeness of wetting, but also in addition it decreases rapidly with increased ends per inch in the cloth. The water held is shown to be directly related to the compactness of the cloth. . . . The type of weave has very small effect . . . but it may affect the water holding capacity through its effect upon the compactness. Thus a twill weave will hold more than a plain weave, and a honeycomb slightly more than a huck or diaper, but these differences become very much less pronounced after mangling."

Carlene[197] further observes:

"the saturation regains of the majority (of fibers) fall between 30 and 45 per cent. Exceptions to this are nylon (10 per cent) and cellulose acetate 17 to 19 per cent. Thus the maximum absorptive capacities of the majority of the fibers in common use today for clothing purposes are approximately of the same order, which is of significance when the merits of different textiles for clothing next to the skin are being considered."

Carlene's papers[38,197] were written in 1944 and 1945, and he has not given consideration to the newer synthetics for apparel purposes.

Fourt, Sookne, Frishman and Harris[432] in discussing the rate of drying of fabrics tabulate the maximum moisture absorbed in various fabrics.

TABLE 55. THE ABSORPTION OF WATER BY MISCELLANEOUS FABRICS
(From Fourt, Sookne, Frishman and Harris[432] "The Rate of Drying of Fabrics")

Description	Thickness* (mm)	Weight (mg/cm²)	Maximum Absorption (mg/cm²)	Water Held Cloth wt.
solidly woven, smooth cottons				
balloon cloth	0.20	7.3	9.1	1.25
poplin (civilian shirting)	.30	11.1	15.0	1.35
sheeting	.38	14.8	19.5	1.32
oxford cloth shirting	.43	12.5	23.4	1.87
herringbone twill, A	.61	27.8	29.9	1.08
uniform twill, 8.2 oz., A	.61	31.0	28.4	.92
sateen, 5-harness, 9-oz.	.63	33.0	25.7	.78
Other cotton fabrics				
absorbent gauze	.38	3.3	10.2	3.10
hand towel	1.27	29.2	63.6	2.18
terry cloth	3.00	44.5	147.8	3.32
continuous-filament fabrics				
nylon A	.20	11.5	6.9	0.60
nylon B	.30	15.4	9.2	0.60
plain-weave "Vinyon"				
light sailcloth	.18	12.0	4.6	0.38
experimental uniform fabric	.36	13.5	8.2	0.61
heavy sailcloth	.56	30.6	11.0	0.36
wool felts				
silence cloth felt	2.53	36.5	175	4.80
sole felt	5.29	129	374	2.90
wool knit or woven fabrics				
tropical worsted	0.67	24.9	33	1.33
covert, all-wool, U.S. Army	1.33	34.2	77	2.25
army blanket, No. 1	2.41	52.5	118	2.25
felted-knit outerwear	4.11	66.9	254	3.80

* Thickness is measured at a pressure of 7 g/cm².

The hydrophilic cotton and wool fabrics hold a great deal more water than hydrophobic "Vinyon" and substantially hydrophobic nylon. There appears to be a direct relationship between moisture regain of the fiber type at standard conditions and the maximum amount of water which a fabric made therefrom can hold. However, yarn and fabric geometry may be even more important factors than inherent fiber property, and can radically change the amount of water held by the fabric.

Dillon[433] points out that hydrophobic fiber fabrics such as "Dacron" can hold appreciable amounts of free water. Since the water cannot be absorbed by the fibers, it wicks via mechanical means around each fiber and yarn. The water is present almost entirely as free water. Hence even if the total amount of water at saturation is low, the fabric will feel wet and uncomfortable to the wearer, due in part to its coming into contact and sticking to the skin. Hock, Sookne, and Harris[196] further discuss the wet and clammy feel of fabrics as influenced by fiber type and fabric geometry, on page 211.

Nowhere in the literature have any data been found which relate the water content of textiles to their feeling of being wet or dry. It would be interesting to ascertain the maximum moisture content of a fiber before it started to feel wet to a person. It must be related to that condition in the fiber where free water starts to appear on its surface. It has been the writer's experience in rearing two small children that woolen crib blankets do not feel anywhere near so wet as their rayon bindings under what are sometimes severe test conditions. The same situation holds in comparing wool against cotton. Apparently, wool can hold more water than cotton or rayon without feeling wet. In addition, the opportunity for the wool blanket to become wet is undoubtedly less than for a cotton blanket or rayon binding because of the irregular surface of the wool blanket. Tests with the above-mentioned offspring have never been placed on a quantitative basis, due in part to their apparent failure to abide by the law of conservation of matter in that liquid output at least appears to exceed liquid intake.

(21) The Effect of Moisture on the Mechanical Properties of Fibers

Data on the wet and dry strengths of fibers have already been listed in Section 2.

Since textile fibers, yarns, and fabrics are to be sized, bleached, dyed, finished, etc., they must have requisite characteristics in tension, torsion, and bending to withstand the required operations. For example, the yield point must not be reduced, by wetting, to a value such that the resulting wet fabric cannot be processed without causing it to be permanently and irrevocably distorted.

A corollary to the above is the importance of being able to finish a fabric in the desired manner *because* of the wet mechanical properties of the fibers from which the fabric is made.   The ability of a fiber to be rendered plastic by water, whereupon it can be "molded" into a required geometric configuration, and then "set" in that configuration by re-drying, is the nub of most finishing operations.   Wool, of course, is outstanding in this attribute since the fiber can be fulled, felted, shrunk, steamed, etc.

Similarly, in considering end-use requirements, if the fiber is to be used in any environment where it is apt to become wet or subjected to high humidity, its properties must be such as to be able to withstand such conditions.   Polyvinyl alcohol fiber, for example, is a perfectly good fiber when dry, having a fair degree of tenacity and extension.   It is water soluble, however, and would be of little value in such an end-use requirement as a bathing suit.

Hindman and Fox[66] report stress-strain diagrams for various synthetic fibers at 0, 65 and 100 per cent R.H. and 70°F (Graph 24). In each case strengths diminish and elongations increase as humidities rise.

Data on the effect of relative humidity on the load-elongation properties of the new synthetic fibers are unavailable.   However, Coplan[424] shows some wet load-elongation diagrams.   They are counterpart to the dry diagrams given in Graph 6 (page 18).   (The dry diagrams are repeated here for comparison purposes.)

As one might expect, for each fiber the greater the degree of hydrophobicity the less is the difference between the dry and the wet diagram.

Nylon, "Orlon," "Dacron," and "Dynel" show small or no differences because they absorb little or no water.

No data are yet available on the wet repeated stress properties of fibers.   It is logical to predict that those hydrophobic fibers which have the same wet and dry load-elongation diagrams to rupture, will have the same wet and dry repeated stress diagrams.   If such fibers, when dry, exhibit acceptable crease retention, wrinkle resistance, dimensional stability, or abrasion resistance, they will also exhibit such acceptability when wet.   This point is further discussed in Chapter 16.

Meredith[30] shows load-elongation diagrams at approximately 0, 65 and 100 per cent relative humidity for cotton, "Fortisan," nylon, silk, viscose, wool, acetate, and casein fiber.

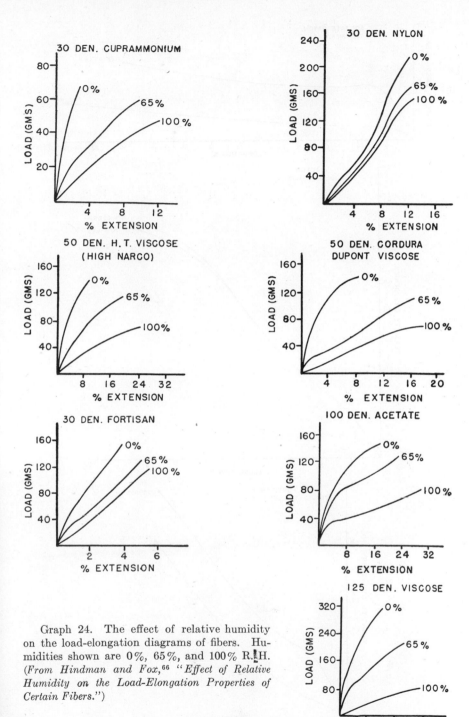

Graph 24. The effect of relative humidity on the load-elongation diagrams of fibers. Humidities shown are 0%, 65%, and 100% R.H. (*From Hindman and Fox*,[66] "*Effect of Relative Humidity on the Load-Elongation Properties of Certain Fibers.*")

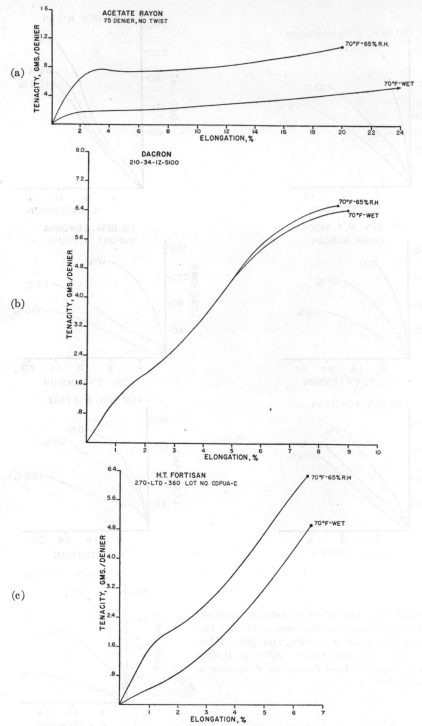

Graph 25. Dry and wet load-elongation diagrams of producers' yarns. (*From Coplan,*[424] "*The Effect of Temperature on Textile Materials.*")

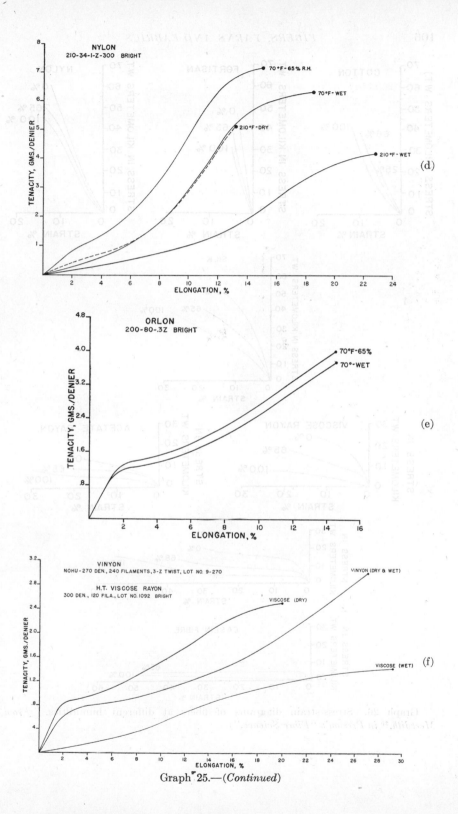

Graph 25.—*(Continued)*

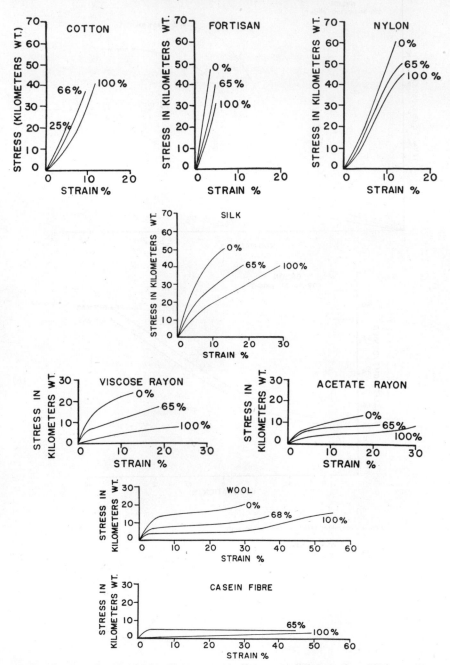

Graph 26. Stress-strain diagrams of fibers at different humidities. (*From Meredith,*[30] *in Preston's "Fibre Science."*)

Meredith states,

"Since nearly all fibers absorb water, the mechanical properties depend on the relative humidity of the surrounding air, and controlled atmospheric conditions are necessary for measuring these properties. As shown in Graph 26, native cellulose fibres, such as cotton, usually increase in strength with increase in relative humidity, whereas artificial and protein fibres decrease in strength. The decrease in strength of rayons is ascribed to the penetration of water molecules which weakens the lateral cohesion on which their strength depends. The increase in strength of native cellulose fibers like cotton, flax, and hemp, is due to the water in the amorphous regions acting as a lubricant, releasing internal stresses in the long chain molecules anchored to the crystalline regions, and so increasing the fiber strength by a more uniform internal distribution of stress. It is interesting to note that the strength of highly tendered cotton decreases with increase in relative humidity in a similar way to rayon.

"The extension at break increases with relative humidity for all fibres. For Fortisan and nylon, the increase in extension is relatively small, but the effect is considerable with cotton, viscose and acetate rayons, silk, wool, and casein; in fact the effect is large in those cases where the mechanism of fiber extension already produces a high breaking extension.

"The resistance to extension, as measured by the initial Young's modulus, decreases considerably as the absorbed water reduces the cohesion of the chain molecules in the amorphous regions. Thus only one-twentieth of the force is required to stretch wet viscose rayon or wet casein fibre by two per cent compared with the bone dry material. Acetate rayon, cotton, silk and nylon require somewhat less than half the force to extend the wet fibre a given amount compared with the dry fibre. Wool[67] is unique in that the absorption of water produces little change in its initial resistance to extension, although the yield stress is considerably lower in wet fibres."

Carlene[38] cites the following references on the effect of moisture on the elastic properties of fibers:

"Speakman's[67] investigations of the elastic properties of wool fibres led him to determine the work required to stretch them 30% at different humidities. The energy required decreased with increasing humidity, and the energy vs. humidity curve was slightly although definitely sigmoid in form. Comparison of this curve with the absorption isotherm of wool afforded additional evidence that absorption occurs at high humidity mainly by capillary space flooding. Dry wool fibres cannot be extended much further than 30% before rupture, but increasing the humidity increases their extensibility. The general form of the load-extension curve does not alter appreciably with changing humidity. But the Hooke's law region, and region of rapid extension decrease in slope with fall in humidity. Mann[68] observed that the breaking load of cotton in general increased with increasing humidity.

"Denham and Lonsdale[69] reported that with rising humidity the breaking load of silk decreased, whereas extension at break increased. With silk yarns[70] the breaking strengths were not affected significantly by a variation in humidity from 33–55%, but above 55% relative humidity, the yarns became weaker."

Speakman's findings that the absorption of water produces little change in wool's initial resistance to deformation when wet is highly significant. It means that a wet wool fabric is no more subject to deformations resulting from small forces than is a dry fabric. This explains in part why wool fabrics, when wet out or exposed to high relative humidities retain their shape, neatness of appearance, and warmth far better than do fabrics composed of other fibers.

The above remarks pertain to low loads only. The following graphs from Harris and Brown[71] confirm the above conclusion, for the slope of the wet and dry curves up to 0.2 g.p.d. are substantially the same.

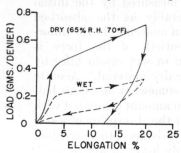

Graph 27. Cyclical loading and unloading diagram for wool fiber tested dry and wet. (*From Harris and Brown,*[71] "*Natural and Synthetic Protein Fibers.*")

The yield point of the wet fiber occurs at about the same extension as the dry fiber, but at about half the load. This means that when a woolen fabric becomes wet (assuming the effects of fabric geometry and structure to be constant, which they probably are not), higher strains or distortions can be produced with one half the force. However, let us now examine the unloading or recovery portion of the curve. If the dry fiber is loaded to any point beyond its yield point, it does not fully recover, but is permanently set. The wet fiber, under the same conditions is more easily distortable but is 100 per cent recoverable. In practical use this means that when wool fabrics are exposed to high humidities or become wet, they are more distortable, but upon removal of stress can revert to their original shape.

It explains why the wearer of a woolen suit on a humid day may induce many wrinkles in it when he sits down, crosses his legs, etc., but when he stands up and moves about, or if he takes the suit off and hangs it up, the wrinkles will "hang out" fairly completely.

It does not mean that a suit can be wrinkled at high humidity, dried out with the wrinkles remaining and then have them removable; they will then stay in. This latter technique is the one used in pressing, i.e., the suit is dampened, and then being more distortable, is pressed and dried; the new wrinkles (creases) deliberately put in tend then to remain. (This subject will be further discussed under crease resistance; it is important to explain the fundamental mechanisms here, however.)

Referring again to Graph 27, a technical term coming into popular and common parlance among textile technologists is one called "the 30 per cent index." Sookne and Harris[72] discuss and define it as follows:

The load-elongation diagram to rupture is determined under water or in a selected medium. The area under the load-elongation diagram to 30 per cent extension when tested under water at pH 5.8 is used as a standard.

"Comparison of the extensibilities of fibers in various solutions is facilitated by calculating the 30% index, which is defined as the ratio of the *energy* required to elongate a treated or untreated fiber 30% in a given medium to the energy which should be required to elongate the untreated fiber 30% in distilled water.

"It has been shown by Speakman[73] that fibers elongated 30% or less, after a twenty-four hour period of rest without load, will give load-elongation curves very nearly identical with the original curves. That the fibers used in this investigation possess this ability was demonstrated by re-extending in distilled water, five individual fibers which twenty-four hours previously had been elongated 30% in distilled water. The mean value of their 30% indices was 0.996."[72]

The 30 per cent index serves a twofold purpose: (1) The fact that an undamaged wool fiber under water can be stretched 30 per cent, allowed to relax under water for (say) twenty-four hours, and then can be stretched 30 per cent again to produce identical load-elongation diagrams and identical energy absorptions, is evidence of the ability of wet wool completely to recover to its original dimension. (2) The technique may be employed to study the effect of chemical treatments on wool. Here the reduction in energy resulting from the treatment as a percentage of the original energy *in the identical fiber* is employed as a criterion of damage to the fiber. It must be remembered that the test is a wet test, and while it is used generally in textile research, it does not necessarily always hold that because the fiber is "damaged" when wet, i.e., the 30 per cent index becomes less than 1.0, that it may not be a useful fiber when dry. The end use must be kept in mind.

Rigidity Properties of Wet Fibers. Again the importance of the subject is evident in terms of compressional resilience and crease resistance at high humidities. In this survey almost no references have so far been found which catalog the wet rigidity, bending, torsion and fatigue properties of fibers. A more thorough searching of the literature might divulge pertinent information, or it might be that research on the subject must be undertaken.

Meredith[30] discusses the effect of moisture on torsional rigidity. He calculates

> "the relative modulus of rigidity, i.e., the ratio of the modulus of the moist fiber to that of the dry fiber is plotted against moisture regain. For wool[52] the modulus of rigidity of the wet fiber is only one-fifteenth of that of the dry fibre whilst for cotton[74] this ratio is one-ninth. It is interesting to note that the shapes of the two curves are different in that the rigidity of the cotton falls off rapidly for the initial absorption of water, whereas the rigidity of wool decreased only slowly at first. Speakman[75] analyzed the curve for wool using Peirce's two-phase theory of moisture absorption, and it was found that the fall in rigidity is complete when approximately one molecule of beta water is associated with each peptide group. Since the cohesion of the keratin structure is governed partly by hydrogen bonding between neighboring peptide groups, it seems probable that the action of water in reducing the rigidity of wool fibers is due to the combination of peptide groups with water molecules instead of with one another."

Carlene[38] also states that the first amounts of water absorbed by dry wool cause little change in fiber rigidity.[47]

> "Subsequent absorption of water results in a linear fall in rigidity up to 22% regain, after which the change observed is again small."

The above rigidity findings are in agreement with wool's wet tensional properties discussed by Meredith on page 107. The fact that the first amounts of water absorbed by dry wool cause little change in tension and torsional rigidity is of applied value in the retention of a wool fabric's shape, crease resistance and compressional resilience.

It is regrettable that so far no data have been found on the wet repeated-stress characteristics of all fibers in tension, bending, torsion, and shear.

Chapter 6

THERMAL PROPERTIES OF FIBERS

(22) Thermal Conductivity and Specific Heat Capacity

Thermal Conductivity. Little data are available on the thermal conductivity of fibers because it is an accepted fact that the thermal insulation ability of a textile fabric is substantially independent of this inherent property. Rather it is a function of the state of aggregation of the fibers in the textile structure. Cassie[4] states that the heat insulation of a fabric comes from the air entrapped in it. This chapter is concerned only with *fiber* properties; the broad topic of heat insulation of textile *fabrics* will be discussed in Chapter 12.

Cassie states that the conductivity of the wool fiber is ten times that of air; silk is fifteen times that of air; plant fibers thirty times; synthetic fibers are more like plant fibers than protein.

Baxter[76] has developed a method for determining fiber conductivity by determining, for various batts of materials, a curve of conductivity vs. density at constant regain, then extrapolating the curve to ascertain conductivity at the requisite fiber density. As regain increases, fiber conductivity also increases. Relative conductivity values, based on air's being unity are given as follows:

TABLE 55A. RELATIVE CONDUCTIVITY OF TEXTILE FIBERS
(From Baxter[76] "Thermal Conductivity")

	Relative Conductivity
air	1.0
wool	7.3
cotton	17.5
viscose	11.0
synthetic fibers (tested in sheet form)	
polyvinyl chloride-acetate	6.3
polyvinyl chloride	6.4
cellulose acetate (transparent)	8.6
cellulose acetate (pigmented)	8.6–13.8
ethyl cellulose	8.9

The conductivity of a molded disc of "Dynel" polymer is given as 0.32×10^{-3} cals/sec/cm/°C.[415]

Specific Heat Capacity. Matthews[77] reports data on the specific heat capacity of various fibers originally reported by Dietz.[78] Specific heat capacity is defined as the ratio of the heat required to raise a given weight of material one degree of temperature to that required to raise an equal weight of water one degree of temperature. By definition the specific heat capacity of water is unity, and all other substances are compared with it.

TABLE 56. SPECIFIC HEAT CAPACITY OF TEXTILE FIBERS

(From Dietz[78] in Matthews[77] "Textile Fibers")

raw silk	0.331	hemp	0.323
boiled-off silk	0.331	manila	0.322
worsted yarn	0.326	sisal	0.317
artificial silk (rayon ?)	0.324	asbestos	0.251
linen	0.321	glass	0.157
cotton	0.319	straw	0.325
jute	0.324	soda wood pulp	0.323
kapok	0.324	sulfite wood pulp	0.319

The above table demonstrates that the heat capacity of most fibers is in the same range, and hence has no bearing on the heat insulation properties of textile structures.

(23) Thermal Stability

Textile fibers may be classified into two main groups with respect to their reaction to heat: those which are thermoplastic and those which

TABLE 57. EFFECT OF HEAT ON FIBERS

(From Newell[3] "Synthetic Fiber Table")

Fiber	Effect of Heat
viscose rayon	loses strength above 300°F; decomposes at 350° to 400°F; does not melt
cuprammonium rayon	decomposes at about 300°F
acetate	loses strength above 200° to 220°F; softens at 400° to 445°F; fuses at 500°F; sticking point 350° to 375°F
nylon	melts at 482°F
glass	strength loss at 600°F; softens at 1500°F
vinylidene chloride	softens at 280° to 320°F
polyethylene	5 % shrinkage at 165°F; melts at 230° to 250°F
"Orlon"	sticking temperature 455°F
"Acrilan"	sticking temperature 455°F
"Dynel"	shrinks above 275°F
"Dacron"	melts at 480°F
"Vinyon" Staple HH	shrinks at 150°F; softens at about 170°F; melts at 260°F
"Vinyon" N	shrinks above 275°F
zein protein	strength loss above 350°F; melts at 470° to 475°F
cotton	yellows at 248°F after 5 hours; decomposes at 302°F
wool	becomes harsh at 212°F; decomposes at 266°F; scorches at 400°F; chars at 572°F

TABLE 58. HEAT SENSITIVITY OF FIBERS

(From Ray[414] "The Role of Synthetic Fibers")

	Melt (°C)	Stick (°C)	Decompose (°C)	Char (°C)
nylon	250	235	......	...
"Dacron"	250	235	......	...
"Orlon"	...	235	......	...
acetate	230	200	95–105	...
viscose	...	...	180	180
cotton	...	...	150	...
wool	...	...	135	300
silk	...	...	150	...

TABLE 59. THERMAL STABILITY OF FIBERS

(From Brown[81] "Chemical Engineering Materials")

cotton	loses strength above 300°F.
silk	rapid disintegration above 170°C.
"Celanese"	loses strength above 200–220°F.
"Fortisan"	loses strength above 266°F.
viscose	loses strength above 266°F.
cupra	loses strength above 300°F.
nylon	150°C for 5 hours in dry air causes yellowing.
saran	loses 50 % of its strength at 212°F.
"Vinyon"	loses strength, shrinks, becomes tacky above 150°F.

TABLE 60. COLOR CHANGES PRODUCED IN UNDYED FABRICS AFTER HEATING FOR FIVE HOURS AT 300°F IN DRY AIR

(From Sherman and Sherman[5] "The New Fibers")

Fiber	Color Change
silk	brown
wool	yellow
nylon	light yellow
viscose	very light yellow
acetate	very light yellow
cotton	very slight yellowing—hardly noticeable

are non-thermoplastic. Typical of the former are acetate, nylon, "Vinyon," "Dacron," and vinylidene chloride; typical of the latter are cotton, wool, silk, and viscose rayon.

Tables 57, 58, 59 and 60 list the effect of heat on the various fibers.

Obviously the degradation resulting from heating must also be affected by time of exposure, relative humidity of the atmosphere, and air circulation. The latter factor is important because most ageing or heat degradation processes involve oxidation, and the greater the air circulation, the greater the amount of oxygen available to the fiber. With respect to ironing and pressing, pressure and heat transfer will also affect the amount of degradation of the textile structure.

Matthews[79] comments that electric iron manufacturers rate the resistance of fibers to heat in the order shown in Table 61. The safe surface-temperature range of home electric flatirons is also listed.   Temperatures shown are for the iron, and it does not mean that the fabric necessarily will reach these temperatures.

TABLE 61.   HEAT SENSITIVITY AND SAFE IRONING TEMPERATURES OF ELECTRIC IRONS
(From Matthews[79] "Textile Fibers," p. 70)

Fiber	Sensitivity	Safe Temp. Range (Flatiron's Sole Temp. in °F)
rayon (including acetate)	most	275 to 325
silk		300 to 400
wool		375 to 450
cotton		425 to 500
linen	least	535

It appears that wool is reasonably resistant to degradation due to heating, is not as good as cotton or linen in this respect, and since it is not thermoplastic, no danger of melting exists.   Cellulose acetate, "Vinyon," "Dynel," vinylidene chloride and polyethylene have fairly low temperature ranges of melting and sticking, and care in processing and ironing them must be taken.

Heat shrinkage may be as critical a factor in the performance of thermoplastic fibers as is water shrinkage for hydrophillic fibers.   Preston lists contraction temperatures and the melting points of fibers in Table 62.

TABLE 62.   CONTRACTION TEMPERATURES AND MELTING POINTS OF FIBERS
(From Preston[434] "The Temperature of Contraction of Fibers")

Fibers or Monofil	Contraction Temp. (°C)	M. P. (°C)
"Vinyon"	80–83	200–210
Rhovyl	90	200–210
PeCe	100–110	200–210
"Vinyon" N	140–145	190–200
saran	145–155	150–160
Perlon U	None	170–175
"Fortinese"	225–230	245
"Terylene"	235–240	250–255
nylon	none	240–250
wool	240	chars
silk	none	chars
"Orlon"	none	chars

Wool is not a thermoplastic fiber, and Preston's observation that contraction occurs at 240°C is interesting and surprising.   The magnitude of the shrinkage is not given.   One can conjecture as to the significance which such a contraction may have with respect to wool fabric shrinkage in milling and pressing.

The thermoplasticity of acetate, nylon, "Dacron," and the like is a disadvantage with respect to garment pressing.   Care must be taken as to iron temperature and pressure to insure that shiny spots are not produced at seams (resulting from higher stress concentrations in pressing), that pressure on buttons do not produce a permanent impression in the fabric, or that creases are not improperly placed, lest it be impossible to remove them. This subject is further discussed in Chapter 19.

(24) Inflammability Properties of Fibers and Fabrics

The importance of the problem of fire-resisting fabrics for apparel and decorative purposes has been widely discussed in the press. The many catastrophes which have taken place within the past ten years has resulted in a concerted effort on the part of government at all levels, the military, safety officers, professional societies, and industry to improve a bad situation. With respect to legislation, the State of California has been a leader in the development of safer fabrics. With respect to product development and test methods of evaluation, the National Research Council via The U.S. Army Quartermaster Corps., the National Bureau of Standards, and the American Association of Textile Chemists and Colorists, have been leaders.

At the outset it is advisable to define the terminology surrounding the inflammability properties of materials. J. M. Church,[82] in a symposium on flame resistance edited by R. W. Little, defines various degrees of fire resistance as follows:

"Fireproof: The use of this term conveys the meaning of total resistance to destruction by fire.

"Flameproof: A material which does not withstand the action of fire without some change in its physical state, but does prevent self-combustion once the igniting source has been removed.

"Flame Resistant: Materials which are poorer than those in the above group, but which do not burn too readily."

In addition to the burning ability or resistance of a material a second important factor must be mentioned: the problem of afterglow once the flame has been extinguished. Church[82] states

"one characteristic of cellulosic materials different from most combustibles is their tendency to be consumed, after the flame has been extinguished, by a glowing, nonflaming type of combustion. In some respects this afterglow may be more serious than flaming, for the heat resulting from it is in most cases more intensive than the flame. It may cause serious damage as well as renewed flaming."

A differentiation between flaming and glowing is necessary in evaluating materials. Flameproofing connotes both nonburning and nonglowing.

Little[83] states that

"fabric characteristics to be considered are (1) Ease of ignition or 'flammability,' (2) Rate of burning or 'combustibility,' (3) Resistance to flame and thermal degradation or 'flameproofness.'"

Let us now examine the various commercial fibers and note their flammability properties.

Sherman and Sherman[5] report tests made by the American Association of Textile Chemists and Colorists as follows:

"(1) Wool, silk, nylon, vinyl resin ('Vinyon') and vinylidene chloride (Saran) polymer fabrics offer no flammability hazard.

(2) Cotton is just as flammable as regenerated-type rayon (viscose and cuprammonium) under identical construction and testing conditions.

(3) Since cotton has a normal moisture content of 6.5%, compared with 11% for regenerated-type rayon, it is reasonable to conclude that cotton will come to the critical point much more rapidly than rayon.

(4) Acetate rayon fabrics, both close knit or woven and pile fabrics gave no flash or burning test. However, acetate rayon netting, even though the rate of burning was relatively slow and the volume of flame small, did burn, dropping a residue of still burning molten material."

Casey and Grove,[84] in a compilation of data on engineering materials, list the following:

"Asbestos: Noncombustible, unaffected by removal of hygroscopic moisture at 100°C.

"Cotton: Highly combustible, but not subject to spontaneous heating unless contaminated.

"Hemp: Highly combustible; heats spontaneously when wet.

"Wool: Not readily ignited, but will burn; not subject to spontaneous heating.

"Cuprammonium Rayon: Burns rapidly.

"Nylon: Melts in flame, but does not propagate when flame is removed.

"Saran: Excellent flame resistance.

"'Vinyon': Doesn't support combustion.

"Viscose: Burns readily.

"Glass: Inert."

Table 63, prepared by General Technical Committee "C" of the British Textile Institute,[419] is intended to be used for the identification of fibers via flame tests. It may be used here, however, to describe the inflammability of fibers.

TABLE 63. BURNING TESTS FOR FIBER IDENTIFICATION

(From British Textile Institute[419] "Identification of Textile Materials")

Fiber	Ease of Ignition	Behavior of Material
asbestos	does not burn	does not melt; glows red; returns to original form on flame removal
glass	does not burn	softens, forming round bead; glows red, then orange; leaves hard white rounded bead
"Vinyon" and Rhovyl	difficult to ignite; self-extinguishing	shrinks from flame; softens and melts forming irregular bead; burns, leaving charred black bead
"Terylene"	difficult to ignite; self-extinguishing	shrinks from flame; softens and melts forming fawnish rounded bead; bursts into flame; leaves hard irregular black bead
nylon	moderately difficult to ignite; self-extinguishing	shrinks from flame; melts forming round fawnish bead; drips and froths; liquid ignites and burns with hissing
saran (foil)	moderately difficult to ignite; self-extinguishing	shrinks from flame; softens and melts; ignites; leaves irregular crisp black bead
cowhair, horsehair	ignite fairly readily; self-extinguishing	burns rapidly with loud crackling noise; leaves charred tangled skeleton-like mass
degummed and Tussah silk	ignite readily; self-extinguishing	burns steadily with very slight sizzle
wool	ignites readily; self-extinguishing	swells; coarsest varieties burn with slight crackle; leaves irregular crisp black inflated mass
angora, rabbit, alpaca, mohair, cashmere, camel hair	ignite readily; self-extinguishing	burn quickly with slight sizzling
"Ardil"	ignites fairly readily; self-extinguishing	bursts into flame; burns quickly with slight hissing; leaves irregular black inflated mass
calcium alginate	ignites readily; self-extinguishing	bursts suddenly into flame; chars, white residue incandescent in burner
unretted flax	ignites readily; self-extinguishing	burns with crackle; smoulders; leaves delicate greyish ash skeleton
manila	ignites readily; self-extinguishing	flares and burns quickly; smoulders; leaves delicate greyish ash skeleton
casein	ignites readily; not self-extinguishing	bursts into flame; slight hissing; leaves firm tangled skeleton

TABLE 63. BURNING TESTS FOR FIBER IDENTIFICATION.—*(Continued)*

Fiber	Ease of Ignition	Behavior of Material
polyacrylonitrile	ignites readily; not self-extinguishing	softens and melts forming black bead; ignites; leaves round crisp black bead
cellulose acetate	ignites readily; not self-extinguishing	melts and burns quickly; leaves irregular charred bead
raw cotton, kapok, retted flax	ignite readily; not self-extinguishing	burns steadily; leaves delicate black or greyish ash skeleton
jute	ignites readily; not self-extinguishing	burns steadily; leaves delicate black ash smouldering to blue color
hemp, sisal	ignite readily; not self-extinguishing	burns steadily; leaves delicate white ash skeleton
ramie	ignites readily; not self-extinguishing	burns steadily and fairly quickly; leaves delicate black ash skeleton
mercerized linen, well-bleached cotton	ignite readily; not self-extinguishing	burns steadily; no ash (?)
regenerated cellulose	ignites readily; not self-extinguishing	burns quickly; slight sizzling, fine grey or black ash
"Rayolanda"	ignites readily; not self-extinguishing	burns steadily; slight sizzling; leaves black or greyish ash skeleton
acetylated cotton	ignites readily; not self-extinguishing	burns steadily; leaves fine white ash skeleton

The state of aggregation which fibers assume in a textile structure (fabric geometry again) is important in the rate of burning. This is so because burning is an oxidation process and the greater the oxygen available per fiber or fiber surface, the faster the rate (dust explosions are an extrapolation of this phenomenon). For materials which do not burn, or burn with difficulty, the state of aggregation may not be important. For highly combustible fibers like cotton or rayons it is important.

H. E. Hager,[85] Chairman of the A.A.T.C.C. Committee on Flammability of Consumer Textiles, states:

> "First we studied fabrics—all, of course, burn, but with varying degrees. Wool and silks and nylons are quite safe; most cellulose dress fabrics burn slowly; many napped, brushed and tufted cottons or rayons flash burn rapidly over the surface; sheer or net fabrics burn fast. . . . "

As recent as within the past year, there has been a flurry in the press and radio concerning the high degree of inflammability of brushed rayon sweaters. The implication in the newspapers was that the rayon was inferior and not of first quality. More careful analysis indicated that the brushed pile was so finely divided that burning proceeded at a very rapid rate. The inflammability of the rayon fiber per se was no greater than normal.

There is little information in the literature on the flame-resisting properties of wool, probably because wool is accepted as not being a hazardous material, while considerable work is reported on cotton and rayons, and application methods of making them flameproof. Church[82] lists the following requisites for such treated fabrics:

(1) Minimum add-on of chemical treating compounds in order to prevent excess weight and poor hand.

(2) Ease of application.

(3) Reasonable permanency to laundering and/or dry cleaning.

(4) Freedom from deleterious action on storing or ageing, i.e., no reduction in effectiveness of treatment or tendering of the fabric.

(5) No decrease in air and vapor transmission.

(6) Compatability of flameproof treatment with other fabric finishing treatments.

(7) No harmful physiological effects to the wearer.

(8) Prevention of flaming and afterglow.

To produce a treatment with all these attributes on cellulosic materials has not been easy, and probably to the present writing, has not been attained. The fact that wool comes by them naturally is an attribute which in many instances is overlooked. Examples of wool's flame-resistance properties are as follows:

In an analysis[86] of causes and treatment of burns in a thousand accidents at the Birmingham (England) accident hospital, it was found that "most of the deaths and the more serious injuries" were caused by the setting afire of the clothing of women and children. Most of the garments involved were usually of a highly inflammable material. This calls attention to the fact that the woolen industry has failed to capitalize on the fact that woolen garments are flame-resistant and that even woolen garments with pile structures will char without spreading the flame. It is pointed out that of the variety of fabrics sold over the counter today, only wool, silk and nylon are found to be noninflammable.

Johnson[87] states that

"The ability of charred wool to resist a flame has been demonstrated and an instrument devised whereby the time taken for a flame to penetrate the charred mass of a wool fabric and mark an indicator paper can be measured. This property of the wool fibre is superior to that of asbestos, although the brittle nature of the wool-ash precludes advantage being taken of this feature in 100 per cent wool fabrics, especially if worn specifically for fire-fighting. Asbestos threads, on the other hand, repeatedly withstand attack by flame and are ideal yarns from which to form a structure which can firmly hold the wool ash. Fabrics constructed with this object in view have been made from wool and asbestos yarns, mixtures of wool and asbestos fibres and compound structures in which the outer layers of the cloth were made from asbestos yarns and wadded with wool threads. The last-named fabrics were most successful in resisting the flames as the charred wool had little chance to escape from the interstices of the asbestos warp and weft. The structures of these cloths were carefully devised so that if garments were made up from the fabric the latter would have a rather more desirable handle than 100 per cent asbestos fabric. It still remains to be seen from full scale tests of made-up garments whether movement in wear will dislodge the ash to any serious extent. If not, then a fabric made on the lines set down from wool/asbestos will have at least three times the resistance to flame of a fabric of a similar weight made from asbestos yarn alone. There are, however, many uses for heat resisting rather than fire-resisting fabric and in these cases wool asbestos may have wider application than an all-asbestos cloth."

An explanation of wool's superiority to cellulosic fibers has not been found. In addition to their different chemical structure which is of obvious importance, a second factor to be considered is moisture regain. The fact that wool has twice the regain of cotton must be of advantage in rendering it more fire resisting. The two above mentioned factors, i.e., structure and moisture regain, could be separated by determining inflammability properties of the bone-dry fibers. Also, the relative humidity of the atmosphere in which the burning takes place may be of consequence.

Nylon. The *Nylon Technical Service Bulletin*[139] states:

"Undyed finish free nylon yarn will melt at temperatures of approximately 480°F if a flame is applied. However, as soon as the flame is removed the melt will drop away and harden, with little or no tendency for further flame propagation. . . . Nylon yarn may therefore be considered flameproof since it does not support spread of the flame after the igniting source has been taken away from the material. Our experiments and experience has shown that nylon is followed by wool, silk, rayon, and cotton in its resistance to burning."

"Orlon": Orlon burns freely and rapidly.[141]

Fiber V ("Terylene"): "Burns slowly."[141]

"Dynel" and "Vinyon" N:

"Dynel is fire resistant and will not support combustion. In contact with an open flame, the fiber will burn but is self-extinguishing when the flame is removed."[140]

The Dropping of Flaming Hot Melts. Many investigators have observed that certain thermoplastic fibers, upon burning, form viscous burning globules which drop away from the fabric and continue to burn. This is an added hazard of fabric inflammability which must be considered in evaluating flame resistance. The writer has noted that polyethylene film is particularly notorious in this respect. "Terylene" is almost as bad. Nylon has somewhat of a tendency to drop burning melt. "Orlon" burns sufficiently rapidly and freely that the dropping melt does not have time to occur. "Vinyon" and "Dynel" do not drop hot melt.

Related to the hot-melt problem is one concerning the formation of fused areas in apparel and decorative fabrics made of thermoplastic fibers which have accidently been ignited or upon which cigarette ashes have been dropped.

The writer tested an all-thermoplastic fiber carpet in comparison with an all-wool carpet being considered for department store usage. Lighted paper matches and cigarettes were dropped on both, some being allowed to burn, others being stamped out with the shoe. In the case of the wool fabric, the burning match rested on the surface of the pile, continuing to burn until it (the match) was completely consumed. An obvious scorch mark was produced on the carpet pile. When brushed, much of the char was removed, leaving a somewhat lesser but still obvious mark. The fibers in the lower part of the pile remained intact.

In the case of the thermoplastic pile carpet, the match, as it burned, melted the fibers and penetrated to the base of the carpet. Upon cooling, a hard crusty melt penetrating to the bottom of the pile was observed. The appearance and the feel of the thermoplastic fiber scorch was far worse than that of the wool. It would appear that use of 100 per cent thermoplastic pile carpeting in public buildings would not be advantageous because of the cigarette smoking problem.

Chapter 7

THE STABILITY OF FIBERS TO ENVIRONMENTAL CONDITIONS

(25) Resistance to Ageing, Sunlight, Weather, and Heat

"Modern Plastics Encyclopedia"[7] and Newell[3] both list the resistance of textile fibers to ageing and sunlight in Table 64.

TABLE 64. THE RESISTANCE OF TEXTILE FIBERS TO AGEING AND SUNLIGHT
(From "Modern Plastics Encyclopedia"[7])

Fibers	Effect of Age	Effect of Sunlight (Prolonged Exposure)
acetate rayon ("Estron"), regular	slight loss of tensile strength	loss of tensile strength
saponified acetate rayon	virtually none*	....
cuprammonium rayon	virtually none	loss of tensile strength
viscose rayon, regular, medium, high tenacity	slight yellowing	loss of tensile strength
nylon, regular, high tenacity	virtually none	loss of tensile strength
protein, zein	none	bleaches; very little strength loss
protein, soybean	none	similar to wool
glass	none	none
vinyl resin, regular, high tenacity	none	none
vinylidene chloride resin (saran)	none	darkens slightly
polyacrylonitrile ("Orlon")	virtually none	slight loss of tensile strength;* superior to cotton
acrylonitrile-vinyl chloride ("Vinyon" N), NOZZ, NORU, NORT	virtually none	darkens slightly; some loss of tensile strength
cotton	virtually none	loss of tensile; tendency for whites to yellow
silk	slight yellowing; slight loss of tensile strength	loss of tensile; affected more than cotton
wool	slight yellowing; slight loss of tensile strength	loss of tensile; dyeing affected; less affected than cotton

122

TABLE 64. THE RESISTANCE OF TEXTILE FIBERS TO AGEING AND SUNLIGHT.—
(*Continued*)

(From Newell[3] "Synthetic Fiber Table")

Fibers	Effect of Age	Effect of Sunlight (Prolonged Exposure)
viscose rayon	slight	loses strength after prolonged exposure very little discoloration
cuprammonium rayon	slight	loses strength on prolonged exposure
acetate	slight on tensile strength. None on color	slight on tensile strength; none on color
nylon	virtually none	loses strength on prolonged exposure. No discoloration. Bright yarn is more resistant than semi dull
glass	none	none
vinylidene chloride	none	darkens slightly
polyethylene	virtually none	prolonged exposure decreases strength
"Orlon"	virtually none	very resistant to degradation by ultraviolet light and atmosphere
"Acrilan"	virtually none	very resistant to degradation by ultraviolet light and atmosphere
"Dynel"	virtually none	darkens somewhat after prolonged exposure with some loss in tensile strength.
"Dacron"	virtually none	loses strength on prolonged exposure. No discoloration. Much more resistant behind glass than in direct sunlight
"Vinyon" staple HH	none	none
"Vinyon" N	virtually none	darkens somewhat after prolonged exposure with some loss in tensile strength
protein	none	very slow deterioration and loss of strength
cotton	little or none	loss of strength; tendency to yellowing
wool	little or none	loss of strength; some effect on dyeing properties

* *Note:* Contrary to the "Modern Plastics" notation, there is evidence to believe that saponified acetate can lose significant amounts of strength strictly from ageing. Also, "Orlon" is considered to be one of the most stable fibers.

Ray[414] shows in Graph 28 the outstanding outdoor exposure resistance of "Orlon" as compared to viscose, acetate, cotton, and silk. Accompanying curves for nylon and "Dacron" were apparently unavailable for inclusion on this graph. Ray states that the curves for these fibers "would probably fall somewhere between those for cotton and 'Orlon.'"

Fletcher[88] has studied the heat and light resistance of twenty-two woven, undyed fabrics and five colored plastic materials, each suitable in weight, texture, and draping qualities for either glass curtains or draperies. While constructions were not exactly the same and hence fabric geometry was an uncontrolled variable, the type was sufficiently the same to allow evaluation of fiber properties.

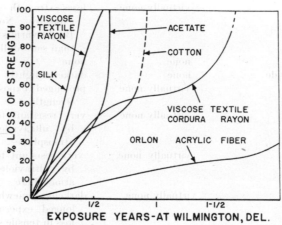

Graph 28. Effect of outdoor exposure on yarn tenacity. (*From Ray,*[414] *"The Role of Synthetic Fibers."*)

The heat resistance test consisted of progressive exposure of the fabrics for times up to two hundred hours at 125°C; the light-resistance test employed a Fade-o-meter. It is obvious that color plays an important part in the ability of fabrics to resist light exposure, in that infrared or ultraviolet absorption or reflection is dependent upon color. To eliminate such an effect, undyed samples were used so that the natural resistance of the fiber could better be measured. Criteria of evaluation are wet and dry strengths and elongations, and light reflectance (change in shade of the undyed samples). Table 65 is abstracted from Fletcher's paper and shows that the acetate and glass fabrics are most durable; silk and nylon are probably the poorest. Wool appears to be inferior to cotton and linen, but better than nylon or silk.

Caution must be employed in drawing conclusions from the data given in Table 65. Since the fabrics are not all of the same weight, and since the light exposure test in particular is a surface reaction, the per

TABLE 65.   EFFECT OF HEAT AND LIGHT ON THE PROPERTIES OF CURTAIN FABRICS
(From Fletcher[38] "Fabrics for Glass Curtains and Draperies")

Weave	Cotton plain	Linen plain	Silk plain	Wool plain	Acetate plain	Viscose basket variation	Nylon plain	Glass basket and plain
weight, oz/yd^2	3.2	2.6	1.8	2.8	2.8	2.8	1.9	2.4
dry strength (warp)								
control	37.2	56.1	50.0	25.8	40.7	38.8	97.2	40.4
after 200 hrs of heat (% remaining)	72.1	65.9	61.6	88.6	102.5	79.8	61.8	105.6
after 200 hrs of light (% remaining)	81.2	90.4	2.7	66.0	92.3	47.5	32.3	114.7
dry elongation								
control	20.3	5.7	33.7	36.0	21.3	20.7	24.7	3.3
after 200 hrs of heat (% remaining)	82.3	75.4	95.0	75.0	97.2	77.3	74.8	100.0
after 200 hrs of light (% remaining)	88.7	82.5	28.8	29.7	79.8	42.0	55.5	100.0
reflectance change								
after 200 hrs of heat (% loss)	−18.7	−21.0	−14.3	−19.7	−2.3	−28.5	−20.0	−6.0
after 200 hrs of light (% loss)	− 8.8	− 9.0	− 6.0	−10.2	+0.5	− 3.8	− 6.4	−2.0
wet strength								
control	39.0	64.1	26.8	17.2	22.7	16.5	81.5	.....
after 200 hrs of heat (% remaining)	53.1	54.7	55.8	73.0	92.5	52.0	46.8	.....
after 200 hrs of light (% remaining)	64.0	71.5	10.5	44.7	74.4	29.4	26.9	.....
wet elongation								
control	17.3	5.3	28.0	57.7	32.0	19.7	27.3	.....
after 200 hrs of heat (% remaining)	90.8	75.5	67.9	91.8	96.9	62.4	61.2	.....
after 200 hrs of light (% remaining)	115.6	100.0	32.1	97.0	75.9	47.2	47.6	.....

cent loss in strength or elongation cannot be accepted as an absolute criterion. Also a stronger fabric (e.g., nylon) may lose more of its original strength after exposure, and still retain more absolute strength than a weaker fabric which lost little or no strength. The condition of the fabric per se, after the designated exposure time must be used as a criterion for evaluation.

Of particular pertinence to nylon's poor light resistance, is the development of finishing compounds which are applied to fabrics for the purpose of filtering out the deleterious rays. A duPont patent[89] states that unprotected nylon, after 600 hours exposure to an ultraviolet carbon arc lamp, loses 83 per cent of its strength; silk loses 91 per cent; viscose rayon loses 16 per cent. By proper treatment, the nylon's resistance is increased so that it loses only 22 per cent.

LaFleur[90] discusses the mechanism of wool's breakdown upon exposure to light. He correlates Fade-o-meter exposure with ease of wetting of the fiber. He states

> "Light exposure modifies the sulphur containing groups of the wool fiber most, the chief one of which is the S-S linkage. There is good correlation between degree of modification and wettability. Exposed wool first becomes whiter, then gradually becomes yellower with increased exposure. This yellowing effect did not penetrate through to the unexposed side, and a gradually increasing color gradient, as well as harshness gradient, was noticeable between exposed and unexposed sides as exposure time was increased. Harshness was very pronounced in swatches exposed for the longest period."

Using alkali solubility as a criterion of damage to the wool, he states that the alkali solubility increased from 1.64 for the control, to 7.33 at 100 hours and 24.8 at 400 hours. These values appear significantly lower than conventional alkali solubility figures. A private communication from Dr. A. C. Goodings[435] states that LaFleur used $0.01N$ alkali instead of the more conventional $0.1N$. Additional references to light exposure studies are cited by Fletcher.[91,92,93]

Appleby[94] has made a thorough search of the literature on the action of light on textile materials. Using per cent loss in strength as a criterion, she concludes that wool is placed in the top position and silk at the bottom, the other fibers falling between these boundaries. No mention is made of the newer synthetics.

(26) Resistance to Chemicals

Table 66 from "Modern Plastics Encyclopedia,"[7] and Table 67 from Newell[3] list the general chemical resistance of fibers. It should be obvious that time, temperature, and concentration of reagent, as well as the state of aggregation of the fibers in the textile structure, will all have a bearing on the reaction rate and degree. Therefore, the data listed in the tables should not be used without thought as to their limitations.

It should also be apparent that a survey of the chemical properties of fibers is an extensive subject, worthy of one or more separate volumes. It is outside the scope of this book. Because wool is of particular interest here, it is deemed advisable to give some details on the chemical reactability of wool as it pertains to wet processing and to environmental conditions.

(27) The Chemical Reactability of Wool

Speakman[95] has reviewed the literature in "Fiber Science" (edited by Preston). This section is quoted entirely from his review.

> "The Reactability of Wool Fibers in Water: The swelling and weakening of wool fibers in water is due to weakening of the attractive forces between the $—COO^-$ and $—NH_3^+$ ions of salt linkages and breakdowns of hydrogen bonds between neighboring peptide groups. In water at high temperatures, however, further weakening is brought about by disulphide bond fission[96] . . . brought about in the following manner:

$$R—CH_2—S—S—CH_2—R + H_2O$$
$$\rightarrow R—CH_2—SH + R—CH_2—SOH$$
$$R—CH_2SOH \rightarrow R—CHO + H_2S$$

> A similar reaction is believed to take place when wool is exposed to light and air during growth, not only because the sulphur content of the exposed tips of the fibers is reduced, but also because the exposed wool reacts to a greater extent than the unexposed wool with p-bromophenylhydrazine[96] and combines with a greater amount of sodium hydroxide at pH 9.5.[97]

> "Reactability of Wool With Acids: The combination of wool with acids (at ordinary temperatures) is due to back titration of the carboxyl groups of salt linkages:

$$R—COO^- —H_3N^+ —R + H^+ \rightarrow R—COOH + H_3N^+ —R$$

> "At high temperatures, the main peptide chains are hydrolysed and the wool is broken down into the constituent amino acids, e.g. by boiling in 20 per cent hydrochloric acid for 16 hours. Some such hydrolysis occurs at ordinary temperatures, but only to a limited extent, though this increases as the internal pH of the fibres falls.

TABLE 66. CHEMICAL RESISTANCE OF FIBERS
(From "Modern Plastics Encyclopedia")

Fibers	Effect of Strong Acids	Effect of Weak Acids	Effect of Strong Alkalis	Effect of Weak Alkalis	Effect of Organic Solvents
acetate rayon, regular and high elongation	decomposed	dissolved by certain weak organic acids, such as acetic	saponified	little or no effect for short periods cold; saponification on long standing or hot	insoluble in dry cleaning solvents generally; swollen or dissolved in acetone, ethyl acetate, many ketones and esters, glacial acetic acid, phenol, and some chlorinated solvents. Softened in alcohol.
saponified acetate	decomposed	resistant	swelling and mercerization; loss of strength in hot concentrated	little effect	resistant
cuprammonium rayon	disintegrated by hot dilute or cold concentrate	similar to viscose	swelling and loss of strength	little effect if dilute	resistant
viscose rayon, regular, medium and high tenacity	similar to cotton	strength deterioration on prolonged contact or hot	swelling and loss of strength	no effect cold; reduced strength hot or on prolonged contact	resistant
nylon, regular and high tenacity	hydrolyzed by concentrated; loss of strength after several hours at 100°F by dilute	varies with nature of acid and concentration	none or slight	virtually none	unaffected by dry-cleaning solvents; soluble in phenol, formic acid, m-cresol, xylenol in cold
protein, zein	embrittled	stable	resistant	stable	resistant
protein, soybean	embrittled	stable	embrittled	little effect	resistant

TABLE 66. CHEMICAL RESISTANCE OF FIBERS.—(Continued)

Fibers	Effect of Strong Acids	Effect of Weak Acids	Effect of Strong Alkalis	Effect of Weak Alkalis	Effect of Organic Solvents
glass	attacked by hydrofluoric and hot phosphoric	stable	attacked	attacked if hot	insoluble
vinyl resin, regular, high tenacity and staple	stable	stable	stable	stable	soluble in ketones and some chlorinated hydrocarbons; swells and softens in ethers, esters, aromatic hydrocarbons, dioxane, propylene oxide
vinylidene chloride (saran)	stable	stable	stable to most; limited resistance to ammonia	stable	swelled or softened by oxygen-bearing solvents (cyclohexanone, dioxane) at elevated temperatures
polyacrylonitrile ("Orlon")	stable	stable	attacked	slight	unaffected by common solvents
acrylonitrile-vinyl-chloride ("Vinyon" N)	generally resistant except to 25% chromic, 70% nitric and 96% sulfuric	not attacked	not attacked	not attacked	unaffected by dry cleaning solvents; NOZZ dissolved by acetone and certain other ketones; other types show improved resistance to ketones
cotton	disintegrated by hot dilute or cold concentrated	stable if cold; strength deterioration if hot	swelling and mercerization	little effect	resistant
silk	dissolved	fairly resistant	dissolved	attacked if hot	resistant
wool	destroyed by hot sulfuric; resistant to others	resistant	attacked	attacked if hot	resistant

TABLE 67. CHEMICAL RESISTANCE OF FIBERS

(From Newell[3] "Synthetic Fiber Table")

	Effect of Acids	Effect of Alkalis	Effect of Organic Solvents
viscose	similar to cotton; hot dilute or cold concentrated disintegrate fiber	strong solutions cause swelling and reduce strength	generally insoluble
cuprammonium	similar to viscose; hot dilute or cold concentrated disintegrate fiber	dilute have little effect; strong solutions cause swelling; loss of strength, and ultimate disintegration	generally insoluble
acetate	concentrated solutions of strong acids decompose	strong alkalis saponify into regenerated cellulose	soluble in acetone and glacial acetic acid
nylon	boiling in 5% HCl ultimately causes disintegration; dissolves with at least partial decomposition by cold concentrated solutions of HCl, H_2SO_4, HNO_3	substantially inert	generally insoluble; soluble in some phenolic compounds and in concentrated formic acid
glass	attacked by hydrofluoric and hot phosphoric only	attacked by hot solutions of weak alkalis and cold solutions of strong alkalis	insoluble
vinylidene chloride	fair resistance to concentrated sulfuric acid; good resistance to others	unaffected by most; limited resistance to ammonium hydroxide	insoluble in most solvents; swelled or softened by oxygen-bearing solvents such as cyclohexanone and dioxane at elevated temperatures
polyethylene	very resistant	very resistant	swollen at room temperatures by chlorinated hydrocarbons, aromatics and aliphatics
"Orlon," and "Acrilan"	good to excellent resistance to mineral acids	fair to good resistance to weak alkalis	not harmed by common solvents
"Dynel"	little or no effect	little or no effect	weakened by 5% phenol; softened by acetone and certain other ketones

TABLE 67. CHEMICAL RESISTANCE OF FIBERS.—(*Continued*)

	Effect of Acids	Effect of Alkalis	Effect of Organic Solvents
"Dacron"	good resistance to most mineral acids; dissolved with at least partial decomposition by concentrated solutions of sulfuric acids	good resistance to weak alkalis and moderate resistance to strong alkalis at room temperature; disintegrated by strong alkalis at boiling temperatures	generally insoluble; soluble in some phenolic compounds
"Vinyon" HH	none	none	soluble in ketones and some chlorinated hydrocarbons
"Vinyon" N	little or no effect	little or no effect	weakened by 5% phenolic; softened by acetone and certain other ketones
protein	resistant (mineral acids up to 10%)	insoluble in caustics up to 10% solutions	insoluble
cotton	disintegrated by hot dilute acids or cold concentrated acids; unaffected by cold weak acids	swelling (Mercerized) in caustics	resistant
wool	destroyed by hot H_2SO_4; resistant to other strong and weak acids even when heated	destroyed by strong alkalis. Attacked by weak alkalis; felts with agitation in mild alkalis	resistant

"Special consideration must now be given to the action of sulphuric acid on wool and the resist effects which are sometimes obtained in carbonizing. Harris, Mease and Rutherford[98] found that when wool is treated with 80 per cent sulphuric acid at 25°C, the gain in weight of the fibres and the gain in sulphur content can be reconciled if the sulphur is introduced as SO_3. They concluded that concentrated sulphuric acid reacts with the basic side-chains of wool to form sulphamic acids:—

$$R \cdot NH_2 + H_2SO_4 \rightarrow R \cdot NH \cdot SO_3H + H_2O,$$

but the possibility that other side-chains might be sulphonated was overlooked. After Speakman and Gaafer[99] had shown that the tyrosine side-chains are sulphonated when wool is treated with 80 per cent sulphuric acid at 25°C, Lustig and Kondritzer[100] made a more detailed study of the reaction. They found that the serine, tryptophane, phenylalanine, arginine and tyrosine contents were all reduced, the serine content by 10 per cent and the arginine content by 25 per cent. Although the reaction between wool and concentrated sulphuric acid is, therefore, more complicated than Harris, Mease and Rutherford[98] assumed, it seems probable that the resist effects obtained in carbonizing are due to the introduction of sulphonic groups into the keratin molecule.

"The Effect of Alkalis on Wool: The action of alkalis on wool is much more complicated than that of acids. Besides causing salt-linkage breakdown in accordance with the following equation:—

$$R \cdot COO^- \overset{+}{H_3N} \cdot R + OH^- \rightarrow R \cdot COO^- + H_2N \cdot R + H_2O,$$

alkalis are capable of causing disulphide bond fission. It was at first assumed that disulphide bond breakdown takes place in the following manner[101]

$$R \cdot CH_2 \cdot S \cdot S \cdot CH_2 \cdot R + H_2O \rightarrow R \cdot CH_2SH + R \cdot CH_2 \cdot SOH$$
$$R \cdot CH_2 \cdot SOH \rightarrow R \cdot CHO + H_2S. \ \ldots$$

"It now appears that the reaction between the disulphide linkages of wool and alkalis may follow two paths:—

$$\diagdown CH \cdot CH_2 \cdot S \cdot CH_2 \cdot CH \diagup \quad \ldots \ (1)$$

$$\diagdown CH \cdot CH_2 \cdot S \cdot S \cdot CH_2 \cdot CH \diagup$$

$$\diagdown C{=}CH_2 + H_2C{=}C \diagup \quad \ldots \ (2)$$

Only about half the cystine of wool can be converted into combined lanthionine by the action of alkalis. When the other half is attacked, each molecule gives rise to two molecules of combined α-amino-acrylic acid (Reaction 2). Only the first reaction takes place with 0.1*N* sodium hydroxide solution at 22°C, whereas both reactions, (1) and (2), proceed side by side in 1.0*N* sodium hydroxide and 0.385*N* baryta solutions at 22°C.[102] The main reaction with a boiling 2 per cent solution of sodium carbonate is the first. Although the alkali-treated wools were found to contain no aldehyde groups which would react with *p*-bromophenylhydrazine, and although examination of the hydrolysates of alkali-treated wool have so far failed to provide evidence of the formation of —S·NH— and —CH═N— cross-linkages, further experiment is necessary before it can be concluded, with certainty, that aldehydes are not formed during the action of alkalis on wool. . . .

"The Effect of Oxidizing Agents on Wool: Among the oxidizing agents, whose action on wool has so far been examined, chlorine peroxide is probably the most powerful. It converts about half the cystine of wool into cysteic acid, the remainder of the sulphur being removed as sulphuric acid.[436] The oxidizing agent of greatest commercial interest is, however, hydrogen peroxide. Smith and Harris[103] have shown that when wool is treated with 10-vol. hydrogen peroxide for 3 hours at 50°C, its sulphur content is unchanged though the cystine content falls from 11.6 per cent to 8.4 per cent. The treated wool is much more easily attacked by alkali than untreated wool. . . . In a later paper, Rutherford and Harris[104] showed that the arginine and lysine contents of wool are unaltered by treatment with 10-vol. hydrogen peroxide for 20 minutes at 50°C, although the acid-combining capacity of the wool was reduced from 0.80 to 0.32 milli-equivalents per gram. These observations could all be reconciled if part of the cystine in wool is oxidized to cysteic acid under the above conditions.

"Smith and Harris[103] also treated wool with 2-vol. hydrogen peroxide for 3 hours at 50°C at different pH values. The extent of attack increases steadily with rise of pH above pH 7, as is indicated by the fact that the cystine content of the wool treated at pH 12 was only about 37 per cent of the original cystine content. The alkali-solubility of the wool also increases with rise of pH between 7 and 10. . . .

"The Effect of Reducing Agents on Wool: When wool is treated with a dilute solution of sodium sulphide, the fibres swell rapidly and pass into solution. This is because the disulphide bonds between the main peptide chains are reduced to cysteine side-chains in the following manner:—

$$Na_2S + H_2O \rightleftarrows NaOH + NaSH$$

$$\diagdown CH \cdot CH_2 \cdot S \cdot S \cdot CH_2 \cdot CH \diagup + 2NaSH \rightarrow 2CH \cdot CH_2SH + Na_2S_2.$$

The cysteine side-chains combine with alkali . . . which causes swelling, and ultimately, dissolution of the fibres. Precisely similar reactions take place in alkaline solutions of mercaptans,[105] e.g. thioglycollic acid ($HS \cdot CH_2 \cdot COOH$), and both these methods of dissolving wool have been used in experimental work on the production of synthetic fibres."

Speakman[95] shows that sodium bisulfite ruptures disulfide bonds in wool as follows:—

$$" \quad CH—CH_2—S—S—CH_2—CH + NaHSO_3$$

$$\rightarrow CH—CH_2—S—SO_3Na + HS—CH_2—CH$$

"About half the cystine in wool reacts readily with sodium bisulfite in accordance with the above equation.[95,106,107,108] . . .

"The Effect of Halogens on Wool: Special interest is attached to chlorine because of its use in making wool unshrinkable. The fundamental cause of unshrinkability seems to be disulphide bond breakdown. This was established by showing that when the cystine cross-linkages in wool are replaced by less reactive cross-linkages by treatment with sodium hydroxide,[109] unshrinkability cannot be imparted to the fibers by means of chlorine. It is well known that chlorine is capable of causing disulphide bond fission: when, for example, dibenzyl disulphide is treated with chlorine, dibenzyl disulphoxide and benzylsulphonyl chloride are among the reaction products.[110] There can be little doubt, therefore, that similar reactions will occur with wool, giving cysteic acid as one of the reaction products. Similarly, the action of sulphuryl chloride in making wool unshrinkable seems to be due to disulphide bond breakdown. . . .

"The action of bromine on wool seems to be similar to that of chlorine, because an aqueous solution of bromine has been used commercially to make wool unshrinkable. Fluorine is also capable of causing disulphide bond breakdown.[111] The first reaction to occur when dry wool is treated with gaseous fluorine diluted with dry nitrogen is as follows:—

$$\begin{aligned} & \diagdown \qquad\qquad\qquad \diagup \\ & \;\; CH \cdot CH_2 \cdot S \cdot S \cdot CH_2 \cdot CH + 7F_2 \\ & \diagup \qquad\qquad\qquad \diagdown \\ & \qquad \rightarrow CH \cdot CH_2F + 2SF_6 + FCH_2 \cdot CH. \ldots \\ & \qquad\quad \diagup \qquad\qquad\qquad\qquad\quad \diagdown \end{aligned}$$

"The action of iodine on wool is less drastic than that of the other halogens. Blackburn and Phillips[112] have shown that when wool is treated with an aqueous solution of iodine in potassium iodide, the retained iodine is of three kinds, viz. absorbed iodine, combined iodine and anionic iodine. The 'combined' iodine is present as 3:5 di-iodotyrosine, while the 'anionic' iodine is formed according to the following equation:

$$R \cdot COO^- \overset{+}{H_3}N \cdot R + KI + I_2 \rightarrow R \cdot COOK + R \cdot \overset{+}{N}H_3{}^- I_3.\text{''}$$
(salt linkage)

(28) The Resistance of Fibers to Perspiration

An investigation of the literature shows a divergence of findings and conclusions concerning the chemical composition of human perspiration.

Mezincesco[113] reports that 53 samples of sweat taken from 7 men showed an average pH of 7.1 to 7.5 with limits of 6.7 and 8.4. Chloride content was about 0.5 per cent. Nitrogen content was 0.3 per cent, 50 per cent of which was in the form of urea, 20 per cent was ammonia.

Marchionini and Hausknecht[114] state that the skin has an acid surface layer resulting from the secretion and evaporation of sweat. The pH of 3 to 5 makes this layer bactericidal. The axillary and genital regions, etc., have a weakly acid or alkaline reaction which is the result of ammonia formation in the sweat when its evaporation is hindered.

Bergeini and Cornbleet[115] state that sweat as secreted contains lactic acid in amounts sufficient to give it some bactericidal action. Evaporation on the skin increases the lactic acid concentration and renders the sweat more effective. The concentration must be such as to give a pH of 5.3 or lower to have much bactericidal effect. Volatile fatty acids of sweat are formed by bacterial action on the lactic acid. They are present in small amounts but relatively more effective (bactericidal ?) in the range of pH 5.3 to 6.2 than is the lactic acid. On incubation, sweat tends to become alkaline owing to the formation of ammonia from the urea by means of bacteria. The ammonia is more volatile than the acids present, and is lost on evaporation.

Barail[116] in a three paper resume of the physiology, biochemistry, and bacteriology of human perspiration and its effect on textiles states that determination of the true chemical composition of perspiration is difficult because of its contamination with sebum and cast off epidermis cells. Filtered perspiration has an average pH of 4.5 and contains 98 per cent water and 2 per cent solids, sodium chloride predominating. Also found in the solids portion are phosphates, sulfates, urea, ammonia, uric acid, cholesterol, and traces of creatinin, serin, aromatic oxyacids, ethereal sulfates of phenol and skatol, albumen, vitamins B_1, B_2, C, and nicotinic acid. He states that sterile acid perspiration is practically odorless, the acidity resulting from the production of fatty acids derived from lipids by hydrolization and oxidation. The perspiration is converted to an alkaline condition via bacterial decomposition, and thereupon assumes its objectionable odor. The bacteria of several types, are derived from the skin, clothing, and the air. Barail states that the various bacteria have a tolerance for a fairly wide pH range, even to a relatively high alkalinity.

The above investigators lead one to conclude that the mechanism of cellulosic and protein fiber degradation due to perspiration is not at all understood or agreed upon. Apparently degradation can come about by three basic mechanisms: (1) the chemicals produced per se may have a deleterious effect on specific fibers, particularly when the fibers dry, and the sweat salts become concentrated; (2) the acidity or alkalinity (pH) per se of the perspiration may be the cause of damage; (3) the fibers may be deteriorated by bacterial action. In the literature, little specific quantitative information was found which ascertains which of the above, alone or in combination, is the true mechanism. Except in severe cases. i.e., where profuse sweating causes repeated soaking and drying of the fabric, can it be concluded that any of the three mechanisms is singly to blame.

After much pondering the writer has come to two conclusions (one of which will be substantiated below): (1) Most apparel textile complaints regarding perspiration stem from dyed fabric color changes rather than from fiber deterioration; thus fiber deterioration is not a serious problem. (2) Where fiber deterioration does take place, it probably is partially bacterial.

Barail contends that (1) sweat is acidic but is converted to an alkaline state via bacteria; and (2) sterile sweat has no deleterious effect on fabrics (he doesn't state the type of fibers). However, Barail's statements cannot be accepted as fact since some of his comments concerning pH are confusing, and he does not specify types of fiber. Certainly no blanket statements covering all fibers can be made and substantiated. Cellulosic fibers would be resistant to alkaline media and therefore if deterioration occurred, it would necessarily be bacterial. Wool, of course, would be more subject to attack. Barail also does not state the nature of the bacteria and whether they have appetites for cellulose or protein.

The synthetic fibers, nylon, "Orlon," "Vinyon," "Dacron," "Dynel," and to an extent cellulose acetate, are probably not subject to bacterial attack since they do not appear in nature; no bacteria capable of digesting them have ever been developed by Mother Nature. These fibers also have good resistance to weak acids, alkalis, and salts, and therefore would be expected to have generally good perspiration resistance.

Nopitsch[117] studied the effect of perspiration on the bacterial damage of wool, cotton, and viscose rayon. Salt solutions adjusted to pH 4.5, 7.0, and 8.5 were used as media to simulate perspiration. The organism used was *Bacillus mesenterricus*. Separate samples were given various treatments including washing, bleaching, loading with $Cr(OH)_3$, and impregnation. It was found that pH exerted the most important influence, especially for wool. The alkaline samples showed the greatest damage, while those in acid media were almost unaffected. The damage was less pronounced on cotton and least extensive on viscose. $Cr(OH)_3$ had a protective action for wool which was almost independent of the perspiration effect.

No clear-cut data have been found in the literature which enables one authoritatively to rank the various fibers in their resistance to perspiration damage. By damage, we mean deterioration of the fiber, not color changes in dyed wearing apparel. In private discussions with the chemists of two Boston department stores the following salient facts were learned:

(1) Most customer complaints stem from color changes rather than fiber damage. This is particularly true for printed silks and rayons.

(2) No definite statements can be made that one fiber is notoriously good or notoriously poor in its degradation resistance. This is because complaints on fiber deterioration are few and far between. The problem is not a serious one, except when complicated by anti-perspirants.

(3) There have been complaints about the poor resistance of viscose rayon, but it has been concluded that the trouble lay with the low wet strength of rayon rather than with bacterial action alone. In other words, the wetting action resulting from the perspiration was sufficient to reduce strength below the requisite minimum and so the fabric failed.

(4) Wool is as good (or as bad) as the other fibers. However, most perspiration damage occurs in the summer and so the opportunity for wool to behave poorly is eliminated. Even in winter, however, few people wear wool directly against the skin where it would have the opportunity of absorbing large quantities of perspiration with resulting damage.

The Effect of Anti-Perspiration Creams on Fabrics. As might be expected, the action of anti-perspirants on fibers is governed by the chemical reactabilities of the two materials. Most anti-perspirants are on the acid side, usually being buffered formulations of aluminum sulfate, chloride, or phosphate. It follows that wool and other protein fibers have good resistance to anti-perspirants while cellulosic fibers do not. Bien[118] states

"A number of different creams of varying amounts were applied to cotton, linen, viscose rayon, acetate rayon, silk and wool, and the fabrics were maintained at varying conditions of time, temperature, and humidity. Conclusions are:

"(1) Silk, wool and acetate rayon are highly resistant under all practical conditions.

"(2) Linen, cotton, and viscose are extremely vulnerable.

"(3) Maximum damage is produced by ironing without preliminary laundering. Creams which contain no buffering ingredient will usually cause complete destruction of cotton, linen and viscose rayon when so treated.

"The degree of fabric damage by creams is not directly dependent on the pH of the cream but rather on the holding together of the emulsion, and the balance of the basic ingredients with the aluminum salts and the 'buffer' (action probably not a true buffering action), provided that the cream is not under a pH of 2.5. Under pH 2.5 there would probably be damage no matter how the balance occurred in the formula."

In all probability many failures ascribed to poor perspiration resistance actually stemmed from poor resistance to anti-perspirants. It was the writer's experience in talking with merchandising people and department store technicians that all complaints were lumped together, no care being taken to separate perspiration damage from anti-perspirant damage.

What apparently is a comprehensive (non-textile) survey of perspiration from the biological and physiological aspects will be found in the bibliography as Ref. 119.

Chapter 8
THE MICROBIOLOGICAL PROPERTIES
OF FIBERS

(29) **Classification of Microorganisms** (by *Leta H. Webber*)

Biological degradation of textile fibers is due for the most part to the growth and reproduction of those microorganisms which are capable of using any or all of the fiber as a food. Since the individual organisms responsible for the damage are microscopic in size, their ubiquitous nature is unnoticed except by the results of their metabolic activity. Their position among biological forms is for this reason little understood by most people. Fungi and bacteria belong to the plant kingdom, and recent classifications have grouped the plant kingdom into ten or eleven divisions or phyla so that any known plant will fit into one of these groups. It is unnecessary here to name all of these divisions; however, complete lists may be found in Emerson[120] or Hylander.[121] The organisms responsible for textile damage belong to two of these divisions, the *Schizophyta* and the *Mycophyta*. A brief summary is given in Table 68.

The organisms in these groups, (with the exception of the *Cyanophyceae* which are autotrophic and can synthesize their own foods from carbon dioxide, water, and mineral salts) are dependent on other organic materials for their food. Many are quite selective in the material they use while others are omnivorous. The majority of plant and animal diseases are caused by these organisms. If the organism is incapable of growth on any substance other than some specific living plant or animal tissue, it is called a parasite and the plant or animal upon which it grows is the *host*. In some cases, no apparent damage is done to the host and the organism may even be necessary for the development of the host (symbiosis). Most often the parasite kills enough tissue to cause serious impairment in normal functioning, so that a disease results or the host may even die. The destruction of tissues is generally due to toxins which are produced by the bacteria. These may be produced and excreted by the living bacterial cell as waste products (exotoxins), or they may accumulate in the bacteria and not be released until they die (endotoxins).[122]

139

TABLE 68. ORGANISMS RESPONSIBLE FOR TEXTILE DAMAGE

Division	Class	Genera Important In Textile Deterioration
Schizophyta (fission plants) unicellular or colonial no organized nucleus no sexual reproduction multiply by fission	(a) Cyanophyceae (blue green algae) pigments present but not in organized plastids autotrophic (capable of manufacturing their own food) not of textile importance	
	(b) Schizomycetes (bacteria) no pigments heterotrophic (organic nutrients necessary for life processes) important in many respects diseases fermentation decomposition	*Bacillus mesentericus* *B. subtilis* *B. mycoides* *Clostridium* *Flavobacterium* *Sporocytophaga*
	(c) Actinomycetae similar to bacteria but plant body thread-like	*Actinomyces*
Mycophyta (fungi) multicellular (except in yeast) total lack of chlorophyll reproduction sexual and/or asexual live either as parasites or saprophytes responsible for most of organic decomposition (of great importance in textile deterioration)	(a) Myxomycetae (slime molds) distinct life cycle of little importance in textile damage	
	(b) Phycomycetae (alga-like fungi) coenocytic (cells multinucleate) reproduction sexual and asexual (definite life cycle)	
	(c) Ascomycetae (sac fungi) enlarged mycelial tip (ascus) in which 8 ascospores are produced reproduction sexual and asexual definite life cycle cells uninucleate	*Chaetomium* *Aspergillus* *Penicillium* *Monilia* *Cephalothecium*

TABLE 68.   ORGANISMS RESPONSIBLE FOR TEXTILE DAMAGE.—(*Contd.*)

Division	Class	Genera Important In Textile Deterioration
	(d) Basidiomycetae (club fungi) enlarged mycelial tip (basidium) on which 4 basidiospores are produced reproduction sexual and asexual definite life cycle cells binucleate clamp connections on mycelia	
	(e) Fungi Imperfecti unknown or incomplete life cycles. (Not a natural group. Forms may be transferred to another class when complete data on life cycle is obtained)	*Trichoderma* *Stachybotrys* *Alternaria* *Stemphylium* *Cladosporium* *Phoma* *Hormodendron* *Fusarium* *Snorotrichum* *Oöspora*

The great majority of bacteria and fungi do not require living hosts for their nourishment but are capable of using nonliving organic material for their growth.   These organisms are called *saprophytes* and the material upon which they grow is the substratum.   Saprophytes are imperative to the balance of nature; not only do they break down into simpler and reusable compounds all the dead plant and animal remains on the earth, but they are also necessary in man-controlled fermentations, including the production of various alcohols and over forty organic acids,[123] the production of antibiotics, the manufacture of cheeses, and commercial enzyme production.[124]   It is not surprising that organisms which are at times capable of utilizing such varied substrata as plant and animal residues in their normal life processes, for the production of useful metabolic by-products for man, should at other times attack, for the same reason, materials which man does not want changed.   An organism might be very useful at one time in the production of ethyl alcohol from grains and quite harmful and wasteful at another time in the spoilage of certain foodstuffs.   Thus the same organisms which are so necessary to man at one time are also the causal agents of decay of textiles, resulting in the loss of millions of dollars of man's useful goods.

The consequences of the voracious and diverse appetites of microorganisms are of the utmost significance in the maintenance of an integral balance of all of the natural biological processes which proceed concomitantly on the face of the earth. The dependence of all green plants upon the gas carbon dioxide as an elemental nutrilite, to be reduced through the photosynthetic process to carbohydrate, imposes the urgent need for equilibrium between the production and consumption of this gas. It is not difficult to realize that unless oxidized carbon is eventually returned to the environment, the available supply of this substance would soon become exhausted, since no inorganic processes are known to produce carbon dioxide in sufficient quantity to satisfy the demand of green plants. The amount of carbon dioxide in the world is definitely limited. The 0.03 per cent present in the earth's atmosphere represents a mere six tons over each acre of the earth's surface, and at the average plant consumption rate it is estimated that this carbon dioxide would be completely exhausted after 35 years.[125]

Therefore, the billions of tons of cellulose produced annually, locking up carbon in its reduced form, has provided the need and consequent selection for those microorganisms with the capacity to liberate this carbon so that it may reenter the carbon cycle as available carbon dioxide for photosynthesis.

Likewise, nitrogen proceeds through a cycle in which green plants incorporate it into complex molecules, such as proteins. It is then liberated in the reduced form as ammonia by microorganisms. The nitrogen of ammonia is not generally available to plants and the microorganisms convert ammonia to oxidized compounds such as nitrites and nitrates, which are the forms in which nitrogen is utilizable by green plants.

At the same time, all other living forms which metabolize complex organic substrata contribute to the breakdown of carbon and nitrogen compounds. However, the magnitude of this contribution is small relative to that of the microorganisms.

These processes are achieved by virtue of specific enzyme systems (organic catalysts) selected through the evolutionary mechanisms which enable these organisms to survive. Insofar as these organisms have survived, we have testimony to their efficiency in performing the essential functions in the carbon and nitrogen cycles. It is also evident that enzyme systems will have been selected to achieve the degradation of the most abundant natural substratum, cellulose. It is not fortuitous, therefore, that we find a wide diversity and high population density of organisms which readily decompose this material. In our particular interest, the cellulosic textile fibers such as cotton, the regenerated cellulosic filaments, and the long vegetable fibers on the one hand; protein fibers such as wool, silk, animal hairs, and the regenerated protein fibers on the other hand provide compatable substrata for microorganisms. In the latter, we have a case of highly complex substances which, relative to the total mass of naturally synthesized materials, occur in small and scattered quantities. Proteins as opposed to cellulose, which is chemically the same irrespective of its origin, are different, depending on the species which synthesized them. This consideration suggests that any one enzyme system which has evolved to degrade a specific protein is not likely to be as ubiquitous as the cellulose decomposing enzyme system.

It may be useful at this time to define some terms commonly found in the literature on biological degradation. Impairment of man's useful goods by physical, chemical, or biological forces is known as *deterioration*. If the forces are of microbiological nature only, it is *decomposition*. This is brought about by the action of bacteria and of fungi (molds).

Some organisms require the presence of atmospheric oxygen for their activities and cannot live in its absence. These are known as *aerobic organisms*. Both bacteria and fungi are found in this group. Aerobic decomposition is decay.

Other organisms cannot live in the presence of atmospheric oxygen. These organisms are termed *anaerobic*. As in the case of aerobic organisms, this group is also made up of both fungi and bacteria. Anaerobic decomposition is called *fermentation*. As in decay, any form of organic matter may be fermented. Common usage of the word usually limits its meaning to only carbohydrate decomposition. A specific word for this type of fermentation is *glycolysis*. Cellulose fermentation is carried out by anaerobic bacteria. Protein fermentation is known as *putrefaction*. Fats may also be fermented (lypolysis). Fermentation is usually associated with odors. Putrefaction particularly is accompanied by unpleasant odors, usually due to the production of sulfhydryl sulfur.

All of these changes have been grouped together and called *mildewing*, *rotting* or *decay* in the textile literature. The words are generic and are used differently by different workers. Some workers use *mildew* to denote the effect produced by any microorganism when textiles are attacked. Others use it only when a "musty" odor or when discoloration of material occurs.[126] Decay or rotting, in this usage, signifies changes which result in loss of tensile strength or *tendering*. If the organisms causing the mustiness or discoloration are allowed to grow, tendering or even complete disintegration of the textile may result. Hence, in most cases, only the time factor distinguishes these terms from one another.

Mention has been made of the effect of oxygen in determining the type of decomposition which will occur. Other factors are of equal importance.   Thus the pH of the substratum will limit the activity of the fungi and bacteria.   Bacteria generally prefer conditions near neutrality, although some are capable of growing under acid or alkaline conditions.   Most bacteria cannot grow below pH 5.   Fungi, on the other hand, have a much higher acid tolerance and will be found growing luxuriantly in conditions too acid for bacteria.

Physiological processes generally occur in aqueous solution and consequently the substratum must be solubilized before assimilation.   For this reason, moisture is an essential factor in the maintenance of growth and reproduction.   Textile decomposition is not initiated unless the relative humidity is above 82 per cent for cotton[127] or 85 per cent for wool.[126]   Above these values, the fibers are able to absorb enough moisture to permit growth of microorganisms.   Wool regain of 25 to 30 per cent allows microorganisms to grow well.   This corresponds to a relative humidity of 95 per cent.   Bacteria do not attack wool unless it is actually wet (about 40 per cent regain).   If precautions are taken to insure sufficient drying of fiber material before storage and if storage conditions are maintained below 80 per cent relative humidity, no damage will result, even though spores of the organisms are present.   If for some reason, drops of moisture should accumulate (as when the temperature is lowered to the dew-point or accidental splashing of water on the fiber occurs) the relative humidity of the atmosphere immediately surrounding the spores will be sufficient to initiate their germination and the subsequent development of the organism will deteriorate the fiber.   This will occur in localized regions resulting in "spots" indicating the site of the original spore.   During respiration (aerobic breakdown of carbohydrates) six molecules of water are released for each molecule of glucose metabolized.   It may thus be seen that unless rapid drying (circulation of air) is maintained, once a fungus starts respiring it will continue to do so, as long as food is available, without a moisture limitation.

The Microorganisms.   The Schizophyta are the smallest and simplest plants known.   Their plant body, as evident in the bacteria, consists of a single cell.   The unstained bacterial cell appears as a transparent, colorless, and apparently homogeneous mass of protoplasm bounded by an extremely delicate cell membrane.   The presence of an organized nucleus is not easily demonstrable.   Reproduction is of the simplest type.   When a cell has reached a maximum size determined by the ratio of the volume to the area, fission occurs in a central plane and a division of the protoplasm results which yields two daughter cells, each capable of functioning independently.   They may remain attached for a time, but the cohesion between cells varies greatly.   They sometimes appear as bead-like filaments, grape-like clusters and packets or cubes of bacteria.

This grouping is most evident in the coccus (spherical) forms, whereas the chains are also found in the bacillus (rod) forms.

The rate of growth of bacteria has been determined to vary between 16 to 20 minutes per cell division.[120] Thus a single organism may yield 1600 trillions in 24 hours under favorable conditions. However, such an ideal environment is probably infrequently enjoyed over the 24-hour period due to the rapid exhaustion of nutrients and the accumulation of toxic waste products.

Many bacteria have the capacity, when conditions are unfavorable for growth, to form an encysted stage, i.e., a *spore*, which can resist extremes of desiccation, temperature, pH, famine and other such conditions of the environment which the vegetative cell cannot withstand. Sporulation is not a means of reproduction, however, since there is no increase in number. Spores readily develop into the vegetative form when conditions of temperature, humidity, and nutrition again become favorable.[122]

Actinomycetes. There is an intermediate, not clearly defined group of microorganisms called *Actinomycetes*, which manifest morphology and physiology akin to both the bacteria and the molds. This group is significant to us in this consideration because of its vigorous attack on wool.

Mycophyta. The *Mycophyta* consist of a group of plants more complex in structure than the bacteria but whose nutrition is much the same. They are saprophytes or parasites and vary in size from single-celled yeasts to very complex and large mushrooms.[120] With the exception of the yeasts, most fungi have, as a part of their plant body, threads or filaments more or less tangled together and of microscopic size. The mass of filaments is called the *mycelium* and each individual thread is a hypha. An interesting method of propagation noted in the fungi is fragmentation of the mycelia. This is similar to "cuttings" in the higher plants. Small portions of mycelia, which have broken away from the parent plant body, are capable of developing into a new plant body if growth conditions are favorable. In some fungi this is the only known method of reproduction.

Myxomycetae. There are five main classes of fungi.[120] The Myxomycetae are commonly known as the "slime fungi" or "slime molds," because at one stage in their life history they consist of a mass of slimy, naked protoplasm called the *plasmodium*. This plasmodium may be found slowly moving in dark and inconspicuous regions, wherever decaying vegetation is available. Nutrients are obtained by selectively absorbing nutrilites from decaying vegetation. Because there are no distinct cross walls in the protoplasm and there are many nuclei, the mass is a *coenocyte*. If conditions become unfavorable for this type of growth, the whole mass assumes an entirely different appearance. It moves toward direct light, becomes stationary, and produces *sporangia*, which are spore-bearing structures. When the sporangia become dry, they break open and the spores are scattered. If suitable conditions are found for germination, new plasmodia are formed and the process is repeated. The Myxomycetae are of little economic importance except for a few forms which cause some plant diseases. Although the Myxomycetes have not been noted as textile decomposers, it is safe to assume that fabrics in contact with the soil may serve as substrata for these organisms.

Phycomycetae. Some of the members of the second class of fungi, the *Phycomycetae*, resemble certain algae in many respects, the only difference being the lack of chlorophyll. No cross walls are formed in the plant body except when the mycelium produces a reproductive structure. Asexual reproduction occurs when a portion of the hyphae is cut off by a cross wall and numerous spores are produced within the tip. These spores are set free when the hyphal wall ruptures, and they are carried either by water or air to a new substratum, where, if conditions are favorable, a new plant will develop. Sexual reproduction occurs by the fusion of nuclei from the same or different plants, depending on the species, to form a zygote, which is similar to a spore, insofar as it is able to withstand adverse conditions. When conditions are favorable, the zygote will germinate by sending out new hyphae, which can develop into a new plant body. Sexual reproduction is not necessary for the propagation of these forms since an asexual mechanism is always available.

Some of the Phycomycetae are parasitic on plants and cause such diseases as "white rusts," "potato blight," "downy mildew of grape" and others, while one species is parasitic on fish. Most of the forms are saprophytic and are important scavengers in helping to break down organic debris. The common bread mold is an example of this type. This fungus and its close relatives are not cellulose decomposers and so are of little importance in textile deterioration. Other Phycomycetae, however, are capable of utilizing cellulose and 3.8 per cent of the types of organisms responsible for tropical deterioration were found to belong to this group.[124]

Ascomycetae. The Ascomycetae are characterized by the production at some time in their life cycle of a sac-like structure, the *ascus*, in which four or eight ascospores (sexual spores) are borne.[120,124] The ascus varies considerably among the various genera in this group, the simplest being in the yeasts, but in other plants large and complex structures are found. Some of the ascomycetes are the fleshy morels which by some are considered the finest edible mushrooms. Since the mycelium of the Ascomycetae has cross walls, it consists of many cells which are uninucleate. Several different kinds of spores besides ascospores may be produced by various forms. In some cases ascospore production is very difficult to observe but unless it has been observed, the fungus must be placed in the heterogeneous class, *Fungi Imperfecti.* Many of the larger Ascomycetes are important in cellulose breakdown in the soil. Some Ascomycetes are parasitic on seed plants and cause such diseases as "powdery mildew" on grapes, lilacs, etc. Ergot is a serious disease of grains, especially rye, in which individual grains become overgrown with the fungus mycelium. If these are eaten along with the healthy grains, serious illnesses result in both man and animals caused by the toxins of the fungus. The blue and green molds have been placed by some workers in the Ascomycetae. Since ascospore production has not been demonstrated in all cases, however, other workers include them in the Fungi Imperfecti. These blue and green fungi are the common molds found on foods such as cheese, jelly, fruit, and smoked meat, and on leather and various textile materials. The general are *Aspergillus* and *Penicillium.* Another genus of this class is *Chaetomium,* an efficient cellulose decomposer, and for this reason is one of the test organisms used to measure the rate at which fabrics are degraded. Other members of the group which are important in textile decay are given in Table 68.

Basidiomycetae. The *Basidiomycetae* is the class of fungi which is made up of mushrooms, puffballs, rusts, and smuts. The members of this class all produce a distinctive type spore called *basidiospore.* Basidiospores are produced on the surface of the fungus on specialized structures called the basidia. This is in contrast to ascospores which are produced within a sac. There are generally only 4 basidiospores produced on a basidium instead of the 8 ascospores produced within an ascus.

The Basidiomycetes are the most important cellulose decomposers in the forest. The plant body consists of large masses of white mycelia which penetrate the forest residues in the course of decomposition. The extent of these mycelial masses is not generally appreciated because they are minute in size and are generally obscured in the forest debris. When enough nutrient material has accumulated in the mycelium, typical fruiting bodies are produced. These are very often large and variously colored. The mushrooms and shelf fungi are typical examples.

The mycelial cells contain two nuclei.[124] Besides this identifying characteristic the hyphae frequently produce peculiar bulges which are known as clamp connections.[128] It may thus be seen that even though no fruiting structures are produced, basidiomycete mycelium can be distinguished from mycelia produced in other classes. Fragmented mycelium is capable of continued growth under favorable conditions, and these forms can often be isolated from textiles which have been exposed to soil.[129]

Fungi Imperfecti. The Fungi Imperfecti are a heterogeneous class including all forms which cannot be definitely placed in some other class. The list includes many common fungi of importance to textile deterioration (see Table 68). Weston[129] in a report on tropical deterioration caused by fungi noted that 80.5 per cent of the mycological flora involved in deterioration belong to the Fungi Imperfecti. As more detailed investigations are made on the life cycle of particular genera, one may presume that many of the Fungi Imperfecti will be reclassified and included in the other classes of fungi. Very often this means renaming the fungus, since the previously unknown portion of the life cycle is actually well known by another name in the correct class. This can be illustrated by the genus *Aspergillus*. For years no ascospore production could be demonstrated for this genus. When, however, they were finally discovered it was found they were those of a genus *Erotium*, in the Ascomycetes. The placing of Aspergillus in its proper class, the Ascomycetes, theoretically requires that the name be changed to *Erotium*. Since *Erotium* is not a well known genus, many workers prefer to continue to keep the name *Aspergillus* which locates them in the Fungi Imperfecti. Weston follows this practice, which may account for the high proportion of textile decomposers located in the Fungi Imperfecti in his report mentioned above.

(30) Microbiological Resistance of Fibers (by *Leta H. Webber*)

As has been shown earlier, cellulose is the most common fiber material. It is not only used in its natural form as cotton, flax, and other long vegetable fibers but also in the regenerated form as viscose, cuprammonium rayon, and "Fortisan." These being all of the same general chemical composition, they are attacked by the same enzyme systems. The number of enzymes involved in the breakdown of cellulose, wherever it is found, apparently are few, whereas the organisms capable of attacking cellulose are widespread. For instance, they are found in the digestive tract of some herbivorous animals, in the soil where most of the accumulated cellulose from dead vegetation is found, in surface waters especially at the mouths of slow moving streams, in fermenting manure, in compost heaps, in decaying sawdust, etc. These organisms are the principal ones concerned in textile degradation.[124]

Cellulose. The breakdown of cellulose to glucose is apparently the result of two enzymes.[124] *Cellulase* converts cellulose to *cellobiose*, and *cellobiase* converts this to glucose.   Organisms breaking down cellulose belong to two main groups, aerobic bacteria and molds, and anaerobic bacteria.   Some of the latter are capable of growing vigorously at temperatures much above the optimum for most organisms.   Such high temperature tolerant organisms are designated as thermophilic, and it has frequently been demonstrated that the spores of these organisms can withstand the temperature of boiling water for as much as three hours.[122]

Cotton.   Since most organisms are a part of the natural flora of soils it is not surprising that they can readily be transferred to textiles.   As soon as the cotton boll matures, the lint is exposed to the atmosphere where air-borne spores from the soil can easily find lodgement.   If this cotton is picked early in the day, before the dew has dried, these organisms can resume growth at once.   During rainy harvest seasons microbial decomposition is enhanced and the tendering and staining that results is readily detectable.   Some of the damaged cotton fibers originate in this manner.   Cotton fibers may be exposed to various cellulose decomposers throughout the entire process of fabrication, and unless proper storage conditions are maintained, damage will result.   One serious source of infection occurs in storage rooms that previously contained samples of badly contaminated cotton.

Long Vegetable Fibers.   The retting of flax involves the solubilization by microbiological action of the materials in the flax stem which hold the fibers together.   This is accomplished either by spreading the hay on the surface of the ground or by placing the hay in streams or tanks where various organisms can digest the cementing materials. Careful control is necessary because, if the process is allowed to go on too long, the cellulose fibers will be attacked by these and other organisms as soon as the protective coat has been removed, and fiber tendering will result.   However, in relation to cotton, these and the other vegetable fibers, having a higher degree of molecular order (crystallinity), present less reactive surface and consequently are more slowly degraded by enzymes.

Regenerated Cellulosic Fibers.   The regenerated cellulosic fibers, viscose and cuprammonium rayons are equally susceptible to microbiological decay since they apparently present the same chemical linkages as native cellulose.   All of the organisms which attack cotton have been demonstrated to decompose the regenerated celluloses.   The *Aspergilli* and the *Penicillia*, as in the case of cotton, do not materially impair the mechanical properties but are capable of imparting discoloration and spotting.

"Fortisan."   The saponified cellulose acetate fiber, "Fortisan," which in effect is pure cellulosic material, is less readily attacked than cotton or regenerated fibers.[7]   However, the rate of degradation is all that appears to be altered, since the course of the decomposition appears to be the same as in the other cellulosic materials.   Since "Fortisan" represents a high degree of molecularly oriented cellulose, we may postulate that the reduced surface accessible to enzymatic activity can account for the reduced rate of decomposition.

Cellulose Acetate.   Cellulose acetate, on the other hand, is not attacked by microorganisms.   Borlaug[130] has subjected cellulose acetate fabrics, in various stages of processing and end-use, to the most severe soil burial and laboratory tests.   *Chaetomium, Metarrhizium,* and *Stachybotrys* were employed as the laboratory test organisms.   No degrading effect other than discoloration by *Stachybotrys* was noted. These results may be explained on the basis of the incompatibility of enzyme and substratum.[131]   Since cellulose acetate is not found in nature, it is not likely, therefore, that one would find enzyme systems selected to react with this substance.

Wool and Animal Hairs.   Since wool and other animal hairs contain a specific protein (keratin) which is limited in amount compared with cellulose, the organisms capable of degrading this more complex substance are not as universally found nor as numerous as are the cellulose decomposing organisms.   Nonetheless, keratin degrading organisms are sufficiently widespread to warrant considerable precaution in this regard in the handling and storing of wool products.   It has been variously demonstrated that wool may be readily degraded by both bacteria and by molds.[132,133,134,135]   The more ostensible effects of microbiological activity result from the action of those several species of *Penicillium* and *Aspergillus* which cause variously colored stains.   This staining, although serious insofar as the stains are difficult to remove and may interfere with subsequent dyeing, is but a superficial effect occurring for the most part as a result of the growth of the microorganisms on fiber surface impurities such as waxes, soaps, suint salts, oils, and nitrogen-bearing degradation products.   Probably a large number of fungi contribute to this staining type of effect.   Species of *Alternaria, Stemphylium, Oöspora* and *Penicillium* are staining organisms but also completely or partially alter the structure of the wool fiber.   Other molds which contribute to this effect include species of *Aspergillus, Dematium Fusarium, Trichoderma,* and *Cephalothecium.*   Aerobic bacilli (rod-shaped bacteria) have been demonstrated to deteriorate wool, while a few coccus (spherical) bacteria cause discoloration without damage to the fiber.   Non-spore forming rods also contribute to discolorations to wool.   *Bacillus mesentericus* is a common test organism for measuring bacterial deterioration of wool.

A more deep-seated influence than that of discoloration by microorganisms results from the action of bacteria, actinomycetes and molds, which decompose the wool fiber substance, keratin, resulting in loss of mechanical properties and structure. There is adequate evidence to indicate that this latter type of degradation does not readily occur unless some previous damage to the fiber has been effected by mechanical injury or through the action of chemicals such as that of strong alkalis, reducing agents, peroxide, or chlorine. It has been demonstrated[136] that the proteolytic enzymes trypsin, pepsin, chymotrypsin, and papain do not attack the fiber unless the scale structure has been mechanically disrupted, but when this has been done, pepsin and chymotrypsin cause considerable weakening and disorganization of the fiber structure. It has also been shown that when the disulfide cross linkage has been broken, attack by these enzymes is greatly enhanced, and the reoxidation restores the original stability of the wool substance.

The proteolytic bacteria and fungi attack the wool fiber under favorable conditions by rapidly loosening the cuticular scales, decomposing the intercortical matrix, and dissociating the spindle-shaped cortical cells. These effects may readily be observed on microscopic examination of decomposed wool fibers. The general conditions favorable for this growth have been discussed previously, but we should reiterate at this point the primary significance of moisture. Added to this limiting factor Burgess[135] has suggested that the amount of soluble nitrogenous material present on the surface of the fiber to initiate the attack is likewise crucial.

Suffice it to say that those processing stages in wool manufacture which expose the wool to moisture and add organic nutrients to the surface of the fiber at temperatures close to the optimum (25 to 40°C) are conditions which would enhance the microbial degradation of wool.

Recognizing the conditions which increase the activity of microorganisms on wool, certain precautions may be exercised to protect against these deleterious effects. Burgess,[135] for example states that the use of chrome in the dyebath imparts to the wool a considerable resistance to the development of the mould fungi chiefly responsible for mildew.

Silk. There is a dearth of reference to the susceptibility of silk to microbial attack; however, silk is generally believed to be resistant to microbial attack.[134] On the other hand, Hayes and Holden[137] have found silk to be "tendered by two kinds of bacteria and that molds sometimes cause discoloration on silk."

Regenerated Protein. Regenerated protein fibers, like the regenerated cellulose fibers, are not markedly altered in chemical nature from the native state, and consequently are generally subject to the same enzyme systems which attack wool.　Casein fibers such as "Aralac" and Lanital are readily attacked by the proteolytic bacteria and fungi, more so than wool because of the lack of protective structure which the wool fiber manifests.

One would expect "Vicara," a regenerated corn protein fiber, to be equally subject to the action of proteolytic organisms as are wool and casein. However, the Virginia Carolina Chemical Corporation,[138] manufacturers of "Vicara," state that, "'Vicara' is resistant to mildew and bacteria, and moths and carpet beetles will not eat it." This may be due to the inclusion of antiseptic agents within the fiber, or a basic chemical modification of the protein which would alter its nutrient properties.

Filaments prepared from soybean protein are susceptible to microbiological attack similar to that of wool.[132]

Synthetic Fibers. The synthetic fibers are formed of chemical substances which do not naturally occur as far as we know.　Consequently, it would be only fortuitous if existing microorganisms could produce enzymes which would specifically attack the chemical linkages to which the synthetics owe their structure.　It is not surprising, therefore, to find these materials completely resistant to microbiological decay.　Cellulose acetate as discussed above is an excellent example of how slight a modification of a natural substratum is required to upset the stereometric fit of the enzyme and its substratum.　The wider deviation from naturally occurring compounds manifested in the synthetics discussed below supports the contention that no synthetic fiber is likely to be subject to microbial attack.　Thus nylon is reported on by its manufacturer as follows:[139]

> "Undyed, unfinished nylon yarns and fabric have been found to be remarkably resistant to molds and other microorganisms, showing insignificant loss in strength after severe exposure to *Chaetomium globosum, Metarrhizium, Stachybotrys sp., Aspergillus niger* and *Penicillium,* and to the microorganisms (particularly the cellulose-destroying organisms) encountered in a soil burial test.　Fabrics exposed to soil burial tests for 21 days retained from 95 to 99 per cent of their original strength and were relatively bright and clean after rinsing in cold water.　Cotton fibers under identical conditions were completely destroyed.
>
> "Molds can be induced to grow upon nylon by applying suitable food materials, but such growth causes little if any loss in strength of the yarn.　Controlled tests have shown that bacteria of any kind do not readily attack nylon.　Nylon fishing lines, both waterproofed and unwaterproofed, when exposed to both fresh and salt water intermittently for a period

of six months lost only about 20 per cent of their original tensile strength."[139]

The manufacturers of "Vinyon" N and "Dynel" state in a technical bulletin:[140]

"In tests in which 'Dynel' fabrics were buried in soil and held under tropical conditions of 87°F and 97 per cent R.H., no deterioration of the cloth could be detected after 6 months. Eight-ounce army duck disintegrated completely in 10 days under the same conditions."

A duPont bulletin[141] states that "Orlon" and Fiber V ("Dacron") exhibit excellent resistance to microorganisms.

Sherman and Sherman[5] mention that vinylidene chloride and polyethylene are not attacked by fungi or mildew.

TABLE 69. NATURE OF THE VARIOUS FIBERS AND THEIR COMPARATIVE SUSCEPTIBILITY TO THE INFLUENCE OF MICROORGANISMS

Fiber	Nature of Fiber	Comparative Susceptibility
cotton	native cellulose	+++
long vegetable	native cellulose	+++
viscose (high, medium, low tenacity)	regenerated cellulose (xanthate)	+++
"Bemberg"	regenerated cellulose, (cuprammonium)	+++
"Fortisan"	saponified cellulose acetate	+
cellulose acetate	modified cellulose	−
wool	native protein	++
animal hairs	native protein	++
silk	native protein	+
"Aralac"	regenerated protein (casein)	++
lanital	regenerated protein (casein)	++
"Vicara"	regenerated protein (zein)	
	regenerated protein (soybean)	++
	regenerated protein (peanut)	++
nylon	synthetic—polyamide	−
"Orlon"	synthetic—polyacrilonitrile	−
"vinyon" N "Dynel"	synthetic—copolymer acrilonitrile and vinyl chloride	−
"Vinyon"	synthetic copolymer vinyl chloride and vinyl acetate	−
Fiber V ("Terylene")	synthetic copolymer terephthalic acid and ethylene glycol	−
saran	synthetic—vinylidene chloride	−
polyethylene	synthetic—polyethylene	−
"Fiberglas"	borosilicate	−
asbestos	mineral asbestos	−

+++ Very susceptible.
++ Moderately susceptible.
+ Slightly susceptible.
− Resistant.

Glass and asbestos, being nonorganic in nature, do not provide suitable substrata for the growth of microorganisms. However, it has been noted in tropical deterioration studies that even these inorganic substances, when coated with organic treatments which can serve as substrata, will be effected by microorganisms through the action of corrosive waste products which have been known to etch glass components of optical systems.

The nature and the comparative susceptibility to the influence of microorganisms of the above discussed fibers are summarized in Table 69.

(31) Animal Biological Damage : Insect and Rodent Resistance

Animal organisms, mostly insects, can damage or infect textiles. Included in this group are the Insecta class consisting in part of moths, beetles, cockroaches, ants, silverfish, lice, and fleas; and the Mammalia class consisting of rats, mice, squirrels, etc. Table 70 summarizes the various classes.

Damage may occur by three mechanisms: (a) The organism may use the fiber in whole or in part as a food, and thus actually will eat the fiber. (b) It may cut through unattractive fibers in order to liberate itself or reach a food source to which it is attracted. (c) It may coincidentally eat an unattractive fiber which is coated or sized or contaminated with an attractive material.

Insect Damage. In addition to those insects mentioned above specific reference should be made to the clothes moth and the carpet beetle larva or buffalo moth. The webbing moth and the casebearing moth are varieties of the clothes moth. The "carpet beetle larvae . . . are known as 'dermestid pests' and among these are the common carpet beetle . . . , the furniture carpet beetle . . . , the varied carpet beetle, and the black carpet beetle."[142]

In addition to damage per se which insects may cause, other undesirable conditions may occur in terms of sanitation and health. For example, lice and fleas are probably more detrimental, since they are harbored in textiles, from a health standpoint than from the damage they may cause.

Fiber Resistance. *Animal Fibers.* Wool, hair, and fur fibers are susceptible to clothes moths and carpet beetles.[142,143,144] From the practical point of view it can be stated that these insects use such fibers as food and actually digest them. However, Zinkernagel[145] mentions that "larvae cannot live on wool which contains no trace of fats or salts."

His article, as printed in *Textil Rundschau*, gives test results which illustrate the degree of attack on various materials by keratin-eating larvae. Mathews[142] states that the loss of money involved in the damage

TABLE 70. ANIMAL BIOLOGICAL DAMAGE OF TEXTILES
Phylum: Chordata

| Subphylum: Invertebrates (no backbone) | | | | | | | Subphylum: Vertebrates (backbone) |
| Class: Insecta | | | | | | | Class: Mammalia |
Moths	Beetles	Cockroaches	Ants	Silverfish	Lice	Fleas	Rodents
clothes moths	carpet beetles (firebrats)		termites (white ants)				Rats, mice, squirrels, etc.
greatest amount of damage to textiles, especially wool.	damage to textiles, acting in substantially the same fashion as clothes moths.	damage to textiles.	damage to textiles, especially cotton.	some damage on cellulose.	present on some textiles and furs.	present on some textiles and furs.	May attack textiles; one source implies that rats do.

caused by two types of moths on woolen and worsted materials and the control of these insects amounts to $100,000,000 to consumers. Mathews mentions that the casein fiber, like animal protein fiber, is subject to the attack of the webbing moth and carpet beetle.

Cotton and Regenerated Celluloses. Under the proper environmental conditions, termites will attack cotton and other cellulosic materials.[144,146,147]

Lailbach[148] states that "silverfish destroy viscose and cuprammonium rayon, but avoid acetate rayon. Neither native cellulose nor mercerized cotton is attacked by this insect." The regenerated celluloses do not however constitute a complete food for silverfish and the larvae cannot develop on it.

According to Micksch and Herfs,[149] rayon fabrics are only subject to attack by clothes moths if they have been finished with a substance containing starch, casein, or glue.

Cellulose Acetate. Mathews[142] states that

> "Acetate rayon appears to be immune to attack by insects, except in a few instances it has been shown that moth or carpet beetle larvae will cut their way through acetate or other non-nutrient fabrics to get at wool fibers."

He also states that cuprammonium rayon is wholly resistant to moths.

Nylon. Sherman and Sherman[5] mention that

> "black carpet beetles, firebrats, and a certain variety of ants eat their way out of nylon and silk fabric, if imprisoned . . . , (but that) neither (clothes moth larvae nor moths) appear to eat nylon for food as they do in the case of wool."

Mathews[142] says that finish-free nylon is not attacked by insects, roaches, or moths except as imprisoned insects may eat them to attain liberation. Nylon containing oily finishes may be attacked by the insects noted above, owing to the food value of the finish.

The *Nylon Technical Service Bulletin*[139] makes substantially the same remarks. Clothes moths, German cockroaches, black carpet beetles, firebrats, and ants will not eat nylon as a food but will cut their way out of it if imprisoned. "The Anthrenus Verbasci beetle has shown more tendency to eat nylon from choice than any other insect which has been called to our attention. Nylon which is perfectly free from oils or other attractive materials is not attacked by Anthrenus Verbasci except upon entrapment. However, if oils which are attractive to this insect have once been applied to nylon, it appears extremely difficult to scour them off to the point where the danger of attack is completely removed."[139]

The above statements are substantially confirmed in an article by R. L. Patton in the *Journal of Economic Entomology*.[150]

"Orlon" and Fiber V ("Terylene"). A duPont Bulletin[141] rates both as "excellent" in their resistance to insects.

"Dynel" and "Vinyon" N. The Carbide and Carbon Chemical Company Bulletin[140] states that "Dynel" fabrics are immune to insect attack.

> "Caged clothes moths and carpet beetle larvae were kept for 4 months with no food source other than 'Dynel.' The insects starved to death rather than eat the cloth."

Polyethylene. This is rated by Sherman and Sherman[5] as excellent.

"Vicara." The Virginia-Carolina Chemical Company Bulletin[138] states that "Vicara" is resistant to bacteria and moths, and carpet beetles will not eat it.

Table 71 from "Modern Plastics Encyclopedia" lists the moth resistance of the various fibers.

Conclusions Regarding Insect Attack. As is the situation for biological attack, the synthetic fibers are far superior to the natural fibers in their resistance to insect attack. Wool of course is particularly susceptible to moths and considerable attention has been given to the development of mothproofing compounds. This has been a chemical development and will not be discussed here. Cellulose is probably more resistant to insects than is wool except that silverfish will attack it under the right contaminating conditions. Again, the fact that the synthetic fibers are not produced by nature in part explains why there are few insects which have appetites for the synthetic fibers.

TABLE 71. MOTH RESISTANCE OF FIBERS*
(From "Modern Plastics Encyclopedia"[7])

acetate rayon ("Estron")	not attacked
saponified acetate rayon	not attacked
cuprammonium rayon	not attacked
viscose rayon	not attacked
nylon	not attacked
protein (zein)	resistant
glass	not attacked
vinyl resin	not attacked
vinylidene chloride resin	not attacked
acrylic	
polyacrylonitrile	not attacked
acrylonitrile-vinyl chloride	not attacked
polyethylene	not attacked
cotton	not attacked
silk	may be attacked, but more resistant than wool.
wool	attacked

* Many fibers are subject to attack via finishes which are edible by the moth larvae.

Rodent Damage. A preliminary search of the textile literature produced no information on this subject.

Chapter 9

THE DYEING CHARACTERISTICS OF FIBERS

This chapter will attempt briefly to describe the various classes of dyestuffs, the fibers to which they are applied, some reference to application methods with particular citation of special problems and techniques, and fastness properties of the dyed fibers.

(32) Dyestuff Classification

After some examination of standard textbooks on dye chemistry, the writer prefers to catalog dyes similarly to the system used by Lewis, Squires, and Broughton in their text entitled "Industrial Chemistry of Colloidal and Amorphous Materials."[151] (These authors are not represented to be dye experts, nor is it implied that their text is a classic of dye chemistry.) The following classification is the writer's nomenclature and is based on dyeing mechanism rather than on chemical structure:

(1) *"Physical" Dyes.* Direct or substantive dyes consisting of water-soluble colors which are taken up selectively by various fibers, the action being a reversible physical-chemical absorption into the fiber rather than a strictly chemical reaction with the fiber.

(2) *"Chemical" Dyes.* Water-soluble acid and basic dyes which are picked up preferentially by both wool and silk. The action is undoubtedly chemical because of the amphoteric nature of proteins.

(3) *Insoluble Dyes.*

"Insoluble[151] colors which can be deposited, apparently within the fiber itself, either by synthesis in situ or by chemical conversion into soluble forms from which the color body can be regenerated after introduction into the fiber."

(4) *Mordant Dyes.* Mordant colors are those which of themselves possess[151] "little direct affinity for the fiber, but which are anchored to it by the use of a third substance with affinity for both fiber and dyestuff." The resulting combination of mordant and dye produces, usually, an insoluble compound or lake. There is also evidence to show in some cases that there is a chemical combination among fiber, dye, and mordant.

158

(5) *Pigment Colors.* In addition to true dyestuffs, a fifth class of colors consists of the insoluble pigments which are applied to textiles in discreet particle form, adhesion being obtained principally by use of binders.

It will be recognized that some dyestuffs will fit more than one of the above classes. A "metallized" color contains the mordant in the dye molecule and is applied in a manner similar to an acid (chemical) dye.

Briefly reviewing the concept of color in its relation to organic chemical structure, Lewis, Squires, and Broughton state that

"organic dyestuffs are molecularly complex but always contain groups which confer color, the so-called chromophores . . . the azo group —N≡N—, the nitro group —NO_2, the nitroso group —N≡O, and the *o* and *p* quinonoid groupings

and . Such a group converts a molecule into a chromogen capable of imparting color, but does not give it dyeing properties. For the latter, auxochromes must be introduced, e.g., groups such as —OH, —NH_2, —$N(CH_3)_2$, —HSO_3, etc. In general, the more complex a molecule and the greater the number of its chromophores, the darker its color."

Continuing the classification of dyestuffs in terms of their dyeing mechanisms, each of the fundamental classes listed above contain several types:

TABLE 71A. CLASSIFICATION OF DYESTUFFS ACCORDING TO DYEING MECHANISMS

Physical	Chemical	Insoluble	Mordant
direct	acid	azoic	chrome
	basic*	ingrain	metallized
		ice	basic†
		vat	
		sulfur	
		mineral	
		acetate	

* For protein fibers (rarely used).
† For cellulosic fibers.

While the dyer will classify dyestuffs in the above fashion, the chemical nomenclature may be entirely different. For example, the various dyestuffs making up the acid dye group are not necessarily related chemically. Two dyes may be chemically different and yet included in the same class because they are applied to the fiber in the same fashion. Of course, many groups of dyes do perform similarly with respect to dyeing and have related chemical structure.

The following listings classify dyestuffs according to dyeing properties. The information is obtained largely from Whittaker and Wilcock's "Dyeing With Coal Tar Dyestuffs."[152]

Direct (Cotton) Dyes. Direct dyes are used primarily on cellulosic fibers, although many will dye silk, wool, and other proteins. An equilibrium condition is obtained between the dye in the dyebath and that on the fiber. To shift this equilibrium and deposit more dye on the fiber, i.e., to help in the exhaustion of the dyebath, dyeing assistants are normally used, e.g., Glauber's salt or common salt. Whittaker and Wilcock list the following classes of direct dyestuffs:

TABLE 72. TYPES OF DIRECT DYESTUFFS

(From Whittaker and Wilcock[152] "Dyeing With Coal Tar Dyestuffs")

Chemical Nomenclature	Example of Popular Name and Color Index
Disazo dyes	Benzopurpurine 4B (C.I. 448)
Trisazo dyes	Chlorazol Black FFS (C.I. 539)
Tetrakisazo dyes	Toluylene Brown R (C.I. 609)
Stilbene dyes	Stilbene Yellow (C.I. 622)
Thiazol dyes	Primuline (C.I. 812)
Dioxazine dyes	Sirius Supra Blue FFRL
Phthalocyanine dyes	Durazol Blue 8GS

Acid Dyes.

"Despite their constitutional variety these dyes are, from the dyeing point of view, all one class since they are normally best dyed from an acid dye-liquor, and hence the name "acid" dyes. The acids commonly used for this purpose are sulphuric, formic, or acetic acids.

"The acid dyes possess a direct affinity for wool, silk, nylon, and casein fibre, and give a most comprehensive range of shades having varying degrees of fastness."[152]

TABLE 73. TYPES OF ACID DYESTUFFS

(From Whittaker and Wilcock[152] "Dyeing With Coal Tar Dyestuffs")

Chemical Nomenclature	Example of Popular Name and Color Index
Nitro	Naphthol Yellow (C.I. 9)
Monoazo	Fast Red (C.I. 176)
Disazo	Croceine Scarlet (C.I. 277)
Nitroso	Naphthol Green (C.I. 5)
Triphenylmethane	Wool Green (C.I. 737)
Xanthene	Erio Fast Fuchsine BL (C.I. 758)
Anthraquinone	Solway Blue SES (C.I. 1053)
Azine	Azo-carmine (C.I. 828)
Quinoline	Quinoline Yellow (C.I. 801)

Whittaker and Wilcox also put Neolan and Palatine dyes (o-hydroxy-azo compounds containing coordinated chromium in the molecule), and the Carbolan dyes (long paraffin chains in the molecule) in this grouping.

They state that the majority of the acid dyes are sulfonic acids usually marketed as sodium salts.

Basic Dyes.

"The basic dyes are so called because the actual colouring principle has a basic character due to the amino groups present in the molecule either as free amino groups or amino groups alkylated in varying degrees, usually $N(CH_3)_2$ or $N(C_2H_5)_2$. They have a direct affinity for silk, wool, nylon, casein, jute, and related fibers and have some affinity for acetate rayon. However with cotton, linen and regenerated cellulosics, it is necessary to mordant the fiber with tannic acid or a sulphurized phenol."[152]

TABLE 74. TYPES OF BASIC DYESTUFFS

(From Whittaker and Wilcock[152] "Dyeing With Coal Tar Dyestuffs")

Chemical Nomenclature	Example of Popular Name and Color Index
Triphenylmethane	Magenta (C.I. 676)
Diphenylmethane	Auramine (C.I. 655)
Acridine	Acridine Yellow (C.I. 785)
Induline	Indamine Blue (C.I. 859)
Oxazine	Meldola's Blue (C.I. 909)
Thiazine	Methylene Blue (C.I. 922)
Azine	Saffranine (C.I. 841)
Azo	Bismarck Brown (C.I. 331)

Azoic Dyes.   These dyestuffs are also called "Ingrain" or "Ice" colors; the latter because the nature of the dye formation requires ice in the preparation of the diazo solution.   They

"are not applied directly as dyes, but are actually produced within the fibre itself by impregnating the fibre with one component of the dye followed by a passage through a diazo solution of the other component."[152]

The two components "couple" to form an insoluble dyestuff within the fiber. The two components used are of the β-naphthol-diazotized p-nitraniline type.   The process is not suited for silk or wool, probably because these fibers usually are dyed at elevated temperatures which would destroy the diazo compound, and in addition the coupling compounds are not substantive to the silk or wool.

Vat Dyes.   The vat dyes are divided into two groups:

TABLE 75. TYPES OF VAT DYESTUFFS

(From Whittaker and Wilcock[152] "Dyeing With Coal Tar Dyestuffs")

Chemical Nomenclature	Example of Popular Name and Color Index
Anthraquinone dyes	Caledone Jade Green (C.I. 1101)
Indigoid dyes	Ciba Blue 2B (C.I. 1184)

"They are insoluble in water and only pass into solution when they are reduced to their leuco compounds which are readily soluble in caustic alkalies. They are applied to fibres in the latter form, the dye then being regenerated and precipitated in the fibre by oxidation."[152]

Since vat dyes require an alkaline reducing bath in order to convert them to the soluble condition, they have, to the present, been used mostly on cotton and cellulosic fibers. In recent years, however, development of vat colors on wool has made appreciable progress.

A sub-group of vat dyestuffs are the so-called solubilized vats or Indigosols. These are soluble esters of vat dyestuffs which are thus applied without the necessity of alkaline reduction to the soluble form. After deposition in the fiber they are "developed" by hydrolysis and concomitantly oxidized to the insoluble form.

Sulfur Colors. The compositions of the various sulfur colors are either unknown or are carefully guarded secrets. Whittaker and Wilcock,[152] and McMyn and Bardsley[153] mention that they are made by fusing sulfur or sodium polysulfide and organic (usually nitrogen) compounds. Matthews[154] mentions that aromatic amines are fused with sulphur and sodium polysulfide to produce sulphur colors. Dinitrophenol is also mentioned as an intermediate. This class of dyestuffs is solubilized by means of sodium polysulfide and alkali. There is some questioning as to the mechanics of this solubilization, whether the alkaline polysulfide reduces the dye, is a solvent for it, or combines with it to make it soluble. Probably each of the three mechanisms acts in specific instances for specific dyes in this group. Probably the reduction mechanism is the most prevalent since subsequent oxidation is required in many cases.

The solubilized color is then applied substantially the same as a substantive color; salt usually is added to aid in the exhaustion. Because of their alkalinity they are used very little on silk or wool, but are used extensively on cottons, particularly because they are cheap. No formal classification of sulfur colors has been found.

Mineral Colors. This class of colors is now substantially obsolete. The dyeing procedure consists of impregnating the fiber with a metallic salt solution and then reacting the salt with another salt capable of producing a colored precipitate. Matthews[154] cites chrome yellow, prepared by precipitating lead chromate (within the fiber) from a soluble lead salt and potassium dichromate. Prussian Blue and mineral khaki are classic examples of this type of dye.

Acetate Dyes. Up to the time that cellulose acetate was first produced, synthetic dyestuffs were manufactured with the objective of dyeing hydrophillic materials—cotton, wool, silk, leather, etc.   Acetate, being much less hydrophillic could not be dyed with the then available water soluble dyestuffs, and an entirely new series of dyestuffs had to be developed to dye this fiber.   The mechanism no longer is the simple diffusion of a water-soluble dyestuff into a permeable, swellable material.

> "The principle employed is the conversion of insoluble azo compounds containing amino groups by means of formalde-hyde-bisulfite into methyl-w-sulfonic acids which are water soluble.   These gradually hydrolyse during the dyeing process, and the regenerated insoluble azo compounds are absorbed by the cellulose acetate."[152]

These types are called the "Ionamines" but are being rendered obsolete because of difficulties in dyeing and shade matching.[152]   They have been replaced by the "dispersion" type

> "which include the Duranol, Dispersol, S.R.A., Celliton, Cibacet, Setacyl, Artisil, Supracet and Serisol dyes.   These dyes are mainly amino anthraquinone derivatives, basic azo compounds . . . which can be brought into a finely divided condition by grinding with dispersing agents."[152]

The particle size is sufficiently small, apparently, to enable the dispersion to be handled as a substantive dye solution.   As such, one might consider such dispersion dyes to be true pigments as classified into Group 5 (see page 159) above.   The question of particle size in its relation to whether a "dye solution" is a true solution or a colloidal suspension, is one which can be argued at length, but we need not so discuss it here (Ref. 155).   Dyeing with the dispersed type is carried out substantially the same as with direct colors on cotton.

Chrome Dyes.   Chrome dyes belong to the mordant class and require an additional component, usually a chromium salt, in order to form a "lake" or insoluble compound within the fiber.   They are normally used only to dye protein fibers, particularly wool.   The dyeing mechanism has been the subject of much discussion.   Some dye men believe that complex compounds are formed between the wool, dye, and chromium salt.   Carlene, Rowe and Speakman[156] state that wool and chromium salts form a complex independent of the presence of a dyestuff, but that there is no evidence that chromium containing cross-linkages are formed between the peptide chains of wool during mordanting.

Some chrome colors are absolutely dependent upon chromium salts (or other trivalent salts) in order to produce a dyed fiber with maximum fastness.   Other colors will dye wool without the absolute necessity for chroming.   However, usually the dyeing is deeper and the shade is much faster if chromium is used.   Depending upon the nature of the dyestuff, the chroming may be carried out either before the dyestuff is applied (bottom chrome), or after the dyestuff is applied (top chrome), or mordanting and dyeing simultaneously in the same bath (metachrome or chromate).

TABLE 76. TYPES OF CHROME DYESTUFFS

(From Whittaker and Wilcock[152] "Dyeing With Coal Tar Dyestuffs")

Chemical Nomenclature	Example of Popular Name and Color Index
Anthraquinone dyes	Alizarine (C.I. 1027)
Monoazo dyes	Solochrome Yellow Y (C.I. 197)
Disazo dyes	Chrome Fast Black FW (C.I. 299)
Oxazine dyes	Gallocyanine (C.I. 883)
Triphenylmethane dyes	Eriochrome Azurole B (C.I. 720)
Nitroso dyes	Gambine (C.I. 2)
Oxyquinone dyes	Alizarine Black (C.I. 1019)
Xanthene dyes	Coeruline (C.I. 783)

Metallized Dyes.   This class of dyes may be considered to be a special class of chrome colors, but where the chromium ion has been introduced into the dye molecule during manufacture.   Luttringhaus[157] states that the majority are chromium co-ordination complexes of azo dyes of the ortho-dihydroxy type.   He lists names as Palatine Fast, Neolan, Chromacyl, and Calcofast.   They are used primarily for dyeing wool, the technique being similar to that used with acid dyestuffs.   Probably a "lake" is formed within the fiber although the literature on this point is not as definite as it is in the case of true chrome colors.   Metallized dyes might be classified as acid colors, which is where Whittaker and Wilcock[152] place the Neolans and Palatines.   Luttringhaus[157] points out, however, that

"since the Palatine Fast dyestuffs contain chromium, they produce fastness properties which approach those of chrome dyeings."

Therefore, it may be concluded that the resulting dye substance must approach, to a greater or lesser extent, the condition of a mordant type of dye.

Pigment Colors.   Pigments are discreet particles of colored material dispersed by means of emulsifying agents in a water or solvent solution which usually contains a resin or binder.   The purpose of the resin or binder is to anchor the pigment particle to the fiber.   Silverman[158] lists the colors most commonly used:

"azo coloring matter, nitroso dyes, vat dyes in the oxidized state, and phthalocyanine blue and green.   Another group is the inorganic pigments such as the precipitated iron oxides, and ultramarine blue."

It is apparent that most of the pigment colors belong to the "insoluble dye" classification listed above. However, instead of converting them to a soluble condition, dyeing the fiber, and then reconverting to the insoluble state, the pigment colors are directly applied (printed) to the fabric.

(33) The Dyeing Properties of Fibers

Table 77 lists each fiber and the dyestuffs which are commercially used to dye it. No classes are included which, while they may dye the fiber, are not satisfactory in terms of color fastness or have other obvious disadvantages.

TABLE 77. FIBERS AND THEIR DYESTUFFS

Fiber	Dyestuffs Used
acetate rayon	acetate colors including dispersed and Solacet types
casein	acid, chrome, metallized, some direct, some acetate
cotton	direct, vat, azoic, ingrain, sulfur, basic
cuprammonium rayon	direct, vat, azoic, ingrain, sulphur, some basic
"Dacron"	dispersed acetate,[163] certain acid, chrome, metallized, basic and vats
"Dynel"	most acetate* most basic, direct*
flax	direct, vat, azoic, ingrain, sulfur, basic
"Fortisan"	direct, vat, azoic, ingrain, sulfur, basic
glass	special colored resin coatings or bonded pigments
nylon	most acetate colors; certain specific acid, chrome, metallized and basic colors
"Orlon"	some acetate,* some basic, some vat, some direct*
peanut protein ("Ardil")	acid, chrome, metallized, some direct, some acetate
ramie	direct, vat, azoic, ingrain, sulfur, basic
silk	acid, chrome, metallized, basic, some direct, some vat
soybean protein	acid, chrome, metallized, some direct, some acetate
saran	colored before extrusion,[7] probably with pigments
"Vicara"	acid, chrome
viscose rayon	direct, vat, azoic, ingrain, sulphur, basic
"Vinyon" N	most acetate colors, "vat and acid dyes give pastel depths"[7]
wool	acid, chrome, metallized, basic, some direct, some vat
"X-51"	selected acetate,* basic,* direct,* vat, soluble vat

* Cuprous ion method.[323]

Cellulosic Fibers. Cotton, viscose, cuprammonium rayon, flax, ramie and "Fortisan" are all cellulosic and can be discussed as a group. Direct colors are generally used, giving a wide variety of shade and fastness properties. It has been stated that individual dyestuffs are like people in that each has its own personality.   Broad statements concerning the dyeability and fastness properties of certain classes must be made with extreme caution.   (We can, for example, say that vat colors on cotton, as a class, are fast to laundering; but we can't say the same about direct colors, as a class.   It depends upon the individual dye.)   Whittaker and Wilcox[152] mention that basic dyes give, in many cases, brilliant shades, but they are not particularly fast to light and to rubbing.   Sulfur colors[152] are cheap, have good wash-fastness, only moderate light-fastness. Azo colors[152] vary considerably in their fastness to various agencies. Vat colors[152] vary in properties but generally speaking there is a sufficient range of them to produce dyeings of excellent fastness to light, washing, bleaching, etc.

By and large, we may conclude that there is a sufficient range of dyestuffs for use on cellulosic fibers to produce dyeings of any selected color and intensity with reasonable fastness to common ambient conditions. The moisture absorption and swelling properties of the cellulosic fibers are sufficiently high to enable the dye solution to penetrate and thereby dye the fiber with relative ease.

Wool, Protein Fibers, and Silk.   These fibers are sufficiently reactive to allow them to be dyed with many classes of dyestuffs.   The acid colors are used where bright shades of "normal" fastness are required, for example ladies' wear.   Chrome colors are used where extreme fastness is desired, both for wear and the manufacturing operations required in making the cloth.   Generally speaking, the chrome colors are duller and darker than the acid colors.   The metallized colors are coming into prominence because they are dyed with the ease of acid colors but approach the fastness properties of chrome colors.   Basic dyes are not widely used because the other types are more easily applied and have better fastness, particularly against crocking.   Exceptions are the Rhodamines which give exceptionally brilliant, but not necessarily fast, dyeings.   Vat dyes are used to a limited extent; but again dyes of other types are easier to apply, cost less, and exhibit equally good fastness properties.   Indigo is useful particularly for navy requirements, where excellence of fastness (especially light) is mandatory.   A problem in dyeing indigo and other vats is the fact that the leuco (soluble) base is prepared in a strongly alkaline-hydrosulfite reducing solution which will damage wool unless precautions are taken.

The same conclusions that were made for cellulosic fibers may be made for protein fibers.   They are sufficiently hydrophillic so that they may be easily and straightforwardly dyed with no special equipment or processes required.   With few exceptions, any color and combination of fastness properties may be obtained.

Acetate Rayon.   Because of its acetyl group substitution for hydroxyl groups in the cellulose structure, cellulose acetate has a lower moisture regain, swells less, and is much more difficult to dye.   As has been pointed out, a special class of dyes had to be developed.

Difficulty is experienced in dyeing deep shades of some dispersed colors because of the inability of cellulose acetate to take up large quantities of color.[152]   Penetration of the dye is difficult because the dye is not truly in solution, but is present as a dispersion.   A limited use of acid colors has been attained by means of swelling the cellulose acetate in alcohol solutions or other swelling agents.[152]   Such a procedure is undoubtedly expensive because of solvent cost, more elaborate dyeing procedures, etc.   A serious problem in the past, and one which in part still prevails is that of "gas fading" of acetate fabrics.   Many of the acetate colors are sensitive to oxides of nitrogen and sulfur so that in urban areas where industrial gases are present, fading may result.

Hydrophobic Fibers.   It appears fair to state that the greater the degree of hydrophobicity in a fiber, the greater is the difficulty encountered in dyeing.   The original development of dyestuffs useful in the coloring of partially hydrophobic cellulose acetate, has proved of significant value in dyeing the more hydrophobic nylon, and completely hydrophobic "Orlon," "Dacron," "Vinyon," "Dynel," "X-51," etc.

However, the successful dyeing of the hydrophobic fibers in all requisite shades, and with acceptable fastness properties has by no means been attained.   To accomplish this objective, new dyestuffs, new equipment, and entirely new processes have been, and are being developed. As additional effort is expended in such research and chemical engineering development, greater degrees of success inevitably will be obtained in the dyeing of these difficult-to-dye fibers.   The progress made, should, in turn, aid in the dyeing of the hydrophillic fibers.

Because of the failure of the more common dyeing procedures to be effective, two new techniques for hydrophobic fiber dyeing are presently being explored:

(1) The use of assistants in the dyebath which act either as swelling agents for the hydrophobic fibers in much the same way that water does for the natural fibers, or as carriers of the dye from the dyebath into the fiber.

(2) Dyeing at temperatures considerably above 212°F with water or steam under pressure, or with dry heat.   (A brief description of the present principal commercial processes employed in hydrophobic fiber dyeing will be given in the next section).

Nylon.   Most of the dye types which will dye protein fibers will dye nylon, but in many cases color fastness is a problem.   Each dyestuff must be individually considered. For example Wool Fast Blue B.L., a wool dyestuff of fairly good lightfastness, dyes nylon beautifully, but with extremely poor lightfastness. Acetate dyes are widely used on nylon; they have a good affinity for the fiber, and can produce dark shades.

In the case of continuous filament nylon (and also for most other synthetic fibers) warp or filling streaks (barre effects) is a continued headache for the dyer. Unless extreme care is taken, streaky goods result from the unequal absorption of dyestuffs along the yarn because of slight differences in filament or yarn tensions during manufacture. The popular explanation is that unequal tensions cause unequal molecular orientation within the filament and lead to unequal dye absorption, it being an accepted hypothesis that a dye cannot penetrate beyond the surface of the crystallite and may largely lie in the amorphous region.[160] If these crystalline and amorphous regions are not uniform along the fiber, unequal dye absorption will result.

"Orlon." The duPont Company bulletin calls "Orlon" a hydrophobic fiber which

"at conventional dyeing temperatures possesses little dye affinity. Near the boil, the fiber absorbs small amounts of dispersed acetate colors and is surface dyed by certain vat colors. Under these conditions, basic dyes also have some affinity. By using assistants in the dyebath at 212°F, noticeable improvements in the absorption of color are obtained, but the resulting shades are still in the light to medium range."

To obtain heavy shades on "Orlon," pressure dyeing (250°F, 15 psi) is suggested.

The duPont bulletin[161] states that good wash-fastness is obtained with acetate dyes used at the boil, while

"light-fastness is suitable for lingerie, lining cloth, and perhaps a few other fabric types. Under pressure at 250°F level shades of good depth are attained, although exhaustion efficiency is relatively low.

The insoluble vat colors dyed at 212°F produce a wide range of shades. However, black, brown, and maroon are obtained only with concentrations of caustic and result in some damage to the fiber. The fastness properties of insoluble vat dyes applied to yarn under pressure at 250°F are suitable for outdoor uses, such as in awning fabrics, sewing threads for tarpaulins, tents, etc."

One dyeing process specific to "Orlon" and to the other acrylonitrile fibers is the "cuprous ion" method. The presence of dissolved copper in the dyebath appreciably increases the absorption of dyestuff. Feild and Fremon[323] comment,

" . . . Copper enhances the pickup of a wide variety of dyes, whether it is present in the dyebath in the metallic form, or as dissolved cupric or cuprous salts. Of the three, dissolved cuprous salts, prepared by interaction in the dyebath between cupric sulfate or acetate and any one of a wide variety of reducing agents—dextrose for example—appears to be the most effective. It was also found that copper is a dye assistant in its own right, not merely a promoter for dye assistants that act by swelling the fiber, and that this "copper technique" is specific to acrylonitrile fibers and is most effective with acid, direct, and soluble acetate dyes."

Feild and Fremon suggest that the cuprous ion mechanism involves the utilization of the copper as a "bridge" between the resin molecule and the dye molecule, analogous to the function of chromium in the chrome dyeing of wool. A second explanation postulates that the copper catalyzes the hydrolysis of nitrile groups to amide or carboxyl groups, which have a greater affinity for water and water souble dyes. Feild and Fremon prefer the former explanation.

"Vinyon" N and "Dynel." The Carbide and Carbon Chemical Company, manufacturers of "Vinyon" N and "Dynel," states that these fibers may be dyed with almost the entire range of acetate colors and many of the acid colors.[162] The acetate colors level particularly well and have a very good fastness to washing. The light stability varies with the dyestuff and concentration used. Acid colors require dyeing assistants to obtain medium and dark shades. Dynel may also be dyed with many basic dyes giving a wide range of brilliant colors which have excellent fastness to washing and crocking. However, their light fastness is poor. Swelling agents (e.g., *p*-phenylphenol) are recommended to aid in the dye penetration.

Dacron ("Terylene"). According to a duPont Company bulletin[163] "Dacron" can only successfully be dyed with dispersed acetate colors, and dark shades are acquired with some difficulty. Three mechanisms are described: (1) Dyeings at the boil (atmospheric pressure) without the aid of assistants. This produces satisfactory light or medium shades. (2) "Carrier" dyeing, i.e., reagents which when added to the dyebath cause a marked increase in color value of the final dyeing.[163] Most of the "carriers" swell the fibers although it has not been conclusively proved that this is the true and sole mechanism. (3) Pressure dyeing at temperatures of about 250°F. These latter two methods give deeper and faster shades. The duPont Bulletin points out that the "carriers" employed (benzoic, and salicylic acids, phenol, *m*-cresol) are expensive in the amounts required for dyeing "Dacron" and are awkward to handle. At the present time research is being carried on to discover new and more practical carriers. Again it may be concluded that this fiber presents many problems to the dyer.

(34) Special Processes for Synthetic Fiber Dyeing

Growing out of the need for proper dyeing of the hydrophobic fibers has been the development of unique dyeing processes, all designed for continuous rather than batch dyeing. Application of these processes to the hydrophillic fibers is equally, and probably more easily attainable. The following gives a brief description of each of the more popular methods.

Pad Steam Process. The dye is padded on the cloth and then passed through a chamber of superheated steam (250°F). The high temperature causes the dye to penetrate, and probably dissolve within the fiber. In the case of vat dyes, the dyestuff and the reducing agent are padded on at the same time. The high temperature steam atmosphere effects the reduction. Advantages of the process are its simplicity of construction of equipment, and the fact that most mills have high pressure steam available.

Uxbridge Submarine System. Instead of conventionally dyeing the fabric at a maximum temperature of 212°F, the entire dyeing apparatus is kept under steam pressure so that temperatures in the range of 250°F can be attained. The fabric is still dyed in an aqueous medium. The higher temperature produces more rapid and complete dyeing than is attained at 212°F.

Williams Unit. When water is used as the dyebath, this process may be considered to dye fabrics in standard fashion at temperatures up to the boil. The equipment consists of a series of narrow, deep, vertical dye baths designed to increase the fabric to dyebath ratio to a maximum for economy of operation, and to lend the method to continuous dyeing.

Williams Hot Oil Process. This process uses the Williams Unit described above, but with hot oil in the baths instead of an aqueous medium. This enables high temperatures to be reached to enhance fiber dyeing. Some dyes such as the sulphur colors, are soluble in the oil and cause uneven dyeing. More care than usual in the subsequent washing operation is necessary, in order to remove all of the extraneous oil.

Standfast or Molten Metal Process. This process makes use of a series of relatively narrow but deep (6 feet) chambers filled with molten metal (e.g., Wood's Metal—melting point 65–70°C) which can be heated to almost any desired temperature at which the material to-be-dyed is not damaged. The dye bath may be floated on top of the "entering" molten metal chamber, or the dye may be padded onto the fabric. In either case the fabric is then passed through the molten metal bath. The liquid metal acts similarly to a large number of squeeze rolls which forces the dye into the fibers. In addition, excellent heat transfer exists between the metal and the fibers; this also aids in the rapidity of dyeing and the degree of dye penetration. The surface area where the fabric emerges from the metal may be covered with molten Glauber salts (for example) to protect the metal from oxidation. In spite of this protection, however, some of the metal becomes oxidized and forms surface scum, which in the case of "Dacron" or wool may be carried out of the bath rather firmly adhered to the fabric surface. Any unoxidized metal carried out by the fabric easily melts and drops out in the hot water wash.

Thermosol Process. The dyestuff in relatively concentrated form is padded onto the fabric and then passed through a hot air chamber at temperatures ranging up to 400°F. The high temperature causes the dyestuff to diffuse into the fiber. Only selected dyestuffs can be employed, but those which are satisfactory permit dyeing to proceed at a very rapid rate.

PART B

THE PROPERTIES OF TEXTILE STRUCTURES WHICH ARE DEPENDENT UPON FABRIC GEOMETRY AS WELL AS UPON INHERENT FIBER CHARACTERISTICS

Chapter 10

YARN AND FABRIC GEOMETRY

(35) The Philosophy of Fabric Geometry

The preparation and performance of any textile structure is dependent upon a combination of inherent fiber properties, as well as upon the geometrical arrangement of fibers in yarns, and yarns in fabric.

In addition to the obvious inherent requisites of fibers, a most significant requirement is the ability of the fibers to be converted to a yarn, and the ability of the resulting yarns to be converted into a fabric. Inherent properties can and do affect the geometry of translation. The more important aspect of the subject is concerned here however, with the effect of geometry on the ultimate properties of the textile structure. Schwarz[164] points out that

> "Yarns form the basic units which relate the properties of fibers to the properties of fabrics. Their geometry and structure should be increasingly well understood, since these may modify the behavior of fabrics by reducing or enhancing the properties of the fibers used. Further, the form assumed by the yarn has considerable effect upon the texture and structure in such matters as sley and pick, covering power, nature of interstices, lustre, abrasion resistance, permeability, drape, thickness and hand."

Hamburger, Platt, and Ross[165] in a paper entitled "A Study of the Effects of Form Factors on the Translation of the Inherent Physical Properties of Textile Fibers into Textile Structures" mention that fiber, yarn, and fabric properties, respectively, are determined (in part) by:

Fiber properties are determined by:
   (A) polymer properties
   (B) geometric modifiers
      (1) orientation of chain molecules with respect to fiber axis
      (2) cross section area and shape
      (3) length
      (4) crimp
      (5) surface contour

Yarn properties are determined by:
 (A) fiber properties
 (B) geometric modifiers
   (1) Fineness
   (2) Twist
   (3) Cross section
     (a) diameter
     (b) compactness
   (4) surface character
Fabric Properties are determined by:
 (A) yarn properties
 (B) geometric modifiers
   (1) tension on yarn components
     (a) tension on elements in weaving process
     (b) compactness of weave
   (2) design

Because of the complexity of fabric geometry studies, the subject has been investigated to a much lesser extent than have the inherent properties. Two approaches to the problems have been made: (a) theoretical analyses of ideal geometric structures and (b) empirical investigations of the effect of geometry on physical properties.

Approach (a) above is the more difficult one and only in relatively recent years have investigators made any attack on the problem. Schwarz[166] has set up classical mathematical formulae for the geometry of singles and plied yarns, and relates helix angle, single and ply twist, and single and ply diameters. F. T. Peirce, in some outstanding classical work on "The Geometry of Woven Cloth,"[167] mathematically relates eleven structural parameters which control the construction of a fabric. They are:

l—total length of yarn between crossovers (intersections) in a fabric (warp and filling)

p—horizontal projections of l, i.e., reciprocal of threads per inch (warp and filling)

c—crimp (warp and filling)

h—maximum perpendicular displacement of the center line of a yarn out of the plane of the fabric (warp and filling)

ϕ—angle of inclination of that length of yarn which is out of the plane of fabric (warp and filling)

D—sum of warp and filling yarn diameters

Any seven of these parameters may be related via simultaneous equations, leaving four variables which are available for process control, etc.

The importance of Peirce's analysis lies in the fact that fabrics can be engineered in terms of yarn size and spacing, fabric thickness, density, opacity, crimp, etc. These factors in turn (in addition to inherent properties, of course) govern those characteristics of the textile which are of value to the ultimate consumer: warmth and resilience, abrasion resistance, crease resistance, water repellancy, shrinkage, air permeability, etc.

Painter[168] has reduced the complexity of Peirce's work by developing graphs to describe the relationships mentioned above.

Other important contributions to the concept of yarn and fabric geometry have been made by Schwarz[12] on yarn structure; Backer,[169] Backer and Tanenhaus,[305] and Pollitt[409] on fabric structure; Platt and Hamburger[170,171] on staple and continuous yarn properties, crease resistance, tensile elasticity, and tear resistance of fabrics; Hamburger[172] on the principles of yarn and fabric elongation balance; and Kaswell[173] and Backer[294] on abrasion resistance.

The geometric factors which we shall discuss are compressional resilience, thermal transmission, air permeability, moisture transmission, water repellancy, crease retention, wrinkle resistance, dimensional stability, abrasion resistance, felting and shrinkage, fabric soiling and cleaning, fabric hand, fabric drape, and fabric luster. Obviously the interrelationships between inherent property and geometric form will encompass much of the discussion.

Chapter 11
COMPRESSIONAL RESILIENCE

(36) Compressional Resilience Nomenclature

The word "resilience" in textile technological parlence is another of those terms which have varying interpretations to various people. Dillon,[174] Mark,[175] Hamburger,[14] and Smith[13] all discuss the definition of the word.

Dillon[174] comments

> "The term 'resilience' enjoys frequent usage in the field of textile research and there is no question that the property or group of properties thus described is very important in textile applications. Yet when the textile literature is perused, one discovers only a few papers in which there is any attempt to study resilience critically. In these few papers there seem to be almost as many different definitions of resilience as there are authors."

Dillon proceeds to list the definitions appearing in the literature, breaking the subject down into the resilience of single fibers and yarns, bulk fibers, and fabrics. Two concepts predominate: (1) resilience is the ability to recover from a deformation (force-deflection-time characteristics); (2) resilience is the ability to absorb and return energy. Dillon concludes that based upon

> "a crude statistical analysis of the frequency of various definitions . . . a reasonable expression for resilience is
> $$R' = \frac{\text{energy of retraction}}{\text{energy of deformation}},$$
> bearing in mind that the deformation may be tensile, compressional, shear, or a complex combination of various types of strains. Retraction here is used to refer to release of strain."

Mark[175] discusses resilience from a very practical point of view:

> "Resilience is primarily a property of fabrics. Whether or not a given fabric exhibits it to an expected degree can, probably, be established with full certainty only by making a

178

suit of this material and wearing it for a certain period. The extent to which the suit keeps its shape and drape, the absence of bulges at the knees and elbows, and the disappearance of wrinkles which are formed during daily use after hanging overnight, will characterize the fabric as to the extent of its resilience."

Using a "clenched fist" test wherein a sample is repeatedly crushed in the hand, he suggests three parameters of judgment.

"(a) How the fabric plies or folds under compression. In order to be resilient, it must offer a certain moderate resistance to the closing of the fist. If it yields too easily it may be classified as 'limp' or 'dead'; if it resists too much it will appear to be 'boardy,' 'stiff,' or 'harsh.' (b) How the fabric behaves upon sudden opening of the fist. A resilient material will spring back rapidly into a fairy open state, demonstrating a certain 'springiness,' 'loftiness,' or 'liveliness.' If it recovers too slowly, it will be characterized as 'limp' or 'slow.' (c) How the fabric appears, after repeated compression, when flattened out on a table. If a fabric is resilient, it will show only the presence of indistinct shallow wrinkles, which will disappear completely in a few minutes. This last property is also referred to as 'crushproofness.'"[175]

Mark does not claim the clenched fist test to be quantitative or reproducible but points out that

"it is remarkable how closely its results match if a number of experienced textile technologists apply it to a number of fabrics."

He uses it only to demonstrate the various factors involved in the problem of evaluating resilience.

Smith[13] discusses resilience as one of a group of terms describing the "hand" of fabrics. Table 78 is taken from American Society for Testing Materials Standards.[176]

Hamburger[14] states that elasticity and resilience have frequently been referred to as

"obscure textile properties. . . . In these definitions an attempt has been made to express tactile or visual impressions in concise terms either verbally or by numerical indices. Actually these so-called "obscure properties" are not properties per se, but are, rather, complex interactions of many factors, both inherent in the fiber and resulting from the geometry of the fabric structure."

He uses the classical scientific definition of elasticity, i.e., "the ability of a material to return spontaneously to its former size, shape, or attitude after being strained whereas (classically) resilience connotes the amount of strain energy present in a stressed system." He emphasizes the quality of "softness" and at the same time the ability to recover from large deflections where the time factor is important.

TABLE 78.   TERMS RELATING TO HAND OF FABRICS
(From American Society for Testing Materials Standards[176])

flexibility	ease of bending	pliable (high) to stiff (low)
compressibility	ease of squeezing	soft (high) to hard (low)
extensibility	ease of stretching	stretchy (high) to non-stretchy (low)
resilience	ability to recover from deformation	springy (high) to limp (low); resilience may be flexural, compressional, extensional, or torsional
density	weight per unit volume (based on measurement of thickness and fabric weight)	compact (high) to open (low)
surface contour	divergence of the surface from planeness	rough (high) to smooth (low)
surface friction	resistance to slipping offered by the surface	harsh (high) to slippery (low)
thermal character	apparent difference in temperature of the fabric and the skin of the observer touching it	cool (high) to warm (low)

We can see that such end-use requisites as retention of shape, retention of drape, wrinkle resistance, hand (including softness, stiffness, harshness, limpness, liveliness, boardiness, springiness, roughness, smoothness), and retention of thickness and bulk, are all dependent upon the "resilience" of the structure.   To evaluate such requirements, we must break the subject down into logical categories of study.   Thus Wrinkle Resistance and Shape Retention will be discussed in Chapter 16, Hand in Chapter 20, and Drape in Chapter 21.   This chapter will continue with the specific subject of Compressional Resilience.   It is an important parameter for evaluating blankets, wearing apparel where warmth is a factor, permanency of pile fabrics including carpets, and for bulk fiber utilization in mattresses, cushions, and the like.

Concerning comfort in clothing, warmth is dependent, among other factors, upon thermal conductivity, air permeability and moisture permeability.   The next chapter will show that thermal conductivity is inversely related to fabric thickness.   Maintenance of thickness is vital to the maintenance of warmth.   Since compressional resilience reflects the ability of a fabric to maintain an original thickness, it may be used as one criterion of warmth.   It is not the sole parameter, of course.

(37) Methods for Measuring Compressional Resilience

The general method for determining compressional resilience is to select a given area of the fabric (e.g., 1 to 25 square inches) and to plot a force-penetration (or thickness) diagram as the material is progressively and uniformly stressed (or strained) over the selected area.   The load (or strain) is then progressively removed and the resulting diagram recorded.   Such a procedure normally gives a diagram typical of that shown in Graph 29.

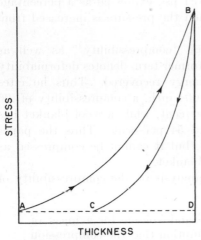

Graph 29.   Stress vs. thickness upon loading and recovering. (*Adapted from Fox and Schwarz,*[177] "*An Instrument for the Study of Compressional Creep and Creep Recovery of Yarns and Fabrics.*")

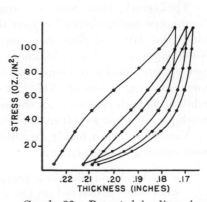

Graph 30.   Repeated loading characteristics. (*Adapted from Fox and Schwarz,*[177] *An Instrument for the Study of Compressional Creep and Creep Recovery of Yarns and Fabrics.*")

If the sample is then repeatedly loaded and unloaded, a diagram shown in Graph 30 results.

The analyses of such diagrams have caused considerable discussion among textile technologists.   Dillon, as well as Fox and Schwarz,[177] as we have noted, suggests the ratio of energy of retraction as a percentage of energy of deformation (area CBD/ABD).

Hamburger[14] criticizes this concept since "two entirely different materials could exhibit identical area relationships."   Instead, he proposes and uses the already mentioned "elastic performance coefficient" (see page 35).   This is as well suited for compressional analyses as it is for tensional analyses, and depicts the degree of perfect resilience of the material. Exactly the same principles of tensional elastic behaviour, the implications of instantaneous elastic deflections, primary creep and secondary creep, are just as valid in compression although not as simple in interpretation, because of the geometric aspect, as they are in tension, and engineering-wise should be handled in the same manner.

Schiefer[178] uses the following criteria of resilience and compressibility:

Standard Thickness: Thickness of the specimen when the pressure is increased to 1 pound/inch².

Compressibility: Ratio of the rate of decrease in thickness with pressure at a pressure of one psi, to the standard thickness.

Compressional Resilience: Work recovered from the specimen when the pressure is decreased from 2.0 to 0.1 psi, expressed as a percentage of the work done on the specimen when the pressure is increased from 0.1 to 2.0 psi.

The reason that Schiefer suggests "compressibility" as well as "compressional resilience" is that the former term denotes deformability while the latter depicts per cent energy recovered. Thus he cites bond paper as having a thickness of .004 inch, a compressibility of .06 inch²/pound, and a resilience of 56 per cent, while a wool blanket has corresponding values of .117, .38, and 54 per cent. Thus the paper exhibits as high resilience as the wool, but it cannot be compressed as much, i.e. it is not as soft as the wool blanket.

Van Wyk[179] in a highly technical analysis on the compressibility of wool summarizes his article:

> "A relation between pressure and volume for a mass of wool fibers is derived on the assumption that the compression of the mass consists solely of the bending of the fibers. It is suggested that compressibility measurements constitute a convenient method of comparing flexural elastic properties of the fibers composing different wool samples."

Rees[180] uses three criteria, namely: (1) the over-all specific volume (volume occupied by a specified weight of fiber); (2) compressibility of the fiber mass; (3) ability of the fiber mass to recover from compression. Specific volume or filling capacity is quantitatively defined as

> "the ratio of the over-all volume (including the volume of the entrained air) under a particular pressure to the weight of the fibers. Compressibility is defined as the per cent reduction in volume of the fiber mass resulting from a specified increase in the applied pressure. The ability of the fiber mass to recover from compression . . . (is expressed) . . . here as the amount of energy returned by the material on the removal

of load, expressed as a percentage of the energy expended in compressing, the material between the same limits of pressure."

(38) Compressional Resilience Properties of Textile Structures

In an article entitled "Characteristics for Warmth in Underwear Fabrics," Cassie[61] discusses the relationships of warmth, heat insulation, air permeability, and resilience. He points out that warmth is due (in part) to thermal insulation which in turn is dependent upon entrapped air at rest. He[61] states that

"fibers entrap air because air clings to a solid surface, and fibers have enormous total surfaces. A fabric composed of thousands of fibers forms a 'wind break' because air clings to the fibers, thus bringing the air to rest. The important consideration for clothing is whether or not we actually use the large fiber surfaces. If the fibers are packed surface to surface, their total surface will not be free to impose drag upon air movement. It is probably in this packing property that fibers differ most extensively from one another. . . . The most densely packed forms of wool in clothing are worsted yarns, bulk density 0.5 gms/cc. Since wool density = 1.3 gms/cc, 1 cc of worsted yarn contains 0.38 cc wool. Thus the most densely packed form of wool is 60% air and 40% wool. Wool seems to have a unique resistance to close packing. Cotton yarns of 80% cotton and 20% air are not uncommon. (Writer's note: Peirce[167] gives values of 60% cotton-40% air. Platt and Hamburger[171] give values of about the same magnitude for staple acetate.) Continuous filament yarns are automatically close packed and it is probable that only yarn surfaces are available for air drag.

"The large surface of fibers being essential for high heat insulation, the question is raised as to how to obtain (and maintain) accessible fiber surfaces. Wool fibers are probably unique in this respect. The open structure of wool yarns may be due to the natural crimp of the fibers, but other mammal hairs, e.g., Angora rabbit, also spin to give open structure yarns, and they have much less crimp than wool.

"Let us therefore look more closely into the elastic properties required of a fiber in a yarn. Fibers in a yarn spiral around one another; an individual fiber will have roughly the shape of an open spiral spring when twisted into a yarn. If a spiral spring is stretched, it may elongate either by uncoiling or by twisting about the axis of the fiber forming the spring. If the fiber surfaces are to be separated from one another, the fibers should uncoil rather than twist when the yarn is stretched; for as the fibers uncoil they also unpack, thus freeing their surfaces, whereas if a fiber merely twists about its own axis, any elongation of the yarn will only tend to pack the fibers more closely together.

"Using engineering concepts and a cylindrical wire as an example: if the wire is easily bent, but resists torsion about its own axis, the spring will uncoil on stretching, but if the material resists bending whilst it twists easily about its own axis, the spring will coil up on stretching. If n is the modulus of torsional rigidity and E is Young's modulus, then the spring will unbend and uncoil when $\frac{1}{n} - \frac{2}{E}$ is negative, and it will coil up when this expression is positive. All ordinary materials (steel, glass, etc.) have plus values and they all coil up on stretching. Quartz is the only known material with a minus value. Values of n for textile fibers are uncertain, but Peirce's data are consistent if not absolute. Table 58 shows that $\frac{1}{n} - \frac{2}{E}$ for wool alone is negative and that it will therefore tend to uncoil rather than tighten up on stretching.

TABLE 79. ELASTIC MODULUS PROPERTIES OF FIBERS

(From Cassie[61] "Characteristics for Warmth In Underwear Fabrics")

Material	E dynes/cm²	n dynes/cm²		$\frac{1}{n} - \frac{2}{E}$	
		Peirce	Other	Peirce	Other
wool	3.5×10^{10}	2.4×10^{10}	1.2×10^{10}	-1.5×10^{-11}	$+2.6 \times 10^{-11}$
silk	10.8×10^{10}	1.4×10^{10}	0.7×10^{10}	$+5.3 \times 10^{-11}$	$+12.5 \times 10^{-11}$
cotton	7.5×10^{10}	2.3×10^{10}	1.2×10^{10}	$+1.7 \times 10^{-11}$	$+6.0 \times 10^{-11}$
viscose	9.0×10^{10}	1.4×10^{10}	0.7×10^{10}	$+4.9 \times 10^{-11}$	$+12.1 \times 10^{-11}$
acetate	3.5×10^{10}	1.2×10^{10}	0.6×10^{10}	$+2.6 \times 10^{-11}$	$+11.0 \times 10^{-11}$
nylon	1.5×10^{10}	....	0.5×10^{10}	....	$+6.0 \times 10^{-11}$
steel	209.0×10^{10}	....	81.2×10^{10}	....	$+0.29 \times 10^{-12}$
glass	60.0×10^{10}	....	25.0×10^{10}	....	$+0.6 \times 10^{-12}$
quartz	52.0×10^{10}	....	30.0×10^{10}	....	-0.5×10^{-12}
phosphor bronze	120.0×10^{10}	....	44.0×10^{10}	....	$+0.6 \times 10^{-12}$

"From Table 79 it becomes apparent that the values of $\frac{1}{n} - \frac{2}{E}$ are roughly in the order of the appearance of the yarns. The greater the positive value, the greater the tendency to produce tightly packed smooth yarns: cotton will give the least tightly packed yarns; viscose, or possibly silk, the most. General conclusions suggested by Table 79 are thus in agreement with our experience of yarns produced by the different fibers. It is unlikely that any fibers other than wool do have minus values for $\left(\dfrac{1}{n} - \dfrac{2}{E}\right)$ because their yarns would be unstable in wear; it is only the directional friction effect of wool fibers that allows yarns with a minus value to be stable.

"The problem for man-made fibers in underwear is to keep $\dfrac{1}{n} - \dfrac{2}{E}$ small, which means that the fibers should have a low bending modulus and a high torsional rigidity. Those people who have been producing man-made fibers have rather aimed at the reverse condition: their ambition has been to make inextensible fibers, difficult to bend, and in aligning the molecules to the fiber direction to give resistance to stretching, they have made lean, cold yarns. Until some means is found for increasing their resistance to torsion, they will retain this character."

The high regard which Cassie has for wool's ability to attain and retain a "lofty" condition in yarn is thus demonstrated.

The following table is taken from Schiefer:[178]

TABLE 80. RESILIENCE PROPERTIES OF VARIOUS FABRICS

(From Schiefer[178] "The Compressometer")

No.	Specimen	Total Compression, pressure range of 0.1–2.0 psi (inches)	Standard Thickness (inches)	Compressibility (in²/lb)	Resilience (%)
3	rug underlay (sponge rubber)	.146	.292	.28	81
10	blanket B, wool	.077	.116	.27	48
11	blanket B, after 1 wash	.097	.134	.27	42
12	blanket B, after 3 washes	.105	.145	.28	36
13	blanket B, after 5 washes	.103	.144	.27	36
14	blanket C, (cotton W, wool F)	.081	.123	.25	45
15	blanket C, after 1 wash	.101	.145	.27	39
16	blanket C, after 3 washes	.101	.148	.26	36
17	blanket C, after 5 washes	.096	.144	.26	36
27	cotton fabric	.0035	.011	.08	41
28	cotton balloon cloth	.0045	.0065	.15	28
29	wool fabric	.003	.015	.07	66
30	silk parachute cloth	.0015	.006	.06	67
31	rayon fabric	.0015	.0095	.05	51

Analysis of the above values shows sponge rubber to have the highest compressibility (softness) in conjunction with resilience. The wool blanket is next; upon washing, it maintains its compressibility while losing 25 per cent of its total resilience. The cotton-wool blanket appears to be fully as good as the all wool. Fabrics 27–31 show a trend towards higher resilience for the wool and silk, but the fabrics are flat and have low compressibility, i.e., they are not soft.

Rees,[180] using the three criteria described on page 182 compares various fibers in various states of aggregation as is shown in Table 81.

TABLE 81. SPECIFIC VOLUME, COMPRESSIBILITY, AND RESILIENCE OF BULK FIBERS (From Rees[180] "The Over-all Specific Volume, Compressibility and Resilience of Fibrous Materials")

Fiber	Source	Specific Volume (cc/g) at			(%) Compress- ibility	(%) Resili- ence
		.001 psi	0.5 psi	1.0 psi		
cotton, bengals	after passing thru Shirley Analyser from bale	42.6	9.0	8.2	80.8	39.1
cotton, Sea Island (St. Vincent)	after passing thru Shirley Analyser from bale	49.7	10.3	9.4	81.1	37.7
cotton, Ishan	after passing thru Shirley Analyser from bale	55.5	9.8	8.9	84.0	38.0
cotton, Texas	after passing thru Shirley Analyser from bale	50.4	9.6	8.7	82.7	37.8
cotton, Giza 12	after passing thru Shirley Analyser from bale	49.3	9.7	9.8	82.0	38.0
wool, 70's	sliver	54.7	9.7	8.2	85.0	55.8
milkweed	unprocessed	68.5	24.7	22.3	67.4	50.3
kapok, prime Java	bale	56.4	15.3	13.7	75.7	44.0
kapok, Ceylon	machine-opened	78.7	22.4	20.4	74.1	41.5
silk, degummed China	1st drafts	41.1	10.8	9.5	77.0	52.2
nylon (waste) 3.4 fil. den.	sliver	22.0	7.9	7.1	67.7	53.0
hollow viscose staple fiber 4.4 fil. den., 1¾-in. staple	bale	38.9	13.1	12.0	69.2	30.7
cellulose acetate staple fiber 8 fil. den., 3-in. staple	bale	64.3	10.6	9.4	85.3	44.6
cellulose acetate staple fiber: (50% 8 fil. den., 3-in. staple, 50% 15 fil. den., 3-in. staple)	bale	64.7	11.1	9.8	84.9	44.4

The cottons, wool, and cellulose acetates have the highest compressibility under the designated conditions of loading. Softness or compressibility must be governed in part by the fiber configuration and also by the state of aggregation of the fibers in the bulk mass. The fact that uncrimped synthetic or regenerated fibers are "slick" and uniform probably explains in part why they, by fitting together more easily and closely, initially produce a less lofty mass and subsequently are compressed to a lesser extent when subjected to compression forces.

Rees's comments on resilience follow:

"The results for cottons show that apart from Bengals, which has a higher value of resilience, there is no significant difference in resilience between any of the cottons listed. The wool specimen has the highest resilience of all the fibres given in the table and the hollow viscose staple fibre the lowest. Nylon waste, silk and milkweed fibre have resilience values approaching that for the wool specimen. The kapok and the cellulose acetate staple fibre specimens have greater resilience than the cottons, but lower resilience than milkweed fibre."

TABLE 82. PROPERTIES OF BLANKET MATERIALS

(From Schiefer[181] "A Study of The Properties of Household Blankets")

Blanket No.	Fiber Composition Wool (%)	Cotton (%)	Viscose (%)	Acetate (%)	Weight (oz/yd²)	Thickness at 0.10 psi (in.)	Thickness at 1.0 psi (in.)	Compressibility in./in. (lbs/in.²)	Resilience (%)	Thermal Trans. Btu/°F/hr/ft²	Air Perm. at 0.5ΔP ft³/min/ft²	Breaking Str. Grab (lbs) W	F	Shrinkage 10 washes (%) W	F	Rel. Thermal Insul/Unit Wt. 150×10⁻³	Thermal Insul. Value
1	100				5.6	.080	.044	0.34	49	1.15	257	32	19	10	3	150	28
5	100				9.5	.172	.099	0.34	49	0.94	261	54	43	3	0	112	41
14	100				10.2	.137	.087	0.28	36	0.99	221	41	32	2	1	99	38
21	100				12.0	.193	.103	0.49	54	0.75	111	50	21	3	10	111	53
30	100				13.0	.228	.115	0.43	39	0.75	187	51	31	4	6	103	53
46	100				14.9	.230	.128	0.37	50	0.78	212	56	36	8	3	86	51
60	100				17.8	.207	.137	0.24	42	0.87	101	75	48	2	1	65	46
65	80	20			8.8	.160	.089	0.38	47	…	…	33	17	…	…	…	…
67	80	20			9.6	.136	.087	0.26	50	0.97	124	46	46	8	12	107	39
82	62	38			12.4	.145	.100	0.21	36	…	…	24	19	…	…	…	…
81	51	49			9.8	.194	.114	0.37	36	0.81	266	35	20	5	7	126	49
83	50	50			14.4	.170	.109	0.27	37	0.86	88	53	59	12	10	81	46
96	37	63			9.9	.120	.071	0.30	38	1.04	124	56	38	14	0	97	35
99	40	60			11.1	.147	.087	0.29	39	0.97	105	63	33	12	0	93	39
103	25	75			13.5	.215	.137	0.30	27	0.84	135	47	45	15	13	88	47
105	25	75			14.2	.213	.135	0.30	29	0.85	116	58	62	12	10	83	47
113	17	83			8.2	.142	.084	0.32	34	…	…	43	8	…	1†	…	…
127		100			9.5	.182	.114	0.38	29	0.84	178	41	13	7	…	125	47
128		100			11.0	.192	.126	0.32	29	0.86	155	38	24	6	4	106	46
131	29	53	18		13.9	.231	.160	0.33	32	0.76	178	43	45	4	9	95	52
138	23	31	46		13.0	.275	.172	0.39	29	0.73	224	41	32	4	1	105	54
141	12	1	87		12.8	.281	.175	0.36	24	0.74	216	33	40	5	7	106	54
145		18	82		13.9	.154	.112	0.22	22	0.91	74	57	57	9	5†	81	43
146		13	87		15.1	.239	.148	0.35	25	0.83	343	49	50	7	10	80	48
147	75			25	15.9	.144	.089	0.29	40	0.87	…	56	61	…	…	72	46
149	50			50	14.7	.110	.070	0.27	30	0.99	…	55	52	…	…	69	38
152	25	26		49	10.6	.286	.153	0.49	30	0.68	331	36	22	11	10	139	57
155				100	14.2	….	.124	0.25	41	0.78	…	55	8	3*	2*	90	51

* After 5 washes.
† Stretch.

Summarizing the data reported by Rees, it can be stated that wool exhibits the highest resilience as well as the highest softness (compressibility) of any fiber tested. Other fibers, viz. nylon waste, silk, and milkweed, are almost as good in resilience but have much less compressibility. In other words, bulk wool has the greatest "loftiness" and the greatest ability to retain that loftiness of any of the materials studied by Rees.

Schiefer and co-workers report on "A Study of The Properties of Household Blankets."[181] One hundred fifty-six various types of wool, cotton, viscose and acetate rayon, alone and in blends, were studied. Data on weight, thickness, compressibility, compressional resilience, thermal transmission, air permeability, breaking strength, and shrinkage are recorded. Table 82 is abstracted from the original article. The data other than for compressibility and resilience, are included for future use. The table shows that maximum compressibility and resilience is obtained with the all-wool samples. Addition of cotton or viscose or rayon depresses the values. The authors state:

"It can be readily seen that there is no correlation between the properties of the blankets and the fiber composition except for compressional resilience. The average compressional resilience, computed for those blankets having similar fiber composition is plotted in Graph 18 against wool content. A linear relationship is obtained for blankets containing a mixture of wool and cotton. The difference in compressional resilience between the groups of blankets is statistically highly significant, except between the 5 per cent wool and the all cotton groups. The addition of 5 per cent of wool does not increase the compressional resilience significantly. If a portion of the cotton is replaced with viscose rayon, the compressional resilience is significantly decreased, and if a portion of the cotton is replaced with acetate rayon, the compressional resilience is increased slightly. Several of the 100 per cent wool blankets were known to be made from all virgin wool. The average compressional resilience of this group was 50 per cent which is higher than the general average of the all wool blankets. Likewise a number of blankets were known to be made from a high per cent of reprocessed and reused wool. The average compressional resilience of this group was only 41 per cent. There seems to be a relationship between compressional resilience of blankets and the quality of wool used. If mechanically damaged wool is used, compressional resilience of the blanket is lowered."

Schiefer,[182] in alluding to what probably is the same investigation, reiterates that the only property related to the thermal insulation ability

of blankets, is compressional resilience. He mentions the linear relation between resilience and wool-cotton ratio (Graph 31), and that viscose
rayon lowers the resilience of wool more than cotton, while acetate lowers
it less than cotton. He points out that since a relationship exists between
thickness, resilience, and thermal insulation, an all wool blanket having
a high compressional resilience probably will retain its original thickness,
and hence its thermal insulation, more nearly than would a blanket
made from cotton or rayon.

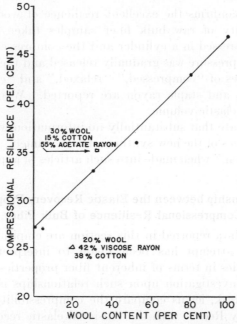

Graph 31. Linear relationship between compressional resilience and wool content
of blankets made from mixtures of wool and cotton. (*From Schiefer,*[182] *"Factors
Relating to the Thermal Insulation of Fabrics."*)

Effect of Moisture Content on Thermal Insulation.[182] A cotton and
a wool blanket of equal weight and thickness were used. Weight, thickness, and thermal insulation of each, when dry and after 100 per cent
water was added, were measured. The addition of water decreased the
thermal insulation of both the wool blanket and the cotton blanket;
the total *decrease* being greater for the cotton. However, the cotton
decreased appreciably in thickness because of the water, thus causing of
itself a decrease in thermal insulation. After a correction for the decrease
in thickness of the cotton was made, it was found that the decrease in
thermal insulation because of the water was exactly the same for wool

and cotton.   However, the advantage of wool is apparent in that it does not lose so much thickness and concomittant thermal insulation loss as does cotton.

Gilmore and Hess[183] report on "The Effect of Fiber Content and Care on Resiliency, Thickness and Thermal Conductivity of Blankets." Various blends of wool, "Aralac," cotton, rayon, and paper were studied.   The all-wool blankets, as a group, were found to be more resilient than the blends; the blends containing wool were usually more resilient than those containing no wool.

Mutschler[184] confirms the excellent resilience of wool in a study of the compressibility of raw bulk fiber samples taken from bales.   A sample was compressed in a cylinder and the compressed volume measured.   Then the pressure was gradually released and the relaxed volume measured.   Values of "compressed," "relaxed," and "elastic" volumes for wool, cotton, and staple rayon are reported.   Wool was found to have the highest elastic volume.

It is unfortunate that substantially no information was found on the resilience properties of the new synthetic fibers, namely, nylon, "Orlon," "Dynel," "Dacron," when made into such articles of apparel as sweaters and coats.

(39) The Relationship between the Elastic Recovery Properties of Single Fibers, and the Compressional Resilience of Bulk Fiber Aggregates

Most of the data reported in this section are empirical.   In most of the articles, no attempt has been made to interpret compressional resilience properties in terms of inherent fiber properties.   It is obvious that a research investigation upon such relationships is needed.   As a start on such a task, let us compare the compressibility and resilience data presented by Rees[180] with the tensional elastic recovery properties of fibers as listed by Meredith[17] (page 38), and the elasticity at low strains as given by Hamburger, Morgan, and Platt[21] (pp. 44–46).   The samples are not of the same pedigree, of course.

TABLE 83

	Compressibility From Rees[180] (%)	Resilience From Rees[180] (%)	Elastic Recovery at 5% From Meredith[17] (%)	I.E.D./Total at 5% From Hamburger, Morgan and Platt[21]	Elastic Index at 5%
cotton	80–84	38	45	. . .	. . .
wool	85	56	89	.38	.57
cellulose acetate	85	44	73	.29	.44
silk	77	52	70	.42	.59
nylon	68	53	98	.38	.49
viscose	69	31	52	.14	.21

Graphs 32 and 33 plot compressibility and resilience, respectively, against elastic recovery and the two elasticity indices.   It will be evident that no correlation exists between compressibility and any of the other measurements, but that reasonably good aggreement exists between resilience and tensional elasticity. When the definition of resilience is reviewed, it is understandable that such a trend should exist, for both "resilience" and elasticity depict the degree of ability of a material to return, after deformation, to its original dimension.

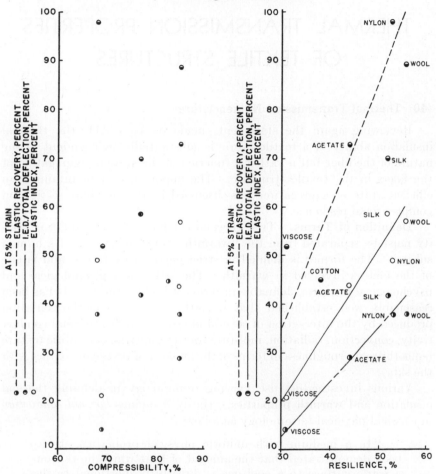

Graph 32. Bulk compressibility vs. elastic recovery properties of fibers.

Graph 33. Bulk compressional resilience vs. elastic recovery properties of fibers.

The above correlation seems to be borne out by Schiefer's work[181,182] for he shows that viscose, acetate, and cotton depress the resilience of wool; that viscose is worse than wool, and acetate is better than wool.

Of course, considerable work must be done before any conclusive proof is obtained that such a correlation as is suggested above does exist, and if so, quantitatively to define it.

Chapter 12

THERMAL TRANSMISSION PROPERTIES
OF TEXTILE STRUCTURES

(40) Thermal Transmission Nomenclature

Reviewing again the statements made on page 111, the thermal insulation ability of a textile fabric is substantially independent of the nature of the fiber but is rather a function of the state of aggregation of the fibers in the textile structure. The importance of maintaining an efficient state of aggregation was discussed in the previous section on compressional resilience.

Definition of Terms. True thermal conductivity or insulating ability must be separated from the "warmth" (or "coolness") of a human subject. The former is defined in strict engineering terms, and is one of the factors involved in warmth. The latter is a physiological and psychological measure, definable in terms of body comfort. It has been reasonably well established that warmth or coolness is the sensation produced by the interaction of several physical criteria: thermal conductivity, convection, radiation, moisture transfer, air transfer, fabric texture (smoothness or roughness in terms of the amount of textile in contact with the skin).

Various investigators use varying terminology in defining thermal insulation and warmth properties. Hardy[185] defines *thermal conduction* in classical physical terminology as follows:

> "In a medium with uniform physical properties, it has been demonstrated that the amount of heat which flows from a warm surface to a cool one is directly proportional to the length of the path, the nature of the medium, and the thermal gradient:

$$H_D = \frac{KA(T_2 - T_1)}{d} t \text{ (g cal)}$$

where

$$H_D = \text{quantity of heat conducted}$$
$$K = \text{thermal conductivity constant}$$

192

T_2, T_1 = temperatures of the warm and cool surfaces
t = time
d = thickness of the conductor
A = area of surface."

He draws an analogy between thermal conductivity and resistance, and electrical conductivity and resistance:

$$I = E/R$$

where I = current, E = voltage, R = resistance.

H_D is analagous to the current; $T_2 - T_1$, the temperature differential or thermal gradient, is analagous to the voltage; and d/KA is the resistance factor.

Peirce and Rees[187] mention:

"*Specific Thermal Resistivity* which is defined as the ratio of the conductivity of air to the 'effective' conductivity of the fabric, i.e., as K_a/K where K_a is the conductivity of air. This may conveniently be expressed as a percentage, i.e., $100K_a/K$.

"*Equivalent Air Thickness* which is defined as the thickness of a layer of still air having the same thermal resistance as the fabric. Denoting this by t_a we have $t_a = K_a t/K$.

"*Thermally Effective Specific Volume* (T.E.S.V.) which is defined as the ratio of the equivalent air thickness to its weight per unit area. If v denotes the over-all specific volume of the fabric, the weight per unit area is t/v, and we have T.E.S.V. = $K_a v/K$. This magnitude has the dimensions of a specific volume and so can be expressed in cc/gram. It is equal to the specific volume of the fabric, changed (in general, decreased) in the ratio that the conductivity of air bears to the effective conductivity of the fabric. It will be seen that the ratio T.E.S.V./Over-all Specific Volume is equal to K_a/K, i.e., to the specific thermal resistivity."

Marsh[188] points out that from an end-use consideration, thermal conductivity alone is not a true criterion of thermal insulation ability. He suggests the term Thermal Insulation Value (T.I.V.). The apparatus consists of a heated surface kept at constant temperature. The heat required to maintain this constant temperature when covered with a textile fabric is determined and is compared to that required to maintain the uncovered control surface. Baxter and Cassie[189] elaborate on the measurement of T.I.V. as follows:

"The T.I.V. of a fabric is the per cent saving in heat loss from the surface due to covering it with the fabric . . . :

$$\text{T.I.V.} = 100\,\frac{(H_0 - H_c)}{H_0}$$

where H_0 = heat lost per second from the uncovered surface
H_c = heat lost per second from the covered surface."

Baxter and Cassie[189] point out the importance of fabric surface emissivity* (radiation effect) in measuring T.I.V.

"The heat flow H_c through unit area of the material is $(T_1 - T)K/d$, where K is the thermal conductivity of the material, d is its thickness and T is the temperature of surface C. This must equal the flow of heat from unit area of the exposed surface, **or**

$$H_c = (T_1 - T)K/d = \sigma(T - T_0)$$

where σ is the emissivity of the outer surface. The heat lost from the uncovered surface at temperature T_1 is

$$H_0 = \sigma'(T_1 - T_0)$$

where σ' is the emissivity of the heated surface."

Baxter and Cassie's final equation shows

$$\frac{P}{100} = 100\,\frac{(H_0 - H_c)}{H_0} - \frac{(K/\sigma')}{(d + K/\sigma)}$$

where P = T.I.V.

They demonstrate by the above equation that "T.I.V.'s can be discussed in terms of fabric thickness, thermal conductivity, and surface emissivity"; the last term depicting the tendency of the fabric to emit "heat" in the form of radiant energy.

Rees[191] suggests the word "TOG" as a unit of measure of thermal resistance. He defines it as (one-tenth of) the ratio of the temperature differential causing heat to flow to the actual heat flow in watts per square meter, namely

$$10 \text{ togs} = 1\,\frac{°C}{\text{watts/meter}^2}$$

* Emissive power[190] or emissivity is measured by the energy radiated from unit area of a surface in unit time for unit difference of temperature between the surface in question and surrounding bodies. For the Cgs system the emissive power is given in ergs/second/cm² with the radiating surface at 1° absolute and the surroundings at absolute zero.

The apparatus which Rees employs in reporting such data is one wherein the energy put into the heater to maintain a steady temperature differential through the thickness of the fabric is measured.

Gagge, Burton, and Bazett[192] use the term "Clo" as a unit of insulation. It is defined in Newburgh's "The Physiology of Heat Regulation and the Science of Clothing"[193] as follows:

> "The Clo is a unit of insulation and is the amount of insulation necessary to maintain comfort and a mean skin temperature of 92°F in a room at 70°F with air movement not over 10 feet per minute, humidity not over 50 per cent, with a metabolism of 50 calories per square meter per hour."

Obviously the Clo value is based upon human physiological factors as well as upon the engineering measurement of thermal characteristics.

(41) Methods for Measuring Thermal Transmission

Marsh[188] lists three basic methods of measurement:

(1) *Disc Methods.* The test fabric is placed between two plates at different temperatures and the rate of heat flow through the fabric is determined.

(2) *Cooling Method.* A hot body is wrapped with the fabric and its rate of cooling measured. The outer surface of the fabric is exposed to the air, and is not in contact with any solid substance.

(3) *Constant Temperature Method.* A body is wrapped with the fabric and maintained at a constant temperature by a controlled supply of energy.

One of the precautions which must be taken in using the disc method is the proper control of fabric thickness. Since the specimen is held between two plates, pressure necessarily is exerted. The magnitude of this pressure, and resulting thickness of the fabric will control, in part, the thermal conductivity.

Marsh[188] comments that in using the Cooling Method, data are reported in terms of cooling time,

> "and apply only to the apparatus and temperature used. They cannot, therefore, be compared to any advantage. . . . Experiments with damp cloth may lead to erroneous results, owing to the absorption of the latent heat of water evaporated."

Marsh prefers the constant temperature method when he states

> "This method has been used in work which may be considered the best of any yet done on the thermal insulation of fabrics. The chief advantage lies in the fact that the measure-

ments of heat are replaced by those of electrical energy and can, therefore, be made more easily and more accurately."

(42) Factors Which Influence Thermal Transmission

Thermal Transmission vs. Thickness and Weight per Unit Area. Marsh[188] reports on the thermal insulation value, weight, thickness, and air permeability of wool and worsted suitings, wool overcoatings, flannels, wool and cotton blankets, cotton knit goods, acetate fabrics, cotton duck, linens, cambrics, silk taffeta, crepe de chine, and wool felt. From the

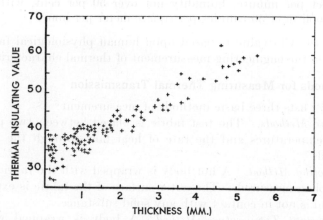

Graph 34. Effect of fabric thickness on thermal insulation value. (*From Marsh,*[188] "*The Thermal Insulating Properties of Fabrics.*")

(The graph depicts a variety of fabrics of miscellaneous fiber types, and miscellaneous yarn and fabric constructions.)

many values ascertained, he plots T.I.V. vs. thickness and shows (Graph 34) that the relationship is substantially linear.

> "The points lie very approximately on a straight line which does not pass through the origin. This linear relationship holds over a very wide range of thickness, covering every type of fabric and raw material. It may be said, therefore, that the chief factor which determines T.I.V. of a fabric is its thickness, the thickness excluding the projecting fibers. There are certainly other factors, but thickness appears to be the predominant one. It should be noted that the average straight line drawn through the points does not pass through the origin, but that for small thicknesses there is a thermal insulating value of about 30 per cent. This is probably due to the breaking up of the convection currents which are responsible to a large extent for the loss of heat from a body in air."[188]

Marsh found very poor (almost no) correlation between T.I.V. and weight per unit area.

Schiefer and co-workers[181] confirm the linear relationship of thermal transmission and thickness:

$$T = \frac{1}{3.0t_{0.1} + 0.63}$$

or
$$R = 3.0t_{0.1} + 0.63$$

where T = Btu/°F/hr/ft² = thermal transmission

$t_{0.1}$ = thickness in inches at 0.1 psi

$R = \dfrac{1}{T}$ = thermal resistance.

"The constant 0.63 is a thermal resistance which is equivalent to an effective thickness of 0.21 inches and is caused by the layer of still air at the exposed surface of the specimen."[181]

Because of this, Schiefer states that

"it is impractical to attempt to measure the effect of construction and other factors on the thermal resistance of thin materials, such as light underwear and dress fabrics, since the thermal resistance contributed by thin fabrics may amount to only some 10–20 per cent of that of the layer of still air."

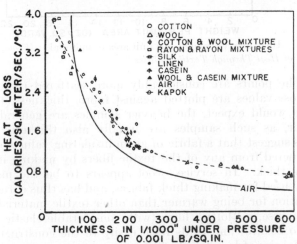

Graph 35.   Variation of heat loss with thickness of material.   (*From Rees,*[186] *"The Transmission of Heat Through Textile Fabrics."*)

Rees[191] made tests on fabrics of cotton, wool, cotton and wool mixtures, rayon and rayon mixtures (?), silk, linen, casein, wool and casein, and kapok, and confirms the "dependence of the thermal insulation of a fabric upon its thickness, irrespective of the type of fiber used. . . . Thickness may not be the only factor which determines the thermal insulation of a fabric but it is certainly one of the most important."[191]

Graph 36 plots similar data for heat loss vs. weight per unit area and shows a much poorer correlation.

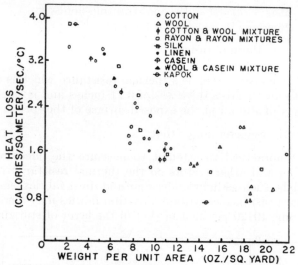

Graph 36.   Heat loss vs. weight per unit area of material.   (*From, Rees,*[186] *"The Transmission of Heat Through Textile Fabrics."*)

"The points are considerably more scattered than when heat loss values are plotted against fabric thickness, though as one would expect, the heavier samples are generally the warmer, as such samples are usually also thicker. These results suggest that a fabric of given insulating value could be constructed from any of the textile fibers by making it sufficiently thick. In service, wool appears to be the material mostly used for making thick fabrics, and has thus earned the reputation for being warmer than other textile materials. It is, of course, a "lofty" fibre (with considerable elastic resistance to flexure) and lends itself easily to the construction of thick fabrics of low density."[186]

Marsh[188] points out the difficulty of comparing the relative values of different fibers for thermal insulation:

"Many comparisons have been made, but it is very easy to misinterpret experimental results on this point. The great difficulty is in the very different types of fabrics produced by different fibers. For instance, the question is often raised as to whether silk is "warmer" than wool. This is very difficult to answer, as very few silk fabrics are more than 0.3 mm thick, while very few wool fabrics are less than 0.5 mm thick. Even if two fabrics, one of silk and one of wool were found to be the same thickness, each would be an extreme of its class and therefore not truly representative.

"A comparison of silk and linen brings out another difficulty in comparing different fibers. Tests were made on a number of silk and linen fabrics whose thicknesses were all 0.1 mm. The linens (sheer linens and cambrics) had T.I.V.'s between 33 and 35 per cent, while among the silks, a crêpe de chine had a value of 30 per cent and a twilled silk for foulards, 37.8 per cent. The (fabric) structure is therefore of the utmost importance. . . . It is therefore unjust to compare the thermal insulation of textile materials by comparing certain fabrics made of each. From this work it is believed that it would be possible to make a fabric of a given insulating value from any of the textile materials. It would only be necessary to make it sufficiently thick and of close structure. The reasons why this is not done commercially are apparently considerations of cost and weight. From a general review of fabrics made, it would appear that wool is the main material for making thick fabrics, and has therefore earned the name for being warmer than other materials."

Marsh's paper was written in 1931, which explains the lack of discussion of the synthetic fibers in the same vein.

Thermal Transmission vs. Fabric Density. Based upon the fact that fiber conductivity has little effect upon a fabric's thermal transmission, plus the above discussed conductivity-thickness relationship, it becomes obvious that state of aggregation of the fiber in the fabric structure is of major importance. So long as the requisite thickness is attained, concomittant insulation will result. However, the ability to maintain that thickness under normal use conditions of compression, tension, bending, laundering, dry cleaning, etc., must be given consideration.

An additional factor which must be discussed, is fabric density. Two fabrics may have the same thickness and hence the same thermal conductivity, but to obtain such equal thicknesses, different amounts of fiber may have to be used, that is aggregates of different fibers may have different bulk densities, so that on a weight basis, in a fabric structure one fiber may exhibit advantage over another.

Using 64's Merino wool, Egyptian cotton, and viscose staple fiber, all in the bulk form of compressed pads of loose fiber, Speakman and Chamberlain[194] plot specific conductivity vs. density in Graph 37.

The authors mention that the density of most textile fabrics varies from 0.15 to 0.60 g/cc. In this range, (as well as over the whole curve), the wool pads are superior to the cotton or viscose.

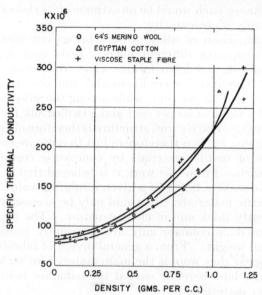

Graph 37. Specific thermal conductivity vs. density. (*From Speakman and Chamberlain,*[194] *"The Thermal Conductivity of Textile Materials and Fabrics."*)

Speakman and Chamberlain[194] give the following relationship among conductivity H, density Δ, and thickness d:

$$1/H = 16 + (801 - 639\Delta)d$$

They show data[194] wherein experimentally determined and calculated values of $1/H$ are compared.

> "With the exception of two fabrics, E_2 and E_1, the formula holds good within very narrow limits for all the types of fabric in common use as clothing materials, and by its use a good approximation to the true value of a fabric as a heat insulator in stagnant air can be obtained from measurements of thickness and density only."

They then use the above formula. . . .

> "to compare fabrics composed of materials other than wool with all-wool fabrics of equal weight and thickness, and in this

way unequivocal comparison of the several textile fibers as heat insulators can be made; for the total heat loss of a given fabric can be determined experimentally, and the total heat loss of a theoretical fabric of identical structure, but composed of wool, may be calculated. The difference between actual and calculated heat loss is given. For woven cotton fabrics, the mean deviation is 23.6 per cent, i.e., wool fabrics are 23.6 per cent more efficient as heat insulators than cotton fabrics of identical thickness and weight. For knitted fabrics the difference appears to be greater, the mean deviation being 32.1 per cent for the three samples tested. Of the four real silk fabrics examined, three show an approximately constant deviation of 23 per cent, while the fourth, a knitted sample, has a deviation of only 11 per cent. Artificial* silk fabrics also show a variable deviation while the mixture fabrics show deviations between the zero of wool and the 23.6 per cent average of the cellulose fabrics. In all cases, wool fabrics appear to be definitely superior as heat insulators to those composed of other fibers."

Table 84 shows some of the authors' data.

This writer gathers, from the above statements, that Speakman and Chamberlain[194] conclude that the wool fiber is inherently a better insulator than other fibers. In light of considerable work reported upon since their article was published, one can not agree with their findings. Presuming exactly the same weight and thickness of fabric, the density of the aggregate structure would have to be appreciably different for those fabrics containing fibers other than wool. This could, in turn, come only from differences in specific gravity between wool and the other fibers: cotton, "artificial silk," real silk, etc. Page 11 shows the specific gravities not to be sufficiently different to explain Chamberlain and Speakman's values. Cotton, for example, is 17 per cent heavier than wool, while silk is 5 per cent lighter.

It can only be concluded that any advantage of wool as a thermal insulator stems from its ability to maintain its given efficient state of aggregation under end-use conditions. Additional attributes, if any, must stem from other physical properties, e.g., heat of water absorption (already discussed on page 89), fabric surface in contact with the skin, etc. Schiefer[181] points this out by using thermal insulation (T.I.) per unit weight as a criterion of insulating efficiency. His results indicate that the efficiency is substantially independent of the type of fiber.

---

* This article was written in 1930 when the term "artificial silk" was used to identify what was probably viscose rayon.

(From Speakman and Chamberlain[194] "The Thermal Conductivity of Textile Materials and Fabrics")

TABLE 84

Fabric No.	Density (g/cc.)	Thickness (cm)	Heat Loss (expl.) (cals/sec/sq cm)	Heat Loss (calc. for same structure in wool) (cals/sec/sq cm)	% Error	Comments
cotton						
C.2	0.363	0.048	31.30×10^{-3}	23.08×10^{-3}	-26.26	pique 20 ribs per inch
C.3	0.341	0.043	29.94	24.35	-18.66	winceyette (fluffy material)
C.5	0.6575	0.018	55.09	43.76	-20.56	normal structure
F.1A	0.5043	0.043	33.87	27.33	-19.32	washed cotton suiting
F.1	0.5672	0.038	38.25	30.61	-19.97	unwashed cotton suiting
F.5A	0.6022	0.023	54.38	39.11	-28.08	sheeting unwashed
F.5	0.7525	0.018	56.99	45.95	-19.36	sheeting washed
O.4	0.3616	0.054	25.66	21.37	-16.72	flannelette (fluffy material)
V.2	0.2294	0.066	24.75	16.89	-31.76	knitted cotton underwear
art. silk						
K.4	0.4989	0.029	47.23	33.35	-29.40	viscose, knitted
O.3	0.3698	0.026	43.49	32.58	-25.20	viscose, hollow fibre
O.9	0.3443	0.033	31.07	28.43	-8.50	open knit, acetate silk
O.8	0.6748	0.018	60.77	44.13	-27.38	normal structure, cupra-ammonium silk
S.3	0.3909	0.054	23.21	21.85	-5.86	viscose, scribbled yarns
real silk						
O.13	0.6030	0.018	53.67	42.60	-20.62	spun silk
O.14	0.2847	0.101	16.93	12.74	-24.75	heavy ribbed knit from underwear
O.15	0.3788	0.038	30.16	26.85	-10.97	plain knit from underwear
linen						
O.5	0.5685	0.029	44.91	34.84	-22.42	plain weave coarse linen
mixtures						
A.2	0.1595	0.119	11.80	10.08	-14.57	gauze weave, wool, cotton
A.3	0.1645	0.091	15.36	12.61	-17.90	gauze weave, wool, cotton
A.4	0.1653	0.098	14.35	11.89	-17.14	gauze weave, cotton, art. silk
A.5	0.2799	0.048	27.36	21.80	-20.32	gauze weave, cotton, art. silk
S.1	0.4273	0.043	28.89	25.83	-10.59	suiting, wool 33.1%, art. silk 66.9%
S.2	0.4289	0.043	29.10	25.86	-11.14	suiting, wool 27.8%, art. silk 72.2%
V.4	0.2108	0.122	11.80	10.28	-12.88	knitted, wool 41.78%, cotton 58.22%
E.7	0.5461	0.068	25.20	21.39	-15.12	suiting, wool, cotton

"In general, the greater the thickness of the blanket, the lower is the value of thermal resistance per unit weight. The correlation is far from good for the blankets as a group. . . . (but) is greatly improved if the blankets are grouped according to compressibility.

$$\frac{1}{TW} = 0.4c - 0.4t_{0.1} + 0.05$$

where T = thermal transmission
W = weight
c = compressibility
$t_{0.1}$ = thickness at 0.1 psi"[181]

TABLE 85. THERMAL PROPERTIES OF BULK FIBERS

(From Peirce and Rees[187] "The Transmission of Heat Through Textile Fabrics, Part II")

Fibers	Wt/Sq yd (oz)	Thickness under pressure of .001 psi (inches)	Thermal Resistance (togs)	T.E.S.V. (cc/g)	Actual Specific Volume under pressure of .001 psi (cc/g)	T.E.S.V. Actual Specific Vol. (Specific Thermal resistivity) (%)
acetate waste	24.9	0.70	5.02	14.9	21.0	70.9
viscose waste	18.9	0.70	4.98	19.5	27.7	70.5
90% acetate waste + 10% wool (50's)	19.9	0.60	4.83	18.0	22.6	79.7
90% viscose waste + 10% wool (50's)	19.9	0.77	6.20	23.1	29.0	79.6
wool (50's)	20.9	0.96	7.90	28.0	34.4	81.5
cotton (bengals)	25.5	0.90	7.37	21.4	26.4	81.0
Java kapok	16.5	1.05	9.58	43.0	47.8	89.9
akund	18.2	1.05	9.15	37.3	43.3	86.2
glass	27.8	1.03	6.70	17.9	27.8	64.4
In the following samples the fibers have been treated with urea-formaldehyde resin.						
viscose waste	13.2	0.85	7.18	40.3	48.2	83.6
cotton (Bengals)	14.4	1.00	8.18	42.1	52.0	81.0
alpaca and viscose staple fiber mixture	14.8	0.79	6.43	32.2	39.9	80.7

Thus the greater the compressibility, the more efficient is the insulator. Referring to the previous section on resilience, since wool exhibits such high compressibility and resilience, it follows that its thermal insulation ability is high and can remain so.

Peirce and Rees[187] compare various bulk fibers for thermal properties by preparing quilted fleeces of the various fibers. They use "Thermally Effective Specific Volume" as one of their criterion of performance.

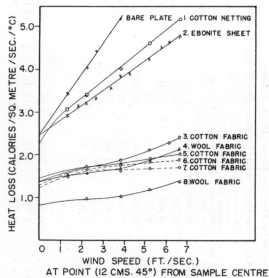

Graph 38. Heat loss vs. wind speed. (*From Rees,*[186] "*The Transmission of Heat Through Textile Fabrics.*")

Reviewing the definition given on page 193, it will be noted that density $\left(\text{actually specific volume or } \dfrac{1}{\text{density}} \right)$ is taken into account. Table 85 lists data on the various fibers. Inspection of the table shows the outstanding properties of kapok and Akund. However, wool is superior to acetate, viscose, and cotton. It is unfortunate that no data are reported for the synthetic fibers. It is worthy to point out that the specific volume of the wool (cc/g at 0.001 psi) is only exceeded by the above mentioned kapok and akund. This of course correlates with the thickness-thermal conductivity relationship already discussed in that a given weight of wool occupies a greater volume.

Effect of Air Velocity on Thermal Transmission. Rees[186] reports on the effect of air velocity on the heat loss of fabrics (Graph 38).

"Curve 1 is for a thin cotton netting of very open structure, and above a wind speed of 1 ft/second (the curve)
appears to be linear. This fabric was very open and afforded
little resistance to the passage of air through its structure.
Curves 3, 4, and 8 show a rapid increase of heat loss at the
higher wind speeds which is not apparent in curves 5, 6, and 7.
The fabrics of curves 5, 6, and 7 are closely woven, whilst those
of curves 3, 4, and 8 have a much more open structure, and at
the higher wind speeds, the air will be circulated in the interstices of the loosely woven fabrics, resulting in greater heat
loss."

Rees thus shows that fabric structure, not fiber property, governs the
effect of air velocity on thermal transmission, and this conclusion is in
keeping with the rest of the evidence presented in this chapter.

The article of Cassie[61] concerning warmth, air permeability and
resilience has already been discussed at some length on pages 183–185
and the advantages of the wool fiber in that it cannot pack as closely
together as many other fibers has been pointed out. He agrees that
geometric structure is important, and elaborates on the subject by discussing the usually blithe statement that

"Underwear fabrics are warm because they 'entrap' air.
. . . Thermal insulation measurements tell us nothing of how
air is entrapped by clothing. . . . Fibres cannot entrap air in
cells or in closed small spaces within a fabric. They entrap
air because air clings to a solid surface and the fibers have
enormous total surfaces. Air clinging to a solid surface is
the well-known foundation of aerodynamics, and it is easily
seen in the aerodynamics of a common hedge. A hedge forms
a windbreak because air clings to its branches, twigs, and
leaves, and the drag on the air from the large surfaces within
the hedge brings it to rest: in short, the hedge does not behave
as a solid wall, obstructing the flow of air; it uses aerodynamic
drag to bring the air to rest. Clothing employs the same
principles as the hedge: indeed, if I were to give a larger scale
analogy of underwear fabrics, I should choose the hedge . . .
if you want to see the general internal structure of a wool
fabric, I would say, look at a hedge. A fabric looks solid
because the large surface of the fibres strikes the eye to give
the appearance of solidity; and a hedge looks solid for precisely
the same reason.

"When we say that fabrics entrap air, we really mean that
their fibres impose a drag on air movement. Let us look then
at the total surface area of fibres to find how effectively they
may perform this function."[61]

Cassie then proceeds to show, assuming that the fibers are cylindrical, that 64's quality 20 μ wool has a surface area of 800 ft^2/lb, silk has 3,000 ft^2/lb and a crossbred wool 400 ft^2/lb. He points out the need for using such large surfaces in cutting down air permeability, and then mentions the importance of preventing the close packing of fibers as has already been discussed on page 183. Cassie in a previous article[195] gives similar data for acetate and viscose rayon. Tables 86 and 87 list fiber surface accessible to air values and their relation to air permeability and fabric structure.

TABLE 86. FIBER SURFACE ACCESSIBLE TO AIR IN WOOL FABRICS

(From Cassie[61] "Characteristics for Warmth in Underwear Fabrics")

Plain Weave 24 warp $\times$ 28 filling—Woolen yarn mean count in finished fabric 4.4 (worsted counts)—Fiber diameter 22.7 μ

Finish	Wt oz/yd^2	Thickness .001 in. at 6 oz/in^2	Bulk Density lbs/ft^3 at 6 oz/in^2	Air Perm. ft/min/inch	Fiber Surface per yd^2 Actual	Accessible	% of Surface accessible to air
grey	14.0	71.0	16.5	388	582	310	53
scoured	13.2	78.3	14.0	173	540	508	94
milled	14.9	98.2	12.7	124	615	684	110
washed off	15.6	97.6	13.4	112	645	726	112
cropped	13.9	67.4	17.2	112	571	527	92

Cassie[195] comments on the acetate and viscose fabrics (Table 87) as follows:

"The fabrics were chosen for the uniformity of their structures, but despite the choice, they do not have the almost uniform packing of fibres that is present in wool cloths. The results are, therefore, not wholly trustworthy, but they seem to indicate that the accessible fibre surface, even in the best of artificial fabrics, in only 70 to 80 per cent of the total surface. It may be, of course, that even in these fabrics, the air flow is largely through the spaces between the yarns, and that the accessibility of the fibres in the yarns is even less than 70 per cent."

His later article[61] more or less confirms his prediction of the superiority of wool, for the tables show that both the accessible fiber surface, the actual fiber surface, and the ratio of the former to the latter are all higher for the wool fabrics than for the viscose or acetate. He then states that

"wool yarns are probably unique in exposing the full surface of their fibres to air. The open structure of wool yarns may be due to the natural crimp of the fibres, but it will be shown that the elastic constants of wool have a unique relationship which would predict an open structure yarn."[61]

TABLE 87. FIBER SURFACE ACCESSIBLE TO AIR IN VISCOSE AND ACETATE FABRICS
(From Cassie[61] "Characteristics for Warmth in Underwear Fabrics")
Plain Weave

Fiber	Fiber diameter μ	Ends and Picks	Counts (wstd)	Weight oz/yd²	Thickness .001 in. at 6 oz/in²	Bulk Density lbs/ft³ at 6 oz/in²	Air Perm. ft/min/inch	Fiber Surface per yd²		% of Surface accessible to air
								Actual	Accessible	
continuous acetate	23	101/49	69/68	2.46	4.2	48.7	50	98.2	77.8	79
continuous viscose	27	34/35	13/13	5.70	18.0	26.4	401	170.0	129.0	75
Fibro	18.25	47/40	23/23	6.85	26.0	22.0	267	302.0	210.0	70
acetate staple	15.5	.....	.....	4.66	17.5	22.2	362	272.0	222.0	81

He then proceeds to analyze the fiber coiling characteristics already discussed on page 184.

It is unfortunate that Cassie has no data or conclusions concerning the inherent aerodynamic drag properties of the various fibers.

Effect of Relative Humidity on Thermal Transmission. Graph 39, taken from Rees's article,[186] shows that the effect of humidity on heat loss through textile fabrics is substantially negligible. (The relative

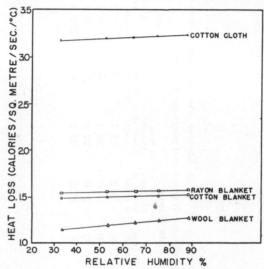

Graph 39. The effect of relative humidity on thermal transmission (heat loss). (*From Rees,*[186] "*The Transmission of Heat Through Textile Fabrics.*")

position of the various graphs for cotton cloth, rayon blanket, etc. are of no consequence since the samples are of various thicknesses.)

(43) Emissivity and the Feeling of Coldness of Fabrics

The importance of emissivity as well as thermal conductivity in its effect on thermal insulation value has already been mentioned on page 194. Baxter and Cassie[189] comment as follows:

> "Clothing, when made up of several layers of loosely fitting fabrics, will have an overall conductivity that depends on the transfer of heat from one fabric to another, and fabrics with low surface emissivities will give clothing of low heat loss.
>
> "Surface emissivities contain two heat transfer factors . . . radiation . . . and convection. Heat transfer by radiation will depend upon the radiation properties of the fibres composing the fabric and on the colour of the fabric. Transfer by convection will depend on the roughness of the fabric surface."

Table 88 lists thermal conductivity and emissivity values for a greatcoat, a worsted and a cotton fabric.

TABLE 88. CONDUCTIVITY AND EMISSIVITY VALUES FOR FABRICS
(From Baxter and Cassie[189] "Thermal Insulating Properties of Clothing")

Fabric	Conductivity cal/cm/sec/°C × 10^5	Emissivity cal/cm^2/sec/°C × 10^4
greatcoat	8.9	2.38
worsted	9.15	2.46
cotton	9.35	2.50

"The milled greatcoat material has both a lower conductivity and a lower emissivity than the others. The low emissivity of the wool clothes is doubtless due to their surface cover which gives them effectively a greater thickness than the measured one. Their low conductivities may be due to the breaking up of pores between the yarns by fibers that always appear on the surface of wool yarns."[189]

Any discussion of emissivity and radiation emanating from the human body brings to mind the recently popular use of "metal-coated" lining fabrics utilized in light weight coats. These are allegedly designed to reflect the radiant energy emanating from the body back towards the body. Thus the conversion of this energy to sensible heat is kept at a minimum and the wearer is supposedly warmer in a lighter weight coat. Herrington[411] analyzes the situation as follows:

"It may be noted at once that the quality of radiation from a very hot source, such as the sun at 6000°K, is quite different from that emitted by low temperature sources near 300°K. This latter radiation is typical of radiation from walls, human bodies and other objects whose temperature on an ordinary scale is from 0°F to 200 or 300°F.

"In common experience the high temperature radiation is associated with visible objects such as the sun or incandescent lamps. Radiation from objects at ordinary temperatures is long infra-red radiation and is invisible. It may of course be felt by the skin, as in the case of a warm wall.

"Radiant energy may be reflected. However, a good reflector for energy from a high temperature source is not necessarily a good reflector for the dark heat from our ordinary surroundings. This point has led to some general misunderstanding in the application of reflective insulation to clothing.

"Since we associate visible reflection with the word 'reflection,' it is often assumed that any shiny surfaced material will provide reflective insulation for dark or invisible infra-red. The misunderstanding has been furthered by the fact that by chance one of the most common reflectors for high temperature sources, aluminum surfaces, is also a good reflector for long infra-red, under certain circumstances. These circumstances are the requirement that the aluminum surface be either uncoated for long infra-red insulation, or else with so thin a coating that the absorbing effect of the organic material is unimportant.

"It is quite unsafe to estimate the long infra-red reflecting character of an aluminized fabric by giving regard to its visible appearance. Technical measurements of long infra-red reflectance are the sole acceptable criteria of the adaptability of such fabrics to insulation uses.

"When spacings of 0.1 to 0.7 inches are used between the plates of a fabric heat conductance measuring apparatus, gains of approximately 15% can be realized by facing the terminal plates with aluminum foil of 0.95 reflectance when the intervening space is filled to a low density with other insulating materials.

"When narrow spaces of the order of 0.1 to 0.2 of an inch are used without a filler, gains of the order of 40% are theoretically possible.

"In order to realize the larger gain in lighter constructions, means would have to be found of preventing contact of the opposed metallized surfaces or any substantial intervening area of fabric or filler. In addition, the fabric surfaces would have to have tested reflectances near 0.95. For applications requiring very low over-all conductance, the larger gain cannot be realized for physical reasons related to the nature of the radiation exchange process.

"It would not be in order to discard the utility of technically improved reflective fabrics in protective clothing or related applications. A flexible and durable fabric of 0.90 reflectance in the long infra-red would have many applications. At the present moment such fabrics as have been developed seem to have their most direct application when used in connection with fire-fighting equipment. Here the requirements for efficient and useful insulation performance are less exacting."

Returning now to the subject of the nature of the surface of fabrics, Baxter and Cassie[189] show that a rough surface wool blanket gives a low surface emissivity compared to a relatively smooth all-wool serge fabric.

"Smooth surfaced fabrics with their relatively large surface emissivities will give good heat transfer from fabric to fabric and presumably from skin to fabric; they will thus give clothing of large heat transfer even though the individual fabrics have the same thermal conductivity and thickness as fabrics with surface cover.   Smooth surfaced fabrics are thus likely to be regarded as 'cold' fabrics, whilst those with surface cover will be regarded as 'warm.'"

Rees[191] discusses the cold feel of fabrics:

"It was frequently observed during tests that the temperature of the hot plate dropped slightly when the fabric was first brought into contact with it.   This is due to the 'coldness' of the sample and is, of course, greater the lower the initial temperature.   The effect varies markedly in different fabrics and

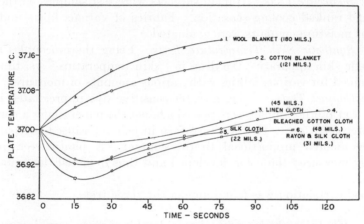

Graph 40.   The cold feel of fabrics.   (*From Rees,*[186] *"The Transmission of Heat Through Textile Fabrics."*)

may be an important feature as regards comfort of putting clothing on next to the skin.   A record of the initial change in temperature of the hot plate when the specimen is first applied gives a measure of this cold feel (Graph 40).   Wool and cotton blankets showed no chill effect and a wool blanket warmed up most quickly.   The chill effect was quite marked with a smooth bleached cotton cloth; a similar linen cloth showed less chilling, a silk one about the same, and a cloth consisting of acetate rayon and silk much more."

Hock, Sookne, and Harris[196] report on "The Thermal Properties of Moist Fabrics" with particular reference to the "chilling effect" or "clamminess" of fabrics:

"Practical experience has demonstrated that moist fabrics in contact with the body produce an unpleasant sensation commonly referred to as a "chilling" effect or "clammy feel." The intensity of the sensation varies with different fibers and fabrics; thus on the basis of general experience, the merits of wool fabrics over similar cotton fabrics have long been recognized . . . the preference usually (is) given to woolen underwear and other garments for use in cold climates under conditions where physical labor causes considerable perspiration."

Recognizing that warmth was not dependent upon fiber or fabric thermal conductivity per se, an investigation was made on the chilling effect of fabrics as the moisture content increased. Three test methods were employed:

(1) *Subjective Tests.* Human subjects wore test samples on the forearm and ranked cooling sensation. Fabrics of various fibers and with various moisture contents were evaluated.

(2) *Synthetic Skin Temperature Tests.* Using thermocouples and a synthetic skin apparatus, the drop in "skin temperature" vs. time was determined for various fabrics with various amounts of moisture.

(3) *Contact Tests.* Using a water sensitive dye impregnated into a paper, wet fabric samples were placed against the paper under a constant pressure of 0.5 psi. The fabric surface in contact caused the paper to become colored proportional to the contact. A photometer quantitatively measured the color developed and thus depicted the amount of contact.

Good correlation was found among the three tests.

"Fabrics which produced considerable chilling in subjective tests were found to make good contact and to cause a substantial drop in skin temperature. Conversely, fabrics which caused little or no clamminess made poor contact and the accompanying drop in temperature was relatively small."[196]

Graphs 41 and 42, taken from Hock, Sookne and Harris's paper, plot temperature drop vs. time (test (2) above), and per cent reflectance vs. per cent moisture (test (3) above), respectively. The former shows that the wool, cotton, and blends thereof show a sharp initial drop in temperature to a minimum followed by a progressive lessening of the temperature drop. The all wool sample is better than the all cotton, the blends exhibiting proportionate curves. The continuous filament fabrics of viscose, nylon and acetate give an entirely different type of curve, showing a rapid and continuing increase in temperature drop. The superiority of the wool and cotton fabrics is apparent. However, since we are comparing spun cotton and wool fabrics with continuous-filament acetate, viscose, and nylon, no absolute conclusions concerning fiber advantages can be made.

Similarly, Graph 42 shows the cotton and wool fabrics to give higher reflectances (i.e., less surface contact) than the synthetics. Obviously it is easier to produce this condition with spun yarns than with continuous filaments.

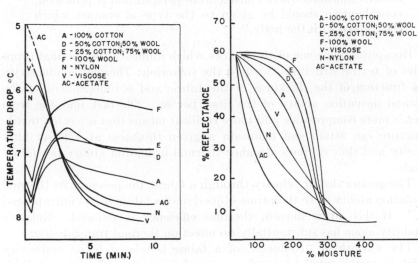

Graph 41. The effect of type of fiber on the "chilling effect" of a "synthetic skin" surface. (Temperature drop °C vs. time.) (*From Hock, Sookne, and Harris,*[196] "*Thermal Properties of Moist Fabrics.*")

Graph 42. The effect of type of fiber on the "surface contact" of fabrics against a paper surface. (Per cent reflectance vs. per cent moisture content.) (*From Hock, Sookne, and Harris,*[196] "*Thermal Properties of Moist Fabrics.*")

The authors make the following conclusions:[196]

"A progressive improvement of the fabrics as their wool content is increased, and the superiority of certain types of construction are clearly indicated. The extent of contact which the fabrics make with the skin appears to be the significant factor. These tests show that those fabrics which make the poorest contact cause the least chilling. From this point of view the desirability of wool fibers which are highly crimped and possess long range elasticity, properties which permit a type of fabric construction which minimizes the extent of contact which can be made with the skin, is apparent. In contrast, cotton which exhibits considerable plasticity when wet is less desirable from the same point of view. However, results show that special types of construction, especially those which produce a napped or fuzzy surface, reduce appreciably the contact which even wet cotton fabrics make, and thereby lessen the chilling effect. It appears therefore that in selecting fabric for warmth, especially when these fabrics are to be worn next to the skin in cold climates, and under conditions where considerable perspiration is produced, consideration should be given to the type of contact which they make with the body."

Recapitulating some of the factors which influence the thermal properties of textile structures, we find the following: Thermal conductivity is a function of the thickness of the fabric and is independent of the thermal insulation ability of the fiber per se. The fact that the wool fiber is more compressible and more resilient means that a woolen textile structure can attain and maintain a given thickness at a lesser bulk density and thus exhibits a higher thermal insulation ability per fabric weight.

The greater the air velocity through a fabric, the poorer is its thermal insulation ability since the prime objective of a fabric is to "entrap dead air." If this air is moved, thermal efficiency is reduced. Relative humidity alone has substantially no effect on thermal transmission.

The warmth or "coolness" of a fabric is related to its emissivity which in turn is related to surface smoothness. Smooth surface fabrics have high emissivities which produce high heat transfer from fabric to fabric and presumably from skin to fabric. The rougher the surface, the lower is the emissivity, the less the heat energy emitted, and the warmer the fabric. Wool fabrics which are made from naturally crimped staple fiber, tend to have low emissivities and a warm feel. Continuous filament fabrics tend to produce the opposite condition. Based on conductivity and emissivity properties, as well as upon the already discussed high heat of moisture absorption (page 91), it can be concluded that fabrics made from wool tend to provide excellent warmth for apparel use, and the popular conception that wool fabrics are warm is undoubtedly a valid one.

With respect to coolness for summer tropical worsted suitings, high thermal conductivity is obviously not the entire answer. Even if fabrics are of sufficient thinness to cause high heat transfer, and are sufficiently open to allow high air transfer, for wool fabrics the nature of the surface in contact is of paramount importance. It is evident that one should strive for as slick and smooth a fabric surface as possible: long staple, low crimped fiber spun into smooth yarns which in turn are woven into a smooth fabric (e.g., a sateen), might do much to increase the surface contact between skin and fabric, and fabric and fabric, thereby increasing the emissivity and heat radiation. At the moment, the writer cannot comment on the implication of heat of absorption in this situation, but in any event, the construction of such a smooth fabric should logically be a step in the right direction of cooler all-wool summer fabrics.

Chapter 13

AIR PERMEABILITY

(44) Air Permeability Nomenclature and Measurement

Air permeability of textile fabrics plays an important part in certain limited end-use requirements: parachute fabrics, sails, clothing where warmth is desired under cold and windy weather conditions, rain wear and other water impermeable fabrics, and industrial air filters. The most important of these, in this book, is concerned with warmth.

The literature on the subject is not extensive and conclusions concerning requisite air permeability values for specific applications, when made at all, are usually only qualitative. For example, no data are found which give the maximum and minimum values of air permeability for parachute fabrics. Carlene[197] comments on an article by Marsh[198] as follows:

> "In connection with his work on the thermal insulating properties of fabrics, Marsh determined the air permeability of a large number of materials. A wide variation in the values for different cloths was observed, knitted and Aertex-type fibers having a high permeability to air, whereas closely woven plain or twill weave fabrics were comparatively impermeable to air. Marsh, however, made no comments on the importance of permeability upon the choice of certain fabrics for clothing, and although in his paper on thermal transmission[188] figures for both T.I.V. and air permeability are given for many fabrics, no mention is made of the connection, if any, between these two physical quantities. In actual fact, no direct relation was observed on plotting the results for all the fabrics examined by Marsh, but certain fabrics such as wool and wool-cotton blankets, and Aertex cotton fabrics fell into groups, the former characterized by high T.I.V. and relatively high permeability, and the latter by low T.I.V. and very high permeability."

The Measurement of Air Permeability. There are two standard air-permeability testers popularly used in the United States, the Gurley

Densometer and the Frazier Air Permeometer. Landsberg and Winston[199] describe their operation as follows:

"*Gurley:* The Gurley machines used in this investigation are equipped with two coaxial circular plates, at the center of each of which is a circular orifice 0.1 or 1.0 square inch in area. . . . The upper plate and its opening serve, respectively, as the bottom of a cylinder and as the end of a tube which extends up through the center of the cylinder. This cylinder . . . is filled with oil (viscosity 60–70° Saybolt at 100°F) to a prescribed point below the upper end of the tube. Air is forced through the open top of the tube by means of an inverted cylinder (with sealed top), weighing 5 ounces, floating freely on the surface of the oil in the outer cylinder. The air pressure thus exerted is equal to 1.26 inches of water.

"The outer surface of the inverted cylinder is scored off into six sections, each of which represents 50 cc of air. The descent of this cylinder forces air through the fabric at a rate indicated by the surface markings. Air-permeability values are obtained by noting the number of seconds required for 300 cc of air to pass through the fabric.

"*Frazier:* The Frazier instrument consists of two chambers, (one above the other), a suction fan, two manometers, a calibrated orifice, and a clamp for holding the specimen. Between the two chambers is mounted one of a series of nine calibrated orifices. The air in (the lower) chamber is pumped out by means of the fan and is replaced by air coming from (the upper) chamber through the orifice. The flow of air from the atmosphere into the upper chamber is determined by the permeability of the specimen, 0.0412 square foot of which is exposed to testing by virtue of the size of the fabric orifice. The removal of air from the lower chamber creates a vacuum across a tube connecting this chamber with a vertical manometer and an oil reservoir. This gage is used to measure the pressure drop across the calibrated orifice. Still another tube connects the upper chamber with another reservoir and an inclined manometer. This gage, open to the air, measures the pressure drop across the fabric.

"Air-permeability values are obtained by noting the vertical manometer readings while the pressure drop across the fabric is maintained at 0.5 inch of water pressure, as indicated by the inclined gage. By a consideration of the size of the calibrated orifice used, these readings can be converted into a figure which expresses the number of cubic feet of air which passes through a square foot of the fabric per minute."

Quantitative relationships between the two instruments have been calculated by the authors[199] as follows: At operating pressure drops of 0.5 and 1.26 inches of water for the Frazier and Gurley instruments respectively, and a 0.1 square inch orifice in the Gurley machine:

$$\log Y_F = \log 533 - 1.02 \log X_G$$

where Y = cu ft/sq ft/minute (Frazier)
     G = time in seconds (Gurley)

Clayton[200] uses two parameters of air permeability:

"(1) Permeability P = the volume of air in cubic centimeters passed per second through 100 square centimeters of cloth, divided by the pressure difference in centimeters of water, i.e.

$$P = 100V/A \cdot p$$

where V = volume of air in cc/second
     A = area of test piece in sq cms.
     p = pressure head of air in cms of water"

"(2) Sectional Permeability Ps. The permeability of a fabric may be considered in terms of three factors, (a) the cross sectional area of each hole, (b) the depth of each hole—or the thickness of the fabric, and (c) the number of holes per unit area. It is therefore conceivable that two cloths may have the same permeability P for very different reasons. For example, a very thick cloth with a rather open weave may have the same permeability as a thinner cloth with a closer weave. If the two cloths were of equal thickness, the closer weave would have a lower permeability. It is therefore desirable to have a figure independent of the thickness, to represent the "air openness" of a fabric; for this purpose the product Px*d*, where *d* is the thickness in millimeters, is used to express the openness of a fabric of unit thickness. This is called the sectional permeability Ps."

(45) Factors Which Influence Air Permeability

Clayton[200] has investigated some aspects of the variation of air permeability with cloth structure as follows:

Series I—Effect of Number of Picks Per Inch. Holding the warp yarn size and thread count as well as the filling yarn size constant, the picks per inch were varied and the permeability determined.

TABLE 89. EFFECT OF PICKAGE ON AIR PERMEABILITY

(From Clayton[200] "Air Permeability of Fabrics")

Ends per inch = 141; Warp count = 44; Filling count = 50; Filling crimp % = 3.5

Cloth	Picks (per inch)	Warp crimp (%)	Cloth weight (oz/yd²)	P*	Thickness (mms)
A	36.1	5.1	2.8	8,290	0.30
B	46.3	6.5	3.0	5,570	0.31
C	56.2	9.7	3.1	2,880	0.29
D	66.3	11.6	3.3	1,070	0.30
E	77.1	15.3	3.7	562	0.29
F	87.5	16.0	3.9	248	0.29
G	98.1	19.1	4.0	128	0.30
H	106.1	24.2	4.2	90	0.30
I	108.4	25.3	4.3	86	0.29

* $P = 100V/A \cdot p$ where V = Volume of air (cc/second)

A = Area of test piece (cm²)

p = pressure head of air (cms H_2O)

Series II—Effect of Filling Yarn Size. Holding the warp yarn size and thread count, as well as the filling thread count constant, the filling yarn size (count) was varied and the permeability determined.

TABLE 90. EFFECT OF FILLING YARN SIZE ON AIR PERMEABILITY

(From Clayton[200] "Air Permeability of Fabrics")

Ends/inch = 141; Picks/inch = 74; Warp count = 44; Filling Crimp % = 3.0

Cloth	Filling count	Warp crimp (%)	Cloth weight (oz/yd²)	P*	Thickness (mms)
A	20.3	27.0	5.4	213	0.37
B	38.9	13.5	3.9	530	0.29
C	51.5	13.2	3.5	555	0.29
D	59.4	10.2	3.4	673	0.28
E	81.5	7.4	3.0	761	0.25
F	101.2	7.0	2.9	1,010	0.25

* See Table 89 for units of P.

Series III—Effect of Constant Cover Factor (attained by proper selection of filling count and pickage). By adjusting filling yarn size and picks per inch a constant "cover factor" (i.e., ratio of fabric surface covered to the whole surface) is attainable according to the equation:

$$\frac{\text{Picks per inch}}{\sqrt{\text{count}}} = \text{constant}$$

Table 91 shows permeability values for various combinations of pick and filling count producing a constant cover factor.

TABLE 91.   RELATIONSHIP AMONG PICK COUNT, FILLING YARN COUNT, COVER FACTOR
AND AIR PERMEABILITY

(From Clayton[200] "Air Permeability of Fabrics")

Ends per inch = 143; Warp count = 43; Warp crimp % = 13;
Cloth weight = 3.7 oz/yd²; Cover factor = 1.04

Cloth	Picks (per inch)	Filling Count	Filling crimp (%)	Cloth Thickness (mms)	P*
A	45.9	19.8	2.0	0.36	3,000
B	66.0	40.2	2.3	0.29	1,040
C	75.3	51.5	3.2	0.29	555
D	80.6	61.3	3.8	0.26	488
E	93.0	82.4	4.5	0.24	274
F	104.7	100.4	5.2	0.24	217

* See Table 89 for units of P.

Series IV—Effect of Filling Twist.   Holding warp and filling thread count constant, warp yarn size constant, and filling size substantially constant, filling twist was varied and the permeability determined.

TABLE 92.   EFFECT OF FILLING TWIST ON AIR PERMEABILITY

(From Clayton[200] "Air Permeability of Fabrics")

Ends per inch = 143; Picks per inch = 75; Warp count = 43; Filling count = 50;
warp crimp % = 13.0; Filling crimp % (except B) = 2.9; Cloth weight = 3.7 oz/yd²

cloth	A	B	C	D	E	F
filling twist factor	2.6	3.1	3.6	4.0	4.7	5.1
P*	507	702	671	755	869	920
thickness (mms)	0.29	0.30	0.30	0.30	0.30	0.29

* See Table 89 for units of P.

The above four series show results which one might expect: (1) as the pickage increases the permeability decreases.   (2) As the filling yarn becomes lighter in weight, the permeability increases, Clayton stating that the relation is fairly linear.   (3) At constant cover factor, attainable by various combinations of pick and count, permeability is not constant. However, linear relationships do exist between (a) log Ps and log number of picks and (b) log Ps and log filling count.   (4) Permeability varies linearly with twist factor.   This last relationship is confirmed by Robertson[201] who states,

> "It is evident that the twist has a profound effect on the fabric porosity (permeability).   This is probably a direct result of the effect of twist in compacting the fiber bundle and the resulting higher yarn densities with high twist.   For a given fabric, no other constructional variable was found to have nearly as great an effect on porosity."

(46) The Influence of Air Permeability on The Comfort Aspects of Clothing

Some discussion of air velocity in its relation to warmth has already been made in the Chapters on resilience and thermal transmission. Cassie's papers[4,61] in particular have pointed out the insulation ability of entrapped air.   A light lofty blanket might keep a person warm in a cold bedroom at low wind velocity but would be obviously of little help in a high cold wind atop Mount Washington.   A second effect of wind velocity is the evaporation of moisture from the skin with concomitant reduction in skin temperature.

In considering the range of fabric air permeabilities and its effect upon body comfort, Robinson[202] comments as follows:

"In air temperatures of 28, 34, and 46°C, varying the air permeability of their clothing from 12 to 40 cubic feet per minute made no consistent difference in working men's rates of sweating, skin temperatures, and heart rates, nor did it alter to any important degree heat exchange by the avenues of radiation, convection, and evaporation.   A change in air movement from 5 to 184 m/min made practically no difference in this relationship.   These results confirmed the author's original observations that the porous British cellular weave does not make cooler clothing than the thinner but more tightly woven fabrics.

"Correlated with the above physiological data are the observations of Fourt and Harris on the effects of wind and fabrics on evaporative clothing.   The tests ranged from mosquito netting to the most tightly woven fabrics and cellophane, and included experiments on bare, wet, artificial skin which was saturated blotting paper.   In still air, the porosity of the fabric is of very little importance, since the resistance to diffusion is largely in layers of still air which contribute up to ten times as much resistance as the cloth itself.   In moving air, the resistance of the clothing and associated air layers falls off with increase in the velocity (V, miles/hour) or air permeability of the fabric (A, ft^3/ft^2/minute at 0.5″ water) so that the rate of evaporative cooling, (E, in kg cal/meter^2/hour/mm vapor pressure difference between skin and air, P) is

$$E/P = 3 + (0.3 + 0.004A)V$$

"Any kind of fabric, even mosquito netting, cuts down the air movement and evaporation by a large factor.   The evaporation from bare wet surfaces, such as face and hands, is much larger than that through any fabric, and is much more sensitive to air movement. Evaporation from wet fabrics is similarly large and sensitive, but is less efficient in cooling the body than evaporation from the skin. This is correlated with the above data which show that in hot environments the wearing of clothing by men greatly increases the physiological strain over that experienced when the skin is bare. Among the strong fabrics used for army clothing, variations in air permeability from $A = 50$ down to zero make little difference unless there is much air movement. Hence both the physical and physiological data show that tight weaving to prevent mosquito bites imposes no more heat burden than that presented by other fabrics such as herringbone twill, and if the tight fabric is thin, may impose less burden."

An amusing application of fabric permeability concerns the development of mosquito-resisting fabrics. Linduska and Morton[410] report on

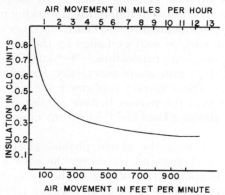

Graph 43. Insulating power of ambient air as a function of wind velocity at 77°F. (*From Belding,*[159] *in "Physiology of Heat Regulation and The Science of Clothing."*)

the resistance of 56 different cloths to biting by mosquitos, using as units the number of bites per 100 mosquitos landing on the sample area. Field tests of sample fatigue suits showed that tightly woven cloths gave substantially complete protection. The use of a net-type undergarment permitted the wearing of a more permeable outer garment. For example, the permeability of a light nylon suit was reduced from 65 per cent to less than 1 per cent by a quarter inch square net.

Belding[159] also shows a plot of insulation in Clo units vs. air velocity (Graph 43) and a plot showing the amount of insulation which must be provided at three different wind velocities (Graph 44). He states

"Wind does not affect the total insulation required but simply the fraction of the total insulation which must be sup-

plied by the clothing; in other words, whereas a total of 4.3 Clo
are indicated as being necessary at 50°F to protect a man
indefinitely while sleeping, only about 81% of this must be
furnished by the bedding if there is no wind, while 95% must
be similarly furnished if there is a 12 mile per hour wind.
This difference is of less practical importance at colder temperatures where total insulation requirements are large, but . . .
wind makes a great difference when a man is nude or lightly
clad."

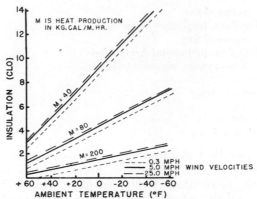

Graph 44. The amount of insulation which must be provided by clothing at
three wind velocities. (*From Belding,*[159] *in "Physiology of Heat Regulation and The
Science of Clothing."*)

Fourt and Harris[203] list the air permeabilities of a wide range of
military and civilian apparel fabrics.

They state,[203]

"Clothing as worn is exposed to moving air, and common
experience indicates the value of relatively porous (permeable)
clothing. For this reason there was considerable surprise at
the first reports from Australian observers that tightly woven,
wind-resistant fabrics were more desirable for wear under
tropical conditions than the more porous (permeable) herringbone twill used in U.S. combat clothing. These reports set off
a series of physiological and physical investigations . . . on
the influence of clothing on comfort and efficiency in hot
climates. Two of the principal results are:
"(1) In the low ranges of porosity, thinness of fabric is
more important than porosity in reducing the heat burden.
"(2) The diffusion layer of relatively still air between the
clothing surface and the general atmosphere reduces the effects

TABLE 93. AIR PERMEABILITIES OF REPRESENTATIVE FABRICS

(From Fourt and Harris[203] "Physical Properties of Clothing Fabrics")

ft^3/ft^2/minute at 0.5 inch water pressure

Fabric	Air Permeability
none—rate of flow which gives 0.5 inch impact pressure	2800
wire screen, ¼ inch	1700
mosquito net	1300
very open weave shirt	395
knit cotton undershirt or T shirt	220
thirteen civilian shirts (broadcloth or oxford weave): range	233–24
average	93
Palm Beach suits—range of five	129–91
light worsteds, gabardines, tropicals—range of six	60–42
seersucker suiting—range of five	41–50
British Cellular Weave—experimental Army fabric	40
herringbone twill—Army; range, eighteen lots	25–6.5
average	13
uniform twill, 8.2 ounce, Army	12
poplin, 6 ounce, Army	6
Byrd cloth, wind resistant	3
JO cloth (special wind resistant)	0.9

of porosity, so that at low rates of air movement, extremely tight weaving of the hygroscopic fibers imposes no greater burden than moderately tight weaving. This is important for military fabrics where wind and rain resistance, strength, and resistance to insect bites are to be combined in the same fabric."

It becomes apparent that for fabrics which are composed of hydrophilic fibers, the air permeability may be set at any desired level without interfering with other factors involved in body comfort, namely, moisture transfer and heat dissipation. The following chapter will similarly show that for hydrophilic fiber fabrics, tightness of structure has little effect on moisture transfer. However, in the case of the hydrophobic fibers this is not so, for unless the weave is sufficiently open and the air permeability is sufficiently high, moisture cannot transfer through the fabric interstices, and discomfort results.

Gregory[204] confirms the wide latitude in permeability without sacrifice of comfort:

"Measurements of permeability to air on the series of fabrics employed in the tests for moisture transfer indicate a variation in this quantity between wide limits (in the ratio of 2,300 to 1). It is shown that, for fabrics of low permeability to air, the pressure difference generated between the two sides of a fabric by even small rates of movement is sufficient to overcome the forces tending to move the fabric relative to the body, so that little ventilation can take place through the fabric. It is obvious that for a fabric of low permeability, ventilation will take place through vents in the clothing, and such a fabric will exert by its movement a more efficient bellows action than a more open fabric. It is a debatable point whether a fabric of high permeability to air will allow of more efficient ventilation than a fabric of low permeability, but in general the former fabric may be preferred, since the air between fabric and body has a choice of passages to the outside air. Assuming that high permeability to air is desirable in a fabric, it is difficult to assess the minimum value of permeability for efficient ventilation beyond stating that a lower permeability factor is permissible for low rates of movement of fabrics in general, and for heavy or stiff fabrics as compared with light or limp fabrics. It is not possible to give any exact figure for this minimum value of permeability owing to the large variation in the forces controlling the stability of fabrics and owing to the dependence of this figure on the degree of motion of the fabric.''

Chapter 14

MOISTURE TRANSMISSION

(47) Moisture Transmission Nomenclature and Measurement

Water vapor permeability of textile structures is another of the important parameters concerned with the suitability of fabrics for apparel purposes. For the human body to be comfortable under both hot and cold environmental conditions, sensible and/or insensible moisture must evaporate from the surface of the skin. This evaporation acts in part to regulate thermostatically the skin temperature. Rees[191] comments as follows:

> "Even though the body remains quite inactive, it is continuously producing perspiration, and this minimal amount is called the 'insensible perspiration.' This is so small that the sweat evaporates as soon as it reaches the surface and the skin remains dry. Now water in evaporating, absorbs a considerable amount of heat (580 calories/gram), and so long as the perspiration remains insensible, it accounts for about 25% of the total loss of heat from the body. For a resting man under ordinary conditions, the insensible perspiration is about 30 grams/hour (1½ pints/day).
>
> "As the temperature rises . . . the body depends more and more on the evaporation of perspiration to maintain its temperature constant. There comes a point where the perspiration ceases to be insensible, when the sweat glands begin to function, and liquid sweat appears."

For the clothed body to be comfortable, moisture must be dissipated, and the moisture diffusion properties of clothing fabrics are of importance in attaining comfort. Rees points out that not only is moisture dissipation important at high temperatures and humidities, but

> "in cold latitudes, man is generally concerned with restricting his rate of loss of heat, and sufficient clothing must be worn to do this under different degrees of activity, not forgetting that the elimination of body moisture must not be unduly restricted, particularly when the body is very active."[191]

226

Carlene[197] lists four principal variables which have a bearing on the subject of moisture and body comfort:

"(a) Permeability to water vapour, i.e., the diffusion of water vapour through fabrics.

"(b) Absorbency of textile, i.e., the amount of absorbed and also mechanically held water in a fabric.

"(c) The heat of absorption of water by fibres.

"(d) The drying of textile materials."

Item (a) is discussed below, the latter three items already having been covered in Chapter 5.

Fourt and Harris[205] describe the following methods for measuring moisture permeability:

"The natural standard of comparison in this field is the resistance of ideal still air to the passage of water vapor by diffusion . . . as a unit, we can take the resistance of one centimeter of ideal still air. In order to compare different fabrics it is convenient to calculate the relative resistance of each as its 'resistance per unit thickness.' This thickness should be measured at a low pressure (Writer's note: e.g., 0.1 p.s.i.).

"The total resistance, R, of a system is given in equivalent centimeters of still air; in terms of Q, the grams of water vapor passing; D, the diffusion coefficient; ΔC, the difference in vapor concentration; A, the area in cm^2; and t, the time in seconds, by the equation

$$R = \frac{1}{Q} D(\Delta C)At \qquad (1)$$

The diffusion coefficient, D, varies with the average absolute temperature, T, and the barometric pressure, p (mm Hg), according to the relation

$$D = 0.220 \left(\frac{T}{273}\right)^{1.75} \frac{760}{p}. \qquad (2)$$

With sufficient practical accuracy, this may be replaced between 0°C and 50°C by

$$D = 0.220 + 0.00147m, \qquad (3)$$

where m is the temperature (°C).

"The concentration difference, ΔC, in g/cm^3 can be obtained from the relative humidities H_1 and H_2, the absolute temperatures T_1 and T_2, and the corresponding saturation vapor pressures p_1 and p_2 on each side of the resistance as

$$\Delta C = \frac{18}{22,400} \times \frac{273}{760} \left(\frac{p_1 H_1}{T_1} - \frac{p_2 H_2}{T_2} \right). \tag{4}$$

For one temperature, this becomes

$$\Delta C = 2.89 \times 10^{-4} \times \Delta p/T, \tag{5}$$

where Δp is the difference in actual vapor pressures.

"To find the permeability under any conditions, the equation can be solved for Q/At and evaluated from the appropriate values of D, ΔC, and R:

$$\frac{Q}{At} = \frac{\Delta C}{R} \times D. \tag{6}$$

The preceding equations (1 through 6) have dealt with the total resistance or over-all permeability of complete systems. The intrinsic resistance of a fabric is defined as the difference in total resistance caused by an additional layer of fabric. The measurement of the intrinsic resistance of a fabric can be made by comparing the total resistance of two systems containing fabric, with one having more layers than the other. All the air spaces in the two systems must be made equal or measured and accounted for."

Fourt and Harris suggest two methods for measuring diffusion: (1) absorption cup method, (2) evaporation method. The former consists of ascertaining the amount of water which will diffuse through the test fabric and into a cup of drying agent (e.g., $CaSO_4$), the test fabric being the cover of the vessel containing the dessicant. The other side of the fabric is exposed to an atmosphere of constant humidity, temperature and air velocity. The amount of water absorbed per unit area per unit time can be calculated by determining the increase in weight of the dessicant at selected time intervals. The authors state that the rate of gain of weight becomes constant after a half hour, and remains so for two hours or more. The evaporation method consists of placing the test fabric over a carefully calibrated cup filled with water to a depth such that the distance between the bottom of the fabric and the water surface is exactly 1 cm (or 2.5 cm according to ASTM and TAPPI standards). Again the assembled cup and fabric is exposed to an atmosphere of constant humidity, temperature and air velocity, and the rate of loss in weight determined.

Peirce, Rees and Ogden[206] develop the following formulae for the resistance to moisture transfer:

"The most convenient method of expressing the results is in resistance units, rather than as rates of transmission. This has the advantage that if we have more than one layer of fabric we may add up the separate resistances to obtain the total resistance just as for the electrical or thermal case.

"Consider (a) porous pot with (a) layer of cellulose acetate sheet. The relative humidity inside the pot is 100%.

"Let E = R.H. of the surrounding air
$\quad F_b$ = measured transmission rate
$\quad R_b$ = over-all resistance of the pot and cellulose acetate sheet

Then we have $\qquad R_b = \dfrac{100 - E}{F_b}$

"Experiments with the porous pot at relative humidities of the enclosure varying from 50 to 90% showed that a linear relation exists between the transmission rate and $(100 - E)$ within this range. With a fabric wrapped around the pot we have

$$R_m = R_b + r = \frac{100 - E}{F_m}$$

where R_m = total resistance
$\quad r$ = resistance of the fabric
$\quad F_m$ = measured transmission rate

"Hence $r = (100 - E)\left(\dfrac{1}{F_m} - \dfrac{1}{F_b}\right)$ and is given in units of R.H./grams/meter^2/second.

"The values obtained for R_b in these units was 12.2×10^2.

"It is more fundamental to express resistance in terms of $\dfrac{\text{vapour pressure}}{\text{grams/meter}^2/\text{second}}$, but in order to do this we would have to know the temperature of the water inside the pot which, owing to the evaporation would be slightly lower than the air temperature. The results included in this paper are given in units of $\dfrac{\text{R.H.}}{\text{grams/meter}^2/\text{second}}$ as no measurement of temperature inside the pot was made during the tests."

(48) Moisture Permeability Properties of Fabrics

Fourt and Harris[205] report on the intrinsic resistance (cm air) and relative resistance ($\times$ air) for various fibers made into various fabrics (Table 94).

They compare the effect of fiber composition by plotting comparative resistance vs. per cent fiber volume (Graph 45). Per cent fiber volume is the fraction of the total volume taken up by the fiber.

"With glass and 'Vinyon,' the resistance increases rapidly with density to twenty times that of air, showing that the main pathway through these materials is the air spaces. With cotton, the tightest weaving produces resistances only four times that of air, whereas for most cottons the range is nearer two times the resistance of air. This indicates that significant amounts of water vapor travel through the substance of the fibers themselves. . . . Nylon and cellulose acetate are intermediate."

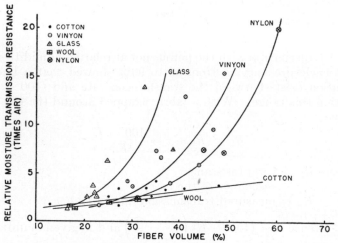

Graph 45.   Comparative resistance to moisture transfer vs. per cent fiber volume. (*From Fourt and Harris*,[205] "*Diffusion of Water Vapor Through Textiles.*")

Note: The curve for wool is not included in Harris and Fourt's original paper, but the plotted values are taken directly from Table 94.

The authors do not discuss wool, but from the graph, it becomes obvious that wool functions in substantially the same manner as cotton, i.e., the water can travel through the wool fiber as well as through the air spaces.

Fourt and Harris conclude that fibers show differences in their resistance to moisture diffusion only when the per cent volume occupied by the fiber exceeds 30 to 40 per cent; above this level the hydrophobic fibers cause sharp increases in resistance;

"below this level all fabrics are closely similar, since the low resistance pathway through air spaces is sufficiently available."

Peirce, Rees, and Ogden[206] arrive at the same conclusions:

"It is thus possible to produce a fabric having a low resistance to the passage of water vapour but very high air and water

TABLE 94. RESISTANCE OF FABRICS TO MOISTURE DIFFUSION
(From Fourt and Harris[205] "Diffusion of Water Vapor Through Textiles")

Fabric	Fiber vol. (%)	Weight (oz/yd²)	Thickness at 0.1 lb/in² (inches)	Air Permeability (ft³/ft²/min. at 0.5 in. w.g.)	Method*	Intrinsic Resistance (cm air)	Relative Resistance (× air)
Cottons							
knit undershirt	13	4.2	0.028	223	A	0.12	1.7
					B	0.07	1.0
balloon cloth	25	2.0	0.007	100	A	0.047	2.61
					B	0.047	2.61
bedford cord (Navy "jungle" cloth)†	27	13.6	0.043	6	A	0.37	3.4
					B	0.41	3.8
herringbone twill, OD 7	27	8.1	0.026	13	A	0.11	1.65
					B	0.13	2.19
Shirley cloth†	33	9.6	0.025	1	A	0.22	3.5
					B	0.27	4.3
poplin, 5 ounce	33	6.2	0.016	6	A	0.09	2.2
					B	0.10	2.46
sateen	34	9.7	0.025	6	A	0.165	2.62
					B	0.185	2.94
uniform twill, 8.2 ounce	35	8.2	0.022	12	A	0.23	4.2
					B	.....	.....
Byrd cloth	37	5.2	0.013	3	A	0.11	3.3
					B	.....	.....
L19 Shirley†	41	7.4	0.016	1	A	0.14	3.4
					B	0.18	4.4
J. P. Stevens 1650	48	7.9	0.015	1	A	0.14	3.8
					B	0.17	4.6
"Vinyon"							
knit	23	4.8	0.021	256	A	0.090	1.7
					B	0.070	1.3
2056	29	4.2	0.014	16	A	0.150	4.2
					B	0.184	5.2
2069	30	4.7	0.013	294	A	0.123	3.7
					B	0.141	4.3
sail cloth, light	35	2.55	0.025	1	A	0.464	7.3
					B	0.473	7.4
2056	36	4.0	0.011	17	A	0.18	6.6
					B	.....	.....
filter No. 8	38	14.8	0.033	9	A	0.34	4.0
					B	0.38	4.5
sail cloth, medium	41	5.35	0.013	1	A	0.43	13.0
					B	0.40	12.2
filter No. 19	44	14.3	0.031	9	A	0.46	5.9
					B	0.42	5.4
filter No. 1	47	13.7	0.028	1	A	0.68	9.6
					B	0.67	9.4
1802	49	3.5	0.007	1	A	0.28	15.4
					B	0.35	19.8
Glass							
CSS-28 extracted	16.5	26.5	0.083	12	A	0.30	1.42
					B	0.33	1.56
CSS-20	20.4	24.3	0.057	8.6	A	0.38	2.62
					B	0.365	2.52
WB 0046	21.6	.....	0.058	.....	A	0.521	3.54
					B	0.438	2.98
WB 0111	22.0	.....	0.074	.....	A	0.423	3.00
					B	0.393	2.78
CSS-27, original	22.4	27.6	0.064	8.5	A	0.42	2.58
					B	0.46	2.82
ECC-11-138	24.7	6.7	0.014	6.0	A	0.22	6.34
					B	0.20	5.56

TABLE 94. RESISTANCE OF FABRICS TO MOISTURE DIFFUSION.—*(Continued)*

Fabric	Fiber vol. (%)	Weight (oz/yd²)	Thickness at 0.1 lb/in² (inches)	Air Permeability (ft³/ft²/min. at 0.5 in. w.g.)	Method*	Intrinsic Resistance (cm air)	Relative Resistance (× air)
ECC-11-128	32.2	7.4	0.012	8.0	A	0.42	13.9
					B	0.33	10.7
no designation	38.8	9.6	0.013	.....	A	0.33	8.0
					B	0.31	7.5
Wool							
wool serge, 16 ounce	25	10.4	0.038	12	A	0.18	1.9
					B	0.26	2.7
serge, 45% viscose, 55% wool	31	11.5	0.033	10	A	0.20	2.4
					B	0.18	2.1
wool felt	18	19.1	0.103	24	A	0.37	1.4
					B	0.67	2.6
wool felt	17	31.3	0.184	16	A	0.80	1.7
					B	1.10	2.4
Nylon							
knit	31	6.5	0.025	108	A	0.16	2.5
					B	0.15	2.3
3-ounce twill	46	3.1	0.008	21	A	0.15	7.5
					B	0.20	10.0
5-ounce twill	49	4.6	0.001	20	A	0.20	7.1
					B	0.18	6.4
mountain tent, calendered	60	3.2	0.006	2	A	0.32	20.0
					B	0.33	20.6

* Method A = absorption; Method B = evaporation.
† Indicates water-repellent treatment on fabric.

penetration resistance by sealing up the interstices of the fabric
with some material which allows water vapour to diffuse
through it, and by making the fabric water repellent. . . .
This work leads to the conclusion that the diffusion of water
vapour through a fabric occurs not only through the interstices

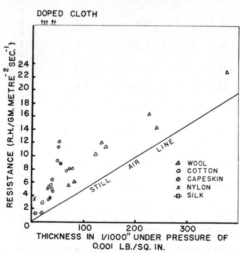

Graph 46. Effect of fabric thickness on moisture resistance. *(From Peirce, Rees, and Ogden,*[206] *"Measurement of the Water Vapour Permeability of Textile Fabrics.)*

but also to an important extent through the fibers themselves. In very close fabrics the latter mechanism has considerable importance, and may in fact become predominant."

Table 95 shows moisture resistance properties of various materials; Graph 46 shows moisture resistance vs. fabric thickness; Graph 47 shows $\dfrac{\text{equivalent air thickness}}{\text{fabric thickness}}$ vs. density. All are from Peirce, Rees, and Ogden.[206]

The straight line on Graph 46 is the "still air" line calculated from diffusion coefficients given in the International Critical Tables.

"Apart from the doped fabrics with very high resistances, there is an obvious correlation between the resistance of a fabric and its thickness, and the relatively low resistance of

TABLE 95. RESISTANCE OF VARIOUS MATERIALS TO THE FLOW OF WATER VAPOR (From Peirce, Rees and Ogden[206] "Measurement of Water Vapor Permeability of Textile Fabrics")

Sample	Threads per Inch warp	Threads per Inch filling	Wt oz/yd²	Thickness in ⅟₁₀₀₀ inch under 0.001 psi	Resistance R.H. gm metre⁻² sec⁻¹	Ratio Equiv. Air Thickness Fabr. Thick.
British Army wool shirting	34	37	7.0	69	5.5×10^2	1.6
British Army wool battledress	57	46	14.1	80	6.0×10^2	1.5
British Army wool greatcoat	40	38	18.3	123	10.4×10^2	1.8
cashmere fabric	76	34	15.0	225	16.3×10^2	1.5
R.A.F. melton	72	66	19.5	135	12.1×10^2	1.8
R.A.F. velour	62	72	19.0	240	14.3×10^2	1.2
U.S. Officers' overcoating	84	61	21.3	142	11.5×10^2	1.6
heavy wool overcoating	50	52	25.5	375	22.9×10^2	1.3
gabardine	196	95	5.5	32	3.5×10^2	2.2
bleached poplin	148	74	3.2	18	1.3×10^2	1.5
close weave cotton fabric No. 1	166	65	7.1	34	3.6×10^2	2.1
close weave cotton fabric No. 2	211	81	6.6	32	5.2×10^2	3.3
close weave cotton fabric No. 3	170	67	8.7	36	5.5×10^2	3.1
close weave cotton fabric No. 4	165	65	7.0	39	4.9×10^2	2.5
close weave cotton fabric No. 5	281	110	4.3	21	2.8×10^2	2.6
close weave cotton fabric No. 6	119	55	9.3	40	4.7×10^2	2.4
scoured cambric	110	85	4.9	39	6.3×10^2	3.3
water-repellent cambric	110	85	5.2	34	5.4×10^2	3.3
cotton tent duck, undyed	55	32	19.6	75	8.0×10^2	2.1
cotton tent duck, dyed sulphur khaki	55	32	19.6	70	7.9×10^2	2.3
cotton tent duck, chrome tinted	55	32	18.6	66	7.8×10^2	2.4
cotton canvas 1	63	30	20.3	53	12.3×10^2	4.7
cotton canvas 2	62	25	18.5	49	9.3×10^2	3.8
cotton canvas 3	50	25	16.5	52	11.4×10^2	4.4
nylon parachute fabric	127	114	1.6	7	3.4×10^2	9.7
silk parachute fabric	115	115	1.6	6	1.2×10^2	3.8
capeskin			13.3	55	8.8	3.2
polyvinyl chloride (PVC) coated cotton fabric		8.3		20	143.5×10^2	144
linseed oil coated cotton fabric			7.9	28	72.0×10^2	51
double texture rubber reclaim fabric			14.4	44	75.0×10^2	34
double texture nitrocellulose fabric			12.6	42	96.5×10^2	46
tin foil			....	7	$> 10,000 \times 10^2$	
bare pot			....	...	12.2×10^2	
impregnated cloth (imitation leather)			6.4	24	$> 10,000 \times 10^2$	$> 9,000$

fabrics to the transmission of water vapour through them is striking. All the fabrics tested so far offer more resistance than does still air of the same thickness, the equivalent air thickness of the one nylon fabric tested being approximately ten times the fabric thickness. For the cotton fabrics the equivalent air thickness is roughly three times, and for the wool fabrics, roughly one and a half times the fabric thickness. The only non-textile material tested was capeskin (water-proofed chrome leather) and this has appreciable permeability to water vapour."

On a density basis the advantages of wool and cotton over nylon are apparent from Graph 47. The authors[206] confirm this point with some theoretical calculations.

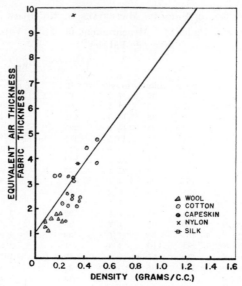

Graph 47. Resistance of moisture passage vs. density. (*From Peirce, Rees, and Ogden,*[206] *"Measurement of The Water Vapour Permeability of Textile Fabrics."*)

We may summarize the moisture transfer situation as follows: Presuming a moisture differential to exist between two sides of a fabric, water vapor may pass via two mechanisms, (1) through the fabric interstices, (2) through the fibers themselves. The contribution of each may vary from zero to one hundred per cent In the case of an hydrophillic fiber fabric, if the weave is open, moisture will pass through the fabric's interstices and through the fiber per se. If the weave is extremely tight, moisture will pass primarily through the fibers. Body comfort in both cases is about equal, probably because sufficient moisture can pass via either path. Thus hydrophillic fibers are comfortable insofar as moisture transfer is concerned under all conditions of fabric structure.

With hydrophobic fibers, if the weave is open, moisture will transfer through the fabric interstices, and the wearer will be comfortable. If the weave is tight, moisture cannot transfer either through the fabric interstices or through the fibers per se, and a wearer may be uncomfortable due to the lack of moisture dissipation. Thus hydrophobic fibers should be used with nominal care to see that fabric construction permits moisture transfer.

Chapter 15

WATER REPELLENCY AND WATER RESISTANCE

An analysis of the water-repellent properties of fabrics again requires consideration of inherent and form effects, and in addition such "external" factors as the amount of water in contact with the material, the time of contact, the temperature of the cloth and the water, the humidity-regain condition of the cloth, the force and energy with which the "raindrop" (or the alleged laboratory equivalent) strikes the fabric, the angle of strike, and the amount of abrasion, weathering, cleaning and other general service conditions to which the material is subjected.

Coated fabrics are not considered in this study since such waterproofed fabrics are dependent almost entirely on the nature of the coating rather than on the actual textile fabric. Because of the moisture transmission-body comfort implications already discussed, one might with confidence, conclude that completely impermeable coated fabrics will probably never supplant water-repellent textile fabrics.

(49) Nomenclature and Methods for Measuring Water Repellency

The 1942 Year Book of the American Association of Textile Chemists and Colorists[212] gives three terms for describing the water resistance of fabrics:

(1) Shower-resisting properties, connoting satisfactory performance of a material in withstanding showery weather or relatively short exposure to medium or heavy rain.

(2) Rain-resisting properties, connoting satisfactory performance in withstanding moderately rainy weather.

(3) Waterproof materials, capable of resisting a hydrostatic head of water, and connoting prolonged resistance to the heaviest kind of rain.

These suggested standards of performance have since been deleted, and the 1951 A.A.T.C.C. Yearbook[213] lists the following definitions only:

"Water Repellency (Textile): The ability of a textile fiber, yarn, or fabric to resist wetting."

"Water Resistance (Fabric): A general term denoting the ability of a fabric to resist wetting and penetration of water."

The American Society for Testing Materials uses identical definitions for water repellency, and almost identical definitions for water resistance. The A.A.T.C.C. Yearbook continues to list the following test methods:

Resistance to hydrostatic pressure
Resistance to absorption of water during immersion
Resistance to penetration of water by impact
Resistance to water spray
Resistance to rain test

Mandikos[214] lists three terms as follows:

"(1) Waterproof
"(2) Water-repellent
"(3) Water-resistant

"In the past, these three terms have been used interchangeably and incorrectly to describe the property of a fabric which prevents water from passing through the interstices and/or the wetting of the surface. The correct use of 'waterproof' has become quite universal now. It is used to describe a fabric which is coated or impregnated to form a continuous wall against the passage of water or a continuous sheet composed of rubber, plastic, and the like. At the present time, 'water-repellent' and 'water-resistant' are used interchangeably, and water-repellent is used more frequently than water-resistant. However, it is the thought of the writer that 'water-resistant' is to be preferred with reference to fabrics which are only partially impervious to water and/or are partially wetted. 'Water-repellent' seems to apply more to a hydrophobic finish or surface, and signifies resistance of a surface to wetting by the spreading of water across it."

Rowen and Gagliardi[215] use only two terms, waterproof and water repellent.

"A waterproof fabric is one in which the pores, the open spaces between the warp and filling yarns and between the fibers, are filled with appropriate substances resulting in a fabric having a continuous surface and a very small air permeability. A water-repellent fabric is one whose fibers are usually coated with a hydrophobic-type compound, and whose pores are not filled in the course of the treatment. The latter types of fabrics are quite permeable to air and water vapor."

Test Methods for Evaluating Water Repellency. Rowen and Gagliardi[215] have surveyed most of the test methods as tabulated in Table 96.

TABLE 96. METHODS AND TESTING CONDITIONS USED BY VARIOUS LABORATORIES
IN MEASURING WATER-REPELLENT PROPERTIES OF TEXTILE FABRICS
(From Rowen and Gagliardi[215] "Properties of Water-Repellent Fabrics")

	Waterproof	Water Repellent
pores	filled	unfilled
water vapor permeability	very small	small or large
air permeability	small	usually large
chief characteristic:	extremely resistant to passage of water even under a hydrostatic head.	resistant to wetting by rain drops and to the spreading of water over the textile surface, but permits the passage of water under a hydrostatic head.

The authors point out the lack of data showing correlation "between the particular test method and the performance of fabrics in the rain." They classify the methods into four main categories

"*Class A.* Methods by which the hydrostatic pressure required to free water through a fabric is measured.

"*Class B.* Methods by which surface wetting and penetration under the influence of falling drops is measured.

"*Class C.* Methods by which the absorption of water by the fabric, when immersed or manipulated under water, is measured.

"*Class D.* Methods by which the wettability of the surface of the fabric is measured by means of the angle of contact or some function of the angle of contact."

Rowen and Gagliardi[215] describe and comment upon each type:

"*Class A:* In this class of test methods, the fabric is subjected to the action of water under pressure. . . . Either the amount of water penetrating in a specified time or the pressure required to force water through the fabric is measured. The most widely used test methods in this class are the A.A.T.C.C. and the Suter hydrostatic pressure tests.

"The hydrostatic-pressure test values are dependent mainly on the pore size and the angle contact.

"*Class B:* The tests in this class are in some cases very different from each other. All of the tests . . . subject the test fabric to the action of water drops. The number, size, frequency, and energy of the drops in the various tests vary considerably. The advantages and disadvantages of these various tests are briefly discussed below:

"(1) The A.A.T.C.C. Spray Test. This test will distinguish qualitatively between treated and untreated fabrics. It is not able, however, to distinguish between obviously different water-repellent finishes or to predict the performance of a fabric in the rain.

"(2) The Drop Penetration Test. This test was developed for and used by the U.S. Quartermaster Corps during the war. The energy of the drops used in this apparatus is approximately 10,000–15,000 ergs. This value is much larger than that of the drops in a cloudburst (3,000 ergs). It appears that by this test one may be able to arrange fabrics in what seems to be a proper order of protection in the rain. The hardness of the fabric backing has a profound influence on the test value. This is probably true also for the other tests in this group.

"(3) The Bundesmann Test. The Bundesmann test was developed in Germany. It can be used in two ways: one, to measure the amount of water penetrating the sample; two, to measure the amount of water absorbed by the sample in a given time. Again the drops of water in the test have energy of from 15,000–30,000 ergs. . . . In this procedure the sample of cloth is in constant motion and is continuously rubbed on the under side during the test. The method seems to offer some advantages over the other tests in *Class B* and has been recently adopted by the British Sub-Committee of the General Technical Committee as a standard test method.

"(4) The Impact Penetration Test. This test involves the spraying of 500 cc of water on the test specimen. At the end of the spray period, a blotter beneath the fabric is weighed. The increase in weight of the blotter represents the amount of water which passed through the cloth. No data are available on correlation with natural rain. . . .

"(6) The Kern Test. This novel method . . . employs a single drop of water of definite size. An electrical circuit is used to detect the penetration of the water to the under side of the test specimen.

(*Writer's note:* The Kern Test appears to be a specific electrical refinement of the A.S.T.M. Water Penetration (Drip) Method[80] which utilizes single drops of water under controlled conditions.)

"*Class C:* All methods in this group measure the resistance which the finish offers to wetting by water. Since droplet penetration is not used in these methods, the part played by the structure of the fabric is less important than in other tests. The water absorbed by the fabric is measured by weighing the test specimen after some form of partial drying. In some of the tests the sample is in motion during the test period. The dynamic types of tests are definitely to be preferred to the static types in this category. Again, it should be pointed out that little, if any, work has been done to correlate these test results with the performance of fabrics in the rain.

"*Class D:* Workers who have used the following three techniques have done so in an attempt to understand the mechanism of wetting. Various methods for measuring contact angles have been described. The three methods which have been applied to fabrics are discussed below.

"(1) Wenzel's Method. Wenzel appears to have been the first to attempt to apply methods of measuring contact angles to fabric. Wenzel measured the contact angle of many materials, waxes, cellulose acetate. . . . His data indicated that the method was applicable to textile surfaces and was very reproducible.

"(2) Wetting Test. This test measures the time for the contact angle on a yarn or strip of fabric to decrease to 90°. This time has been called the "wetting time." Baxter and Cassie[216] claim that the wetting test is more sensitive to proofing efficiency than either the Bundesmann test or the hydrostatic pressure test.

"(3) Contact Angle by the Tensiometer Method. Wakeham, Strickland, and Skau[217] found that, by modifying an ordinary interfacial tensiometer and forcing a circular piece of fabric through the surface of the water, they obtained a relationship between the pressure necessary to force the disk of cloth through the surface of the water and the angle of contact of the water to fabric.

"The above review of the methods used to measure water repellency indicates that no one method completely measures the phenomenon. It appears necessary that a combination of tests be used to evaluate the water repellency of a fabric."

(50) The Mechanics of Wetting and the Factors Which Influence Water Repellency

Baxter and Cassie[216] briefly discuss the physics of wetting as follows:

"Liquids are distinguished from gases by the attraction and close approach of neighboring molecules. One result of the molecules holding together is that the surface of a liquid contracts to the minimum value consistent with other conditions it has to fulfill. Thus water falling freely forms a spherical drop . . . because the sphere has the minimum surface required to contain the water in the drop. If the drop is deformed to give a larger surface work must be done on it to increase the area of the surface. The tendency of the surface to contract is best measured by the energy required to form the surface. It is known as the surface energy or surface tension of the liquid and is usually measured in ergs/cm^2 or dynes/cm; compared with 20 to 40 dynes/cm for most organic liquids, water has quite a high surface tension" (72 dynes/cm).

"Water is known to spread on some solid surfaces such as clean glass and to refuse to spread on others such as paraffin wax. It spreads on clean glass because glass molecules hold water molecules more firmly than water molecules do. There is thus less energy in the glass-water interface than in a water-water interface of the same area, and as all the systems come to equilibrium with the minimum possible potential energy, the water spreads over the glass surface. Paraffin wax, on the other hand, does not hold water molecules so powerfully as water does, and work must be done on the system to make a paraffin wax-water interface. The water does not spread because the potential energy of the system is increased by spreading. When a drop of water falls onto a paraffin surface, the impact energy spreads the drop over the surface, but as this is not a state of minimum potential energy, the water forms itself into a drop or drops, to give the state of minimum energy. Surfaces that behave as paraffin wax does, are known as water-repellent surfaces, but it should be noted that the apparent repellency of the surface is due to the surface energy of the water rather than to any repulsive force exerted by the paraffin surface."

The contact angle which a drop of water assumes when placed upon a plane surface is a function of the interfacial tension between the liquid-air, the liquid-solid, and solid-air interfaces as is shown in Figure 8 (γ_{l-a}, γ_{l-s}, and γ_{s-a}, respectively).

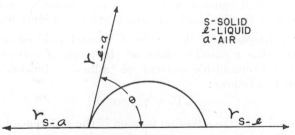

S-SOLID
ℓ-LIQUID
a-AIR

Figure 8. Forces acting at equilibrium on drop-solid system. (*From Rowen and Gagliardi,*[215] *"Properties of Water Repellent Fabrics."*)

The following diagrams illustrate the principle of contact angle in terms of the shape assumed by a drop when placed first, upon a plane surface, and second, upon a series of yarns, one set repellent and the other set nonrepellent. Angles greater than 90° depict water repellency; angles less than 90° depict wettability.

Rowen and Gagliardi[215] say that

> "the tendency of a solid to resist wetting is a function of (a) chemical nature of the solid surface, (b) the roughness of the surface, (c) the porosity of the surface, (d) the presence of other molecules on the surface."

Briefly considering the first three of these factors they state[215]

> "(a) *Chemical Nature of The Solid Surface:* When purified, the natural fibers, cotton, wool, silk, etc., are hydrophilic in

SOLID SURFACE

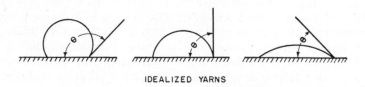

IDEALIZED YARNS

Figure 9.   Shapes of drops on solid surfaces and upon idealized yarns.   (*From Rowen and Gagliardi,*[215] *"Properties of Water Repellent Fabrics."*)

character and hence the drops assume shapes similar to B (in the idealized yarn portion of Figure 9). It is common practice therefore to treat fabrics intended to be water repellent with various hydrophobic compounds. . . . When (thus) properly treated with a water repellent agent, the surface of the fabric will cause a water drop to assume a form very similar to A (in the idealized yarn portion of Figure 9).

"(b) *Roughness of the Surface:* Wenzel pointed out that roughness has a peculiar effect on the angle of contact. He employed Freundlich's concept of 'adhesion tension' which is defined as follows:

$$\text{A.T.} = \gamma_{\text{l-a}} \cos \Theta$$

It is noted that the adhesion tension is the difference between the work of adhesion . . . and the surface tension. Wenzel recognized that (the above) equation was true only in the case where the surface was a mathematical plane. Since most surfaces are not of this type, there is associated with each surface a roughness factor R which is the ratio of actual surface to the geometric surface. Wenzel showed the validity of the following equation:

$$\text{A.T.} = \gamma_{\text{l-a}} \frac{\cos \Theta}{R}$$

"(c) *Porosity of the Surface:* Since textile fabric surfaces are not smooth continuous surfaces, but rather porous screen-like surfaces, one must examine the (contact angle) considerations and see how they apply to textiles. . . . If the angle between water and the surface of the fabric is larger than 90° the equilibrium position of the water level of a drop of water will be, as indicated by the line aa (Figure 9), well outside the fabric. If, however, the angle of contact is much smaller than 90°, the water will penetrate the pores and the level will fall to some position bb. Baxter and Cassie[216] have shown that in the case of porous surfaces the apparent angle of contact is related to the continuous surface-water angle of contact in the following way:

$$\text{Cos } \Theta_a = f_1 \cos \Theta - f_2$$

where Θ_a = the apparent angle of contact

f_1 = the fraction of the plane geometrical area of unity parallel to the rough surface occupied by the solid-liquid interface.

f_2 = the fraction of the plane geometrical area of unity parallel to the rough surface occupied by the liquid-air interface.

"They also derived the relationships between the "f" variables, the distance between the fibers in the yarns, the radius of the fibers, and the angle of contact:

$$f_1 = \frac{r}{r + d} \left(1 - \frac{\Theta}{180°} \right)$$

$$f_2 = \frac{r}{r + d} \sin \Theta$$

where r = radius of the fibers

d = ½ the distance between the fibers

Θ = contact angle between the water and the fiber.

"Baxter and Cassie[216] pursued the idea of the roughness factor and showed that the apparent adhesion tension of a porous surface was given by

$$AT_a = \text{Cos } \Theta_a \gamma_{\text{l-a}} = \gamma_{\text{l-a}}(f_1 \cos \Theta - f_2).$$

Using a hexagonal idealized yarn pattern as a model, the above workers showed that σ, the bulk density of the yarn, was related to the radius of the fibers in the following way:

$$\sigma = \frac{\pi}{2\sqrt{3}} \frac{\rho r^2}{(r + d)^2}$$

where ρ is the density of the fiber. With the aid of (the above equations) they were able to obtain plots of contact angle vs σ. These plots showed that the angle of contact approaches 180° as σ approaches small values (about 0.1 gram/cc). Their theory led them to the position that fabric structure was extremely important in the production of water repellent fabrics."

The Pressure Required to Force Water into Yarns. Continuing with a direct study of Baxter and Cassie's article,[216] they state that for yarns made from wool fibers of 20 μ diameter and

"with a moderate degree of proofing, then (the contact angle) θ will be greater than 90°, and for yarns with a density as low as 0.2 gm/cc more than 35 cms. of water pressure are required for penetration. For an average greatcoat yarn density of 0.4 to 0.6 gm/cc, the pressures are in excess of 60 cms of water. Gabardines have densities of as high as 0.8 gm/cc and the pressures required to force water into them will be in excess of 110 cms of water."

The Pressure Required to Force Water through Fabrics

"The hydrostatic pressure test measures the pressure required to force water through a cloth and uses the value so obtained as a measure of the water repellency of the fabric. Typical proofed greatcoat materials give values for the breakdown pressures of roughly 25 cms. This value is much lower than the calculated pressure required to force water into the yarns of the fabric, and shows that the water, in being forced through the fabric, does not pass through the yarns themselves, but through the pores between the yarns. Similarly typical proofed gabardines give breakdown pressures rarely above 40 cms, which is considerably below the estimated pressure of 110 cms or more required to force the water into the yarns.

"If we assume that the water passes through the pores between the warp and weft yarns of the fabric, then the pressure required to force water through the fabric will be given by the usual formula for a spherical surface

$$P = \frac{2\gamma}{R}$$

where R, the minimum radius of curvature of the water surface is given by

$$R \text{ (min)} = a \cos \Theta_D + \sqrt{(a + b)^2 - a^2 \sin^2 \Theta_D}$$

where Θ_D is the effective yarn advancing contact angle and $2a$ is the diameter of the warp and weft threads (assumed to be equal) and $2(a + b)$ is the distance apart of the threads."[216]

(51) The Water Repellent Properties of Textile Fibers and Structures

Some rapid and reasonable conclusions concerning the inherent water-repellent properties of fibers may be obtained by referring to Tables 46 and 47 on standard and saturation regain values. The natural fibers can absorb and transfer water, and of course are not water repellent; the same holds for regenerated cellulose and protein fibers. It follows that these fibers can only be utilized for wet-weather wear if external water-repelling finishes or treatments are applied. Cellulose acetate and nylon have lower water absorption capacities while "Vinyon," "Orlon," "Dacron," and "Dynel" have substantially zero regain. These latter fibers have an advantage in that they do not need protection per se. However, the fabrics into which they are made may be of a construction such that a water repellent treatment might still be needed to prevent the water's rolling or wicking through the interstices of the yarns and fabrics, thereby failing to give proper protection.

The natural fibers in their natural state undoubtedly have a fair amount of repellency, wool and animal hairs probably being superior to the cellulosic fibers. Wengraf and Schwarz[218] point out that

"Primitive men used animal furs and skins which repelled water by the natural state of their hairs. Later on, clothing for cool weather used to be wool which was spun and woven only insufficiently scoured and cleaned, and thus furnished sufficient water repellency . . . it is assumed that the Greeks and Romans were satisfied with natural protection which the wool provided."

This line of reasoning is no longer valid since people no longer use incompletely scoured wool or incompletely cleaned furs; one of the objectives of modern wool scouring is to free the wool so completely of grease that subsequent wet finishing operations can be expeditiously accomplished. In addition, Baxter and Cassie point out that even in the popularly cited example of the duck's feathers, their water-repelling properties are directly attributable to structure rather than by having any superior water-repellent proofing agent.

Examination of the literature brings out the point that yarn and fabric construction play a far greater part in controlling water repellency than does inherent fiber properties. Admittedly the hydrophobic fibers have an initial advantage over the hydrophillic ones, but this advantage can be negligible where water repellency rather than water proofness is desired.

Relationships among Water Repellency Tests. According to Scott[219] (as published in an article by Slowinske[220]) a fabric should fulfill the following requirements in order to be "water repellent"; (1) "strong resistance to water under some pressure"; (2) "moderate resistance to penetration by falling water"; (3) "resistance to actual wetting by water." Table 96 shows typical values for fabrics of various constructions made from various fibers.

We have here a heterogeneous collection of samples of various weights, constructions, thicknesses and fiber types; thus conclusions concerning properties are limited. The following points can be made, however.

TABLE 96a.   HYDROSTATIC, SPRAY, AND IMMERSION TEST DATA ON FABRICS TREATED WITH A DURABLE WATER REPELLENT

(From Slowinske[220] "The Evaluation of Water Resisting Textile Finishes")

Material	Hydrostatic Pressure Tester Reading (cm)		Spray Tester Rating†		Immersion Tester Absorption (%)	
	untreated	treated	untreated	treated	untreated	treated
cotton voile	0	2*	0	100	50	19
cotton broadcloth	0	31	0	100	71	21
cotton corduroy	0	14	0	100	88	16
cotton gabardine	0	31	0	100	68	19
cotton twill	10	33	0	100	57	19
cotton duck	28	55	50	100	21	14
linen sheeting	0	8	0	90	67	26
viscose rayon crepe	0	13	0	90	83	49
acetate rayon taffeta	0	15	0	100	39	19
cuprammonium rayon dress	0	15	0	100	80	18
silk lining	0	33	0	100	72	27
wool melton	14	28	70	100	99	13

* Value too low to measure accurately.

† The A.A.T.C.C. spray test[213] procedure is the following:

A six-inch diameter test specimen is mounted 45° from the horizontal and is sprayed under controlled conditions with 250 ml of water. The excess water is removed by smartly tapping the edge of the frame in a prescribed manner, and the fabric is then inspected and evaluated as follows:

     100   No sticking or wetting of upper surface
      90   Slight random sticking or wetting of upper surface
      80   Wetting of upper surface at spray points
      70   Partial wetting of whole of upper surface
      50   Complete wetting of whole of upper surface
       0   Complete wetting of whole of upper and lower surface

(1) Water-repellent treatments enhance properties under all three test conditions.

(2) Of the untreated samples, the cotton duck and wool melton offer the best resistance to a hydrostatic head and spray test. In addition, the cotton duck offers the best resistance to water absorption. These two fabrics are probably the thickest and most tightly woven, and it would be expected that they would offer higher resistance on this basis alone. Furthermore, the cotton duck, probably, has natural repellency because of the waxes present on its unbleached fibers. The resistance of the wool melton will be discussed below in conjuncton with Baxter and Cassie's work[216] on the "Ideal Structure for Rain Resistance."

(3) The fact that the untreated melton in the immersion test picks up the greatest amount of water is one disadvantage which mitigates against its use for outer rain wear. The reason for this is that even if wool fabrics originally resist wetting they ultimately do become wet; the added weight in many cases becomes too great a burden for the wearer. This condition is of particular concern in military apparel where weight must always be considered.

Baxter and Cassie[216] discuss the ideal structure for rain resistance at great length, and their comments are quoted as follows:

"Rain resistance is obtained from a structure that gives large apparent advancing and receding contact angles. The structure should therefore have as large and uniform a separation of the component fibres as is possible. If the separation of the fibres is too great, rain drops will pass freely through them, and the rain resistance will be negligible. Experiment shows, however, that average rain drops will not penetrate between the fibres in a wool felt of density as low as 0.1 gm/cc; such a fabric is much too fragile to withstand wear, and it may be taken that strength requirements rather than penetration by rain gives the lower limit for fibre packing. The fibre density for rain resistance should therefore be as low and uniform as possible consistent with strength requirements.

"The second principle for rain resistance is that the structure should be designed to avoid film formation as far as possible. This is best attained by a large fibre separation and by avoiding fibres crossing over one another to give areas bounded on all sides by fibres. Thus, it is useless to have loose fibres separated by a large distance as surface tension forces will pull the fibres together and make film formation relatively easy. Animals' fur illustrate this requirement very well; the outer ends of the fibres in a fur are free to move, and in rain these ends are pulled together by surface tension forces; films are formed, and the outer surface of the fur is wetted out in tufts characteristic of a fur exposed to rain.   Near the skin the fibres are held apart, film formation is difficult, and the fur remains dry.

"Nature has solved the problem of a rain resistant structure most admirably in the duck's feathers, which on examination show that the water repellency of a duck is obtained by satisfying exactly the requirements of the above analysis rather than by having any superior water repellent proofing agent.   The main stem of a feather is known as the rachis and from it extends on either side a system of parallel fibres known as the barbs.   The barbs for the breast feathers of a duck have a diameter of 46 μ and their axes are separated by a distance of 270 μ, i.e., $(r + d)/r = 5.9$.   Projecting from the barbs are very fine fibres known as the barbules, and barbules on one side of each barb are fitted with hooks whilst on the other side they are filled with notches.   This ingenious system of hooks and notches fixes the barbules and barbs rigidly so that they cannot be drawn together by surface tension forces.   The barbules have a diameter of 8 μ and their axes are 38 μ apart, i.e., $\dfrac{r + d}{r} = 4.7$.   The feather is so constructed that the outer surface consists of a single parallel layer of barbules, and the ratio $\dfrac{r + d}{r} = 4.7$ corresponds to a fabric density of .053 gm/cc.   Using the rachis of a feather the values of θ_A and θ_R were seen to be approximately 95° and 60° which indicates quite mediocre proofing.   The effective advancing angle is seen to be 150° and the effective receding angle is 143°.   These estimated values are roughly correct according to experimental observation.   The high effective receding contact angle for ducks' feathers is maintained at a high value as shown by the ability of water to pearl off its back indefinitely.   This excellent characteristic is due to the physical structure of the feathers which maintains the spacings of the barbs and barbules in spite of surface tension forces and eliminates the interlacing of fibres that makes film formation possible.   High values of the effective advancing and receding contact angles can only be obtained when the liquid does not penetrate the porous surface.   If the advancing contact angle θ_A is reduced to a small value then the water will pass through the pores of the porous surface and complete wetting will ensue.   This has been shown very effectively by Caryl and Ericks[221] who had a duck swimming in a tank of water.   On pouring a wetting agent into the tank the duck sank, due to the value of θ_A being reduced to zero and water consequently penetrating through the feathers to the skin, and thus expelling the air entrapped between the feathers which gives the duck its buoyancy.

"The requirements of a water-repellent fabric are (a) that the fibres shall be spaced uniformly and as far apart as possible and (b) that they should be held so as to prevent their ends drawing together.

"These deductions are contrary to the conception of the gaberdine as a rain resistant fabric. It does show a large breakdown pressure in the hydrostatic pressure test because its fine yarns can be woven closely together to provide small pores, and this result has given rise to the idea of it as a rain resistant fabric. Actually the high density yarns give just the conditions for low effective contact angles and ease of formation of films between adjacent fibres, i.e., those conditions for ease of wetting and breakdown under rain.

"It has been shown that wetting takes place more readily on surfaces of high fibre density and in a fabric where there are regions of high fibre density such as in the yarns, the peripheries of the yarns will be the first areas to wet out and when the yarn peripheries are wetted water can pass unhindered through the fabric. Thus the highest efficiency will be obtained in a fabric where the density is as uniform as possible: the yarns should be soft so that their density is not very different from the over-all density of the cloth.

"It is interesting to note that the Scottish tweed, which has long been regarded by the countryman as the best rain resistant fabric, conforms more closely to these requirements than other fabrics. Indeed, only the wool felt, animals' fur and feathers fulfill the requirements more closely.

"Experimental cloths were made to determine whether or not the conclusion is correct that a fabric should be as homogenous as possible and have a low bulk density for rain resistance. A typical proofed gaberdine of 10 oz/sq yd was compared in a shower test with a proofed cloth of the same weight made from open wool gauze with wool fibres lightly felted on to the gauze. The second fabric had a density of 0.1 gm/cc, and its air permeability was 500 ft/min for 1 inch of water gauge, as compared with 15 for the gaberdine. The gaberdine showed a breakdown pressure in the hydrostatic pressure test that exceeded 40 cms, whilst the light felt had a breakdown pressure of 10 cms. When subjected to the shower of 3 inches of rainfall per hour, the gaberdine showed penetration within a few minutes, whilst the experimental fabric showed no penetration after indefinite exposure to the shower."

The above remarks demonstrate the apparent advantages of wool type rain-wear, and were it not for the water absorption problem possibly it would have wider application. Kennedy[222] points out that

> "the abandonment of wool in outer garments of Army combat clothing has been one of the most important changes in military textiles during the war. The fact that an overcoat itself weighs seven pounds and can absorb in a moderately heavy rain an additional nine pounds of water was one factor contributing to this change. Most important, however, was the fact that lighter weight cotton textiles showed themselves to be far superior in wind and water resistance in all controlled laboratory and field tests as well as in actual combat. By making this substitution, wool could then be relegated to its real task of providing insulation in under layers of clothing beneath the outer cotton water-resistant garments."

The above commentary cites two important factors involved in water repellency. The first is the unique ability of the cotton fiber to swell in water, thereby enabling cotton fabrics of the proper construction to close their interstices, making the resulting garment water-repellent after initial wetting, yet maintaining an air permeable open structure when dry. Such a fabric was developed during World War II at the Shirley Institute; it consisted of an oxford weave of high thread count but with soft yarns. The second factor concerns the resilience properties of the outer fabric and/or the under layers of clothing which enables them to withstand the impact forces of raindrops.

The Capacity of Fabrics to Absorb Kinetic Energy in the Form of Falling Rain. A falling raindrop has a certain amount of kinetic energy, depending upon its mass and velocity. Apart from the problem of wetting the fabric which it strikes, the kinetic energy of the drop must be converted into strain energy within the fabric. The ability of the fabric to absorb continuously this "impact energy" is related to the resilience characteristics of the rainwear and under-fabrics.

Baxter and Cassie[216] list terminal velocities and kinetic energies of various types of drop in Table 97.

Wakeham, Strickland and Skau[217] say that

> "softness and elasticity lengthen the time of impact of falling drops and so some of the energy of the drop is absorbed in bending the fibers or moving the fabric instead of forcing the water through the available capillaries."

TABLE 97. PROPERTIES OF RAINDROPS

(From Baxter and Cassie[216] "The Water Repellency of Fabrics")

Type of Drop	Radius (cm)	Terminal Velocity (cm/sec)	Kinetic Energy (ergs)
cloud burst	0.15	700	3460
excessive rain	0.105	600	870
heavy rain	0.075	500	220
moderate rain	0.050	400	42
light rain	0.0225	200	0.95
drizzle	0.01	75	0.012
Bundesmann	0.32	540	20000

(It is noted that the laboratory Bundesmann test is more severe than even a cloudburst.)

Tests on cotton materials have illustrated the importance of resilience as achieved by a backing material or by doubling the fabric. For example,

"if a piece of water repellent cotton poplin is stretched over a piece of glass and exposed to the rainfall tester, the first drop will penetrate the poplin and hit the glass. If a resilient material is placed beneath the poplin (e.g., several layers of gauze), it takes a lot of drops to go through the poplin."[217]

Again illustrative of the effect of nonresilience in easing water penetration, is the fact that a raincoat wets out very quickly at the shoulders where the coat has the most solid support. Raincoats are often made double at the shoulder to offset this condition.[224,225]

Kärrholm and Kärrholm[225] comment on the compressional elastic properties of water repellent fabrics and their backing.

" . . . the type of support has a great effect on the amount of water penetrating through the fabric. If a rigid support is used, a large amount of water will pass through as compared with a more elastic support. The effect of different types of supports in a rain tester has been investigated. Much more water passed through the fabric when the backing was made from a wire net with small meshes (0.33 mm side) as compared with a wire net with large meshes (10 mm side). With the latter net, the penetration first occurred at the places in contact with the wires. It is also well-known that leakages of rain usually occur first at the shoulders where the coat is supported. These examples demonstrate the effect of the pressure on the penetration of a fabric by water. If the backing is rigid, the fabric cannot yield to the drop . . . (and high pressures result). . . . This confirms our theory that plain (flat) fabrics must be constructed to withstand high pressures."

TABLE 98. WATER REPELLENCY PROPERTIES OF COTTON FABRICS

(From Slowinske and Pope[226] "Correlation of Water Repellent Garment Performance and Laboratory Penetration Tests")

Part A
Physical Properties, Spray, and Immersion Absorption Values of Seven Cotton Fabrics, All Treated with the Same Water Repellent Finish

Fabric Code #	Fabric Weave	Average Spray Test Rating	Average Immersion Absorption Test Value (%)	Average Air Permeability (ft³/min/ft²)	Average Thickness (.001 inch)	Average Weight (oz/yd²)	Average Count per inch Warp	Filling
1	poplin	100	20.9	7.34	15.6	6.20	107	54
2	sateen	100	17.7	4.72	22.8	8.78	112	70
3	oxford	100	19.3	2.37	19.1	8.50	132	49
4	poplin	100	22.6	9.15	12.6	4.86	109	63
5	poplin	100	23.2	60.0	14.2	4.39	117	42
6	twill	100	22.9	40.3	16.1	5.21	118	55
7	gabardine	100	20.6	27.6	28.7	9.06	133	75

Part B
Rain Test Data—Penetration in Five Minute Test Period
(Grams of Water Absorbed by a Blotter behind the Test Fabric)

Fabric	No. of Thicknesses	Hydrostatic Pressure Head on Nozzle of Rain Tester						
		2 ft	3 ft	4 ft	5 ft	6 ft	7 ft	8 ft
No. 3, oxford	1	0.0	0.0	0.1	....	....	...	0.5
No. 2, sateen	1	0.1	0.3	0.9	0.7	7.9	9.0	13.8
No. 1, poplin	1	0.2	0.8	2.8	6.5	14.4	...	....
No 4, poplin	1	2.2	7.6	14.1	....	....	...	....
No. 7, gabardine	1	11.7	...	....	....	....	...	....
No. 6, twill	1	12.7	...	....	....	....	...	....
No. 5, poplin	1	13.0	...	....	....	....	...	....
No. 3, oxford	2	....	...	....	....	....	...	0.0
No. 2, sateen	2	....	...	....	....	....	...	0.0
No. 1, poplin	2	....	...	....	0.0	0.1	0.1	0.3
No. 4, poplin	2	....	...	0.0	0.1	0.3	0.5	3.0
No. 7, gabardine	2	....	...	0.0	0.3	0.7	0.6	3.0
No. 6, twill	2	....	0.0	3.6	13.8	....	...	....
No. 5, poplin	2	0.5	3.1	14.6	....	....	...	....

Part C
Rain Test Data—Time to Start Penetration and Time for Four Grams Penetration
Using a Fixed Pressure Head of Three Feet on the Nozzle

Fabric	Number of Thicknesses	Average Time for Initial Penetration seconds	Average Time for 4 gm Penetration seconds
No. 3, oxford	1	930	3600*
No. 2, sateen	1	116	3600†
No. 1, poplin	1	20	1500
No. 4, poplin	1	8	120
No. 7, gabardine	1	1	14
No. 6, twill	1	1	4
No. 5, poplin	1	1	2
No. 6, twill	2	305	1420
No. 5, poplin	2	8	180

* Less than 0.1 gram penetration at end of test (3600 seconds or 1 hour).
† Average of 3.5 grams leakage at end of test (3600 seconds or 1 hour).

TABLE 98. WATER REPELLENCY PROPERTIES OF COTTON FABRICS.—*(Continued)*

Part D

Bundesmann, Drop Penetration, Impact Penetration, and Hydrostatic Pressure Test Data

Fabric	Number of Thicknesses	Average Bundesmann Test Penetration (cc/20 mins*)	Average Drop Penetration Test Times (min.)	Average Hydrostatic Pressure Test Readings (cms)†	Average Impact Penetration (g)
No. 3, oxford	1	0	54	72	0
No. 2, sateen	1	0.2	8.8	43	0
No. 1, poplin	1	1.8	3.7	42	< 0.1
No. 4, poplin	1	3.9	3.2	37	< 0.1
No. 7, gabardine	1	20	1.3	26	1.1
No. 6, twill	1	59	0.77	27	1.6
No. 5, poplin	1	99	0.72	19	11.4
No. 3, oxford	2	0	60+	97	
No. 2, sateen	2	0	60+	55	
No. 1, poplin	2	0	22	52	
No. 4, poplin	2	0.2	22	46	
No. 7, gabardine	2	< 0.1	8.8	29	
No. 6, twill	2	0.3	1.7	29	
No. 5, poplin	2	3.0	1.1	21	

* The Bundesmann Test was run for 20 minutes instead of the specified time of 10 minutes. This was done in an effort to obtain measurable penetrations on all of the fabrics in single thicknesses. However, even with the 20-minute time the penetration for one thickness of No. 3 oxford was zero and the penetration for one thickness of No. 2 sateen was only 0.2 cubic centimeters. When the time was further increased to 60 minutes, the observed penetration was only 0.1 cubic centimeter on additional samples of both the sateen and oxford in single thickness.

The tabulated 20-minute Bundesmann Test data indicate that No. 4 poplin is definitely superior to No. 7 gabardine in single thickness, but slightly inferior in double thickness. Additional tests, made with a time of 60 minutes, confirmed the relative inferiority of No. 4 poplin in double thickness; two thicknesses of No. 4 poplin allowing a penetration of 19 cubic centimeters and two thicknesses of No. 7 gabardine allowing a penetration of only 2.6 cubic centimeters.

† The Hydrostatic Pressure Test was run with a rate of increase of head of one centimeter per second, as specified in the 1945 A.A.T.C.C. Year Book. As an experiment, No. 3 oxford also was tested with an increase of head of 0.5 centimeters per second. A single thickness of the fabric gave an average reading of 71 centimeters, while two thicknesses of the fabric gave an average reading of 97 centimeters.

A private communication from M. Kärrholm[429] points out that falling drop test methods may be used for testing fabrics with compressible surfaces if the kinetic energy of the drop, as it strikes the fabric is not too high. If the drop intensity is great, the water jets may compress the surface layers, and the fabric will have insufficient time to recover from the excessive impact.

Fabric Structure and Its Relation to Water Repellency. Considerable information is reported on the effect of construction on the water repellency of cotton fabrics. Sookne[223] mentions that poplins, oxfords, and sateens resist penetration better than twills because they have a lesser number of holes, the number being a function of weave and thread count.

Slowinske and Pope[226] tabulate a considerable amount of data on various fabric constructions and evaluate them by means of several water repellency tests shown in Table 98.

It should be emphasized that all of these fabrics have been treated with a water repellent finish so that the influence of fiber wetting is held to a minimum. The tables substantiate the point that the oxford and sateen constructions are best. Three poplins are involved with weights of 6.20, 4.86 and 4.39 ounces per square yard. The heavier poplin approaches the repellency characteristics of the oxford and sateen; the lighter poplins approach the properties of the twill.

The outstanding improvement obtained by the use of two layers of fabrics is borne out in the table. This is due to the fact that a double layer affords greater energy absorption under impact; furthermore, a very low order of probability exists that two holes in a fabric will superimpose "to form a continuous path through both fabrics . . . Because the hole is probably not continuous, the raindrop in order to get through both fabrics will have to take a round-about path, and this requires more energy."[223]

Table 99 gives additional data by Sookne on the effect of two layers of fabric.

TABLE 99. COMPARISON OF RAINFALL RESISTANCE OF A SINGLE AND DOUBLE LAYER
OF COTTON POPLIN FABRIC

(From Sookne[223] "The Problem of Water Repellent Fabrics")

	Cotton Poplin	
	Single Layer	Double Layer
no water repellent treatment	6 seconds	8 seconds
slight water repellent treatment	15 seconds	44 seconds
more water repellent treatment	40 seconds	700 seconds
better water repellent treatment	51 seconds	8500 seconds
best water repellent treatment	65 seconds	10000 seconds

The literature contains little information on the repellency properties of fabrics made from synthetic fibers and the economics of using synthetics vs. cotton is probably one reason for this situation. If the fibers are hydrophobic, or nearly so, then fabric structure, as has been stated, will be the controlling factor. The fact that most synthetic fibers can closely pack is conducive to making tight fabrics from them. However, if the fabric is sufficiently tight to repel water via high "jamming" of yarns, the problem of moisture vapor transfer and body comfort appears, since, because the fibers are hydrophobic, water vapor cannot transfer via the fiber itself. Presuming that a compromise can be made between tightness of structure and body comfort by means of chemical water repellent treatments, it can be concluded that fabrics made from inherently water impermeable synthetic fibers should provide excellent "rain resistance."

Reviewing the methods whereby fibers can be formed into water repellent fabrics, there appears to be three distinct mechanisms for attaining such fabrics:

(1) Close packed structures composed either of hydrophobic or hydrophillic yarns with chemical water-repellent finishes as they might be needed. This group is the most popular and includes water-repellent treated cotton fabrics.

(2) Relatively open hydrophillic wool or fur constructions wherein the fibers are uniformly spaced and held as far apart as possible so that water droplets which strike become absorbed only with difficulty.

(3) Soft cotton yarn constructions such that the initial portion of water striking the fabric, swells the fibers and thereby closes the interstices.

The shortcoming of wool in terms of its high moisture absorption capacity can, in part, be overcome by the application of water-repellent finishes. But it should be remembered that such treatments only slow down the rate of moisture absorption and do not usually change the final equilibrium. Thus in a prolonged heavy rain, the amount of water absorbed would ultimately be high, thus presenting the same disadvantage to which reference has already been made.

Chapter 16

CREASE RETENTION, WRINKLE RESISTANCE, AND DIMENSIONAL STABILITY

(52) Nomenclature and Methods for Measuring Crease Retention and Wrinkle Resistance

Introduction to crease retention and wrinkle resistance has already been made via the discussion on "Resilience" in Chapter 11, Section 36.

Descriptive terms are used rather loosely. It is felt that the terms given in the above title describe requisite properties most accurately, for people do not want their clothing to become or remain wrinkled, while they do want to be able to impart and permanently maintain creases. Armour[227] points this out:

> "The crease and the wrinkle, there isn't much doubt,
>   Are alike in a number of ways,
> But the crease is the one that so quickly comes out
>   While the wrinkle's the one that stays."

It is apparent that fabrics which have the attribute of resisting wrinkling, also have the disadvantage of being difficult to crease. This situation can be overcome, in part, by the application of heat and/or moisture, and pressure during pressing.

The somewhat conflicting, yet popular term "crease resistance," will be used only when quoting source material.

Buck and McCord,[228] in an extremely thorough review of the entire subject define crease resistance and resilience as follows:

> "Crease resistance may be thought of as that property of a fabric which causes it to recover from folding deformations that normally occur during its use. The recovery may be almost instantaneous in which case there will be an apparent resistance to the formation of a crease. Recovery may be slower in other cases, with the crease mark disappearing gradually. The speed and completeness of a fabric's recovery from creases is the measure of its crease resistance. . . . Resilience

256

(is) the property of a fiber that enables it to recover from deformation, and thus to influence the crease resistance of a fabric."

Methods for Evaluating Wrinkle Resistance. Buck and McCord[228] have written a complete description of various laboratory test methods, and that portion of their report is repeated here substantially as originally printed:

"During the past twenty years at least a dozen methods for the evaluation of fabric crease-resistance have been suggested, both in this country and abroad. Some of these methods have been used rather extensively, although each leaves something to be desired, either in ease of operation or in the amount of information which they provide on the creasing characteristics of the fabric.

"If the crease-resisting characteristics of fabrics are to be improved, comparative tests must be available so that the relative crease-resistance of a treated fabric to an untreated one can be determined. It is also desirable to know the relative crease-resistance of different fabrics so that the influence of construction and fiber content may be better understood. Methods for measuring crease-resistance which give some clue to the resilient characteristics of the fabric, work recovered on unfolding, and specific information on different time and pressure effects represent a further step in the evaluation of textile creasing properties. The ultimate development in test methods would be a method that could duplicate the creasing which occurs during actual garment use, and which would provide data which could be correlated directly with the performance of a fabric in a garment. At this time, there is no instrument that approaches this goal, although methods now in use do reproduce at least some of the conditions of normal garment use.

"For most purposes, such as the development of improved crease-resistant finishes, or for demonstrations in the merchandising of fabrics, a simple testing device that provides reasonably accurate comparative results is preferred by technologists. Several such devices reveal the relative crease-resistance of treated and untreated fabrics, or of different fabrics. A brief description of a number of testing methods that have been used for evaluating textile crease-resistance will be set down here, together with references to other work on the subject.

"*The Clenched-Fist Method.* One of the earliest methods of qualitatively estimating the wrinkle-resistance of a textile was crumpling a specimen of cloth, about a foot square, and squeezing the small wad of fabric tightly in the clenched fist. When the fist is suddenly opened, a resilient fabric such as wool will spring out and creases formed in the crumpling will disappear rapidly. Less resilient fabrics will either remain partially wadded or crumpled, or will recover their original shape only partially and retain creases and wrinkles easily discernible to the eye. While this method is quick and easy, and suitable for demonstrating comparative crease-resistance where large differences in fabric exist, it is obviously qualitative and not suited to the type of control necessary for determining smaller differences between textiles. Nevertheless, the method will undoubtedly continue in use as a supplement to other techniques.

"The clenched-fist method produces a wrinkles fabric that is examined visually. The principal objection to wrinkles is the change which they cause in the appearance of fabric. This change in appearance is most noticeable and most objectionable when the angle of creasing or folding is sharp. The fabric surfaces on each side of the crease reflect light to the eye from different angles, the difference in the intensity of the light from each surface depending in part on the luster characteristics of the surface, as well as upon its color. The line formed by the crease sharply divides the two adjacent surfaces of different light-reflecting properties, and thus the presence of the crease is made evident in a manner displeasing to the eye, especially when numerous creases form irregular patterns in the fabric. On the other hand, if two adjacent fabric surfaces which reflect light differently are separated by a section in which the light-reflecting characteristics of the one shade gradually into those of the other, a soft and not displeasing effect will result. The importance of the creasing angle has been recognized in a number of the tests which are used to evaluate crease-resistance.

"*The T-B-L Method.* The Tootal-Broadhurst-Lee Company, pioneers in the development of crease-resistance for cellulosic fabrics, utilized for many years a rather simple technique for measuring the improvement in resistance to creasing brought about through the application of the T-B-L finish (Figure 10). A fabric cutting 4 cm long and 1 cm wide is folded across its narrow dimension and placed beneath a 500-g weight for 5 minutes. It is then allowed to recover for 3 minutes while hung over a horizontal wire or pin at the crease. The distance between the ends of the partly recovered specimen is taken as a measure of the crease-resistance of the specimen. In the more resilient fabrics this distance will be greater than in those which recover less from the folding.

"Disadvantages cited for the T-B-L methods include the following:

"(1) Differences between materials of poor crease resistance (forming small angles) are easier to detect than differences between more resilient fabrics since the measurement of crease-resistance in this case is proportional to the sine of the creasing angle. For large angles, differences in this value become increasingly small.

"(2) The curvature of the fabric on either side of the pin, affected by the weight and stiffness of the material, constitutes an additional error.

"(3) Curl or twist common in many fabrics causes difficulty in obtaining an exact measurement of the distance between the ends of the cutting.

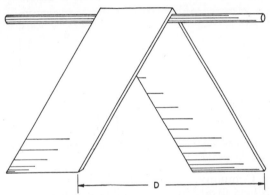

Figure 10. T-B-L method for measuring crease recovery. "The[228] distance D measures the creasing recovery." (*From Buck and McCord*,[228] *"Crease Resistance and Cotton."*)

"*Mercury Method.* A small rectangular cutting of fabric is folded across its short dimension and placed under a standard weight for a specified time. After removal of the weight, the folded cutting is floated on edge on a surface of mercury and allowed to recover, following which either the angle of creasing or the distance between the ends of the cutting can be measured. (Figure 11.) This method eliminates errors due to the weight of the fabric and the curvature of the fabric ends. The results, however, are said to be influenced by the condition of the surface of mercury, and the method is also influenced by handling of the cutting during transfer to the mercury surface. It is believed that this method is not widely used at the present time.

"*Creasing-Angle Method.* This method is essentially a modification of the T-B-L method, and involves measurement of the angle of crease rather than of the distance between the two ends of a folded cutting. The angle method has the advantage of better sensitivity at wide angles than is possible with the T-B-L technique, and the twist or curl of the fabric is also not significant at, or close to, the crease itself. Furthermore, the effect of curvature or droop of the fabric ends is at least partially eliminated, although it still remains as a source of error which may be large with limp cloth.

"*Monsanto Method.* A modification of the creasing-angle method designed to minimize some of the variables of earlier techniques was developed by the Shirley Institute and further refined by the Textile Resin Department of the Monsanto

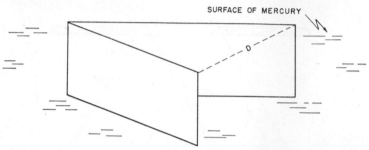

Figure 11. Mercury method for measuring crease recovery. (*From Buck and McCord,*[228] "*Crease Resistance and Cotton.*")

Chemical Company. In this method one end of the creased cutting is held firmly in a jaw while the other hangs free and is brought into coincidence with a vertical line of the meter. (Figure 12.) The angle which the free end makes with the clamped end after a specified time of suspension on the meter is a measure of the recoverability of the fabric. The influence of fabric weight and stiffness is largely eliminated by holding one end of the cutting in the clamp and arranging the other end in vertical suspension. The instrument is simple yet well designed, is portable, and gives results that are adequate for most developmental or merchandising purposes.

"*Roller Creasing Method.* The Stamford Research Laboratories of the American Cyanamid Company have suggested a modification of creasing-angle methods which is said to provide a more uniform creasing pressure than is obtainable by other techniques. A looped cutting, held by its two ends in a special clamping device, is inserted from below between two steel rollers, each ½-inch in diameter. (Figure 13.) The rollers are brought together and held thus at a standard

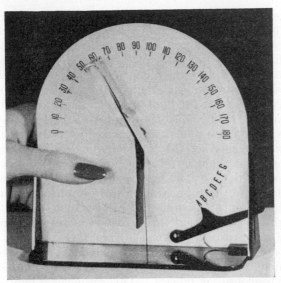

Figure 12. Monsanto wrinkle recovery tester. (*Courtesy, Monsanto Chemical Co.*)

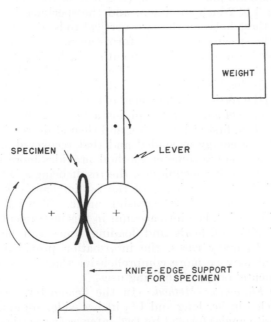

Figure 13. American cyanamid roller pressure tester. (*From Buck and McCord,*[228] *"Crease Resistance and Cotton."*)

pressure determined by a weight-and-lever system. Rotation of the rollers passes the cutting down between them, creasing it and dropping it upon a knife edge situated immediately beneath the line of tangency of the rollers. The silhouette of the crease angle thus formed is projected on a rotatable translucent screen, and the angle is measured at the apex with the aid of cross hairs on the dial. Time for the relaxation of the fabric and the roll pressure are specified. Advantages claimed for this method are a uniform pressure nearly independent of the compressibility of the fabric and the elimination of all handling of the clipping from the time it is placed between the rollers of the tester. The testing device is portable, although more elaborate than the Monsanto instrument. The curvature and weight of the material will still contribute to error, although it is stated that this error is minimized by measurement of the creasing angle at the vertex.

"Compressometer Method. A sensitive, modified compressometer has been used for measuring the "compressometer flexural resilience" of fabrics. This resilience is defined as the ratio of energy recovered by a fabric compressed in the above device to that which is expended in compressing the sample. Three holes are punched along each side of the longer dimension of a 3 × 2-inch specimen, and the specimen is mounted through these holes on the two vertical rods of a special rack so that the specimen in profile forms an S. This specimen is then placed beneath the instrument's 1-inch-diameter circular presser foot, which can be lowered by a rack-and-pinion arrangement. The load is indicated by a dial on the top of the instrument and the vertical displacement of the sample is read from the circumference of a disc on the pinion axle. A number of readings are taken, first at increasing and then at decreasing loads, and both the energy expended and that recovered are calculated. The compressometer method provides more information than any other techniques, the result being a better indication of the true resiliency of the fabric than is obtainable from measurement of the creasing angle. The influence of fabric stiffness is taken into account in this instrument and the effect of different loads and loading times can be readily studied. In many cases, the information provided by this instrument may be more comprehensive than is required for developmental or merchandising uses.

"The Flexometer Method. In the flexometer, two specimens, each 4 inches long and $1\frac{3}{4}$ inches wide, are mounted in the opposite angles formed by two intersecting vertical plates. One of these plates is stationary and the other intersects the first plate and is rotatable about the axis intersection. As the

plate is rotated to compress the two fabric specimens, the torque exerted by the specimens in resisting the folding can be measured by a series of cantilever springs. Readings are taken first at decreasing angles and then at increasing angles and the expended energy of folding as well as the energy of recovery is calculated. The ratio of the energy recovered to the energy expended is termed the 'flexural resilience.'"

In addition to certain miscellaneous methods also cited by Buck and McCord, Jaumann[229] describes a qualitative method wherein the sample (yarn and fibre tufts, cloth specimens 6 × 3 cms) is gripped by the thumb and forefinger of each hand, twisted through 180°, and one grip released after 10 seconds. The samples are then compared by means of a series of photographs.

Very recently Hebeler and Kolb[230] have described a new testing apparatus used to measure "wrinkling." In this test the property of wrinkle resistance is separated from the property of wrinkle recovery, and actual values may be obtained for each. The tester is called the "Wrinklometer," and it attempts to provide measurable results of wrinkling that occurs during a process thought to simulate service testing very closely.

After the 10 × 4-inch fabric samples have been wrinkled in a "random" but "standardized" manner by inserting them in a glass test tube, they are allowed to lie in a standardized manner on a platform that moves to different lateral positions so that several different contour curves (usually four) may be recorded by a Leeds and Northrup "speedomax" recorder.

The length of the trace is measured and the area under it determined by means of an integrator. From these, the mean wrinkle height $\bar{h}$ of the fabric is calculated.

"After[230] each Wrinklometer analysis, the fabric sample is suspended from a wire with clips for 24 hours to permit it to recover under its own weight, after which four more traces are made. This process is repeated for five successive days. The results are then plotted as mean wrinkle height (mm) vs. time (days). In addition to the graph, two empirical relations have been designated as measurements of the wrinkle-resistance and wrinkle-recovery. They are as follows:

Wrinkle-resistance index: $10/\bar{h}_0 (\text{mm}^{-1})$
Wrinkle-recovery index: $100(\bar{h}_0 - \bar{h}_4)/\bar{h}_0$ (limits: 0–100)

where $\bar{h}_0$ and $\bar{h}_4$ are the mean wrinkle heights immediately after wrinkling and after four days' recovery, respectively; large values of both indices are desirable for resilient fabrics. Values of the wrinkle-resistance index usually range between 1 and 40."

Concerning the relationships between laboratory test methods and service performance, Buck and McCord[228] are careful to point out that

"none of the instruments or test methods available are thought to duplicate the conditions of actual garment use, and it is probable that the complicated combination of conditions accompanying such use will never be accurately copied by a testing method. There is some question as to how closely the available test methods approach the conditions of garment use. By the crease-angle test, for example, and in many cases by tests which measure recoverable energy, some crease-proofed cellulosic fabrics are indicated to be almost comparable to or even equal to woolen and worsted fabrics. When these treated cellulosic fabrics are subjected to a severe crushing, however, they do not recover as well as they should according to crease-angle or recoverable-energy test methods. Woolen fabrics, crushed in the same manner, still recover remarkably well. This suggests that a method for severely crushing and rumpling a fabric sample in a random yet standardized and reproducible manner might satisfy a need for more knowledge on the wrinkling of fabrics than we can at present obtain from the available techniques."

Whether Hebeler and Kolb's method (published after Buck and McCord's paper) is a step in the right direction remains to be seen.

(53) The Mechanics of Wrinkle Resistance

Gagliardi and Grunfest[18] employ an engineering approach to the mechanism of creasing:

"Let us first examine the nature of the creasing phenomenon of a homogeneous material, and then see how fabrics behave in folding. If we take any continuous sheet or rod material and subject it to bending stresses, a permanent crease or wrinkle may form if the deformations which accompany the fold exceed the elastic limit of the material. Figure 14 shows a homogeneous rod being bent to a close fold. On the outside of the bend in this rod, elements of the material must be stretched while the bend is being made, and on the inside of the bend other elements must be compressed. Somewhere in the middle of the rod there are elements which are neither stretched nor compressed. These are in the neutral plane of deformation. The amount of deformation suffered by any element in the bend is determined by its distance from this plane. During the formation of a close fold (i.e., 180° bend) in a homogeneous material, the tensile deformations which occur are of the order of 100%. Since very few materials can recover from such deformations, the strains produced in the fibers of a fabric in a close fold must be of a much lower order of magnitude. How this reduction in strain may be brought

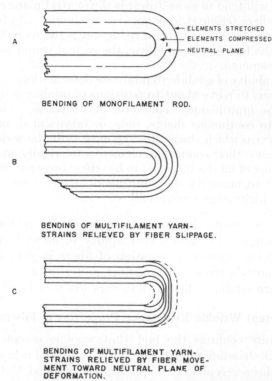

Figure 14. Bending of monofilament and multifilament materials. (*From Gagliardi and Grunfest,*[18] *"Creasing and Crease-proofing of Textiles."*)

about in creasing a fabric is shown by Figures 14-B and 14-C. These figures give a schematic view of a multifilament yarn which, unlike the homogeneous rod of Figure 14-A, is composed of fibers that have some freedom of motion relative to each other. During the bending of a fabric, and consequently of the yarns, the strains produced in the individual fibers can be relieved by two mechanisms. As shown in Figure 14-B, the fibers can slip if their freedom of movement is not hindered by high frictional forces caused either by twist or the presence of sizing agents. If the freedom of movement of the fibers in the bend were completely unhindered, the fibers could adjust themselves around the bend, and hence suffer minimum deformation.　This cannot ordinarily take place except in fabrics the yarns of which have zero twist.

"The second method by which fiber strains can be minimized is shown in Figure 14-C.　Again, if the fibers' movement is not completely hindered during the formation of the fold, the fibers will tend to move towards the neutral plane of deformation, where tensile strains are at a minimum.　As to which of these two methods of strain reduction is the more likely to occur in the folding of any fabric, the second would appear to be more common.

"The ability of a fabric to minimize deformations by allowing its fibers to move about to positions of minimum strains is due to the multifilament character of its yarns.　This is in contrast to continuous sheets, rods, or fabrics made of monofilament yarns which, during folding must suffer large deformations because their composing elements are rigidly fixed.　In the finishing of fabrics intended to be crease resistant, it is very important to maintain this multifilament character in order to obtain high crease recovery."

It becomes apparent that the crease resistance performance of a fabric depends upon (1) the inherent ability of fibers to recover from strain, and (2) the state of aggregation of fibers in yarn and yarns in fabric which controls the amount of fiber and yarn movement relative to fiber and yarn strain.　These two factors will now be discussed.

(54) The Inherent Wrinkle Resistance Properties of Fibers

The literature confirms the fact that wool is accepted as having excellent wrinkle-resisting properties.[228,229,231]　Indeed it has, to the present, probably been accepted as a standard.　Buck and McCord[228] state:

"The ability of fabrics made from wool and silk to resist the formation of wrinkles is well recognized, as is the tendency toward wrinkle formation in linen, cotton, and certain rayon textiles.　Fiber characteristics responsible for these differences . . . are related to the chemical and physical structure of the fiber itself."

For an excellent analysis of the effect of molecular structure on fiber wrinkle resistance properties the reader is referred to Buck and McCord's paper, pages 10 and 11.

Since, in creasing a fabric, strains are produced, we must return to a study of the inherent tensional properties of fibers when subjected to repeated strains below rupture. Grunfest and Gagliardi,[232] and Hamburger, Morgan and Platt[21] state that in creasing a fabric, strains in the order of magnitude of 5–10 per cent result, and it is well to consider recovery properties at this level. Tables 18 through 25 show instantaneous and/or delayed strain recoveries.

Table 20 shows strain and work recovery values of Beste and Hoffman.[236] The remarks made on page 41 concerning these data, summarize the relative position of fibers as they inherently bear on wrinkle resistance. At both 65 per cent R.H. and 90 per cent R.H. the strain and work recovery of nylon, wool, and "Dacron" surpass all other fibers, and one would predict that these fibers would produce fabrics (when properly engineered) of high wrinkle resistance.

The data given in Table 23 by Hamburger, Morgan, and Platt[21] similarly rank silk, wool, mohair, and "Terylene" (equivalent to "Dacron") as having high instantaneous elastic recovery properties. These also enable a prediction of high wrinkle resistance. Cellulose acetate and nylon are intermediate, while viscose rayon and "Orlon" are far inferior.

Table 100 from Susich and Backer[233] is identical with Table 24 except that the fibers are tabulated in decreasing order of Instantaneous Elastic Recovery, and increasing order of Permanent Set, after straining to 5 and 10 per cent extension. (The non-textile fibers, e.g., polyethylene, Saran, are excluded.) The greater the amount of I.E.R., and the lesser the amount of P.S. the better the fiber should be in wrinkle resistance. Here somewhat conflicting ranking occurs. Wool and "Vinyon" NOZZ are near the top. Nylon has low permanent set but its instantaneous elastic recovery is not high, and if this is a prerequisite for proper wrinkle resistance, one would predict that nylon would be somewhat inferior.

It would be nice at this point to present data on the wrinkle-resisting properties of fabrics of identical construction (yarn and fabric) and then to compare their relative merit with the rankings given above. At the moment, the writer has found this to be impossible for two reasons: first, no comprehensive quantitative data on constant-construction fabrics composed of the various fibers are available. Secondly, if they were available, the problem exists of selecting quantitative tensional recovery parameters which do correlate. The writer has spent considerable time in attempting to decide on which criteria of those mentioned above most logically reflect wrinkle resistance; he has come to the conclusion that additional work and analysis is needed before such correlations can be attempted. Hamburger, Morgan, and Platt,[21] as mentioned on page 43, are preparing a paper on "The Elastic Behavior of Fibers at Low Strains" wherein they hope to present some information on the subject. Preliminary findings indicate reasonably good correlation between Instan-

TABLE 100.   PER CENT IMMEDIATE ELASTIC RECOVERY AND PER CENT PERMANENT
SET COMPONENTS OF DESIGNATED TOTAL STRAINS
(From Susich and Backer[233] "Tensile Recovery Behavior of Textile Fibers")

5% STRAIN

	I. E. R. (%)		P. S. (%)
"Vinyon" NOZZ	61	wool yarn	0
"Vinyon" NORU	58	nylon	3
wool yarn	56	"Vinyon" NORU	4
acetate multifil	54	"Vinyon" NOZZ	5
acetate staple	48	stabilized casein	6
H.T. "Fortisan"	46	"Vinyon" N staple	7
cotton yarn 50/1	44*	"Orlon"	8
"Vinyon" CF-HST	42	acetate staple	10
"Orlon"	42	"Vinyon" CF-HST	10
"Vinyon" N staple	42	Fiber V	10
silk	41	acetate multifil	11
Fiber V	38	silk	18
nylon	38	cotton 50/1	23*
viscose multifil	37	H.T. "Fortisan"	24
viscose staple	34	cotton 12/1	28
cotton 12/1	32	viscose staple	30
		viscose multifil	31

10% STRAIN

	I. E. R. (%)		P. S. (%)
wool yarn	40	nylon	5
"Vinyon" CF-HST	30	wool yarn	12
"Vinyon" NOZZ	30	"Vinyon" NOZZ	20
nylon 300	28	"Vinyon" NORU	20
"Vinyon" NORU	28	"Vinyon" CF-HST	22
"Vinyon" N staple	27	Fiber V	27
acetate multifil	27	"Vinyon" N staple	28
Fiber V	27	"Orlon"	30
"Orlon"	27	acetate multifil	41
acetate staple	26	silk	42
silk	25	acetate staple	48
viscose multifil	22	viscose staple	54
viscose staple	22	viscose multifil	54

* Data taken at approximately 4.5% strain.

taneous Elastic Deflection, Instantaneous Elastic Energy, and Elastic Index values, and the data of Hebeler and Kolb[230] on "The Measurement of Fabric Wrinkling."

Beste and Hoffman[236] also discuss the quantitative relationship between fabric crease recovery, and fiber tensile recovery and work recovery. They show plots of crease angle vs. work recovery and tensile recovery respectively (see Table 20) for different materials. Unfortunately, they have not identified the various fibers studied with the exception of Nylon 66. It is recognized that the primary purpose of their paper was to discuss the efficacy of an evaluation technique. However, had the fibers been identified, some conclusions might have been made concerning fiber ranking, as well as the validity of their concept of evaluating fiber crease resistance via tensional recovery properties. Graph 48 is representative of their results.

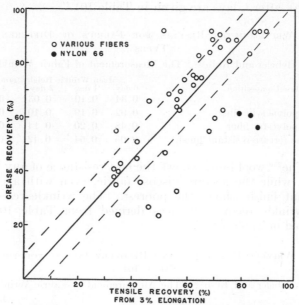

Graph 48. Fabric crease recovery vs. fiber tensile recovery from 3 per cent elongation. (*From Beste and Hoffman,*[236] "*A Quantitative Study of Resilience.*")

Broad statements can be made concerning relative ranking of fiber wrinkle-resistance properties. Unquestionably wool is near the top of the list as is "Dacron." Viscose and cotton are at the bottom. The relative position of the newer synthetics is difficult to ascertain—nylon, from Beste and Hoffman's work, appearing to behave in a somewhat unorthodox manner.

Various reports on the subject of inherent wrinkle-resistance are included below:

(1) Using the test described on page 263, Jaumann[229] compared the amount of recovery shown by various samples composed of viscose rayon, acetate, cuprammonium staple fiber, wool, and cotton in the wet and dry states via a series of photographs. Wool was considered best with regard to "elasticity" and "fullness" (body, resistance to distortion).

(2) Hebeler and Kolb[230] report as follows:

"Results illustrate how the Wrinklometer separates fabrics of different chemical types on the basis of wrinkle resistance and recovery. Each of the fabrics contain spun yarns of 2/32 worsted count with approximately 14 turns per inch in both singles and ply, and is of tropical worsted weave with a count approximately 48 × 39. The mean wrinkle heights, $\bar{h}_t$ (mm), after t days are given in Table 101."

TABLE 101. WRINKLOMETER RESULTS FOR FABRICS OF DIFFERENT CHEMICAL TYPES

(From Hebeler and Kolb[230] "The Measurement of Fabric Wrinkling")

	Mean Wrinkle Height (mm) after:				
Fabric Composition	0 day	1 day	2 days	3 days	4 days
wool	0.34	0.10	0.03	0.03	0.03
experimental polyacrylic fiber	0.92	0.19	0.10	0.06	0.05
experimental polyester fiber	0.48	0.20	0.14	0.12	0.12
acetate/viscose (crease-resistant finish)	2.05	0.64	0.42	0.36	0.36

"The[230] wool fabric shows the best resistance of any in the group, while the acetate/viscose fabric, even with a crease-resistant finish, shows the poorest. The wrinkle resistance and wrinkle recovery indices derived from Table 101 are reported in Table 102."

TABLE 102. WRINKLE RESISTANCE AND RECOVERY INDICES FOR THE FABRICS OF TABLE 101

(From Hebeler and Kolb[230] "The Measurement of Fabric Wrinkling")

Fabric Composition	Wrinkle Resistance Index $10/\bar{h}_0$ (mm^{-1})	Wrinkle Recovery Index $100\dfrac{(\bar{h}_0 - \bar{h}_4)}{\bar{h}_0}$
wool	29	91
experimental polyester fiber	21	75
experimental polyacrylic fiber	11	95
acetate/viscose (crease-resistant finish)	5	82

"Since [230] high values of either index represent favorable performance, wool shows itself to be an outstanding fabric, with both high resistance and high recovery. The fabric made from the experimental polyester fiber has excellent resistance, while that made from the experimental polyacrylic fiber has excellent recovery. Neither matches the wool sample in both resistance and recovery. However, it is known that yarn and fabric construction variables contribute significantly to the test results and that the results of Table 102 can be changed to some extent by altering the constructions."

(3) Using the American Cyanamid Roller Pressure Tester (R.P.T.), Dewaard, Hvizdak and Stock[234] list the following data on crease angle for various types of fabrics:

TABLE 103. CREASE ANGLE OF VARIOUS FABRICS

(From DeWaard, Hvizdak, and Stock[234] "Improved Evaluation of The Wrinkle Resistance of Resin Treated Fabrics")

(Tested at 65 % R.H. and 70°F)

| | Crease Angle (Degrees) | | |
	Rubber Faced Rollers	Metal Rollers	M/R
wool flannel	146	141	0.97
spun viscose rayon gabardine	136	121	0.89
acetate rayon	125	107	0.86
rayon sheer	122	96	0.79
rayon suiting	112	89	0.79
mercerized cotton twill	111	88	0.79
cotton percale	89	55	0.62
cotton voile	72	42	0.58

Two points are worthy of comment concerning Table 103. First, acetate rayon is generally considered to be better than viscose for wrinkle resistance; the fact that the reverse condition exists here can possibly be explained by the glib expression, "fabric geometry." Second, the metal rollers in the R.P.T. tester obviously compress the test specimens a greater amount than do the rubber rollers, as is demonstrated by the fact that in all cases the metal roller values are lower than the rubber roller values. The column marked M/R in Table 103 is a means of comparing the efficacy of fabric springback after creasing under two different pressure conditions. The obvious advantage of wool here is

TABLE 104. COMPARISON OF MONSANTO (W.R.T.) AND CYANAMID (R.P.T.) CREASE-RESISTANCE TESTERS

(From Fabric Research Laboratories, Inc.[235] "Investigation of Methods for Evaluating Crease Resistance" Report Prepared for The A.A.T.C.C. Committee for the Evaluation of Durable Finishes)

| | Recovery Angle at 65 % R.H. and 70°F. | | | |
| | Warp | | Filling | |
	Monsanto	Cyanamid	Monsanto	Cyanamid
cotton gingham				
untreated	80	60	88	73
crease-resisting finish*	118	102	117	107
spun viscose rayon				
untreated	90	92	101	98
crease-resisting finish*	140	148	143	152
60% spun rayon/40% wool				
untreated	128	137	137	140
crease-resisting finish*	138	153	142	153
wool				
untreated	148	152	156	154

* The treatments are not necessarily the same for each fabric.

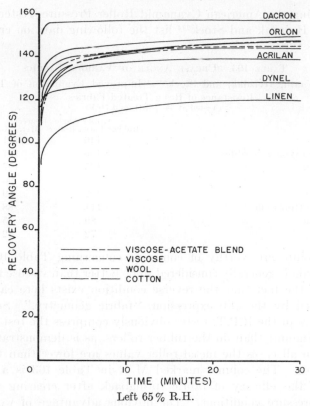

Graph 49.   The effect of time on the Monsanto crease recovery angle of fabrics tested at 65 per cent and 90 per cent relative humidity.   Left, 65% R.H.; right 90% R.H.   (*From Gantz,*[241] *"Textile Fibers from Synthetic Textiles."*)

that it can be creased under a greater force than any of the other fibers and recover the greatest amount.

(4) The T.B.L., Monsanto, and American Cyanamid Testers all utilize the crease recovery angle as a laboratory measure of crease resistance.   In the United States, the Monsanto Tester has had, in recent years, the most widespread use.   General experience with it has resulted in the more or less informal conclusion that materials which exhibit crease angles of 120° or greater will probably reflect proper service performance.   Such a statement is of course hazardous to make in the sense that many other factors, among them the humidity effect, may mitigate against using such a standard.

The American Association of Textile Chemists and Colorists' Committee on The Evaluation of Durable Finishes has conducted an interlaboratory evaluation program which compares the Cyanamid and Monsanto testers.   Typical results are given in Table 104.

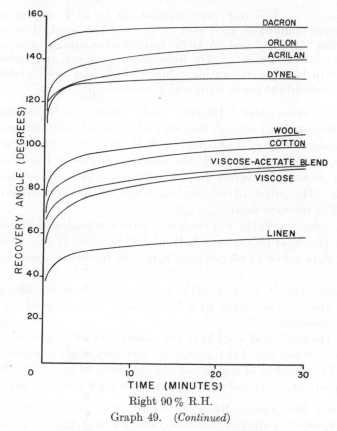

Right 90% R.H.

Graph 49.   (Continued)

The table demonstrates the high recovery angle of wool and the low angles for cotton and rayon when tested at 65 per cent R.H. The advantage of applying crease resisting finishes to cotton and rayon is evident. The addition of 40 per cent wool to rayon enhances the rayon's crease resistance. Looking at it another way, the rayon may be considered to be a diluent to wool.

Both crease testers rank the fabrics in substantially the same manner, but this does not mean that if the crease recovery angle on one tester is known, that the value for the other tester can be calculated.

(5) A limited amount of quantitative information on the wrinkle resistance properties of the hydrophobic synthetics has been found in the literature.

Gantz[241] compares the crease recovery angles for a series of fabrics tested on the Monsanto tester (Graph 49)

"Fabric samples made of spun yarns of several synthetic fibers were obtained and compared with wool, cotton and rayon. . . . The tests were carried out at 70°F and at two relative humidities, 65% and 95%. . . . The wool, 'Dacron,' 'Orlon,' 'Dynel,' and 'Acrilan' fabrics were similar in weight and construction. . . . The linen, cotton, viscose, and viscose-acetate blend were suiting fabrics which had been given a crease-resistant finish with urea formaldehyde resins."

Gantz's curves show "Dacron" and "Orlon" to be outstandingly good. Resin-treated cotton, viscose, and a viscose-acetate blend appear to be as good as wool at the 65 per cent R.H. level (full lines in the graph). However, at 95 per cent R.H. the recovery angles of the hydrophillic fibers are reduced—severely for the cellulosic fibers and somewhat for the wool. The effect of relative humidity on recovery angle will be discussed in the next section.

(6) Coplan, in Table 105 compares recovery angles of various fibers and fiber blends at 65 per cent R.H. and 92 per cent R.H. Considering only the data taken at 65 per cent R.H., the following conclusions may be made.

(i) Employment of a wrinkle resistant finish raises the recovery angle of the viscose fabric to a level which is considered to connote "wrinkle resistant."

(ii) "Dacron" and wool have the same order of magnitude of recovery angle. When blended together the recovery angle remains high.

(iii) The blending of approximately one-third "Dacron" with viscose, for this particular blended fabric, produces a high recovery angle. How

TABLE 105. CREASE RECOVERY ANGLES AT SELECTED HUMIDITIES
(From Coplan[242] "A Study of Wrinkle-Resistance at High Relative Humidities")
(American Cyanamid Roller Pressure Tester)

| | Recovery Angle (Degrees) | | | | | |
| | Warp | | | Filling | | |
Fabric	65% R.H.	92% R.H.	% Change	65% R.H.	92% R.H.	% Change
untreated spun viscose	91	39	57	75	38	49
urea formaldehyde resin treated spun viscose	140	92	77	120	77	36
100% wool (tropical worsted)	141	127	10	141	126	11
100% "Dacron" (tropical worsted)	131	133	1.5*	134	130	3
30% "Dacron"—70% viscose (tropical worsted)	141	117	17	139	117	16
55% "Dacron"—45% wool (tropical worsted)	139	134	3.5	142	132	7

*Gain.

much of this increase is due to the contribution of the "Dacron" and how much is due to what may be a fortuitous geometric configuration, is not known, but certainly the "Dacron" is of appreciable assistance in maintaining a high recovery angle.

(7) Staudt[243] describes the "heat-setting" process applied to nylon as having a stabilizing effect on its molecular structure. Helmus[244] says this "heat-set" process applied in the manufacture of nylon has been responsible for making nylon an excellent crease-resistant fabric, and the effect is permanent even when these fabrics are subject to laundering and wear. Furthermore, desired creases may be set in the fabric that last permanently. Such are the claims made about nylon's crease resistance; yet the general opinion is that nylon exhibits good, but by no means excellent, crease-resisting properties.

(8) Crease recovery data[171] on a pedigreed series of staple and continuous filament cellulose acetate fabrics show that at standard conditions of 65 per cent R.H. and 70°F, this fiber exhibits fairly high crease recovery angles as measured on the Monsanto tester.

(55) The Effect of High Humidity and Wetting on Wrinkle Resistance

The point has already been made that apparel textiles are used under ever-changing ambient conditions. In the summertime the relative humidity in close proximity to the human body may approach or reach the saturation point. It appears in order, particularly for summer apparel wear, to consider the crease-retention and wrinkle-resistance properties of fabrics at a humidity higher than the 65 per cent standard currently employed in most textile laboratories.

Because of the relationship between wrinkle resistance and tensional elastic properties, consideration must also be given to these tensional elastic properties at high humidities, or when wet. Some attention to this subject has already been given on pages 101–110, and the reader is invited to re-examine this portion of the text.

Fibers which are capable of absorbing water, normally have their elastic properties altered by the absorption, usually in a detrimental fashion.

Buck and McCord[228] comment,

"The extensibility of every textile fiber that absorbs water is increased as larger amounts of water are taken up by the fiber. The water by swelling and opening up the fiber structure, appears to act as a lubricant, thus permitting better movement of the fiber's molecules. Probably the water molecules become associated with the fiber molecules so that intermolecular forces are neutralized. It is not likely that the water hydrolyzes or breaks the type of intermolecular cross-linkage that is found in wool.

"Since fibers become more plastic as water is absorbed, or as the humidity of the ambient atmosphere increases, both creasing and crease recovery are markedly affected by humidity. Fibers that are strained while partially plasticized by water and then dried in the strained position will tend to remain in that position. In drying in the deformed position, intermolecular attractions between the molecules have been developed, and these forces hold the molecules together in the new position. If the fiber is re-wet, these newly formed attractive forces are again broken and cross-linking bridges will then act to restore the molecules to their original position. Conversely, this restorative force will be absent in those fibers which do not have cross-linked molecules, and the re-wet fibers will recover their original dimensions only after a long period of time, if at all.

"The wool fiber has properties almost ideally suited for providing fabrics with resistance to creasing and wrinkles, and at the same time for making it possible for the fabric to hold a crease where desired. The wool fiber has an intermediate modulus of elasticity, an area of delayed recovery, and a complete recoverability when wet. Most creases and folds of reasonably short duration in wool fabrics will show immediate recovery. In other cases, where the creasing time is long, or where the creasing pressure is high enough to exceed the immediate elastic limit of the fiber, the fabric will recover more slowly from the deformation. The ability of woolen and worsted fabrics to hold a crease results from 'stretchiness' (long-range elasticity) and the property of the fiber which permits it to assume a 'temporary set' in which it is maintained in a strained position by secondary intermolecular attractions such as ionic, polar, and van der Waals forces. The fiber recovers from the set when secondary forces are neutralized by water, the primary valence forces of the cross-linking cystine bridges acting to restore the keratin molecules to their original positions."

Graph 27 on page 108 and Graph 50 following, show why wool is superior to cotton and other cellulosic fibers in crease-resistance at high humidities. The latter graph shows wool to recover completely from the applied strain, while cotton does not.

Coplan[242] shows (Table 105) that in the absence of a "crease-resisting finish" the viscose fabric loses 53 per cent (warp and filling average) of its recovery angle when the humidity increases from 65 to 92 per cent. Upon application of a urea-formaldehyde treatment the recovery angle at both humidities increases significantly, the average per cent change remaining about 57 per cent (here the standard deviation is high). Whether recovery angles of 92° × 77° at 92 per cent R.H. are sufficiently high to demonstrate acceptable wrinkle resistance under humid service conditions is problematical. There appears to be a general opinion that a crease recovery angle of at least 125° is necessary in order for a fabric to exhibit acceptable performance. This minimum may be independent of relative humidity. On the other hand the possibility exists that such a standard is based upon the general experience of textile

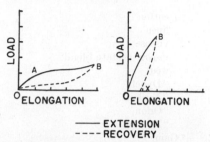

——— EXTENSION
- - - - RECOVERY

Graph 50. Typical stress-strain-relaxation curves for wool and cotton. Left—wool fiber (wet), Right—cotton fiber (wet). (*From Buck and Mc-Cord,*[228] "*Crease Resistance and Cotton.*")

technologists who know that when applying standard types of resin finishes to cellulosic fibers, if the recovery angle is above 125° at 65 per cent R.H., an acceptable fabric will result, regardless of a depression in recovery angle at a higher humidity.

There appears to be a need for the specification testing of wrinkle resistance at humidities higher than the present 65 per cent R.H. standard. The A.A.T.C.C. Committee For The Evaluation of Durable Finishes, of which the writer is a member, has recently recommended a 90 per cent R.H. tentative standard for men's summer suiting fabrics.

Coplan[242] further shows an approximately 10 per cent reduction in the recovery angle of wool as the humidity is raised from 65 to 92 per cent. "Dacron" exhibits a negligible difference in recovery angle as the humidity increases, demonstrating here the value of an hydrophobic fiber. Blends of wool and "Dacron," and viscose and "Dacron" show proportionate reductions in crease angle with increasing humidity.

Gantz[241] in Graph 49 and Table 106 is in agreement with Coplan's data on the per cent loss in recovery angle with humidity for viscose and "Dacron." He shows a greater loss for wool than does Coplan. Additional investigation must be made to ascertain more precisely the effect of high humidity on the wrinkle resistance of wool.

The new synthetic fibers "Orlon," "Vinyon," "Dynel," "Dacron," "Acrilan" and "X-51" all have substantially zero moisture regains (Tables 46 and 47). They are impervious to water and their physical properties as unaffected by changes in humidity. Nylon may be placed in almost

TABLE 106. CREASE RECOVERY ANGLES OF FABRICS MEASURED AFTER FIFTEEN MINUTES OF RELAXATION

(From Gantz[241] "Textile Fibers From Synthetic Textiles")

(Average of Warp and Fill—Monsanto Wrinkle Resistance Tester)

| | Recovery Angle in Degrees | | |
	65% R.H.	95% R.H.	% Change
cotton	143	97	32
linen	118	56	52
viscose	144	85	41
viscose-acetate blend	144	87	40
wool	144	101	30
"Dynel"	128	131	2*
"Acrilan"	138	137	1
"Orlon"	147	144	2
"Dacron"	157	155	1

* Gain.

the same category, although it has a regain of 3.5 to 4 per cent. Tables 52, 53, and 54 show the per cent changes in diameter, length and cross-sectional area upon wetting the various fibers. It follows that the greater the degree of hydrophobicity inherent in a fiber, the less change in dimension will result when the fiber is exposed to water. If, then, a fiber exhibits proper elastic recovery properties and concomittantly high wrinkle resistance when dry, and it maintains these properties upon water exposure because it is hydrophobic, it is bound to be good in crease resistance under moist or wet conditions.

One might predict that any fiber of zero regain *with proper dry tensional recovery properties* will exhibit satisfactory crease resistance under all normal ambient conditions, and will be independent of such conditions. Wool must have inferior dimensional stability to such fibers. In spite of the fact that wool's wet tensional recovery is high, the opportunity exists for it to become distorted when wet, and then dried into a new configuration (wrinkle). This has already been pointed out on page 109.

The data indicate that "Dacron" exhibits high wrinkle resistance and dimensional stability when dry. Because of its hydrophobicity the same properties will obtain when it is wet. Its advantage over wool, for example in a man's suit, becomes apparent. However, additional factors in addition to wrinkle resistance play a part in selecting fabrics for such an end use. Physiological comfort, appearance, hand, and drape are subjective parameters which bear on consumer acceptance. Sewability, cleanability, and alterability of apparel textiles also will control selection. Future chapters discuss these subjective and objective parameters (excluding physiology). With respect to men's suits (the example cited above), manufacturers are not using 100 per cent thermoplastic hydrophobic fibers. For a number of reasons, cost and custom undoubtedly among them, hydrophilic and hydrophobic fibers are being blended together.

(56) Chemical Methods for Improving the Wrinkle Resistance of Cotton and Rayon

The extremely poor crease resistance of cotton, viscose rayon, and linen has been ascribed to their poor elastic recovery. To improve this recovery, enormous effort has gone into the application of chemical treatments to cellulosic fibers. Gagliardi and Grunfest[18] comment as follows:

"The modification of cellulose fiber properties required to increase the elastic recovery of the fibers and to produce resistance to creasing of fabrics appears to involve the formation of cross-linkages between adjacent cellulose molecules. The formation of such cross-linkages reduces the extent of internal molecular slippage, which is responsible for the creep or plastic flow at high stress application and increases the Hooke's law region in the fibers, i.e., the amount of true elasticity.

"How such fiber modification may be brought about by chemical means has been the subject of considerable interest to many chemists. The simplest compound that has been widely investigated for this modification is free formaldehyde, which can form methylene bridges between cellulose molecules.

"A large number of other compounds have been synthesized for the purpose of achieving the same general effects produced by formaldehyde, but with greater ease of application and more uniform fiber modification. Of the many products which have been suggested and investigated . . . relatively few have been accepted for general use by the textile industry. The more widely used products are members of the urea and melamine series of resins.

"Table 107 contains data on the modification of fiber properties produced by various formaldehyde treatments. . . . These data were obtained by treating a 150/40 filament viscose rayon yarn with the appropriate solutions and curing the specimens at 120°C for 20 minutes. The fiber properties were examined by using the Scott IP-2 machine. It is noted that the main changes resulting from the formation of cross-linkages between cellulose molecules are the increase in elastic recovery and increase in modulus, i.e., a decrease in fiber extensibility."

"These[18] same treatments carried out on fibers were repeated on a spun viscose rayon and on cotton fabric. The change in crease-resistance is demonstrated by the data in Table 108. These show that the improvements in crease-resistance closely parallel the improvements previously noted in the fiber elastic recovery and the increase in modulus or fiber stiffness. From the general concept of multifilament character it would appear that the increase in fiber stiffness is also an important factor in obtaining high resistance to creasing. The stiffer fibers not only will better resist the action of bending stresses, but also in the formation of a close fold in the fabric such fibers can more readily adjust themselves to a position of minimum strain than can limp fibers. (Note: this point, in the opinion of the writer, is open to discussion.) While this increase in modulus appears to aid in producing resistance to creasing, at the same time the higher modulus produces fabrics with less capacity for energy absorption and consequently lower resistance to abrasive action and lower resistance to ripping and tearing forces."

TABLE 107. MODIFICATION OF FIBER PROPERTIES BY ACID-FORMALDEHYDE TREATMENTS ON A 150/40 VISCOSE YARN

(From Gagliardi and Grunfest[18] "Creasing and Creaseproofing of Textiles")

Concentration Applied	Tensile Strength (g/den.)	Elongation at break (%)	Load at 2% elongation (g/den.)	Elastic Recovery (2% elongation) (%)
none (control)	2.3	14.7	1.0	20
1% CH$_2$O	2.0	9.2	1.1	30
2% CH$_2$O	2.0	6.0	1.1	55
3% CH$_2$O	2.1	4.4	1.5	75
5% CH$_2$O	2.2	3.5	1.6	83
10% CH$_2$O	2.3	2.4	2.0	95

TABLE 108. IMPROVEMENT IN FABRIC CREASE RESISTANCE PRODUCED BY MODIFICATION OF FIBER PROPERTIES WITH ACID FORMALDEHYDE

(From Gagliardi and Grunfest[18] "Creasing and Creaseproofing of Textiles")

Concentration Applied	Fabric Crease Resistance (% Angle Recovery)	
	Rayon Challis	80^2 Cotton
none (control)	52	47
1% CH$_2$O	51	52
2% CH$_2$O	60	64
3% CH$_2$O	79	77
5% CH$_2$O	83	87
10% CH$_2$O	89	85

The problem of lower abrasion and tear resistance resulting from the application of crease resisting resins may be a serious one. Chapter 3, Section 10 discusses the bending stiffness properties of fibers as well as their fatigue resistance to repeated bending. Tables 27 and 28 show a reasonably good correlation between fiber stiffness and the number of 180° angle bends to cause fracture. Gagliardi and Grunfest show in

Graph 51 that chemical crease resisting treatments cause appreciable increase in stiffness. It follows that the fatigue life in terms of repeated flexing will be diminished for fabrics so treated. Rayons are poor in their flex resistance to start with, and when resin treatments further stiffen the fiber, as is born out by the change in the stress-strain diagram, the flex resistance further diminishes.

Reduction in abrasion resistance of resin treated fabrics may be explained in part by the curves given in Graph 52. Chapter 17 will discuss abrasion and wear in detail. At this point, however, it can be

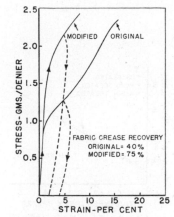

Graph 51. Effect of crease-resistant treatment on 150/40 viscose yarn. (*From Gagliardi and Grunfest,*[18] "*Creasing and Creaseproofing of Textiles.*")

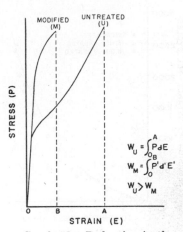

Graph 52. Reduction in the energy absorption of fibers as a result of the decrease in extensibility. (*From Gagliardi and Nuessle,*[237] "*Modification of Fiber and Fabric Properties by Wrinkleproofing and Stabilizing Agents.*")

stated that there is sound reason to accept the principle that abrasion resistance is in part a function of the ability of a material repeatedly to absorb energy under repeated stress applications below rupture. Hamburger[9] proposes that a measure of this energy is obtained by ascertaining the area under the stress-strain diagram after permanent set has been removed by mechanically conditioning the specimen at some stress or strain below rupture. Gagliardi and Nuessle[237] utilize this concept to show the diminution in area under treated vs. untreated fiber diagrams (Graph 52).

The authors also plot abrasion resistance vs. toughness as shown in Graph 53.

"The [237] relation between increase in elastic modulus of fibers and reduction in tear and abrasion resistance of fabrics was well established by measuring the mechanical properties of samples of a viscose rayon fabric which had been treated with a number of different types of wrinkleproofing and stabilizing agents. All of these reduced fiber extensibility without significantly affecting fiber tensile strength. The properties examined were tensile strength of fabric, elongation at break, tear strength, and resistance to abrasive action at high stress application as measured by the Tootal, Broadhurst,

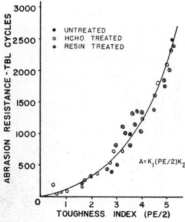

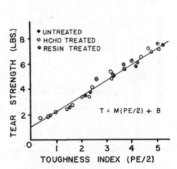

Graph 53. Reduction in abrasion resistance as a result of the decrease in fiber extensibility and fabric toughness. (*From Gagliardi and Nuessle,*[237] *"Modification of Fiber and Fabric Properties by Wrinkleproofing and Stabilizing Agents."*)

Graph 54. Reduction in fabric tear strength as a result of the decrease in fiber extensibility and fabric toughness. (*From Gagliardi and Nuessle,*[237] *"Modification of Fiber and Fabric Properties by Wrinkleproofing and Stabilizing Agents."*)

Lee Abrasion Machine. Correlation was made between fabric toughness as measured by one half the product of tensile strength and extensibility (writer's note: this is an approximation; see page 26), and tear and abrasion resistance. Fabric toughness is directly related to fiber toughness. (Writer's note: fabric geometry being constant.) Since tensile strength of fabric was not greatly changed by the various resin treatments, reduction in toughness index was due directly to decrease in extensibility."

Gagliardi and Nuessle[237] similarly point out the loss in trapezoid tear strength resulting from treatment. (Graph 54.)

Thus it is seen that to the present, application of crease resisting treatments on cotton and viscose rayon cause what sometimes may be serious losses in other physical attributes. At best such chemical treatments are compromises between improved crease resistance on the one hand, and loss in wear and tear properties on the other.

The engineering approach tells us that the elastic recovery of cellulose yarns must be increased in order to enhance crease resistance. Practical experience shows that resin *surface coating* of fibers so far has not produced enhanced recovery properties. Gagliardi and Grunfest[18] point out that

"In order to be effective as a crease-proofing agent, a compound must not only have the property of being able to form chemical or physical cross-linkages between the cellulose molecular chains, but it must also be diffusable in the cellulose phase. In the case of resin-forming material, it can be demonstrated that if a product is not essentially monomeric, it will not diffuse through a cellulose membrane. It will not modify the stress-strain properties of the fibers, it will not produce increased resistance, and it will simply deposit resins on the surface of the fabrics."

The two most widely used crease-resisting resin treatments on cellulose are urea-formaldehyde and melamine-formaldehyde types. An additional disadvantage to both of them is their sometimes marked tendency to form obnoxious odors upon ageing and storage. Fluck, Keppler, Cooke, and Zimmerman[238] have reported on the problem as follows (abstract of their paper):

"Textiles that have been treated with thermosetting aminoplasts, such as urea- and melamine-formaldehyde resins, develop unpleasant odors under certain conditions. A mechanism for the formation of odor in fabrics that have been treated with these nitrogen-containing resins has been proposed. This mechanism suggests that the development of odor is due to the formation of amines. These amines can be formed by (1) a reaction between the ammonium ion of ammonium salt catalysts and formaldehyde liberated from the resins during curing, (2) a reaction between the ammonia liberated from either the ammonium salt or non-ammoniacal-nitrogen-containing catalysts and formaldehyde, or (3) decomposition of the non-ammoniacal-nitrogen-containing catalysts into odor-producing amines. The addition of a formaldehyde acceptor, such as urea, to the resin bath was found to prevent odor formation in the treated fabrics. A sensitive, reproducible odor test for resin-treated fabric was developed."

Having listed the shortcomings of crease-resisting resins on cellulosic fibers, it is only proper now to list any additional advantages over and above their prime utilization for crease resistance. These include increased dimensional stability, decreased shrinkage, (sometimes) increased wet strength (for rayons), and (sometimes) increased fastness of the dyes to washing.[228,239,240] These same melamine resins are applied to wool for substantially the same reasons, the particular objective being the attainment of shrink resistance.

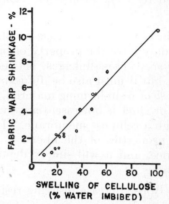

Graph 55.   Relation between reduced swelling of cellulose and stabilization of fabrics against shrinkage.   (*From Gagliardi and Nuessle,*[237] "*Modification of Fiber and Fabric Properties by Wrinkleproofing and Stabilizing Agents.*")

Sherman and Sherman,[5] for example, state that the methylol melamines, which are used advantageously on cotton and rayons, also may be used to stabilize woolens and worsteds, reduce felting, and make

> "it possible to wash these resin-modified fabrics without excessive shrinkage. . . . The rayons so modified take on much of the resilience of wool, the wools so modified take on much of the washability and shrinkage resistance of cotton."

These statements may over-simplify the problems of stabilizing both cotton and wool, but the general idea is valid.

The mechanism whereby crease resisting resins also cause general dimensional stability and shrink resistance control is related to the extent of fiber dimensional changes when exposed to high humidity or water. Gagliardi and Nuessle[237] show a plot of warp shrinkage vs. the swelling of cellulose (Graph 55).

Representative fiber swelling and fabric shrinkage data taken from Gagliardi and Nuessle's paper follow:

TABLE 109. REDUCTION IN SWELLING OF CELLULOSE FILMS AND FABRIC SHRINKAGE
RESISTANCE

(From Gagliardi and Nuessle[237] "Modification of Fiber and Fabric Properties by
Wrinkleproofing and Stabilizing Agents")

	% Swelling	% Warp Shrinkage
control	100	10.0
3% formaldehyde	19	2.2
3% glyoxal	26	2.2
5% urea-formaldehyde	51	6.7
20% urea-formaldehyde	26	2.1
5% melamine-formaldehyde	49	5.5
20% melamine-formaldehyde	22	2.1
15% ketone-formaldehyde	48	4.3

The subject of shrinkage and felting will be discussed in detail in
Chapter 18.

(57) Geometric Factors Which Influence Wrinkle Resistance

The following lengthy quotations are taken, for the most part, from
the article by Buck and McCord:[228]

"A survey of the literature fails to reveal many extensive
studies on the influence of construction on fabric crease-resistance. From the little that has been published, however, and
from advice of technologists in the industry, it is possible to
set down some general statements on this subject. Apparently
this is a subject which is now occupying the attention of a number of textile scientists, and some of what is said here may be
controversial in the light of studies now underway.

The physical dimensions of fiber undoubtedly affect the
crease-resistance of fabrics made from them, but it is not easy
to distinguish the influence of dimensional factors from the
more pronounced characteristics resulting from the physical-
chemical make-up of the fiber."

Effect of Staple Length

"It is recognized that when fibers are too short, fiber-to-
fiber cohesion in yarns is low, and folding may displace fibers
in the yarn so that their failure to return to their original
positions produces permanent deformations. On the other
hand, continuous filaments and exceptionally long staples
appear to have little advantage over medium-length fibers.
Continuous filaments do have the advantage of permitting
relatively low-twist yarns in which strain due to twist is at a
minimum. When strain in the fiber is as low as possible
before folding stress occurs, there is a better chance that the
elastic limit of the fiber will not be exceeded."[228]

Platt,[171] in a research being conducted for the United States Army Quartermaster, reports on a series of cellulose acetate pedigreed fabrics, already referred to above. At comparable yarn twists, and comparable weaves and textures (threads per inch), 1½ inch staple acetate and continuous filament acetate fabrics have crease recovery angles which are substantially alike. This holds for cellulose acetate, but it is not to be construed that such a statement means that for all other fibers, 1½ inch staple and continuous filament fabrics will have the same crease-recovery angle.

Effect of Fiber Diameter and Fiber Shape

"Fiber diameter influences crease-resistance, the fibers with the largest cross section having the greatest bending and

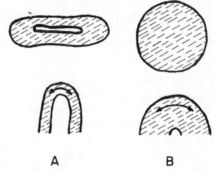

A   **B**

Figure 15. Effect of fiber cross-sectional shape on crease recovery. A is more easily bent than B, but greater strains are probably developed in B. (*From Buck and McCord,*[228] *"Crease Resistance and Cotton."*)

torsional rigidity with which to resist deformation. Since most fabric strains from folding are relatively low, resistance to deformation probably contributes to freedom from wrinkles in fabrics. The actual shape of the fiber cross section is an uncertain factor, although from a mechanical viewpoint it is probable that a fiber with a circular cross section will resist wrinkle formation better than one with a flat, more ribbon-like shape. Once a sharp crease is formed, however, strain in a fiber with a circular cross section would be greater than that in a flat fiber, and the former would therefore recover less easily[228] (Figure 15)."

The Effect of Yarn Construction and Yarn Twist

"The construction of the yarn, as well as of the fabric, should be such that fiber strains are at a minimum. Twist that is too high will place the fibers in a position of strain, causing them to reach their elastic limit quickly upon additional stresses. Where twist is too low, the resultant low fiber cohesion increases the possibility of actual displacement of the fibers in the yarn at or near the point of folding so that a permanent deformation results from the failure of these fibers to return to their normal position in the yarn[228] (Figure 16)."

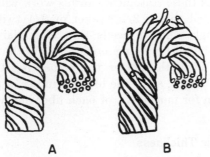

A   **B**

Figure 16.   Effect of twist on crease recovery.   Fiber strain, as in A, contributes much more to creasing than fiber displacement shown in B.   (*From Buck and McCord,*[228] *"Crease Resistance and Cotton."*)

Platt[171] reports that for cellulose acetate yarns at comparable weaves and textures, twists above six turns per inch, on 300 denier filament yarns, have a negligible effect on crease-recovery angle.

The Effect of Yarn Diameter

"The coarseness of the yarn also affects a fabric's ability to resist creasing. Coarse yarns cannot be creased as sharply as fine yarns, and therefore the strain on the fibers will be less. Moreover, there will be more fibers in a given cross section of a coarse yarn than of a fine yarn, and therefore a better distribution of stress. Still another factor in favor of the coarse yarns is the lower twist generally used in the heavier constructions."[228]

It might be well, at this point, to review the diagram given in Figure 14, page 265, and the statements of Gagliardi and Grunfest[18] which show that a multifilament yarn has a better opportunity for adjusting in a bend than a monofilament yarn of equivalent diameter because the strains are relieved by fiber slippage.

The Effect of Weave

"The important factors in constructing fabrics for maximum crease-resistance are much the same as those for yarns. Wherever possible, the fibers should be as relaxed and free from strain as possible. Plain one-and-one weaves, especially those with high count, place the fiber under a maximum strain and limit the flexibility of the fabric. It is recognized that fabric flexibility increases as weave pattern becomes more complicated, and generally sateens, broken twills, and other similar weaves, wrinkle and crease less than plain-woven fabrics."[228]

Platt[171] confirms these statements in his work with cellulose acetate, wherein he has found that a 2/2 basket or 3/1 twill weave exhibits a crease recovery angle which exceeds that of a plain weave. He also states that everything else being constant, the lower the number of picks or ends per inch, the better the crease resistance. This would appear logically to follow, since the lesser number of picks and ends, the greater the freedom for movement of each fiber and yarn without excessive strain.

The Effect of Fabric Thickness

"The thickness of a fabric is, in most cases, determined by the coarseness of its yarns, and thicker fabrics will be more resistant to creasing than thin fabrics for the reasons stated above. The differences between woolen and worsted fabrics exemplify the influence of thickness, although the higher twists in the worsted yarns also contribute to the greater creasability of worsteds. Woolen fabrics are harder to crease than worsteds, and a woolen suit will not retain the neatly pressed appearance of a worsted suit. On the other hand, wrinkles either do not form in the woolen material or fall out quickly when the suit is placed on a hanger."[228]

The general state of aggregation of the fiber in a woolen fabric in contrast to a worsted reflects, it is felt, the fact that creases and wrinkles in a woolen fabric are less obvious visually than in a worsted fabric. This is because woolen surfaces are rough, heterogeneous, and sufficiently broken so that minor defects and imperfections are not easily visible. Of course in some woolen fabrics the defects are so thoroughly and uniformly dispersed that they no longer can be considered defects. A worsted is a slick, smooth and uniform fabric; every interruption, distortion or slight modification of the surface appears as a defect. This problem will be further discussed below, when we talk about the optical effect and its relation to crease resistance.

The Effect of Fiber Position in the Yarn and in the Fabric

"The orientation of the yarns and fibers in the fabric affects the fabric's crease-resisting properties. It will be noted that velvets, plushes, corduroys, and other similar fabrics in which some fibers are perpendicular to the fabric's surface have good resistance to crease formation. Even napping and brushing results in improved crease-resistance. It may be that the improved crease-resistance of these fabrics is partly due to increased thickness, but the improvement is also due in part to the placement of the fibers in a position in which they are better able to resist distortion."[228]

Probably an additional reason why pile fabrics and plushes and corduroys show such good crease-resistance is the optical effect. It has been the experience in another research conducted at the Fabric Research Laboratories that the greater the extent of three-dimensionality of a fabric, the less the tendency toward exhibiting wrinkles. A seersucker fabric is a good example. Whether this is because the wrinkles are truly less apt to form or whether it is a visual and optical condition of their being less visible can be debated. Probably both contribute their share. Buck and McCord[228] state that "knit constructions," for example,

"are notable for their crease-resisting properties. The knit constructions are generally much looser than woven constructions, with less fiber strain and greater freedom of movement for the yarns. Warp knit fabrics, such as those of the tricot type, are significantly superior to woven fabrics of equivalent weight. One reason is that, for a given weight, knit fabrics are usually thicker than woven fabrics. Another reason is that the more complicated configuration of the yarn in knit fabrics probably means that in a crease a smaller proportion of the yarns are subject to the same type of strain. Other yarns which are unstrained or strained in a different manner, or to a different degree, have a better opportunity to bring about recovery to the fabric.

The relatively high tensile elasticity of knit fabrics would itself suggest that the crease-resisting properties of knit goods should be better than those of woven fabrics."

Here, the implication is that the three dimensionality of the knitted structure lends itself to a less obvious condition of a creased and wrinkled appearance.

Buck and McCord[228] further comment on the optical effect as follows:

"Optical effects deserve consideration in any study of the creasing or wrinkling of fabrics. The visibility of wrinkles is, after all, largely due to differences in the character of the light reflected from the sections of fabric adjoining the wrinkle, and therefore the luster characteristics of the textile are involved. Bright satins show wrinkles more readily than fabrics with a matt surface, since the amount of light reflected from satins reveals large differences with changes in the angle that the fabric makes with the eye. The crease-resistance of velvets, plushes, and similar constructions may be partly an apparent effect, which is the result of the softer creasing angle caused by the raised fibers on the surface of the fabric."

In another article, Buck and McCord[245] list the reflectance values of some fibers.

TABLE 110.   RELATIVE REFLECTANCE VALUES OF FIBERS
(From Buck and McCord[245] "Luster and Cotton")

	Reflectance Value
mirror	100
acetate rayon	80
viscose rayon	70
silk	40
cotton	4
magnesia	0

The Effect of Fiber Blending.   With the blending of different fibers continuously becoming more popular, it is well to consider the effect of blending on crease resistance. Literature on the subject is sparse. Attention is called to Table 105 which presents some data on wool-"Dacron", and viscose-"Dacron" blends.

Powers,[246] commenting on the utilization of chemical crease resisting treatments for rayon states:

"A great many blends have been produced in an effort to obtain fabrics with adequate wrinkle or muss resistance. It is surprising how little wool (in low concentrations) improves the resilience of rayon, and how much rayon hurts the resilience of wool. Certainly it is recognised both in this country and particularly in England and on the Continent that resin finishing is the only satisfactory method of imparting true resilience to rayons and more recently to cottons."

Whewell[231] also gives figures on the reduction of crease recovery angle which develops when wool is diluted with rayon (Table 111).

"Incorporation of up to 50 per cent of either 'Fibro' or 'Rayolanda' does not seriously alter the crease resistance, but when more than 50 per cent is present the dominating influence of the rayon which has a low resistance to creasing becomes apparent. The standard urea-formaldehyde process for improving the crease resistance of fabrics is satisfactory for application to cloth containing high percentages of cellulosic rayons and greatly improves the character of the material. Not only does it have improved crease resistance, but it feels fuller and more substantial."

TABLE 111. WOOL-RAYON RATIO VS. CREASE RECOVERY

(From Whewell[231] "The Finishing of Fabrics Containing Wool and Other Fibres")

fabric number	A	B	C	D	E	F	G	H	I	J	K
per cent wool	100	62.5	50	25	12.5	...	...	62.5	50	25	12.5
recovery from folding*	2.9	2.9	2.4	2.2	1.6	1.5	1.5	2.9	2.7	2.5	2.0

* Maximum value possible: 4.0.

In a study[248] of a controlled series of navy melton fabrics composed of blends of wool and other fibers, crease recovery angles were found to be the following:

TABLE 112. EFFECT OF FIBER BLENDS ON CREASE RECOVERY ANGLE

(From Fabric Research Laboratories, Inc.[248] "Development of Navy Meltons From Wool Blends"; Report to The United States Naval Clothing Depot)

(All fabrics are from a controlled series of meltons)

Fabric Number	% Wool	% Viscose	% Cotton	% Nylon	Crease Recovery Angle W	F	Thickness (inches)	Weight (oz/yd²)
0 melton (control)	100	0	0	0	143	146	.0373	10.6
1 melton	63	22	0	15	133	132	.0326	10.2
2 melton	72	28	0	0	141	138	.0285	8.9
3 melton	73	0	27	0	132	133	.0271	8.7
4 melton	74	0	0	26	137	139	.0283	8.8
2A covert	72	28	0	0	132	139	.0320	9.8
2B venetian	72	28	0	0	142	135	.0341	10.4

Among the meltons, the all-wool control has the highest recovery angle. However, it is the thickest and heaviest fabric, and these, according to Buck and McCord, would tend to cause higher recovery angles. The wool-viscose venetian weave, not too different from the melton since both are made from the same yarns and finished in substantially the same way, approaches the all-wool control in weight, thickness and recovery angles. It becomes obvious that no definite conclusions concerning the effect of blending on crease resistance can be made from these data.

(58) Dimensional Stability and Shape Retention

Concomitant with the problems of crease resistance exist the problems of shape retention and the dimensional stability of apparel textiles. The consumer usually is not interested in "crease" or "wrinkle" resistance in the strict sense, but is concerned with whether the garment he buys will retain its new look after use, or will become distorted, shrunk, mussed, etc. Wrinkle resistance is probably only one aspect of this broader problem.

The topic of shrink resistance in relation to wet laundering and dry cleaning is discussed in Chapter 18. Here we shall discuss dimensional stability in terms of normal useage of garments, with particular emphasis on the effect of changing relative humidities.

Gould,[249] and von Bergen and Clutz[250] list two types of cloth shrinkage: (1) relaxation shrinkage and (2) felting shrinkage (the latter being reserved for the most part for wool fabrics). Gould[249] states that

"relaxation shrinkage is the dimensional change which takes place when a fabric is thoroughly wet out after fabrication. This type of shrinkage results from release of strains set up in the fiber during manufacturing operations. Relaxation shrinkage is common to most fibers. The well-known "Sanforizing process" and the so-called "London shrinking" or "sponging" treatments have been devised to minimize this in cotton and wool textiles respectively. Because of the great elasticity of wool, it is particularly important to minimize relaxation shrinkage in knitted wool goods by avoiding overboarding. The reason is that no amount of wool shrinkage control can guarantee the dimensional integrity of garments boarded rather than knitted to size."

Felting shrinkage is the continued reduction in fabric area and the continued increase in fabric density due to continued application of heat, moisture, and mechanical action or motion occasioned usually by water washing.

von Bergen and Clutz[250] list an additional distorting influence—particularly for wool fabrics—produced by ambient changes in relative humidity. They state that this effect

" . . . has been found to play an important part in the appearance of lightweight men's suitings such as the tropical worsteds. This effect was observed especially in suits worn in sections of the country where high humidities prevail—for instance, Florida."

This humidity effect with and without accompanying application of stresses or strains is of the highest significance in relation to dimensional stability.

"The study of the correlation of the swelling of wool fibers with the motion of wool fabrics with changes in humidity has

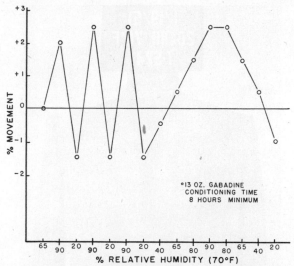

Graph 56.   Movement of a gabardine fabric with relative humidity.   (*From Von Bergen and Clutz,*[250] *"Dimensional Stability of Woolen and Worsted Fabrics."*)

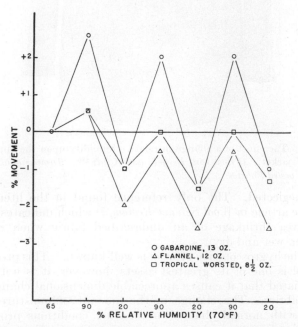

Graph 57.   Movement of gabardine, flannel, and tropical worsted fabrics with relative humidity.   (*From Von Bergen and Clutz,*[250] *"Dimensional Stability of Woolen and Worsted Fabrics."*)

Figure 17.   The effect of a change in relative humidity upon the appearance of a wool worsted jacket.   (*From von Bergen and Clutz*,[250] "*Dimensional Stability of Woolen and Worsted Fabrics.*")

been neglected.   The only reference found in the literature was the article in *Wool Science Review*,[251] which indicates a per cent area shrinkage of an undescribed fabric when cycled between wet and dry.

"The hygroscopicity of wool is well-known.   This property of wool is one of its greatest assets; however, it is not fully appreciated that it causes appreciable dimensional changes in wool fabrics.   The change in the amount of moisture in a fabric with normal changes in weather conditions produces very significant effects in garments.   These effects reflect themselves in two ways—change in the size of the tailored garments, and changes in their general appearance.

Figure 17.   (*Continued*)

"The moisture content of a fabric corresponds to equilibrium at a certain relative humidity.   By studying the correlation of the motion with changes of relative humidity, a measure of the fabric's sensitivity to changes in atmospheric conditions is obtained.   (The dimensional change of the fabric with changes in relative humidity is termed R.H. motion hereafter.)

"In measuring the dimensional changes in fabrics with changes in relative humidity, the fabric is conditioned to a standard atmosphere at 65% R.H. and 70°F.   It is then marked in three locations, and brought into equilibrium with 90% R.H.

"After the fabrics are conditioned . . . the dimensional change is measured using steel trammels on a beam which has been directly calibrated in percentage change. The fabric is then brought into equilibrium with 20% R.H., which for practical purposes requires not less than 8 hours. It is measured and again brought to equilibrium with 90% R.H. and remeasured. This completes one cycle; three cycles are run on each sample."[250]

The effect of R.H. cycling is given in Graphs 56 and 57 for a gabardine, flannel, and tropical worsted. The authors conclude that

"in general, gabardines move more than other fabrics. This can be attributed primarily to the weave structure and the predominance (in weight) of warp yarn."

The photographs shown in Figure 17 are from von Bergen and Clutz.[250] The picture on p. 294 shows a freshly pressed 100 per cent wool worsted jacket at equilibrium in a 20 per cent R.H. atmosphere. The picture on p. 295 shows the same jacket, untouched in any manner, but in an atmosphere of 90 per cent R.H. The stress relaxation accompanying the moisture absorption by hydrophillic wool has caused the jacket to change from a smooth, "well pressed" and "fresh appearing" garment to one which is wrinkled, puckered and "mussy looking."

To explain the mechanics of dimensional stability or instability, reference again is made to pages 101–110, 284–285, and the comments of Collins[377] on shrinkage starting on page 388. It is reiterated that the degree of hygroscopicity of the various fibers governs the extent to which they are humidity sensitive to dimensional change. Wool, cotton, and rayon will swell the most; the low or zero regain fibers will swell the least. The advantage of the hydrophobic fibers in maintaining an originally satisfactory appearance lies in the fact that they have minimum or zero amounts of radial and longitudinal swelling with concomitant minimum yarn and fabric distortion. If the jacket on the left in Figure 17 were composed of hydrophobic fibers, the increased relative humidity would have had no effect, and the two photographs would have been identical.

The application of any finishing treatments on wool, rayon, or cotton, e.g., melamine formaldehyde, will tend to slow down the rate of moisture absorption or desorption, and thereby reduce the tendency to rapid change in fabric dimension. The final equilibrium of the treated may be the same as the untreated, however.

The following discussion, taken from an article by King,[252] discusses the inhibition of swelling due to the application of melamine formaldehyde.

"Mr. R. B. Whitehead: Is the prevention of shrinkage in a woolen fabric by the application of a hydrophobic melamine resin due to a reduction in the swelling propensities of the wool fiber?

"Mr. King: Insofar as swelling assists the felting of wool, any method which inhibits the swelling should reduce fabric shrinkage.

"Mr. G. Landells: There is no doubt that fiber swelling is one of the fundamental causes of dimensional change in cellulose fabrics, and that certain resin treatments produce various degrees of stability depending on their effectiveness in reducing swelling. Fiber swelling is instrumental in bringing about crimp changes in the yarns, and these appear to be the main factor in determining the amount of shrinkage. A number of other factors also play a part; the rigidity of the treated yarns is one which may be important in connection with resin treatment, and any factor which is likely to prevent crimp changes is of interest for stabilization purposes."

Chapter 17

ABRASION AND WEAR RESISTANCE

(59) Nomenclature and Methods for Measuring Abrasion Resistance

"Abrasion resistance" and the related topics of "wear" and "serviceability" are subjects which have been given considerable attention by textile technologists. For the most part empericism has been employed, with the expected result that little progress has been made in ascertaining true mechanisms.

Apparently agreement does exist as to definition of the terms "abrasion," "wear," and "serviceability," and it is well to start by defining them.

Serviceability: The 1937 Annual Conference of the British Textile Institute chose for its subject "The Serviceability of Fabrics for Clothing." A series of papers on the subject were presented by Whittaker,[267] Peirce,[268] Binns,[269] Harwood,[270] Bradley,[271] Cunliffe,[272] Petrie,[273] Lester,[274] Gibson,[275] Davis,[276] Lomax,[277] Mann,[278] Hall,[279] Williams,[280] and Pritchard.[281]

A fabric which serves the functions for which it is intended may be defined as being "serviceable." When it ceases to perform such functions, it is no longer serviceable. The word is a broad one and encompasses all those criteria of performance which permits a fabric to be accepted or rejected for use. Peirce[268] points out that

> "serviceability is not concerned only with the formation of holes in the fabrics. A collar that strangles its wearer is no longer serviceable, however intact; baggy trousers are not fashionable, nor are the seats thereof intended to warn oncoming traffic."

He[268] also cites the following causes of loss of serviceability:

> "Wearing into holes, and threadbareness of shirts, sheets, hose, rubbered raincoats, upholstery, overalls for uses from clerking to sand-blasting.
> "Tearing at seams of overalls, etc., fraying of limbrics and sateens.
> "Creasing and resultant abrasion.

298

"Loss of pile of velvets and of nap of flannelettes.
"Roughening and loss of lustre in sateen linings.
"Shininess of gabardines.

"Loss of shape: shrinkage of shirts and overalls, sagging of rayon vests, shrinkage of hangings and blind-tapes, stretching of corsets and hose, change of shape of wagon-covers and tent canvass, loss of tautness of doped aircraft fabric, stretching of spindle bands, shrinkage and bursting of shoe-linings. Puckering of seams. Curling of book covers. . . . "

Wear is a more confining word, and describes the ability of a fabric to withstand the effects of abrasion (defined below) concomitant with stressing, straining, laundering, dry cleaning, pressing, creasing, etc.

Abrasion: Ball[282] defines "abrasion," in contrast to "wear," as follows:

"Abrasion, derived from the verb 'to abrade' very distinctly suggests a 'rubbing off.' The word 'abrasion' as an adjective might properly be applied therefore to those machines or tests in which rubbing is the only, or at least the major characteristic.

"The term 'wear' is believed to be more closely associated with the thought of the conditions surrounding every-day use and service, and implies the combined effect of several factors of which abrasion or rubbing is only one. A household or garment fabric may wear out from a variety of causes. Thus, a towel is discarded because it has broken down under the combined influences of abrasion, the application of tensile forces in a dry and wet state, and washing, drying, and ironing. The lining of a coat is worn out as a result of abrasion, perspiration, dry or wet cleaning, and pressing. It is suggested therefore, that 'wear' be considered as a broader scope than 'abrasion' and be used to apply wherever other important destructive actions, with or without abrasion, are existent or are intentionally introduced by the machine or test method."

Zook,[283] in an excellent review entitled "Historical Background of Abrasion Testing" sums up the problem of relating abrasion and wear:

"The fundamental question: 'To what extent should the laboratory wear test approximate service during wear?' is still not answered and proponents of two philosophies are noted in the research literature of this field, as hereinafter reviewed.

"In the year 1934, the late H. DeWitt Smith . . . expressed the philosophy held by many in the textile field by stating the following at a U.S. Institute of Textile Research Conference:[284]

"'I should like to see fabrics classified as to use, the most important classes in which wearability is a factor grouped, the cause of wear determined, machines designed to duplicate service results, and properties which affect wearability determined.'

"The duplication of service wear, however, has been complicated by the fact that the essential factors in service life are not known to an exact degree. Skinkle[285] has explained that service life depends on such personal factors as size, weight and occupation of the wearer of the fabric, on the climate around him and on the extent to which it may make him perspire, on the fit of the garment, and on the laundry methods used, together with the infinite variety of mechanical details involved in the motion of a fabric while being worn—all at low standard rates—mostly slower than laboratory abrasion tests.

"Recognition of these difficulties induced Pierce[263] to denounce imitative tests *as a snare and a delusion* and to add:

"'Tests should be devised to measure characteristics defined by behaviour under the simplest conditions. Their validity depends not on imitative features in the testing procedure, but on intelligent interpretation, based on empirical correlation with service experience.'

"Ball[282] has suggested that the wear-testing machines should be planned to reproduce those influences which account for the major part of the destructive effort; and Lomax[277] further has suggested that it is not required that service life be forecast in some unit of time, but rather that the problem should be one of comparing one fabric with another. This reduces the requirements of the apparatus and the selected procedure need not, then, duplicate the actual conditions of use, but only rank fabrics in order of merit. Kaswell,[173] in his work on three combat-course fabrics in connection with the Quartermaster Depot, agrees with this latter philosophy when he makes the statement that a laboratory test need not duplicate an actual set of service conditions, if wear produced by the abrasion machine can be correlated with service wear in such a way as to predict the abrasion resistance of a fabric.

"Skinkle adds that wear may be caused by direct forces, impacts, and flexing or bending applied to the fabric, with consequent friction of fiber on fiber and yarn on yarn, as well as the factors in what have been above designated as abrasion. Stoll[286] goes even further and suggests that, numerically, the mechanical factors involved in normal wear can be assumed approximately as '30 per cent plane abrasion, 20 per cent edge and protection abrasion, 20 per cent tear, and 10 per cent other mechanical action.' He cites results obtained from salvage analyses on various types of field uniforms conducted by the Army Quartermaster as the primary basis for these conclusions, but cautions that the order of relative importance of these factors is directly related to certain inherent fiber properties.

"Abrasion has been cited by Mann[278] and by Tait[292] as the most important single factor in wear. For this reason, many textile technologists have simplified the problem by studying the resistance of fabrics to abrasion rather than to wear in general.

"The two philosophies—the one of duplicating actual conditions of wear and the other of selecting the most important causes of wear and correlating them with service tests—have led to the development of more than fifty abrasion and wear-testing machines. These are listed, described, and explained by Dawson;[287] the principles of each have depended upon the philosophy of the person or persons developing the equipment. To Dawson's list should be added the instrument described by Dean[288] of the Shirley Institute, the Improved Single Unit Schiefer Abrasion Testing Machine,[289] and the Stoll machine,[286] as well as the list of German wear-testing instruments published in January 1948 by Schiefer, Fourt and Kropf."[36]

Description of Certain Abrasion Testers. Zook[283] mentions that Tanenhaus and Winston[290] determined, via letter ballot, that the three abrasion machines most commonly used in the United States are the Taber, the U.S. Testing Company, and the Wyzenbeek Abrasion testers. To these certainly must now be added the Schiefer and Stoll Abraders.

The following short descriptions are taken, for the most part, from "Tentative Methods of Test for Resistance to Abrasion of Textile Fabrics,[291] A.S.T.M. Designation D-51T, 1951."

"(A) Inflated Diaphragm Method (Stoll Abrader):
"This method is intended for use in determining the resistance to abrasion of woven and knitted textile fabrics when the specimen is inflated over a rubber diaphragm under controlled air pressure and rubbed either unidirectionally or multi-directionally against an abradant of given surface characteristics under controlled pressure conditions.

"(B) Flexing and Abrasion Method (Stoll Abrader):
"This method is intended for use in determining the resistance of woven fabrics to flexing and abrasion when the specimen is subjected to unidirectional reciprocal folding and rubbing over a given bar under known conditions of pressure and tension.

"(C) Oscillatory Cylinder Method (Wyzenbeek Abrader):

"The oscillatory cylinder method is used for determining the abrasion resistance of textile fabrics when the specimen is subjected to unidirectional rubbing action under known conditions of pressure, tension, and abrasive action. The abrasion resistance is evaluated in terms of an objective end point. . . . The apparatus (consists) of an oscillating cylinder section furnished with edge clamps to permit mounting a sheet of abrasive material over its curved surface. Three or four specimen-holding arms (are) provided to permit testing of several specimens simultaneously. Each arm (consists) of a set of controlled tension clamps and a controlled pressure pad . . . shaped to (fit) the curve of the cylinder surface."

The cylinder oscillates, thereby causing the specimen held against it to be abraded unidirectionally.

"(D) Rotary Platform, Double-Head Method (Taber Abrader):[291]

"The Taber instrument[173] consists of a 4-inch diameter turntable which rotates at a constant rate in a horizontal plane. The fabric is mounted on this turntable. Above the turntable is a frame containing two rubber-emery composition wheels mounted in such a manner that they are free to rotate in a vertical plane. At the start of the test, the frame and wheels are lowered so that they rest on the turntable. The weight of the frame can be varied, and in this manner the pressure on the sample may be controlled. Various wheels of different abrasive intensity may be used. The lines of abrasion are in the form of two arcs crisscrossing each other, resulting in a circular path covering an effective area of approximately 100 cm². The turntable is driven; the wheels are not. A counter records the cycles.

"(E) Uniform Abrasion Testing Machine Method (Schiefer Abrader):[291]

"The essential parts of the uniform abrasion testing machine are two contacting plane surfaces (one the abradant and the other the specimen supporting surface) which rotate in the same direction at very nearly the same angular speed on two parallel non-coaxial axes. The abradant is enough larger than the specimen supporting surface so that the entire abraded surface of the specimen is in contact with some portion of the abradant at all times. The result is that every point of the abraded area of the specimen is abraded equally in all directions with each rotation of the two surfaces. The slight difference in speed allows each part of the specimen to come into contact with a different portion of the abradant at each rotation."

(60) The Mechanics of Abrasion

Having described five laboratory abrasion instruments, consider now the criteria for evaluating abraded textiles. Ball comments:[282]

> "How may the effects of abrasion be measured? We are here dealing with the problem of finding a means of evaluating the work done upon a textile by a frictional force. Its measurement should yield a quantity proportional to the effect of the frictional force; in other words, the selected measure should be one that is reasonably sensitive and proportional to the work done upon the sample.
>
> "Various measures have been suggested of which the important ones are the changes produced in the (1) tensile strength, (2) thickness, (3) weight, (4) surface luster, (5) air permeability, (6) color, (7) character of abraded materials, and (8) appearance of surface."

Zook[283] adds "the appearance of a hole" and the "appearance of broken threads" to the above list.

In selecting a criterion, the problem of serviceability must not be overlooked. For a satin dress, surface luster might be the selected measure; for a military combat uniform, strength might be a factor.

Ball[282] comments on his suggested list:

> "The first six represent properties which it is possible to measure physically, and this is a feature considered to be an advantage by those who prefer to have numerical values to back up their opinions of a fabric. The last two would be determined with the aid of a microscope, and possibly by comparison with established standards, but are of such a character that the personal equation enters to some degree in the formation of an opinion. Which measure should be selected for a particular investigation would primarily be governed by the nature of the service conditions of the cloth being tested. . . .
>
> "The changes in certain of the properties mentioned above are not always in the same direction nor proportional to the work expended. Some fabrics, for example, first increase in thickness with increasing rubs, and then begin to decrease as the abrasion is continued. This is due to the cutting and breakage of the fibers, and the teasing of them out of the yarn, resulting in a rough, fuzzy surface of greater thickness than the original. . . . Further abrasion finally reaches a point when these fibers become detached from the surface faster

than new fibers are raised up and the thickness begins to decrease. Other cloths have such structures or yarns that they load with particles of the abradant and their own detritus. The result is an increase in weight in the early stages of a test, followed later by the anticipated decrease if the abrasive action is continued far enough. The permeability of a fabric to air depends upon the extent to which the test has progressed and the resultant degree of closure of the interstices with the roughening of the surface and with loading. While the fabric at first exhibits a decrease in permeability followed by an increase, another fabric may show a continuous increase from the start. Whereas it is observed that tensile strength almost always decreases with the number of abrasive strokes, it is not always in a manner proportional thereto."

By his remarks, Ball implies that the rate of change of property with the number of abrasion strokes is a better method for evaluating abrasion resistance than to attempt to abrade to a specific end point, e.g., the formation of a hole or the breaking of one or more yarns. Hamburger[9] states

"The selection of an end-point is undesirable in that it precludes a study of the rate at which the sample is proceeding to destruction, coupled with the fact that it is usually impossible to define and reproduce the end-point quantitatively."

Concerning strength loss as a measure of abrasive action, Hamburger[9] states,

"While strength is not all that could be desired as a criterion for evaluation of damage, it appears to offer the least objectionable features. . . . It should be pointed out, however, that it is used strictly as a measure of the extent of damage from abrasion, and should not be taken to reflect values of durability from the standpoint of strength per se."

Zook[283] cites the work of Schiefer, Crean, and Krasny,[289]

"who developed a capacitance method for measuring abrasion. . . . The method is based upon the change occurring in the electrical capacitance of the abraded samples as a result of abrasive action. A percentage value for the degree of destruction is derived from a mathematical treatment of the difference in capacitance of the original specimen and the capacitance after a specified number of abrasion cycles, with corrections made for deviations resulting from the influence of air. These percentage values are projected onto a diagram of the test specimen—resulting in the formation of an iso-ruin map of the test area."

Suggested Mechanisms for Explaining the Inherent Abrasion Resistance of Textile Fibers. While the textile literature is replete with articles on empirical evaluations of abrasion resistance, little has been reported toward explaining the inherent physical properties of fibers which contribute to good or poor abrasion resistance.

The papers of Hamburger,[9] and more recently, Backer[294] are the only references found which attempt to explain the relationship between classical physical properties (more particularly the stress-strain diagram of fibers) and abrasion resistance. Hamburger and Lee[295] remark

"A review of the various contributions to the literature during the past twenty years indicates, in almost every instance, that the investigations emphasize an evaluation of the *resultant destruction* of the specimen rather than a determination of the basic cause or causes of failure."

Vogt,[296] in 1928, suggested a possible relationship between the energy absorption and abrasion resistance of rubber. His data were inconclusive, however.

Hamburger[9] proposes the same idea but recognizes the importance of measuring energy absorption after secondary creep deflections are removed. Reference is again made to his remarks on page 35 wherein he states

. . . "to resist destruction, the specimen must be capable of absorbing energy imparted to it upon stress application, and of releasing this energy upon removal of the stress without the occurrence of failure."

To this he adds

"Abrasion[9] is definitely a repeated stress application, usually caused by forces of relatively low orders of magnitude which occur many times during the life expectancy of the material. . . . Energy is work done, and may be defined as a function of the average force and the distance through which the force acts. Hence, the primary creep and secondary creep . . . as well as the instantaneous elastic deflection, all contribute to the energy absorption capacity of a material.

"It has been shown[15] that the secondary creep may be removed by means of a relatively few loading and unloading cycles. For a material to resist abrasion, it must withstand many cycles. While secondary creep is an energy-absorbing component of the total deflection, its contribution under

repeated loadings is negligible since it is removed in the course
of the first few cycles.   Both the immediate elastic deflection
and the primary creep deflection are recoverable upon load
removal.   They contribute both to the absorption and the
return of energy necessary for proper performance under
repeated stress, the contribution of the creep deflection being
dependent upon the rate of primary creep and the time intervals between stress cycles."

He thus proposes that abrasion resistance should be correlative with
the energy absorption of mechanically conditioned—secondary creep
free fibers; the greater the area (energy) under the mechanically conditioned stress-strain diagram, the higher the abrasion resistance.   He lists
five requirements for high abrasion resistance:

> "(1) Low modulus of elasticity.
> "(2) Large immediate elastic deflection.
> "(3) High ratio of primary to secondary creep.
> "(4) High magnitude of primary creep.
> "(5) High rate of primary creep."

The following paragraphs on the correlation between energy and
abrasion resistance are taken from his article:[9]

"In order to investigate the relationship between the
factors summarized above and the resistance to abrasion,
some satisfactory means of laboratory abrasion and a proper
evaluation of the effects upon textiles must be established.
The Taber Abraser was selected as the laboratory means of
creating destruction by abrasive action.   This selection was
made because of the simple operation of the instrument—the
fact that it abrades multidirectionally to the specimen as a
whole, but essentially unidirectionally to any given point on
the specimen; and because the abradant, while not absolutely
constant, may be reasonably controlled, and, essentially,
nothing other than plane abrasion takes place upon the
specimen.

"In order to eliminate the effect of form on the samples
investigated in this work, filamentous yarns, with a minimum
of twist, were employed.   A special technique for subjecting
the specimens to the action of the Taber machine was developed, whereby the yarns were wound parallel on panels and
abraded serigraph fashion.

"The predominant method for the determination of extent
of damage as revealed in the literature is to select an end point
based either upon a given number of machine cycles . . . or
the formation of a hole . . . and evaluate the result of abra-

sion at such an end point. The selection of an end point is undesirable in that it precludes a study of the rate at which the sample is proceeding to destruction, coupled with the fact that it is usually impossible to define and reproduce the end point quantitatively.

"Per cent loss in unabraded ultimate strength versus abrasion cycles has been selected to depict both the 'durability,' which connotes time to reach a given degree of destruction, expressed in abrasion cycles, and 'rate of destruction,' which connotes the path of the per cent-loss-versus-cycles curve. The use of per cent-loss-in-strength as an ordinate permits comparison of materials of unlike strengths. The plot of per cent-loss-in-strength versus cycles may be interpreted as a rate-of-destruction curve or, conversely, as depicting the rate and extent of resistance to destruction. If, then, a mean ordinate is calculated and the slope to this mean is determined . . . the ratio of per cent loss in strength to cycles will represent a rate of mean failure. Inasmuch as the mean ordinate is obtained by dividing area by abscissa, which represents a selected number of cycles to destruction, the durability as well as the rate of destruction is reflected by the slope to the mean. Since a large number of abrasion cycles for a given extent of failure is desirable, the ratio of cycles to per cent-loss-in-strength will be used and termed "durability coefficient"; the higher the value, the greater the resistance to destruction of the material.

"It has been stated . . . that the effect of frictional forces on a textile material should be proportional to the work done on the test specimen. Conversely, the resistance of the material to destruction should be proportional to the energy absorption capacity of the material.

"If, then, the resistance of a material to destruction is proportional to the energy absorption capacity of that material, it would be expected that a proportionality exists between energy coefficients and durability coefficients of various materials.

"Acetate, viscose, and nylon yarns of specifications indicated below were abraded . . . on the Taber Abraser to complete destruction (100 per cent loss in strength) and rate of destruction curves were plotted: (Graph 58)

Acetate (bright)	150 den., 40 fil., 3 t.p.i.
Viscose (bright)	150 den., 40 fil., 3 t.p.i.
Nylon (dull) (unshrunk)	60 den., 20 fil., 1 t.p.i.
Nylon (dull) (shrunk in steam at 250°F for 30 minutes)	60 den., 20 fil., 1 t.p.i.

"Mechanically conditioned load-elongation curves were plotted for each of the four yarns.

"Graph 59 depicts the load-elongation characteristics of the four yarns before mechanical conditioning, adjusted to a unit strength basis by plotting per cent of ultimate breaking load in each case versus per cent elongation.

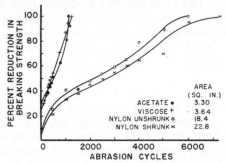

Graph 58.   Comparison of abrasion rate curves.   (*From Hamburger,*[9] "*Mechanics of Abrasion of Textile Materials.*")

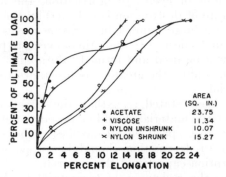

Graph 59.   Per cent ultimate load vs. per cent elongation curves.   (Materials not mechanically conditioned.)   (*From Hamburger,*[9] "*Mechanics of Abrasion of Textile Materials.*")

"Graph 60 is a plot of the loading and unloading characteristics in terms of per cent strength versus per cent elongation after mechanical conditioning at a load equal to 90 per cent of the ultimate breaking strengths, respectively, of the four yarns.   In this graph, as in Graph 59, the strength values have been adjusted to a unit basis to permit comparison of yarns of unlike strengths on an equal basis.

"It will be observed that the shapes of the rate of destruction (abrasion) curves are similar to those of the load-elongation curves, an interesting fact in light of the results of this investigation."

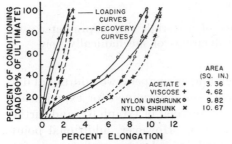

Graph 60. Load-elongation curves. (Materials at conditioned cycle, 90% of ultimate load.) (*From Hamburger,*[9] *"Mechanics of Abrasion of Textile Materials."*)

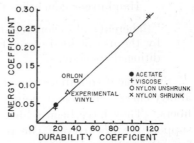

Graph 61. Correlation of energy coefficients and durability coefficients. (*From Hamburger,*[9] *"Mechanics of Abrasion of Textile Materials."*)

Table 113 compares Energy Coefficients E obtained from stress-strain diagrams after 90 per cent mechanical conditioning, with Durability Coefficients D obtained from loss in strength-abrasion cycle diagrams.

TABLE 113.   COMPARISON OF ENERGY COEFFICIENT "E" WITH DURABILITY COEFFICIENT "D" FOR VARIOUS FIBERS

(Data taken from Hamburger[9] "Mechanics of Abrasion of Textile Materials")

	Shrunk Nylon	Unshrunk Nylon	Acetate	Viscose
Energy Data from Load-Elongation Curves (After 90% Mechanical conditioning)				
% elongation	10.90	9.70	2.54	2.94
% ultimate strength (mean ordinate)	39.1	40.4	52.9	63.0
energy coefficient E $\left(\dfrac{\text{% elongation}}{\text{% ultimate strength}}\right)$	0.280	0.240	0.048	0.047
Durability Data from Abrasion Curves				
abrasion cycles	7300	6000	1150	1200
% loss in strength (mean ordinate)	62.5	61.5	57.5	60.5
durability coefficient D $\left(\dfrac{\text{cycles}}{\text{% strength loss}}\right)$	116.7	97.5	20.0	19.8

Hamburger[9] states

" . . . it is apparent that . . . a perfect rank correlation of energy coefficient E with durability coefficient D exists for the four yarns.   Graph 61 is a plot of energy coefficient vs. durability coefficient for the four yarns studied.   The points lie well along a straight line through the origin.   Thus it is evident that a linear relationship exists between energy coefficients and durability coefficients, which permits comparisons on a quantitative basis."

Hamburger concludes that

"(inherent) abrasion resistance of materials can be predicted by the use of load-elongation diagrams of mechanically conditioned specimens."

Subsequent to publication of Hamburger's paper, two additional durability-energy coefficient points have been determined for experimental fibers. They have been added to the original of Graph 61, and further support the linearity of the relationship. However, additional points for other fibers should be ascertained in order to confirm or refute Hamburger's hypothesis.

With further reference to Hamburger's work, the question as to the level at which mechanical conditioning should be conducted (i.e., per cent of ultimate load), possibly bears investigating. Ninety per cent of rupture load is more or less a logical level in that it is a severe criterion of performance and would thus point out the outstandingly good fibers. However, in the light of other work by Hamburger, Platt and Morgan[21] on the elastic behavior of fibers at low strains, the possibility exists that in the course of *normal wear* (if such a thing exists) stress values may be of a lower order of magnitude, and some of the fibers which show up poorly at high stress levels might show better at lower levels. In any case, the fact remains that for the four fibers tested, and with conditioning at 90 per cent of rupture load, Hamburger did get linear correlation with Taber abrasion resistance.

Backer[294] discusses the mechanism of abrasion in the sense of critically analysing the effect of an abrasive particle upon a fiber surface:

"Consider first the action which takes place when a protuberance of a foreign surface comes in contact with the surface of the fabric. The term protuberance is used loosely and implies both a microasperity in the case of a smooth surface or a grit in the case of a rough abrasive surface. The average normal force present between the rubbing surface and the fabric plane may range between 0 and 5 pounds per square inch (for apparel fabrics), while the tangential force depends only on the over-all shear resistance of the fabric surface and the areas of contact. It is customary to consider the relative motion between the two surfaces to occur at constant velocity, although this is not always the case in actual use.

"The single fiber touched by the projection of the foreign surface will react in different ways depending on the nature of the contact:

"(1) By reason of firm anchoring in the fabric, and hard backing of the other fibers in the yarn, the fiber will be subject to frictional wear such as occurs when smooth metal surfaces are rubbed together (with a condition of boundary lubrication between). Wear of this type will take place when the foreign body is quite smooth, say, for example, the surface of polished furniture.

"(2) Where surface projections of the abrading surface are small relative to the diameter of the fiber, the fiber will be subjected to the surface cutting process such as occurs in metal cutting or grinding. Such wear will occur when a very fine abrasive or emery surface is rubbed across a fabric.

"(3) Where the surface protuberances of the abradant are large compared to fiber diameter and the normal forces between the abradant and cloth planes are high, the fiber will be plucked much like a violin string by the finger of a musician. This plucking develops components of force along the fiber axis of higher magnitude than those imposed in the direction of the relative motion (as a result of the geometry of the force system). Release of these axial loads may take place by rupture of the stressed fiber or its slippage from the body of the yarn or its vertical displacement beneath the path of the abradant projection.

"Here are represented elements of (1) direct frictional wear, (2) surface cutting, and (3) fiber rupture or slippage. The nature of the abrading surface and the normal pressures of the rubbing determine which is the more severe under a given set of conditions. However, the mechanism of fabric abrasion is not as simple as has been pictured. Consider, for example, the fact that the forces developed in the plane of the material as a result of either friction or cutting themselves develop components along the fiber axis and thus contribute to axial tensile or bending rupture or to fiber slippage in the yarn structure. Fiber slippage, cracking in bending, or tensile rupture may take place suddenly on first contact of the fiber with protuberances of the abradant, or may follow repeated abrasive stress applications involving dynamic fatigue of individual fibers. It follows that pure friction and cutting may have an indirect effect on fabric wear which may exceed in magnitude the direct effect. The fact remains that the infinitesimal quantities involved in direct frictional wear have limited accumulation of experimental results regarding its mechanism although recently developed electron microscope and tracer techniques are helping to correct the deficiencies of past investigations."

Backer[294] then discusses the fundamental implications of the above three elements of abrasion. With respect to surface cutting, he states that it "involves formation of a complex stress pattern within the individual fibers"—tensile, torsional, and shear, and emphasizes the lack of information on the latter two. He cites the work of Clegg[297] who shows some excellent sketches of the effects of harsh abrasion and surface cutting of individual fibers.

Concerning forces along the fiber axis, Backer[294] states:

> "It has been shown that stresses along the fiber axis can develop from horizontal forces transverse to the fiber axis and arising from surface friction, shallow cutting or actually snagging. Since such stresses may cause fiber rupture or slippage in their first occurrence or after numerous applications, it is desirable to prevent their occurrence or at least reduce the magnitude. Assuming a given yarn and fabric, transmission of high stresses along the axes of the surface fibers may be reduced markedly by having the fiber yield readily until it can slip under the protuberance of the abradant. Not only must a fiber yield in this manner, but it must return quickly upon release of its load so as to be able to assist in carrying the horizontal load of the abradant surfaces."

Backer then cites Hamburger's[9] work which has already been described. It is apparent that he believes that Hamburger's correlation pertains mostly to forces along the fiber axis, and does not necessarily explain frictional wear and surface cutting.

Backer[294] discusses the relative hardness of the abradant and the fabric-to-be-abraded:

> (There appears to be an) "inherent assumption in severe textile wear that the abrading surface will possess a much higher order of hardness than (will) the fiber. . . . It therefore becomes desirable for the polymeric surface to "give" completely with each passage of an abradant particle to prevent the setting up of critical tensile or shear stresses at concentrated points. Behaviour of the surface upon approach of the second and subsequent abradant particles will depend of course upon the recovery of the material to its original position and on its continued ability to give. On the other hand, where normal service brings the textile in contact with material of an equivalent order of hardness, this property assumes greater significance. Here one observes the possibility of reversal of abrasion performance from field to laboratory depending upon the relative hardness of the rubbing surface."

(61) The Inherent Laboratory Abrasion Resistance Properties of Fibers

Some of the references cited below will demonstrate that the relative abrasion resistance position of the various textile fibers will depend in many cases upon the specific methods by which the abrasion was conducted and the technique of evaluation of results. It is emphasized that *at the moment* we are discussing abrasion resistance as measured by laboratory instruments in contrast to "wear," and that inherent properties, uncomplicated by fabric geometry effects, are being evaluated.

Hamburger and Lee[295] compare selected viscose and acetate yarns of substantially the same twist and denier, and lining fabrics of substantially identical construction made from these yarns. Table 114 compares the two yarns.

On an absolute strength-loss basis, viscose is far superior to acetate. On a per cent-loss basis, they are very nearly the same. Here a point of argument can be raised as to whether viscose rayon is or is not superior to acetate (presuming of course that these yarns are representative of their class). Hamburger and Lee use per cent loss rather than absolute loss since it permits comparison of materials of unlike strengths. Thus

TABLE 114. ABRASION RESISTANCE PROPERTIES OF A VISCOSE AND ACETATE YARN
(From Hamburger and Lee[295] "A Study of Lining Fabric Abrasion")

	Acetate	Viscose
Filament Properties		
number	40	40
diameter (microns)	24.5	24.7
strength (grams)	6.9	9.9
Yarn Properties		
denier	145	159
turns per inch	2.97 S	3.07 S
strength (grams)	181	306
tenacity (g.p.d.)	1.25	1.92

	Strength Loss Upon Abrasion			
Abrasion Cycles	Breaking Load* lbs	% Loss	Breaking Load* lbs	% Loss
0	60.1	0	108.8	0
10	52.8	12.1	91.1	16.3
25	48.1	20.0	85.5	21.4
50	44.3	26.3	80.8	25.7
100	39.0	35.1	75.4	30.7
150	37.8	37.1	73.2	32.7
200	36.6	39.1	68.7	36.9
250	36.2	39.8	66.1	39.2
300	35.3	41.3	61.8	43.2
350	34.1	43.3	59.3	45.5
400	32.1	46.6	56.0	48.5
450	31.8	47.1	54.2	50.2
500	28.5	52.6	50.9	53.2
750	23.5	60.9	32.6	70.0
1000	11.6	80.7	14.6	86.6
1100	4.7	92.2	7.2	93.4

* A panel of yarns was abraded and tested as a serigraph group.

it can be considered a "coefficient" of abrasion resistance. Their philosophy is based upon the point that before any abrasive action takes place, the two yarns, independent of their strength (which, as has been stated, is employed only as a yardstick), are of equivalent utility, i.e., one is as good as the other.   After abrasion to 1100 cycles, both have lost most of this utility.   The slopes of the per cent-loss curves depict the

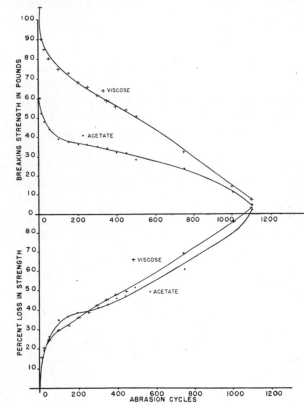

Graph 62. Abrasion resistance properties of viscose and acetate yarns.   Top: breaking strength vs. abrasion cycles; Bottom: per cent loss in strength vs. abrasion cycles.   (*From Hamburger and Lee,*[295] "*A Study of Lining Fabric Abrasion.*")

rate of change in utility and demonstrate that the acetate is better than the viscose in the sense that it shows a lesser change per abrasion cycle. They therefore conclude that "Celanese (acetate) manifests a greater resistance to abrasion than does viscose for the materials investigated."

Looking at the problem from another point of view wherein residual strength (or more properly residual energy) is a true attribute of a fabric and is therefore a criterion per se of abrasion, a different conclusion is warranted. On this latter basis, the viscose is always better than the acetate, and even if, upon abrasion, it loses strength at a rate equal to or greater than the acetate, it will always be stronger and more capable of withstanding stresses accompanying abrasion. The practical application of this difference may be seen by examining Table 115 and Graph 63 which give data on the corresponding fabrics.

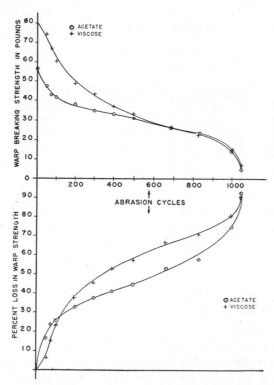

Graph 63. Abrasion resistance of a viscose and acetate lining fabric. Top: warp breaking strength vs. abrasion cycles; Bottom: per cent loss in breaking strength vs. abrasion cycles. (*From Hamburger and Lee,*[295] "*A Study of Lining Fabric Abrasion.*")

The higher viscose yarn strength is reflected in the higher viscose fabric strength but not in direct ratio, thus demonstrating the effects of geometry. In the initial stages, the acetate loses strength at a faster rate, but at approximately 275 cycles a reversal occurs and the viscose loses faster than the acetate; by the time 1050 cycles are reached, both have lost about 90 per cent of their original strengths. But again because the viscose fabric is stronger to start out with, it remains significantly stronger than the acetate for at least the first half of its abrasive

TABLE 115.   ABRASION-RESISTANCE PROPERTIES OF A VISCOSE AND ACETATE LINING FABRIC

(From Hamburger and Lee[295] "A Study of Lining Fabric Abrasion")

Fabric Properties	Acetate	Viscose
yarn count (per inch)	144 × 68	144 × 72
weight (oz/yd²)	4.19	4.29
construction (fabric)	2/1 twill	2/1 twill
construction (yarn)	singles × singles	singles × singles
twist (per inch)	3.25 S × 3.74 S	2.52 S × 2.33 S
crimp (%)	5.92 × 2.23	5.40 × 2.43
number of filaments	40 × 40	40 × 40
denier	156 × 156	156 × 159

Strength Loss Upon Abrasion (warp only)

Abrasion Cycles	Breaking Load (lbs)	% Loss	Breaking Load (lbs)	% Loss
0	56.5	0	79.4	0
50	47.3	16.3	74.0	6.8
75	43.0	23.9	67.1	15.5
100	42.0	25.7	60.8	23.4
200	38.1	32.6	49.3	37.9
300	35.1	37.9	43.3	45.5
400	33.4	40.9	37.5	52.8
500	31.6	44.1	33.4	57.9
666	26.8	52.6	26.4	66.8
832	23.9	57.7	23.0	71.0
1000	14.5	74.3	15.7	80.2
1050	4.3	92.5	7.6	90.4

life.   It is only at the 666-cycle level that the two fabrics have equal strengths.   In order to evaluate these fabrics for suit lining, the question must then be asked, "What is the threshold limit of strength, below which the lining will rapidly fail?"   If it is below (say) 30 pounds (i.e., so long as a lining maintains a strength of at least 30 pounds), it will not make a particle of difference as to which fiber is selected (all other factors being identical, of course).   If, on the other hand, the threshold limit is (say) 40 pounds, the advantage of the viscose fabric is obvious.

The question of minimum strength values in order for apparel wear to render acceptable service is worthy of note.   Williams[280,298,299] has made a study of apparel garments returned to a department store by complaining customers.

He states that[280]

"The useful strength of a fabric is its excess over the maximum tension or pressure occurring in ordinary conditions of use.   The term Normal Stress is used to designate this tension or pressure.   Tests on fabrics which tore in use or which had been discarded as worn out show that for a wide range of uses, the Normal Stress may be taken as equal to a tension of 40 pounds on a 4-inch grab test,* or as a pressure of 37 pounds per square inch."

He gives the following minimum grab strength values for light weight fabrics and bed sheets. (Grab strength was selected as being more correlative with use than strip tensile tests.)

TABLE 116. LIGHT-WEIGHT FABRICS AND MINIMUM PERFORMANCE GRADING OF (From Williams[299] "The Wearing Qualities of Fabrics")

(a)

TENSILE STRENGTH—TWO-INCH GRAB TEST*

	Air Dry	Wet
Grade 1	40 lbs or over	30 lbs or over
Grade 2	32½ lbs or over	22½ lbs or over
Grade 3	25 lbs or over	15 lbs or over
Grade 4	20 lbs or over	12½ lbs or over
Grade 5	17½ lbs or over	10 lbs or over

(b)

Cotton Bed Sheeting
Air Dry

Grade A	204 lbs or over on 2-inch grab test
Grade B	136 lbs or over on 2-inch grab test
Grade C	90 lbs or over on 2-inch grab test
Grade D	60 lbs or over on 2-inch grab test
Grade E	40 lbs or over on 2-inch grab test

* A private communication from Williams states that the 2-inch grab test utilizes a 3-inch wide specimen and 2-inch wide jaws. The 4-inch grab test uses 4-inch jaws. In both cases the standard 3-inch initial jaw separation is used.

Williams[280] plots a graph of customer complaints vs. tensile strength but, from the data shown, the 40-pound minimum which he sets does not appear to be conclusive.

One gathers from Williams's papers that he has been concerned mostly with cotton goods, where the orders of magnitude of extensions are the same. Therefore his suggested strength levels are probably valid in that energy absorption capacities are approximately proportional to strength. However, the hazard of using strength as a sole criterion for comparing fabrics of different fiber types cannot be over emphasized. Materials of lower strength (than 40 pounds) but with high strain and proper strain recovery might perform equally well in that they would absorb energy via *high deformation*, thus preventing high stresses from developing. Graph 64 demonstrates this principle. Assume two hypothetical load-elongation diagrams such as OA and OD. Assume that in being subjected to a given amount of abrasion the fabric will be called upon to withstand an amount of energy depicted by the area OBC or the equivalent OB'C'. It is obvious that under such demands, the load built up in case A (ordinate CB) will be greater than that built up in case D (ordinate C'B'). The potential advantage of low modulus materials, provided they have the proper repeated stress characteristics is demonstrated. This undoubtedly explains the excellent abrasion resistance of wool in spite of the fact that it is a weak fiber, while a high strength fiber such as glass is poor in abrasion resistance because "it is too brittle."

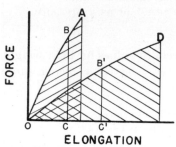

Graph 64. The absorption of energy by two different load-elongation mechanisms. (*From Kaswell,*[10] *"Low Temperature Properties of Textile Materials."*)

Williams[299] is not unmindful of the importance of extension-recovery properties. He lists the following minimum standards:

TABLE 117. MINIMUM ENDURING EXTENSIONS OF FABRICS*
(From Williams[299] "The Wearing Qualities of Fabrics")
(After 20-pound tension on 2-inch grab test)

Grade 1	½% or less
Grade 2	1%
Grade 3	1½%
Grade 4	2%
Grade 5	3%

* The[299] standard of 20-pound tension is used because this is the maximum tension normally occurring in properly fitting garments.

Continuing now the comparison of inherent abrasion resistance properties, Hicks and Scroggie,[300] employing Hamburger's[9] technique for testing yarn panels on the Taber Abraser, report the following fiber ratings:

TABLE 118. ABRASION RESISTANCE RATINGS OF YARNS AND FABRICS
(From Hicks and Scroggie[300] "Taber Yarn Sheet Abrasion Test")

Type	Production	Luster	Tenacity (g.p.d.)	Elongation (%)	Abrasion Rating yarn	fabric
acetate rayon (B)	commercial	bright	1.4	28	75	70
viscose rayon (A-1)	commercial	bright	1.9	19	100	100
viscose rayon (A-3)	experimental	bright	2.7	18	150	110
fiber G rayon (C)	experimental	bright	4.8	6	250	125
polyacrylonitrile (D)	experimental	bright	4.3	18	275	140
nylon (E)	commercial	bright	5.5	25	1000	750

The authors use an end point criterion, the danger of which has already been pointed out. Fiber G and polyacrylonitrile are believed to be a high tenacity viscose and "Orlon," respectively, but the writer has not checked to confirm these points.

Schiefer, Fourt and Kropf[36] list the following wear indices on an absolute and normalized basis, wool being taken as a standard at 100 per cent.

TABLE 119. APPROXIMATE RELATIVE LABORATORY WEAR INDICES
(From Schiefer, Fourt and Kropf[36] "Serviceability Evaluation of Textiles")

Fiber	Corrected Wear Index	%
nylon	330	500
wool	65	100
viscose	20	30
acetate	15	25
casein	5	8

The duPont Company[141] reports the following data on relative laboratory abrasion resistance of some synthetic yarns:

TABLE 120. LABORATORY ABRASION RESISTANCE OF TEXTILE YARNS
(From E. I. duPont de Nemours, Private Communication[141])

	Yarn on Yarn Abrasion Resistance Cycles
Textile Yarns	
Fiber A ("Orlon")	500
nylon (type 100)	16500
"Cordura" (viscose rayon)	260
Fiber V-111 ("Dacron"?)	7000
High Tenacity Yarns	
No. 237 "Cordura"	60
nylon type 300	19100
Fiber V, type 130	4000

Stout and Moseman[301] report on the effect of abrasion upon breaking strength and elongation of fifty-eight clothing fabrics of cotton, rayon, wool, and various blends. Table 121 lists pertinent results, again using loss in strength as a criterion. A direct comparison of data is impossible since the fabrics are not pedigreed; they are not of the same strength, and unfortunately their weights per unit area are not given; their geometric properties are not constant. Obviously the extent of abrasion of any particular set of yarns is a function of their availability to the abradant. To put the data on a reasonably comparable basis, two calculations have been made: first, individual per cent losses in strength have been calculated; second, the sum of the warp and filling strengths and the per cent loss of this combined value has been calculated in order to average out the effect of warp and filling yarn position, in the sense that if the fabric has suffered predominant warp damage, the filling will be protected, or vice versa. Kaswell[173] shows this to be the case for Army fatigue uniform cotton fabrics.

TABLE 121. EFFECT OF ABRASION ON STRENGTH AND ELONGATION OF CLOTHING FABRICS

(From Stout and Moseman[301] "Effect of Abrasion on Clothing Fabrics")

Fabric	Abrasion Cycles	Strength, lbs.			Strength Loss %			Elongation %	
		W	F	W + F	W	F	W + F	W	F
gingham	0	36.6	22.5	59.1	0	0	0	7.4	8.0
(75 × 58)*	100	28.7	20.4	49.1	21.5	9.3	16.9	7.0	6.8
	200	24.3	18.9	43.2	33.6	16.0	27.0	5.7	6.4
chambray	0	35.7	25.3	61.0	0	0	0	11.5	9.4
(88 × 63)*	100	29.8	25.6	55.4	19.5	1.2†	9.2	9.2	8.2
	200	26.2	24.3	50.5	26.6	4.0	17.2	8.3	8.3
rayon twalles	0	30.1	30.5	60.6	0	0	0	16.4	14.6
(96 × 72)*	100	26.7	29.9	56.6	11.3	2.0	6.6	13.4	14.8
	200	24.8	29.4	54.2	17.6	3.6	10.5	13.0	14.9
rayon challis	0	32.8	24.8	57.6	0	0	0	18.1	19.0
(70 × 58)*	100	27.9	18.5	46.4	14.9	25.4	22.9	13.8	14.9
	200	23.2	12.7	35.9	29.2	48.8	37.7	10.5	9.8
rayon crash	0	38.9	38.6	77.5	0	0	0	16.4	20.9
(47 × 46)*	100	38.7	27.9	66.6	0.5	27.8	14.1	14.4	15.1
	200	36.6	19.1	55.7	5.9	50.5	28.1	13.7	13.1
wool flannel	0	23.9	16.8	40.7	0	0	0	21.5	24.1
(63 × 48)*	100	23.8	16.0	39.8	0.5	4.8	2.2	18.1	19.5
	200	23.5	14.4	37.9	1.7	14.3	6.9	16.6	15.2
	300	22.6	13.0	35.6	5.4	22.6	12.5	17.7	13.8
	400	21.6	12.0	33.6	9.6	28.6	17.3	13.6	13.1
	500	21.3	10.9	32.2	10.8	35.0	20.9	17.9	12.0
wool crepe	0	21.6	15.2	36.8	0	0	0	24.4	22.1
(51 × 46)*	100	18.8	10.5	29.3	13.0	30.9	20.4	14.7	11.5
	200	15.7	8.1	23.8	27.3	46.7	35.3	12.5	9.3
	300	13.4	6.8	20.2	38.0	55.2	45.0	11.7	7.9
wool suiting HBT	0	21.5	12.9	34.4	0	0	0	19.9	21.1
(31 × 25)*	100	21.9	13.2	35.1	1.9†	2.3†	2.3†	18.7	20.4
	200	21.3	12.6	33.9	0.9	2.3	1.5	16.5	19.1
	300	21.0	12.4	33.4	2.4	3.9	2.9	18.0	20.4
	400	19.8	11.6	31.4	7.9	10.1	8.7	17.8	16.8
	500	19.2	11.2	30.4	10.7	13.1	11.6	19.8	15.7

TABLE 121. EFFECT OF ABRASION ON STRENGTH AND ELONGATION OF CLOTHING FABRICS.—(*Continued*)

Fabric	Abrasion Cycles	Strength, lbs.			Strength Loss %			Elongation %	
		W	F	W + F	W	F	W + F	W	F
rayon-cotton crash	0	37.3	31.5	68.8	0	0	0	13.2	14.4
(41 × 35)*	100	39.5	28.4	67.9	5.9†	9.8	1.3	11.1	13.1
	200	37.7	29.8	67.5	1.1†	5.4	1.9	9.5	11.9
rayon-wool suiting	0	28.5	22.9	51.4	0	0	0	14.9	20.4
(26 × 22)*	100	25.1	24.1	49.2	11.9	5.7†	4.3	13.4	19.5
	200	26.4	19.3	45.7	7.4	15.7	11.1	12.7	15.4
	300	26.4	17.7	44.1	7.4	22.8	14.2	29.2?	15.3
	400	21.7	14.1	35.8	23.9	38.4	30.4	13.4	14.0
	500	17.6	10.8	28.4	38.3	52.7	44.9	13.6	13.0
rayon-wool twill	0	41.3	36.2	77.5	0	0	0	16.6	20.5
(83 × 74)*	100	42.3	36.9	79.2	2.4†	0.8†	2.2†	16.3	18.6
	200	40.6	29.8	70.4	1.7	17.7	9.2	14.5	17.5
	300	39.5	31.8	71.3	4.4	12.2	8.0	16.0	18.0
	400	37.6	28.2	65.8	8.9	22.1	15.1	16.1	14.4
	500	35.6	24.8	60.4	13.8	31.5	22.1	17.4	16.2
rayon-nylon twill	0	51.9	46.5	98.4	0	0	0	28.2	22.8
(84 × 76)*	100	44.4	40.7	85.1	14.5	12.5	13.5	27.6	26.9
	200	51.9	47.0	98.9	0	1.1†	0.5†	20.3	21.7
	300	45.5	43.5	89.0	12.3	6.5	9.8	22.4	22.4
	400	41.6	39.2	80.8	19.8	15.7	17.9	25.7	21.7
	500	44.7	42.0	86.7	13.9	9.7	11.9	21.8	33.8?

* Warp and Filling thread count.
† Gain.

All fabrics have been abraded for 200 cycles and so let us examine the fabrics at this "cycle station" (Table 121).

Cotton gingham loses 27 per cent of its original 59 pounds.

Cotton chambray loses 17 per cent of its original 61 pounds.

Rayon twalles loses 10 per cent of its original 61 pounds.

Rayon challis loses 38 per cent of its original 58 pounds.

Rayon crash loses 28 per cent of its original 78 pounds.

Wool flannel loses 7 per cent of its original 41 pounds.

Wool crepe loses 35 per cent of its original 37 pounds.

Wool suiting loses 1.5 per cent of its original 34 pounds.

The hazard of drawing conclusions regarding the relative abrasion resistance of the fibers making up these fabrics is apparent. Fabric constructions are so different that their effect obscures inherent properties. It follows that an injudicious selection of a yarn and/or fabric construction can completely nullify the excellent inherent abrasion resistance of a fiber. Conversely a fiber with poorer resistance can be made into fabrics of high abrasion resistance by proper design. No conclusion between cotton and rayon can be made, but it would appear that wool is better than both.

Similar analysis of blended structures gives the following:

Rayon-cotton crash loses 2 per cent of its original 69 pounds.

Rayon-wool suiting loses 11 per cent of its original 51 pounds.

Rayon-wool twill loses 9 per cent of its original 78 pounds.

Rayon-nylon twill loses 0 per cent of its original 98 pounds.

The rayon-wool suiting appears to be inferior to the all-wool HBT suiting, while the rayon-wool twill is inferior to the rayon-nylon twill. It follows that rayon adversely dilutes wool, and nylon enhances rayon more than wool does.

In light of the data given in Tables 118 through 121, it appears reasonable to conclude that in the laboratory, when tested "dry," (i.e., at 65 per cent R.H. and 70°F), nylon is in a class by itself. Wool is a good second, with the probability that "Dacron" is in the same category; whether it is better or worse than wool cannot be stated here. "Orlon" is probably superior to viscose, with acetate following the viscose. It is surprising that no data have been found which enable a clear-cut ranking of cotton.

Backer[294] confirms the general ranking given above and also positions cotton:

> "Discounting the occurrence of isolated reversals in the ranks of the various textile fibers . . . one may conclude from the published data that the following order, from highest to lowest abrasion resistance applies to the most common fibers:[37,300,302,36,303] nylon, cotton, wool (also reported as superior to cotton[37]), viscose rayon (medium-high tenacity), cuprammonium rayon, viscose rayon (normal tenacity), acetate rayon (also reported as superior to normal-tenacity viscose rayon[9,304]), casein."

(62) Comparison of the Inherent Wear Resistance Properties of Fibers

Let us turn now to the broader topic of wear resistance wherein the results of actual service tests may be considered. The number of papers that report on the direct comparison of various fibers is limited. Some information is available on the effect of yarn and fabric construction upon wear, holding the fiber type constant, and this subject also is discussed below.

Schiefer, Fourt and Kropf[36] report on the work in Germany of Schachenmayr, Mau, and Cie:

> "The performance tests directed by Oestermann were made on men's socks. The socks were knitted without any

reinforcing. One sock of each pair was made from standard wool yarn and the other from the experimental yarn to be evaluated for effect of kind of fibers, fiber blend, or yarn construction. The experimental sock was made structurally as nearly like the wool sock as possible. A pair of the socks was worn by a man, who wore each one alternately on the left and the right foot. No other specifications were prescribed for the performance tests; the frequency of laundering and the method of laundering were left to the discretion of the wearer. The length of service which was obtained from each sock of a pair was recorded. The comparative wear was based upon the results of tests of ten pair of socks which were worn by ten different men. For each pair, a value of 100 was assigned to the wool sock and the result for the experimental sock was expressed as a percentage of the value for the wool sock. . . . The approximate results of service wear tests on men's socks made from different fibers are given in Table 122. Nylon was found to be about three times as durable as wool, whereas viscose rayon, acetate rayon, and casein were about $\frac{1}{3}$, $\frac{1}{7}$, and $\frac{1}{20}$ as durable as wool, respectively. Cotton was about as durable as wool."

TABLE 122. APPROXIMATE RESULTS OF SERVICE WEAR TESTS ON MEN'S SOCKS (From Schiefer, Fourt and Kropf[36] "Serviceability Evaluation of Textiles")

	Days	%		Days	%
nylon	60	300	viscose staple	7	35
wool	20	100	acetate staple	3	15
cotton	20	100	casein staple	1	5
cuprammonium staple	8	40			

Backer[294] discusses a Quartermaster research on the wear properties of blends of wool, cotton, and rayon made into 18-ounce worsted serge.

"The possibility of a wool shortage (during the war) was real, and every preparation was made for relieving the critical wool shortage with one of several constructions. As it happened, the need to convert was overcome, and the results of the field tests reported in Table 123 were held in readiness for further emergency changes in specification requirements. The results point to the superior durability of the cotton-wool blend over the all-wool product. However, the loss in other desirable characteristics, such as hand, drape, crease retention and crease resistance, served as a deterrent to the immediate adoption of fabric No. 4 (in Table 123). The rayon blends, on the other hand, (both viscose and acetate) were shown to affect the wear life on the fabrics significantly, depending upon the percentages of the blend. It was indicated that 15%

rayon could be included in the fabric without seriously reducing its wear life or affecting its crease-resistance properties. However, it was deemed inadvisable to include more than 15% rayon from the standpoint of fabric warmth and appearance."

TABLE 123. WEAR TESTS OF FIFTEEN SERGE FABRICS

(From Backer[294] "The Mechanics of Fabric Abrasion")
(Tests conducted at U.S. Army Quartermaster Combat Course)

Fabric No.	wt/yd 56-in. wide (ounces)	Yarn	Texture w	f	Fiber Composition	Spinning System	Wear score*
1	16	2/28	70	50	100% wool	worsted	101 ± 11
2	16	2/32	76	64	100% wool	worsted	141 ± 30
3	20	2/22	68	54	100% wool	worsted	158 ± 19
4	18	2/25	68	54	70% wool, 30% cotton	Merino French worsted	89 ± 11
5	18	2/24	68	54	85% wool, 15% viscose	worsted	157 ± 26
6	18	2/24	68	54	70% wool, 30% viscose	worsted	151 ± 14
7	18	2/28	72	60	70% wool, 30% viscose	worsted	169 ± 12
8	18	2/24	68	54	55% wool, 45% viscose	worsted	188 ± 19
9	18	2/24	68	54	40% wool, 60% viscose	worsted	171 ± 20
10	18	2/24	68	54	40% wool, 60% viscose	cotton	224 ± 20
11	18	2/24	68	54	85% wool, 15% acetate	....	153 ± 15
12	18	2/24	68	54	70% wool, 30% acetate	....	219 ± 20
13	18	2/24	68	54	100% wool (standard)	worsted	139 ± 14
14	18	2/24	68	54	85% wool, 15% acetate	....	149 ± 21
15	18	2/24	68	54	70% wool, 30% acetate	....	183 ± 24

* Based on combat-course wear scores on 8 trousers of each fabric type. (The higher the wear score, the less durable the garment.)

Backer[294] also reports on two wear experiments concerning gloves

"worn by men engaged in heavy manual labor; in one instance leather shells were worn over the inserts and in the other the inserts were worn alone. Data shown in Table 124 demonstrate the general superiority of the nylon-wool, and particularly the nylon inserts over the all-wool inserts in the harsh abrasion to which the items were subjected when worn alone. With the same type of action, but restricting the abrasive surface to the inside of the leather shell, little or no difference was noted between certain of the all-wool inserts and the nylon blends."

The wear data show that nylon is outstanding, followed by wool and cotton, with viscose and acetate inferior. Unfortunately, no data on the new synthetics were found.

TABLE 124. WEAR-RESISTANCE PROPERTIES OF GLOVE INSERTS WITH VARYING
PERCENTAGES OF WOOL AND NYLON

(From Backer[294] "The Mechanics of Fabric Abrasion")

Type	Without Shell Ave. No. of Traversals	Rank	With Shell Ave. No. of Traversals	Rank
75 wool, 25 nylon	27.4	3	83.7	7
100 wool, fulled, unbrushed	17.6	7	71.0	9
100 wool, shrink-resistant, fulled, unbrushed 56's	9.0	9	71.5	8
100 wool, medium brushed, no shrink resistance	10.6	8	102.2	4
65 wool 56's, 35 nylon, 6-den., fulled, medium brushed, shrink-resistant	20.3	6	83.8	6
65 wool 56's, 35 nylon, 6-den., fulled, medium brushed, untreated	25.7	4	85.4	5
35 wool 56's, 65 nylon, 6-den., fulled, medium brushed, shrink-resistant	43.6	2	105.6	3
100 nylon, 6-den., fulled, medium brushed, shrink-resistant	56.6	1	108.4	1
100 wool 56's fulled, medium brushed, shrink-resistant	22.0	5	107.0	2

(63) The Relationship between Abrasion Resistance and Wear Resistance

The limited service wear and laboratory abrasion tests discussed above, rank the various fibers in substantially the same order. One should by no means conclude, however, that the laboratory can easily, quickly, and accurately predict how fabrics will perform in use. The very fact that Backer's data show two different conclusions regarding wear resistance on the same articles of apparel is evidence of the complexity of relating laboratory and service performance. Referring again to his three elements involved in abrasion, namely friction, cutting and flexing, Backer[294] discusses potential reasons why different service (and laboratory) conditions might produce different wear (and abrasion) results.

"The difference between the elements . . . which appear to favor fabric surface softness and the hardness thought to be desirable for minimum damage to a metal surface, lies in the inherent assumption that in severe textile wear, the abrading surface will possess a much higher order of hardness than the fiber (except perhaps in the case of glass fibers). It therefore becomes desirable for the polymeric surface to give completely with each passage of an abradant particle to prevent the setting-up of critical tensile or shear stresses at local points. Behavior of the surface upon approach of the second and subsequent abradant particles will depend, of course, upon the recovery of the material to its original position and upon its continued motility. On the other hand, where normal service brings the textile in contact with material of an equivalent order of hardness, relative hardness assumes greater significance. Here one observes the possibility of reversal of abrasion performance from field to laboratory depending upon the relative hardness of the rubbing surface, or reversals depending upon the type of field use to which the fabric is put. In working with military garments, one must consider the activities of a clerk who sits at a desk the major portion of the day, and of a man who spends his time in vigorous fatigue or combat duty. Uniforms provided for varying activities are usually made of different materials, but frequently the same materials are exposed to widely diverse abrading surfaces. Quartermaster test data show that changing of the rubbing surface does not often reverse the abrasion ranking of materials, but it does enlarge or reduce degrees of difference among the materials."

Gagliardi and Nuessle[293] discuss the relationship between laboratory and service, and the reversal in laboratory abrasion resistance values:

" . . . unfortunately there is still a very prevalent idea that the numbers obtained from laboratory abrasion tests can be used to draw far-reaching conclusions as to the behavior of textiles in practical use. Probably the most unfortunate thing connected with abrasion testing of fabrics is that many management decisions regarding the acceptance or rejection of a finished product have been made on the basis of whether a certain so-called minimum abrasion value has been met, the implication being that such a minimum value is necessary for good wearing qualities. . . . A laboratory abrasion test may . . . be a useful test to make, but the results mean little by themselves unless they are considered along with the many other chemical, physical, and mechanical properties of a fabric. Moreover, in the actual life of a garment in practical use, a fabric is subjected to relatively low abrasive forces, i.e. low stresses and strains, the cycles of which are, on the average, far apart so that there is always time available for stress and strain relaxation. In spite of the precision and accuracy of laboratory abrasion machines, the general criticism that can be made against them is the rapid rate at which a specimen is destroyed by application of repeated stresses more severe than those commonly encountered in the normal wearing of garments. . . . Consequently, the mechanism by which fabric destruction takes place in such machines must be very different from what is encountered in normal wear."

The caution advised by these and other authors regarding the extrapolation of laboratory data to service conditions is too often unheeded and leads to erroneous or potentially erroneous conclusions on the part of the general public as well as the non-scientific portion of the textile industry.

Returning to Gagliardi and Nuessle's comments:[293]

. . . "Since the basic difference in the abrasive actions of laboratory machines and actual wear on a fabric is that of the rate at which destruction takes place, a systematic study was initiated to learn the dependence of apparent abrasion resistance on rate of destruction. For these studies the recently developed Schiefer abrasion machine was used since it could be adapted for either very slow or very fast testing. By varying the applied load on the specimen, we were able to cause fabric destruction through the application of abrasive forces of varying orders of magnitude. In the first experiment, samples of a viscose rayon fabric were treated with different concentrations of five creaseproofing and stabilizing compounds so as to produce about the same degree of shrinkage control and crease resistance. In all cases, the treatments were made according to the practice recommended by the manufacturer and involved acid catalysis and high-temperature curing. The finished fabrics were then tested for abrasion resistance by the TBL machine and the Schiefer machine at varying applied loads. The test results are shown in Table 125.

TABLE 125. APPARENT ABRASION RESISTANCE OF FABRICS MODIFIED BY CREASE-PROOFING AND STABILIZING COMPOUNDS

(From Gagliardi and Nuessle[293] "The Relation Between Fiber Properties and Apparent Abrasion Resistance")

	TBL Abrasion Cycles	Schiefer Abrasion Cycles at Varying Loads				
Resin Used		25 lbs psi	10 lbs psi	5 lbs psi	3 lbs psi	1.6 lbs psi
untreated fabric	3100	160	1100	6500	19,000	94,000
experimental resin A	2110	130	700	6200	53,000	500,000
experimental resin B	1650	120	580	3400	41,000	400,000
commercial A	810	60	300	3600	40,000	300,000
commercial B	800	70	360	3000	24,000	230,000
commercial C	600	30	200	2500	19,000	125,000

"These data show that, according to the TBL and the Schiefer machines, all of the chemical treatments decreased the number of cycles necessary for destruction of a specimen under conditions of testing where rapid destruction takes place (loads of 25 and 10 pounds per square inch), different treatments giving different results. When tests were conducted at lower applied loads (lower stress) the difference between the apparent abrasion resistance of the untreated and the modified fabrics was found to decrease, so that at a particular load, the modified fabrics showed higher abrasion resistance than the original material. This phenomenon is better illustrated by a plot, on log-log paper, of the number of cycles to destroy the fabric as a function of the applied load, as is shown in Graph 65. From this, it is seen that different values of abrasion resistance of treated and untreated fabrics can be

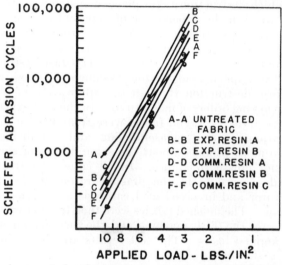

Graph 65. Apparent abrasion resistance of resin treated fabrics at various loads. (*From Gagliardi and Nuessle,*[293] "*The Relation Between Fiber Properties and Apparent Abrasion Resistance.*")

obtained depending on the method of testing. It is important to note that the point where each sample crosses the curve for the untreated cloth varies with the resin used. To our knowledge this apparent improvement of abrasion resistance at low stresses has not been previously noted, since abrasion testing of modified rayon fabrics has been mainly confined to very rapid tests, corresponding to the conditions present at the left lower-half of Graph 65."[293]

Dean[288] also cites reversals in laboratory abrasion results when abrading cotton and wool faced sateens using grey and mineral khaki-dyed canvas as the abrasive, viz:

| | Abrasive | |
	Grey	Khaki
Wool	690	240
Cotton	770	52

(64) The Influence of Yarn and Fabric Geometry on Abrasion and Wear Resistance

It will be apparent from the foregoing that any intelligent approach to the problem of designing fabrics for particular end-use objectives must include consideration of the external wear conditions to which the item will be exposed. Knowing this, attempts can be made to produce fabrics with the requisite inherent and geometric properties. The former having been given some attention, let us consider now some of the geometric problems and their relation to typical external abrasive and wear influences, after which we will return to a discussion of the multiple inherent physical properties of the various fibers requisite for good wear resistance.

Backer and Tanenhaus[305] discuss "Textile Geometry and Abrasion Resistance" in thorough and excellent fashion. The following factors which affect abrasion are examined:

Geometric aspects

(1) Geometric area of contact between fabric and abradant

(2) Local pressures or stress concentrations developing on specific yarn points or areas (i.e., true area of contact)

(3) Threads per inch

(4) Crown height (i.e., the extent of deformations out of the plane of the fabric resulting from the intersection of warp and filling yarns)

(5) Yarn size

(6) Fabric thickness

(7) Yarn crimp

(8) Float length

(9) Yarn cohesiveness

(10) Compressive compliance (i.e., compressional resilience of the fabric and backing)

(11) Fabric tightness

(12) Cover factor

Abrasion aspects

(1) Direction of abrasion

(2) Magnitude and direction of tensions developed during abrasive action.

These authors are quoted at length in the following pages.[305]

Geometric Aspects:

(1) Geometric Area of Contact Between Fabric and Abradant.

"Burwell[306] points out that the bulk flexibility of viscoelastic materials permits numerous protuberances to come into contact before the load between surfaces is completely supported and this is accompanied by a load reduction at each such point. As a result the proportion of points undergoing plastic deformation will be considerably reduced. The geometric area of contact of individual fibers has been studied by Finch[307] and has been shown to depend on the normal load at the point of contact, the principal curvatures of the fiber, the contour of its cross section and its bulk modulus. When dealing with fabric structures, one notes that bulk modulus is a major factor influencing contact area under a given load. Actually, one must consider the apparent bulk modulus of the fabric as affected by the compressibility of its backing support during use."

(2) Local Pressures or Stress Concentrations Which Develop on Specific Yarn Points or Areas.

"A low apparent bulk modulus, or high over-all flexibility, serves to bring as many yarn crowns in geometrical contact with the abrasive surface as is consistent with the fabric structure. The more numerous the crowns in contact and the more area per crown or projecting yarn float, the less will be the local load at a fiber point. As local load is reduced, the true area of contact at each point is also reduced and the abradant protuberance will descend into the yarn structure to a lesser degree. As a result, there will be (1) less frictional wear at the local point of contact, (2) less local frictional resistance to develop axial components of fiber stress, (3) reduced surface cutting of the fibers, and (4) less fiber plucking, slippage and tensile fatigue."

(3) Threads per Inch.

"When[305] all other factors are held constant, the abrasion resistance of the warp-flush fabrics is improved by increasing the number of warp crowns per square inch of fabric, thus reducing the normal load per warp crown. . . . This same trend is observed in fabrics varying in weave and yarn diameters, as is indicated in the work of Tait,[292] summarized in Graphs 66 and 67."

The authors[305] go on to show that in most cases the higher the thread count the better the wear resistance as tested on the Camp Lee Combat Course of the U.S. Army Quartermaster Corps.

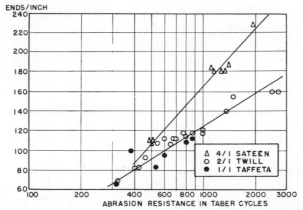

Graph 66.   Effect of weave on the abrasion resistance of rayon linings.   (*From Backer and Tanenhaus,*[305] *"Textile Geometry and Abrasion Resistance," who originally abstracted it from Tait.*[292])

Note: All fabrics are made of 150 denier 40 filament yarn, warp and filling. Fabrics in all cases are viscose or viscose-acetate combinations.

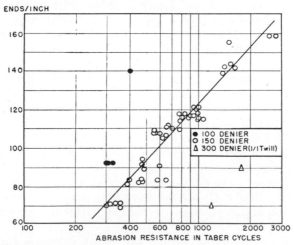

Graph 67.   Effect of warp yarn count on the abrasion resistance of viscose rayon linings.   (*From Backer and Tanenhaus,*[305] *"Textile Geometry and Abrasion Resistance," who originally abstracted it from Tait.*[292])

(4) Crown Height.

The intersection of a warp and filling yarn will produce a "crown," or elevation of one yarn over the other.   The extent to which this causes the crown to be displaced out of the fabric plane will depend upon the weave, yarn thickness, yarn crimp, thread count, and the interaction of these parameters between warp and filling.   These crowns will bear the brunt of abrasive action, the resulting destruction being dependent upon the nature and direction of the abradant and the height and number of crowns. The greater the number of crowns, the less will be the stress concentration per crown. Backer and Tanenhaus[305] discuss the design of a fabric where the warp yarns are to receive the major abrasive action:

"The greater number of warp crowns per square inch of fabric surface must not be obtained by increasing the warp texture to the point of jamming the warp threads, and markedly reducing the flexibility of the fabric structure. Likewise the filling texture should not be excessive nor the warp float so short that the warp crowns become rigid knuckles, incapable of absorbing abrasive energy without early rupture of surface fibers. . . . The abrasion of textile fabrics is so complex a mechanism that the effect of local crown loads on durability is often masked by interactions with other factors. A large part of this complexity is eliminated when the cloth specimen is constructed of monofilament yarns. A single row of vinylidene monofilament crowns rubbed with emery paper shows . . . the effect of a reduction in crown pressure on depth of cut. Here the total load on the abradant was held constant and the number of crowns supporting the load was varied . . .

"While many elastic solids give evidence of a straight line relationship between load and abrasion damage[308] the yarn crowns (here) do not. One reason for this is the change in crown-abradant contact area which occurs as the monofilament is worn down. The yarn crown in a plain weave resembles a torus. . . . If sections of this torus are sliced off perpendicular to the Z axis, the area of the exposed surface will vary in a nonlinear fashion. The relationship between these sectional areas and the depth of cut . . . has been determined by mechanical integration and is pictured . . . for tori with varying inner and outer radii.

"Using[305] these curves one can easily calculate the local bearing surfaces in a plain weave textile fabric as its thickness is reduced in abrasion. This is of course the most elementary case corresponding to the type of monofilament fabric used for seat covers in railway coaches. In ordinary spun fabrics, where the fibers are not retained in a matrix of starch or other coating material, the surface fibers spring up a fuzz after abrasive rupture and the yarn structure is radically altered. . . . In addition the contact areas calculated for the torus do not take into account the effect of compressive changes in the form of the torus itself resulting from normal loads. It suffices to say that in textile materials the contact area will increase as a consequence of wear but only in the case of monofilament materials can this increase be predicted. It may be expected that the wear rate under constant conditions of abrasion will fall off as the contact areas between fabric and abradant increase."

(5) and (6) Yarn Size and Fabric Thickness.

"The[305] association of greater wear life with increased thickness of a given material has been reported many times and implies a direct relationship between the loss in thickness and the number of rubs in an abrasion machine. . . . Increased fabric thickness and larger yarn diameters are generally related and provide marked improvement in abrasion resistance of textile structures. However, the relationship between yarn diameters and fabric thickness is not a simple one. For a given set of balanced yarns, fabric thickness can be varied from the sum of the yarn diameters to $\frac{3}{2}$ the sum, simply by controlling crimp. The abrasion resistance of the fabric during this change will vary significantly, but by no means proportionately to the change in thickness, indicating that once the surface yarns have been severely abraded, the remaining thickness of the specimen does little more to prolong the life of the fabric.[309] In other words, abrasion resistance is related to the thickness or diameter of that element of the textile structure which is exposed at the rubbing surface.

"Both yarn[300,310] and fabric abrasion studies[304,292] have indicated the effect of the diameter of exposed yarns on abrasion life of textile materials. Tait's[292] detailed data, plotted in Graph 64 and 65, show significant increases in abrasion life of lining fabrics as heavier yarns are used.

. . . "It should be emphasized that the largest diameters of the abrasion bearing yarns must be accompanied by yarn uniformity if increased wear life is desired. Non-uniform heavy yarns actually serve as focal points in fabric degradation because of the high pressure concentrations which occur at their crowns."

(7) Yarn Crimp Distribution.

"Crimp distribution determines the relative vertical displacement of each set of yarns above and below the plane of the fabric. As defined in studies of cloth geometry[311,167] true crimp, c, is the ratio of the differences between the axis length of a yarn, l, and its horizontal projection, p, to the horizontal projection (Figure 18). Crimp is usually determined by measuring the difference between yarn length in the fabric and its length when unravelled from the cloth and straightened. Crimp values obtained in this manner apply to the unit cell of a plain weave but must be multiplied by a weave factor, M, when other cloth structures are considered. M is determined from the weave pattern; for example for warp yarns, $\dfrac{1}{M_w}$ is the ratio of warp crossovers per repeat to the number of filling

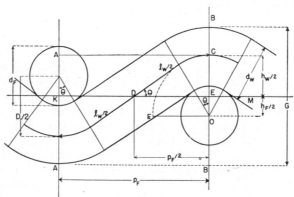

Figure 18. Crimp diagram. (*From Backer and Tanenhaus*,[305] "*Textile Geometry and Abrasion Resistance.*")

threads per repeat. M can be easily computed, e.g., in the case of twill constructions one up to the right:

a $\dfrac{5}{5}$ fabric has M equal to $^{10}\!\!/_{2}$, or 5

a $\dfrac{3}{2}$ fabric has M equal to $^{5}\!\!/_{2}$, or 2.5

a $\dfrac{4}{2}\dfrac{1}{2}$ fabric has M equal to $^{9}\!\!/_{4}$, or 2.25.

The sum of the vertical displacement of the crimped path of each yarn system, h, and its diameter, d, will determine which yarns will project at the rubbing surface of the fabric, and therefore will be subjected to maximum damage in abrasion.[312,313] An expression relating yarn displacement, h, to true crimp, c, and yarn spacings, p,

$$h_W = 4p_F \sqrt{c_w}/3$$

has been found to apply over a wide range of fabric structures.[311,167] Thus if the fabric (made of twisted yarns) is designed with a value of $(h_W + d_W) - (h_F + d_F)$ greater than

d_w one may expect the warp to suffer complete abrasive destruction without damage occurring to the filling.

"More[305] recently a surface coefficient, K_n,[314] has been proposed to establish the protruding yarn system based upon the fabric geometry. Here $K_n = 0.667 n_w N_w / n_f N_f$, where n_w and n_f are the fabric densities in warp and filling directions respectively and N_w and N_f are the corresponding warp and filling yarn numbers. Thus, if K_n is less than 1.0, the warp threads protrude at the surface of the fabric and if K_n exceeds 1.0, the crowns of both yarns lie in the plane of the fabric surface.

"In studies of plain weaves possessing high warp and low filling crimp, the curve showing warp strength vs. abrasion cycles demonstrates a steep negative slope indicative of a high rate of damage, while the filling-strength curve is quite flat until the warp is almost worn away.[315,316,317] In similar studies[173] dealing with twill, sateen, and herringbone-twill weaves, negligible wear damage is noted in yarns which are buried below the rubbing surface, and conversely, maximum abrasion takes place on the surface yarns.

"With the importance of crimp distribution established, it is conceivable that the abrasion characteristics of a fabric can be altered by any factor which will modify the crimp balance. Comparison of fabrics in the loom state with high warp crimp vs. the finished state in which the warp crimp has been significantly reduced have shown significant difference in abrasion performance. Laundering of the finished fabrics and subsequent shrinkage similarly modify crimp distributions and therefore the abrasion mechanism of the fabric changes,[317,309] but here the effect of the increased number of threads per inch must also be considered. Finally, slight modifications in fabric construction or weaving conditions, e.g., reed width and warp tensions, may significantly alter the surface of a fabric and its abrasion performance.[318] In effecting crimp changes through control of "in-loom" construction or weaving and finishing conditions one must have full cognisance of the geometric limitations resulting from yarn jamming[311,167] and the physical limitations imposed by inherent yarn properties, particularly stiffness. Abrasion experiments have illustrated the importance of this requirement. In one case,[309] fabrics were constructed with high filling and low warp crimp, resulting in great damage to the filling in wear and little damage to the warp. In lightly modified constructions, the warp texture was increased, resulting in greater filling crimp. The experimental series was extended until the jamming point was reached, beyond which warp texture increases simply reduced filling crimp. Just before the jamming point, protection to the warp yarns was noted to be highest. The protection of the filling yarns, on the other hand, was not at a minimum at this point for their twisted structure tended to rupture long before the final fiber was worn away.

"In few instances will tension during an abrasion test or during the wear life of a fabric be sufficient to alter the crimp balance in the material.[315] However, wherever the stresses are of sufficient order to reduce crimp in either direction, modified abrasion results may be expected. This is particularly true in novelty and fancy fabrics where long floats at irregular intervals cause a maldistribution of tensile stresses, or where ribs occur, or where intermittent heavy yarns in warp and filling cross one another and create projecting crowns.[273] Thus, it may be expected that a fabric which does not possess over-all dimensional stability will give trouble in laundering, pressing and subsequent wear."

(8) Float Length.

"Where[305] twills or sateens are considered it becomes evident that many of the assumptions of the simplified cloth geometry no longer apply. The longer the float, the less the restraint on the yarn system. Here yarns are no longer restricted to alternating from one side of the fabric to the other, but bend sideways and allow for the closer packing characteristic of twills and sateens. In particularly long floats, such as are found in the Army five-harness sateen, . . . the torus-cylinder form of alternating yarns is modified and a general arc-like form is assumed. This, when combined with a tendency of adjacent yarns to over ride one another, . . . results in higher projection of the yarn system containing the greater number of floats on each side of the fabric, despite the distribution of crimp. This tendency is used to good advantage in protecting from surface abrasion the system of yarns which bears the major stresses during service. In Army utility garments, Kaswell has observed that the longitudinal yarns, normally the warp, bear the major stresses during combat or fatigue activity of the wearers.[173] Damage to the warp is further affected by the relative direction of the yarn twist and of the twill,[319] the more pronounced twills suffering earlier loss in strength.

"Combat course tests have shown that the filling-flush sateen[173] offers more protection . . . to warp threads during harsh abrasive wear than does the structure of the herringbone twill. In the case of herringbone twill and sateen arranged so that the filling floats were exposed, filling damage was three to six times that of the warp in the herringbone twill and fifteen to twenty times that of the warp in the sateen. In short, the sateen showed least warp damage of all fabrics tested. When cross sections of the fabrics in question are observed, . . . the additional protection afforded the warp by the longer filling float of the sateen becomes evident.

"Laboratory tests . . . conducted on sateen, herringbone twill, and uniform twill with reciprocating and rotating type abrasion machines have consistently shown the sateen structure to furnish maximum warp protection when the filling floats are subjected to rubbing. No reversal in this tendency was noted as a result of change in abrasion direction. Conversely, maximum damage occurred to the filling floats of the sateen weave.

"It has thus been shown to be characteristic of the five-harness sateen that the warp yarns project on one surface and the filling yarns on the other. In tightly woven, high warp-cover plain or denim (twill) weaves, the warp yarn projects on both face and back and is subject to immediate damage, regardless of the surface abraded. In the herringbone twills the warp yarns project on the face but are almost flush with the filling floats at the back. The wave height of an alternating yarn is generally related to the relative float lengths of the projecting yarn, for it is evident that the longest float will balloon out most. Measurements of float length in selected experiments[173] . . . (have) shown that the back of the sateen construction has the longest filling float and the highest ratio of filling to warp floats. Recall that the warp yarns are to be protected in use and therefore protrusion of the filling yarn at the outer surface of the fabric is desired.

"Comparison between the several fatigue fabrics of the various (military) services has further demonstrated the influence of weave and float length on yarn projection and relative protection of the two systems from surface abrasion. Two herringbone twills were evaluated here, one with a float of two cross yarns, the other with a float of three. The other fabrics were a five-harness sateen and a 2/1 denim construction . . . all the twills lose significantly in warp breaking strength after reciprocating warpwise rubbing (face up). However, when the fabrics are reversed, the sateen, with the maximum filling float length, is the only material which demonstrated almost complete warp protection under the conditions of abrasion used.

"The most striking example of the warp protection mechanism is seen in the results of combat course tests plotted in Graph 68. Here the plain-weave fabric possessing tight warp crowns and with filling float length of one cross-over, has poorest (highest wear score) resistance, while the sateen with a filling float length of four cross-overs is the best. Intermediate wear scores are evidenced in the case of the oxford, all of which have the filling float passing over two cross yarns. As Kaswell points out,[173] the important part of this geometric

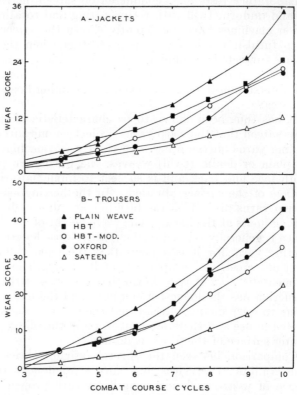

Graph 68. Effect of weave variations on combat course wear test results. (*From Backer and Tanenhaus,*[305] *"Textile Geometry and Abrasion Resistance."*)

consideration is the protection of the tensile stress bearing yarns, which in the case of combat course wear are the warp.

"Finally, it should be stressed that irregularities in the weave pattern should be avoided to prevent one portion of the repeat from projecting above the other and receiving the brunt of the wear. An example of this is seen in the herringbone-twill fabric which at one point in the repeat reduces the length of the filling float by 50 per cent. This throws the warp thread, crossing the filling at this point, out of the plane of the fabric surface and subjects it to excess wear at an early stage.

At another point in the herringbone twill, where a filling float is increased 50 per cent causing it to arch out of the plane of the back surface of the fabric, maximum wear is again noted. . . ."

(9) Yarn Cohesiveness.

"The importance of cohesion of fiber, yarn, and fabric has been stressed by many investigators. . . . The surface wear of fabrics can consist of fiber damage with either partial or complete rupture of the individual hairs, or a whole plucking of the fiber from the yarn structure.[315,320] For good wear the tearing-out action can be reduced by a firm binding of the fibers.[313] This binding may be accomplished by increasing yarn solidity with higher twists, or by use of tighter weaves. . . . Based upon results of more recent yarn tests, it would appear that lower twists afford poor fiber binding, while high twists stiffen the yarn to a point where very little contact is had between yarn and abrasive. This in turn results in high local abrasive pressures and early breakdown of the yarn structure. However, when materials are laundered to a greater extent than abraded, the poor fiber binding of low twist yarns plays a major role in causing early breakdown. . . . It is seen . . . that the compressional characteristics of a yarn and its cohesiveness play dual roles in determining abrasion resistance as its twist is altered. . . . Different abrasion behavior may be expected in fabrics of varying yarn twists, depending upon the normal loads between the rubbing surfaces.

"In[305] considering endpoints, twist becomes a significant factor in determining the loss in yarn strength which may be expected for a given depth of cut at the crown of the yarn float. Yarn twist will bring different fibers to the surface in any float length. The number of different fibers at any surface will depend upon the float length, the turns per inch, and the fiber and yarn diameters. . . . In many instances all the fibers lying at a given depth (abraded depth of crown) from the yarn surface rise to the surface at each float or at adjacent floats, thus degrading yarn strength by an amount proportional to their cross-sectional area."

(10) Compressive Compliance.

"The[305] influence of backing materials in abrasion testing is well known although little is reported in the literature since most investigators standardize on the type of backing used in a given test. The various degrees of backing softness on a man's body will have effect on the relative wear of different portions of his garment. This factor is believed to play an important role in the variation in wear scores recorded in combat course tests of Army clothing, although it is not assumed for a moment that a major factor does not coexist in the wearing habit of the individual, that is, what portions of his body he brings into contact with the different abrasive elements which occur during traversal of the course. Soft backing, extra padding thickness, or napping of the fabrics in test will add to the compressive give and thereby to the ability to escape damage at the abrading surface. . . .

"Finally it is concluded that the compressive behaviour of the surface structure itself bears on its wear performance and it may be expected that a low compressive modulus and high rate of recovery will enhance abrasion resistance, reducing the normal pressures at local protuberances."

(11) and (12) Fabric Tightness and Cover Factor.

"Reduction[305] in the extent of fiber plucking during wear, by closer weave or high twist, should not be carried at the expense of local rigidity at the fabric surface. There is sufficient evidence to demonstrate that tightly woven, knuckled fabrics possess low wear resistance.[173,321,322] This is caused by the inability of the surface fiber to translate and avoid the path of the abradant particle. As a result stresses are set up in the fiber which may exceed the multidirectional shear or tensile strength at the localized point of contact, or the axial tensile tenacity in the case of macrosnagging. . . . In general, the motility required to alleviate surface stresses on individual fibers can be achieved by flattening the yarn structure in compression as indicated above, or through rotation of the yarn, or yarn translation within the fabric structure. . . . .

"For the case of macrosnagging the amount of yarn rotation will depend upon yarn twist and fiber tensile modulus, for these factors determine the torsional rigidity of the yarn. If the yarn rotates enough to permit the surface fiber to slip from under the abrasive asperity little immediate damage will occur, although long-time cumulative effects may be present, such as removal of secondary creep and bending fatigue. However, if the surface torque developed during yarn rotation is of such a magnitude as to cause fiber rupture, damage will be evident after the initial passes of the abradant surface over all parts of the fabric. To avoid excessive torques one may use a fiber of lower tensile modulus or a yarn of lower twist. Finally, the use of longer floats (assuming the same torsional rigidity of the yarn system) will reduce the magnitude of stress at the surface fiber.

"Geometric studies have shown that the number of picks which may be woven in a fabric is limited by the number of warp ends per inch, assuming fixed yarn sizes. The limiting construction of picks for a given sley, or vice versa, is known as the jammed condition.[311,167] The quantitative expression of tightness as a ratio of actual picks (or ends) per inch to the maximum number per inch for a given cover factor, K, in the opposite direction is quite useful in fabric development. It will be recalled that cover factor is the ratio of threads per inch to the square root of the yarn count (cotton system).

" . . . The cover factor of the threads which protrude at the surface is the primary factor in determining the geometric area of contact of the fabric with the abradant, while the modified cover or tightness factor reflects the extent of fabric mobility afforded the protruding yarns by the fabric geometry. It follows that fabrics with high values of M (weave factor, see page 334) can pack considerably more yarn per unit area without increasing fabric tightness, thus avoiding reduction in abrasion resistance through loss of mobility. Meanwhile the increased bearing surface of the higher textured fabrics results in reduced abrasive pressure per crown or float and less abrasive damage. Conversely, when textures are kept constant, the M values of a given structure determine yarn mobility and therefore are a measure of the ability of the yarns to redistribute stress concentrations in abrasion and also in tearing or snagging.

"In[305] . . . (Graph 67) the sateen fabric with the weave factor of 2.5 in both warp and filling shows the maximum . . . abrasion resistance and tear resistance together with the lowest tensile (strip) strength. The plain weave with M_w, $M_f = 1, 1$, respectively, shows the poorest abrasion and tear resistance, while the herringbone twill and oxford fabrics with weave factors M_w, $M_f = 1.5, 1.5$ and 1.2, respectively, show intermediate values of tear and abrasion resistance. This ranking has been attributed to the protective protrusion of the longer filling floats, but it is highly probable that yarn mobility plays a significant role in determining the relative abrasion life of the fabrics whose warp yarns protrude at the rubbing surface, in this case the plain, oxford and herringbone twills. Obviously there is a limit in float length at which increased snagging of the protruding yarn vitiates the advantages of longer floats. In addition, the conditions of abrasion may be such that the yarn mobility may be inoperative, for example as a result of fine abrasives moving at a high speed over the surface of the fabric."

Abrasion Aspects:

(1) Direction of Abrasion.

"Major[305] differences exist in the abrasion performance of textile fabrics when the direction of rubbing is altered with respect to warp and filling coordinates.[309,303] The advisability of analyzing field wear to establish the predominant direction of wear and stress has been noted in early abrasion studies.[315,312] In experiments where fabrics have been rubbed in warp and filling direction, as high a ratio as 2:1 has been observed in the number of strokes required to form a hole.[288]

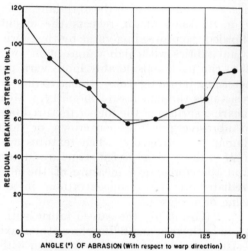

Graph 69.   Effect of direction of rubbing on the abrasion resistance of army poplin.   (*From Backer and Tanenhaus,*[305] "*Textile Geometry and Abrasion Resistance.*")

Generally, the yarns which project on the rubbing surface of the fabric will suffer greatest damage when abrasion takes place in a direction perpendicular to their float lengths,[173,313,303] e.g., Graph 69.   Where it is evident that abrasion and tensile stresses occur in one direction, it becomes desirable to increase the perpendicular set of yarns as to frequency and diameter and bring them to the surface to absorb the wear.[173]   Under these conditions, unfortunately, the cross yarns will absorb maximum damage during a period of rubbing.   Maximum resistance will be achieved when the non-stress-bearing yarns are presented at the rubbing surface with their floats running in the direction of rubbing.[313]   Since the direction of service wear and stress is often the same, the maximum abrasion life of the fabric is not often realized.   Wherever possible, however, the design of the garment or lay of the fabric in the pattern should be altered so as to eliminate perpendicular rubbing of the surface yarns during the wear life of the item. This matter is done more easily in the manufacture of fatigue garments for Army use than in dress uniforms or civilian clothing. One feature that can be modified quite easily is the exposure of face or back of the material to the rubbing element depending on which side exposes the non-stressed yarns. Fabric reversal of this nature is resorted to in a number of Army garments."

(2) *Magnitude and Direction of Tensions Developed During Abrasive Action.*

Abrasive and wear action produce stresses in a fabric. To prevent tensional failures from occurring, it is mandatory that the fabric be sufficiently strong to withstand such forces. Obviously end-use will govern both the magnitude and direction of the stress requirements. Backer and Tanenhaus[305] sum up the situation as follows:

"In designing more durable cloth to meet the requirements of the above conditions, it is recommended that strong yarns be used in the direction of applied stresses and that these yarns be buried below the exposed surface. Protection of the stress-bearing yarns may be effected by the control of crimp in the design and manufacture of the cloth. Geometric relationships in plain-weave fabrics have been developed to the point where the relative protrusion of one system of yarns above the other can be readily designed and implemented in the course of fabric weaving and finishing.

"Maximum[305] damage in wear of a fabric will occur when the direction of rubbing is perpendicular to the exposed floats. It is therefore desirable to orient the fabric in the design of clothing, so that exposed floats are parallel to the predominant direction of rubbing. Unfortunately this is not possible where abrasion and tensile stress directions coincide as in the case of Army fatigue garments."

(65) The Inherent Physical Properties of Fibers Requisite for High Wear Resistance

The attention given throughout this book to the importance of mechanical properties of textile fibers under various conditions of temperature, humidity, repeated stressing, and rate of load or strain, should make it apparent that such parameters are all pertinent to an explanation of wear resistance. It would seem that sufficient tabular data on fiber properties have been reported in the literature and included here, to enable their utilization in calculating relative wear rankings. The problem of how to weight the various contributing criteria still exists, however.

Schiefer, Fourt, and Kropf,[36] reporting upon the work of Bohringer and Schieber,[37] tabulate and weight a series of physical measurements. They call the integrated effect a "Quality Index" (see page 63). Equal weight is given to tensile strength, specific elastic work, knot strength, elongation at break, relative wet strength, tensile fatigue resistance, and flexural endurance. The following average quality indices result:

nylon	678
wool	463
silk	336
cotton	232
rayon	100

A similar technique is reported by the same authors,[36] describing work done on sewing thread in the research department of A. G. Gutermann (Germany):

TABLE 126. EVALUATION OF GENERAL WEAR PERFORMANCE OF SEWING THREADS: AN INDEX NUMBER OF QUALITY

(From Schiefer, Fourt, and Kropf[36] "Serviceability Evaluation of Textiles")

Physical Property	Egyptian Cotton	Russian Cotton	Mercerized Cotton	Spun Silk	Spun Rayon	Rayon
dry strength	73	68	100	80	53	64
wet strength	81	78	100	63	40	45
dry knot strength	78	75	83	100	43	47
wet knot strength	100	95	98	85	39	30
elastic recovery	99	100	96	94	85	69
flex resistance	95	100	41	16	15	4
serviceability	96	100	100	88	64	56
abrasion resistance	68	100	36	54	54	18
strength after laundering	58	55	100	28	45	41
index number	83	86	84	68	49	42

In both of these examples, the properties selected encompass most, and perhaps all of the parameters requisite for evaluating such a complex problem as wear.

This writer has attempted to calculate analogous indices for the different fibers by selecting tabular data already included in this report, weighting each parameter in what may have been a logical fashion,

TABLE 127. NORMALIZED VALUES OF INHERENT FIBER PROPERTIES WHICH MAY INFLUENCE THE WEAR RESISTANCE PROPERTIES OF TEXTILE FABRICS

(Wool Values by Definition Equal 100)

	"Fiber-glas" 1	Cot-ton 2	"For-tisan" 4	Viscose Regular 7	Viscose Hi ten. 10	"Or-lon" 12	"Da-cron" 13	Silk 14	Acetate 16	Nylon 18	"Vin-yon" NOZZ 9	"Vin-yon" NORU 20	Cu-pram-monium Rayon‡	Casein 22	Wool 21
Dry properties															
strength to rupture	720	190	830	230	310	520	640	540	150	680	450	350	220	110	100
elongation to rupture	10	20	20	50	50	50	60	60	60	70	50	100	40	110	100
energy to rupture	30	50	80	90	120	170	260	270	90	360	140	210	70	90	100
elastic modulus*	1	5	5	40	20			30	80	20	20	60	30	200	100
torsional rigidity†	80	80	80	30				110	30						100
shear tenacity	130	160	200	100	140	280	210	225	100	220	200	160		70	100
instantaneous elastic recovery after 5% strain	0 (rupture)	80	80	70	60	80	70	70	100	70	110	100		130	100
delayed elastic recovery after 5% strain	0 (rupture)	70	80	70	80	70	120	90	80	130	80	90		50	100
permanent set after 5% strain*	0 (rupture)	80	80	70	70	90	90	90	90	100	95	90		90	100
Wet properties†															
strength to rupture	1100	400	1100	170		860	1070	670	140	920		580		58	100
elongation to rupture	5	20	15	45		30	40	70	60	50		60		90	100

Notes: The major portions of the data come from Susich and Backer[233] "Tensile Recovery Behaviour of Textile Fibers." The numbers directly under the fiber name refer to their samples, with the exception of Cuprammonium rayon. Values in each case are rounded to the nearest ten.

* Higher numbers in each case connote an advantage; thus a high number reflects a low amount of Permanent Set.
† Susich, George; Private communication, see Bibliography reference 325.
‡ These data do not pertain to Susich and Backer's[233] samples.

summing the resulting numerical indices, and finally arriving at an average wear rank.   Parameters selected were:

breaking strength	delayed elastic recovery after cycli-
breaking energy	cal 5 per cent strain
breaking elongation	permanent set after cyclical 5 per
elastic modulus	cent strain
torsional rigidity	residual energy to rupture after
shear tenacity	cyclical 5 per cent strain
instantaneous elastic recovery after	wet breaking strength
cyclical 5 per cent strain	wet breaking elongation

It is believed that such a list is reasonable unto itself and also encompasses the five factors influencing abrasion resistance as listed by Hamburger[9] on page 306.

Inconclusive results were obtained, as may be noted by examining Table 127.   Therefore no final conclusions are drawn.   The reasons are twofold: first, in spite of the large amount of data already presented in the various tables, many blank spaces exist which preclude the calculation of an average value.   For example, reliable torsional rigidity values for all fibers are not available.   An important omission is the residual energy remaining after cyclical straining at the 5 per cent level, the original data of Susich and Backer[233] potentially contain such information, but it is not available at the present writing.   The second reason concerns the relative importance of each parameter, i.e., how each should be weighted in the calculation of an over-all index.

To select an arbitrary weighting system is hazardous, and this writer, after considerable thought, has decided against listing any weighting factors because they can lead to erroneous results.   For example, the wet strengths of the hydrophobic fibers, relative to wool, are extremely high.   They can far outweigh other factors which may be of greater importance.   Employing weighted indices usually implies linearity of requirement which may not be justified.   Referring again to the comments on pages 316–318 concerning minimum or threshold requirements of textile structures, it is obvious that the degrees of importance of specific parameters may vary, depending upon their closeness to the minimum requirements.   A high tenacity fiber with an excessively high elastic modulus may exhibit poor abrasion resistance because of its brittleness.   The retention of high strength when wet is of little advantage here, being of secondary importance.   However, if all other requirements for good abrasion are met, then high wet strength will further enhance the fiber's value.   Thus weighting factors must vary, depending upon the "weakest link" principle.

Chapter 18

FELTING AND SHRINKAGE

(66) The Mechanics of the Felting and Milling of Wool

At the present writing, it appears safe to say, wool and the other animal fibers are the only ones which will felt in the accepted commercial and practical sense. Numerous claims have been made for the ability of certain unique fibers, synthetic and natural, to felt, but there is no evidence to support the fact that any have ever been of practical value.

The wool fiber has particular properties which permits its conversion into nonwoven felts, flannels, and the host of woolen and worsted fabrics prepared through the fulling of greige goods to effect an increase in weight and density, and a reduction in dimension. These same properties work to the disadvantage of wool products in that they normally exhibit excessive shrinkage when wet laundered. The mechanisms are the same. Let us now examine those factors which influence shrinkage and felting.

Bogaty, Sookne, and Harris[351] sum up the requirements of felting as follows:

"Sufficient advance in the theory of the mechanism of the felting of wool has been made in recent years so that there is general agreement as to the contribution of such factors as the frictional and mechanical properties of the wool fiber. Thus, it is now recognized that in order for felting to be possible, a fiber must possess a surface scale structure, must be easily stretched and deformed, and must possess the power of recovery from deformation."

Alexander[349] discusses the broad aspects of the mechanism of felting:

"The fundamental causes of felting are much more complex than was thought even a few years ago. Felting depends on fiber migration and consists essentially of fibers moving into entanglements of other fibers and the pulling together of these denser areas so as to consolidate and reduce in area the whole fabric. Wool possesses the unique surface property known

347

as the differential friction effect (D.F.E.) of having a greater coefficient of friction in one direction (tip to root) than in the other.

"It[349] is widely held that this property is responsible for the pulling together of the entanglements. Thus, the root end of a fiber protruding from an entanglement moves into another entanglement and because of the D.F.E. the two will be pulled together. At first, the D.F.E. was thought to be a natural consequence of the scale structure, but this view must be abandoned since, as we shall see, there are a number of chemical treatments which remove the D.F.E. while leaving the scale structure largely intact. There are two distinct new theories for the D.F.E., the first attributed to Prof. Speakman of Leeds University, who believes that the extreme tips of the scales are flexible, rather like rubber. A macro model of a wool fiber constructed out of wood and recent electron microphotographs taken in Australia support this view. The other theory is that the actual molecular structure (alignment of the molecules) of the scale substance and not its morphological shape is responsible for the D.F.E. It is assumed that the molecules are more easily displaced in the tip than the root direction. There is a considerable body of indirect evidence to support this view and so far no clear-cut decisive experiment capable of choosing between the two theories has been found.

"One of the strongest pieces of evidence supporting the theory that felting is caused by the D.F.E., is that chemical anti-shrink treatments reduce the D.F.E. (that the friction in both directions tends to become equal). This is achieved either by decreasing the friction in one direction or increasing it in the other. The correlation is, however, not complete and in our laboratory we, have found a number of reagents (mild permanganate treatments and certain chloramides) which almost completely eliminate the D.F.E. without, however, producing unshrinkable wool. Moreover, many treatments which remove the D.F.E. produce wool which does not felt in alkali media but does shrink in acid media. The simple picture of felting is thus seen to fail and we were frankly at a loss for all explanations until Dr. Milton Harris put forward his theory that curliness of the fibers alone can produce entanglements. The curliness is attributed to differences in elastic properties between the scales and cortex which are removed by chemical attack.

"I[349] think we shall find that neither theory completely represents the facts but that there is a measure of truth in both and that a synthesis of the views is required. One thing is clear and in accord with all theory and that is that the property leading to felting resides in the surface of the wool and that removal of scales always prevents felting."

While the D.F.E. may be reduced without serious reduction in felting, the fact remains that if the D.F.E. is eliminated by scale removal, felting will cease. Martin[348] points out that to the present the D.F.E. is obtainable only via scales.

"Until some very queer kinds of crystal (structure) quite different from anything known at present can be produced, it is unlikely that a substance showing a D.F.E. can be made. . . . A result of this theory is to convince the author that no wool substitute that will felt will be produced, at any rate in the near future."

(67) Factors Which Influence the Rate and Degree of Wool Felting

Differential Friction Effect. The difference in dry friction coefficients of wool fibers in the root-to-tip and tip-to-root directions has already been cited in Table 36. Consider now the wet frictional characteristics of fibers as they pertain to felting. Speakman and Stott[331] discuss the subject:

"Milling has been the subject of many investigations and although a number of different theories have been advanced to explain the shrinkage which wool fabrics undergo in the process, none of these has met with widespread acceptance. The only fibres to which the process can be successfully applied are those possessing a surface scale structure, and the conclusion seems inevitable that the scales are in some way directly responsible for the felting and shrinking of wool fabrics in a milling machine. It was at first thought that under the influence of pressure, moisture, and heat, the fibres are forced into intimate contact and retained in this formation by the interlocking of the scales of contiguous fibres. This view has now been abandoned, mainly on the grounds that microscopic examination of a milled fabric fails to reveal fibres showing such intimate scale contact. The generally accepted view of the manner in which scales promote milling shrinkage is based on the observations of Ditzel . . . which have recently been confirmed and extended by Arnold. . . . These authors were able to show from experiments carried out with locks of wool, that when the fibres are subjected to longitudinal rubbing action, they tend to travel in the direction in which the scales do not oppose motion, i.e., in the direction of the root-end. When two locks were placed end to end, with their root-ends in contact, the action of the felting machine caused rapid inter-penetration of the fibres from each lock, whereas when the tips were in contact, no inter-penetration could be observed. It seems clear from these experiments that the fibres composing a wool fabric will similarly tend to travel in the direction of their root-ends under the action of the milling machine. It remained for Shorter[352] to show that such unidirectional freedom of motion could cause the shrinkage of fabrics. His explanation is, briefly, that fibres travelling in the direction of the root-end through a loose mass of fibres can carry along with them those fibres with which they are mechanically entangled. Under the action of the milling machine, there will therefore be a continuous tightening-up of the structure with decrease in its surface area and increase of thickness as a result.

"On[331] the basis of the preceding view of the cause of milling, it is to be expected that the rate of shrinkage of a fabric in a milling machine will be determined by the magnitude of the difference between the frictional resistance to motion of a fibre in the direction of the root-end, and that in the direction of the tip, the friction being greater in the latter instance. In the absence of complicating factors, this difference in friction and the rate of shrinkage should be directly related. Such a view receives support from a comparison of the scale structure of, say, merino wool and mohair. As seen under a microscope, the former has well-defined scales projecting to a marked extent from the body of the fibre, whereas the scales of mohair are indistinct and adhere closely to the fibre throughout their length; as would be expected, therefore, merino wool felts far more rapidly than mohair under identical conditions of experiment."

Table 36, taken from Speakman and Stott,[331] lists the D.F.E. for various wools, confirming the D.F.E.-felting relationship for wool and mohair. However, poor correlation exists when comparing the different types of wool:

"For[331] example, Speakman and Goodings[353] found the following values for the percentage shrinkage in area of cloths possessing the same structure milled for the same time under identical conditions, but made from different wools:

Wool	% Shrinkage in Area
Wensleydale	33.7
Oxford Down	28.0
Southdown	16.3

"The wools in question were those used in measurements of scaliness, and reference to Table 36 indicates that the order of milling efficiency is exactly the inverse of the order of scaliness. Evidently in these cases properties other than scaliness determine milling efficiency whereas with merino wool and mohair, the scales on the one are so pronounced and on the other so ill-defined as to make scaliness the dominating factor in determining their relative milling properties. Wools intermediate in type do not appear to differ sufficiently in scaliness to allow of this being the predominating cause of shrinkage differences."

The work of Sookne, Bogaty, and Harris[361] does not confirm the above findings (page 364), for they found little significant differences in the shrinkage of wools of different qualities ranging from 58's to 70's, nor in the D.F.E., nor elastic properties of the wools. The only explanation which can be given is that Speakman and Goodings[353] employed a milling test while Sookne, Bogaty and Harris[361] employed what is tantamount to a laundering test.

The other factors which affect milling shrinkage will in due course be discussed below.

Martin and Mittlemann[334] show data on the wet frictional properties of fibers as they pertain to the felting mechanism, the presumption being that the greater the D.F.E., the greater the rate and degree of milling.

TABLE 128. DIRECTIONAL FRICTION COEFFICIENTS OF WET FIBERS
(From Martin and Mittlemann[334] "Some Measurements of The Friction of Wool and Mohair")

Friction Coefficient (μ)

Direction	Mohair vs. Mohair	Mohair vs. Wool	Wool vs. Mohair	Wool vs. Wool	Wool vs. Glass	Mohair vs. Glass	Tension (mg)	Comments
tip-to-root	0.285	0.365	0.520	0.601	0.532	0.342	50	pH = 1.6
root-to-tip	0.194	0.250	0.321	0.365	0.391	0.237	50	
D.F.E.	0.091	0.115	0.199	0.236	0.141	0.105		
tip-to-root	0.112	0.132	0.206	0.211	0.241	0.263	2000	pH = 1.6
root-to-tip	0.074	0.096	0.091	0.107	0.201	0.167	2000	
D.F.E.	0.038	0.036	0.115	0.104	0.040	0.096		
tip-to-root	0.305	0.267	0.582	0.550	0.385	0.090	50	
root-to-tip	0.142	0.129	0.288	0.262	0.264	0.048	50	
D.F.E.	0.163	0.138	0.294	0.288	0.121	0.042		10% Sodium Oleate
tip-to-root	0.142	0.140	0.184	0.186	0.196	0.088	2000	
root-to-tip	0.080	0.084	0.100	0.100	0.146	0.055	2000	
D.F.E.	0.062	0.056	0.084	0.086	0.050	0.033		

The D.F.E. values for wool-vs.-wool are higher than for mohair, and in keeping with Speakman and Stott's[331] comments, one would expect the wool to felt more than the mohair, in both acid and soap milling. The mohair-vs.-wool and the wool-vs.-mohair columns give apparently inconsistent results, and this can possibly be explained by the apparatus employed wherein one fiber is considered to be the test specimen and the other is considered to be the rubbing surface.

King[347] discusses D.F.E. and felting:

> "It is well known that the felting of wool is accentuated in aqueous solutions, and many investigators have shown that the frictional coefficients also increase in the presence of water. . . . According to Martin[348] all chemical reagents which swell

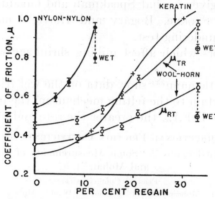

Graph 70. The effect of moisture regain on friction coefficient. (*From King,*[347] *"Some Frictional Properties of Wool and Nylon Fibres."*)

> wool fibers increase their D.F.E. and he states that this occurs at high regains, in the absence of free liquid."

Graph 70 shows plots of μ vs. regain for nylon-vs.-nylon and wool-vs.-horn.

> "In[347] the majority of cases the swelling action not only increases both coefficients of friction . . . but also the frictional difference. This is in keeping with Martin's[348] suggestion that the action of swelling agents increased the D.F.E., an effect which is difficult to explain by Makinson's theory of the D.F.E. of wool fibres. Deformation of any surface asperities naturally becomes much easier in the swollen state and interlocking of these surface asperities with the scales would then become less effective in resisting slip."

Lindberg and Gralen[337] discuss the effect of pH and temperature upon the coefficient of friction of wet wool fibers. They show that friction is only slightly dependent upon pH, there being a slight trend downward from pH 2 to 6, a slight increase at 7 and then a slight decrease to pH 9. The D.F.E. remains substantially constant.

"Since[337] the directional frictional properties are generally regarded to be the primary cause of the felting of wool, the increased rate of felting in alkaline and acid media is sometimes supposed to be due to a change in the frictional properties. Bohm[350] claims to have obtained results which prove that this change in the felting properties is entirely due to the difference between the frictions in the both directions. There has been some doubt about the significance of his results . . . , and Mercer and Makinson,[338] and Martin and Mittelmann[334] in their measurements have not obtained the same close relationship between the felting properties and the friction. . . . Our results . . . support the view of Mercer[338] and Martin.[334] . . . Assuming d (Writer's note: $\mu_2 - \mu_1$) and the felting to be directly proportional, and the absolute friction and the felting inversely proportional (since no accurate figures for the relation is given yet, it is a matter of convenience to adopt the most simple relation) leads to the equation suggested by Speakman.[331] (Writer's note: See page 74.)

$$\text{scaliness} = \frac{\mu_2 - \mu_1}{\mu_1} \cdot 100$$

or by Mercer . . .

$$\delta = \frac{\mu_2 - \mu_1}{\mu_2 + \mu_1}$$

Mercer called δ the directional frictional effect (D.F.E.). The only difference between these two expressions is the denominator . . . Both d and δ are fairly constant over the whole measured range of pH. The increased rate of felting cannot therefore be explained by a change in the frictional properties. Both μ_1 and μ_2 seem to have maxima at pH 7 and minima on both sides of pH 7."

Lindberg and Gralen[337] state that

"the friction of wool fibers is dependent on temperature, and both the with-scale and the anti-scale frictions decrease with increasing temperature, measurements being performed up to 70°F."

They report that as temperature increases μ_2 and μ_1 decrease markedly with μ_2 falling faster than μ_1. Thus d and δ both decrease slightly. Since it is well known that the feltability of wool is extremely dependent upon temperature, it must be concluded that the D.F.E. is not the *sole* factor in explaining the mechanism of felting, for the D.F.E. decreases while felting increases. We shall therefore consider what else is involved.

The Swelling and Elastic Properties of Wool Fibers, and Their Relation to Felting. The work of Menkart and Speakman,[354] and Bogaty, Sookne, and Harris[351] emphasize the necessity of proper swelling, deformation, and recovery characteristics of fibers if they are to be feltable. The former authors[354] comment:

"A satisfactory explanation of the existence of an optimum temperature for soap milling and its non-existence for acid milling, is . . . to be found if Shorter's[352] theory of milling is combined with Arnold's[355] theory of felting. Such a combination was first proposed in 1933, and the large amount of work which has since been carried out lends considerable support to the views then expressed. According to Arnold, when loose wool is felted the fibres migrate in much the same way as an earthworm crawls, i.e., by alternate extension and contraction. As stated in 1933, 'it is easy to imagine that, during milling, the entangled fibre will be stretched while piercing the loose entanglement. On release, the stretched fibre will attempt to return to its original length, and, if the scales are directed correctly, will cling to the loose entanglement and draw it towards the place of tight entanglement.' Contrary to Shorter's recent statement . . . the motion envisaged does not imply that the fibre must possess 'a muscular equipment similar to that of an actual worm'; the fibre is visualised as *being stretched*, not as stretching itself.

"According[354] to this combined theory, fibers must not only be easily deformed, but must possess power of recovery from deformation, if milling shrinkage is to be possible. The ease of deformation of wool fibres in water increases steadily with rise of temperature up to 100°C., and the hysteresis between extension and contraction, expressed as a percentage of the work for extension, decreases with rise of temperature up to about 35°C. Above 35°C, however, the percentage hysteresis increases, i.e., the power of recovery, relative to the resistance to extension, falls, and an optimum temperature for milling is clearly possible. It is the temperature above which the effect of increasing ease of deformation is balanced or overwhelmed by the effect of a decreasing power of recovery from deformation. In alkaline solutions, just as in water, the ease of deformation of wool fibres increases steadily with rise of temperature, but the power of recovery decreases at a greater rate, i.e., the percentage hysteresis *increases*,[356] and a critical temperature for milling in alkalis is even more likely than in water. In acid media, the ease of deformation increases steadily with rise of temperature, but the power of recovery decreases at a smaller rate, i.e. the percentage hysteresis *decreases*, and there is thus no reason to expect an optimum temperature for acid milling. This difference in behaviour of wool fibres in solutions of acid and alkali is, of course, due to the stability of cystine linkages in acid and their instability in alkali. The modified theory of milling shrinkage is thus capable of explaining the existence of an optimum temperature for soap milling and its non-existence for acid milling."

Bogaty, Sookne, and Harris[351] studied the elastic and swelling properties of individual fibers in a series of organic and inorganic solutions, and compared their single fiber results with the felting characteristics of fiber masses in the same solutions.

"Felting shrinkage of the (64's grade) top was determined in various reagents by a top-shrinkage test[357] . . . which involves tumbling lengths of the wool top in 1 liter of liquid and measuring the length changes occurring as a function of time of tumbling; this test has been shown to relate to the felting shrinkage in conventional machine-laundering of fabrics made from top treated for shrink resistance. . . .

"Mechanical measurements were made with a single fiber extensometer. Generally 2-inch fibers were used, and these were extended 20% and retracted, both at a rate of 30% per minute. These measurements were first made in water and then in the reagent under study, the use of this calibrated fiber technique enabling the calculations of relative work for extension, or the 20% index. (Writer's note: See page 109.) From each load-extension curve, the resilience of the wet fiber, defined as the ratio of the work recovered from extension to that required for extension, was determined.

"The swelling of the fiber in the various reagents relative to the equilibrium diameter in water was determined microscopically."

These investigators continue:

"Wool felts more readily in media that swell the fiber, and . . . felting is inhibited in reagents which hinder fiber swelling. The over-all relationship between top shrinkage and relative fiber diameter is plotted in Graph 71.[351]

"As might be expected from the close relationship between fiber swelling and extensibility, a similar curve is obtained when the top shrinkage is plotted as a function of work for extension (Graph 72). These curves describe good general relationships, especially when the variety of systems included is considered. In fact, no swelling system has been found in which felting is retarded, nor a deswelling system in which shrinkage is accelerated.

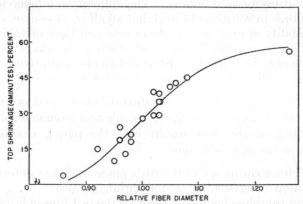

Graph 71.   The relationship between felting of wool top and the swelling of fibers in various reagents (fiber diameter in water = 1.0). (*From Bogaty, Sookne and Harris,*[351] *"The Felting of Wool."*)

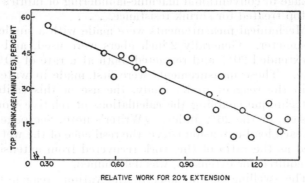

Graph 72.   The relationship between felting of wool top and the relative work for extension of fibers in various reagents. (*From Bogaty, Sookne and Harris,*[351] *"The Felting of Wool."*)

"Many of the neutral salts, e.g., the chlorides of sodium, potassium, and calcium, are seen to depress the felting of wool in proportion to the concentration of salt present. . . . Depression . . . also occurs with isopropanol solutions, the top shrinkage decreasing as the concentration of alcohol increases. These materials exert a deswelling action on the fiber, the diameter in the reagent being less than in water. . . . The decrease in relative fiber diameter is accompanied by a

TABLE 129. FELTING SHRINKAGE OF WOOL TOP, AND MECHANICAL AND SWELLING PROPERTIES OF SINGLE FIBERS IN VARIOUS REAGENTS

(From Bogaty, Sookne and Harris[351] "The Felting of Wool")

Reagent	Top Shrinkage (%) 4 min.	Top Shrinkage (%) 10 min.	Relative fiber diameter*	Relative work for 20% extension†	Fiber resilience‡
H_2O	28	47	1.00	1.00	0.49
KCl, 4M	21	34	0.98	1.14	0.38
NaCl, 1M	29	46	....	....	....
3M	21	40	....	1.03	0.45
5M	19	34	0.96	1.25	0.35
Saturated	12	26	....	1.30	0.32
$CaCl_2$, 1.6M	24	39	0.96	1.25	0.40
3M	6	13	....	....	....
LiCl, 1M	30	49	....	....	....
5M	18	35	....	....	....
LiBr, 1M	34	50	....	....	....
5M	29	48	1.02	0.80	0.54
KI, 5M	29	45	1.03	....	....
KCNS, 1M	35	50	....	....	...
5M	39	53	1.02	0.69	0.62
HCl, 0.1M	35	52	1.03	0.59	0.68
HCOOH, 2%	38	54	1.03	0.72	0.66
9%	43	58	1.06	0.67	0.71
20%	45	59	1.08	0.55	0.75
Phenol, 5% (pH 7)	44	55	....	0.62	0.72
10% (pH 8)	56	68	1.26	0.31	0.89
Urea, 1M (pH 7)	31	48	....	....	....
5M (pH 7)	41	55	1.05	0.83	0.59
4M KCl + 0.01M HCl	13	27	0.97	0.96	0.33
4M KCl + 0.1M HCl	18	34	0.98	0.91	0.34
5M NaCl + 0.1M HCl	12	23	....	....	....
5M NaCl + 0.01M HCl	10	20	0.95	1.18	0.24
3M NaCl + 0.1M HCl	19	34	....	....	....
Sat. NaCl + 0.1M HCl	10	19	....	1.10	0.24
Sat. NaCl + 0.1M HOAc	11	21	....	....	....
Sat. NaCl + 0.05M H_2SO_4	12	21	....	....	....
i-PrOH, 99%	4	8	0.86	§	....
89%	15	25	0.92	1.97	0.23
84%	17	37	....	1.33	0.31
49%	35	54	1.03	1.05	0.48

* Ratio of fiber diameter in the reagent to that in water.

† Ratio of work to extend fiber 20% in reagent to that required in water.

‡ Ratio of work recovered to that required for 20% extension in the reagent.

§ Fibers could not be extended 20% in this medium without breaking.

corresponding increase in stiffness of the fiber, as shown by the larger values for work required for extension; and the retractile ability of the fiber is lowered, as indicated by the decreased resilience.

"The resilience of the fiber in any of the solutions shows very good correlation with the felting behaviour . . . (see Graph 73). . . . It therefore appears that a very close relationship exists between felting and the elastic properties of the single fiber, although it is impossible to state that this is a cause-and-effect condition."[351]

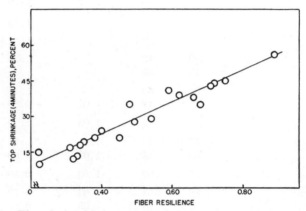

Graph 73.   The relationship between felting of wool top and the resilience of fibers in various reagents.   (*From Bogaty, Sookne and Harris,*[351] *"The Felting of Wool."*)

Wool is unique in that it exhibits greater strain recovery when wet than when dry, already discussed on page 108.   The other hydrophyllic fibers, i.e. cotton, viscose, synthetic proteins, do not exhibit such a property.   The hydrophobic synthetic fibers conceivably could have dry elastic properties which might satisfy that portion of the felting requirement when "wet out" in water; but they do not swell in water.

Summarizing, three distinct criteria are necessary to effect felting: (1) a D.F.E.; (2) proper wet elastic properties; (3) the ability of the fiber to swell.   The only fibers which satisfy all of these requirements are the animal fibers.   Presuming that points (2) or (3) could ultimately be attained in synthetic fibers, the D.F.E. requirement, presently obtained only via scales, would still be lacking.   Martin's conclusion on page 349 that no wool substitute that will truly felt will be produced in the foreseeable future appears justified.

The Carrotting of Fur Fibers.   In any discussion of felting, mention must be made of the carrotting process for enhancing the ability of fibers to felt.   The process is particularly adaptable to rabbit and other furs.

Classically it involves treating the tip ends of the fibers with oxidizing agents such as a solution of mercuric nitrate in nitric acid. More recently Menkart and Speakman[324] cite the use of sodium meta-bisulfite as a reducing agent which ruptures disulfide bonds.

In either case these investigators state that the tips of fur fibers are coarser than the roots, and the carrotting process makes the tips more flexible and deformable. Hence they are able to follow the finer root ends through entanglements which would otherwise have obstructed further movement and felting.

The important effect is apparently one of differential stiffness, attainable either via softening the tip half of the fiber or hardening the root half, or both.

Table 130 shows the effect of both softening and hardening treatments on selected portions of fur fibers. In each instance a maximum degree of felting occurs when a portion of the fiber is softened or hardened.

TABLE 130. THE EFFECT OF CARROTTING AGENTS ON THE FELTABILITY OF WOOL
(From Menkart and Speakman[324] "Felting of Animal Fibers")

Softening Treatment with Sodium Meta-Bisulfite

Fraction of Lock Treated	Degree of Felting
none	0.717
tip ¼	0.814
tip ½	0.826
tip ¾	0.720
whole lock	0.609

Hardening Treatment With Mercuric Acetate

Fraction of Lock Treated	Degree of Felting
none	0.717
root ¼	0.761
root ½	0.694
root ¾	0.545
whole lock	0.387

Section 70 shows that some of the same types of chemical treatments which are used for carrotting are also used as anti-shrink processes. Thus it will be evident that felting can be enhanced or inhibited, depending upon the technique of application. Table 130 shows that treatment of the entire fiber does depress feltability relative to an untreated control, and thus confirms the importance of proper control in processing. Section 70 discusses chemical anti-shrinking processes in detail.

Other Factors Which Influence the Rate and Degree of Felting of Wool. Menkart and Speakman[354] discuss the effect of pH and lubricants on felting:

" . . . the modified theory of milling shrinkage is capable of explaining the relationships between the rate of shrinkage and the pH of the milling agent. It has been shown that the scaliness of wool fibers in buffer solutions is sensibly independent of pH between 4 and 9, but increases with fall of pH below 4 and with rise of pH between 9 and 11. If scaliness were the only factor involved in milling shrinkage, therefore, the rate of shrinkage should be least between pH 4 and 9, should increase with fall of pH below 4 and with rise of pH between 9 and 11. Results in fair agreement with these deductions have been obtained by fulling fabric in the fulling stocks at room temperature, the rate of shrinkage being independent of pH between 4 and 8, increasing with fall of pH below 4 and rising between 8 and 10. Above pH 10 the rate of shrinkage again fell, and the existence of an optimum pH for milling in alkaline media was the second important piece of evidence used in deriving the modified theory of milling which is now under discussion. Rough general confirmation of the preceding results is provided by Mercer's determinations of the rate of shrinkage of a 3/16s yarn on shaking for 6 minutes in buffer solutions at different temperatures, the optimum pH for shrinkage in alkaline media lying between 10 and 11. The fabric and yarn used in the preceding experiments would, however, contain small amounts of adsorbed acid-soap, and there is a possibility that the maximum rate of shrinkage at pH 10 is due to its conversion into normal soap by reaction with the alkali used as the nominal milling agent. It has been shown that soap is particularly effective as a milling agent because of its lubricating action on the fibres and some evidence that there may be no optimum pH for milling in alkaline media when soap is absent is provided. . . . The results . . . were obtained by milling the same fabric, under the same conditions as before with sulphuric acid solutions, water, or sodium carbonate solutions. . . .

" . . . the[354] relationship between shrinkage and pH was normal at pH values below 6, but the shrinkage decreased steadily with rise of pH above this value, as shown in Graph 74."

"The absence of any effect due to absorbed soap is, presumably, due to the salting-out action of the buffer solutions. Summarising the preceding observations, it seems probable that the rate of shrinkage of fabrics decreases steadily with increasing alkalinity of the solution used as the milling agent, in the case of simple alkalis, and that there is no optimum pH for milling in alkaline media in *complete* absence of soap.

"It is, however, the decrease in shrinkage in alkaline media which is important as regards the theory of milling shrinkage. Fortunately, the scaliness measurements to which reference has already been made, were carried out in the same buffer solutions as the preceding shrinkage measurements. The increased shrinkage at pH values below 4 is paralleled by increasing scaliness, but in alkaline media the effects of variations in pH on scaliness and shrinkage are diametrically opposed. That the rate of shrinkage should decrease so rapidly in spite of a constant or increasing scaliness indicates that the rate of shrinkage is determined by factors other than

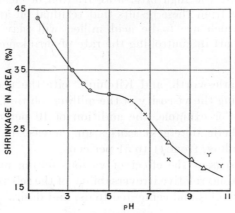

Graph 74. The effect of pH on area shrinkage of wool. (*From Menkart and Speakman,*[354] "*The Felting of Animal Fibers.*")

the scaliness of the fibres. As before, these factors may well be the ease of deformation of the fibres and their power of recovery from deformation, for, whereas both the resistance to deformation and the percentage hysteresis both decrease with fall of pH below 5, the decreasing resistance to deformation in alkaline solutions is opposed, in its effect on milling shrinkage, by increasing hysteresis. At 25°C, the percentage hysteresis is 79.4 at pH 11.29, compared with 35.9 at pH 1.03, and the modified theory of milling is thus capable of explaining not only why acid milling should be more rapid than alkali milling, but also why milling shrinkage should decrease with rise of pH in alkaline media."

In a later article, Peryman and Speakman[358] point out the importance of the presence of a lubricant during milling.

"Soap, for example, is much more effective than sodium carbonate at the same pH value because it lubricates the fibers . . . and the rate of shrinkage in acid solutions is increased by adding a lubricant such as sulphonated castor oil."

Data are shown which compare ether- and alcohol-extracted wool samples with unextracted, but reasonably "clean" samples. Shrinkage in the unextracted samples is sometimes as high as six times that of the extracted, the effect being particularly obvious in acid milling . . .

" . . . there can be little doubt that the low shrinkage of extracted patterns is due to the restraint placed on fibre movement by the high inter-fibre friction of clean wool. It will be clear from these results that residual oil and soap left in pieces which are to be acid milled will play a specially important part in controlling the rate of shrinkage during the process."[358]

Whewell, Charlesworth, and Kitchin[359] cite the use of gelatin as a means of increasing the viscosity of the milling solution, thereby increasing shrinkage. For example, the addition of 10 per cent gelatin to a 5 per cent synthetic detergent causes an increase in shrinkage, after 60 minutes of milling, from 41 to 51 per cent.

LaFleur[360] discusses the effect of various felting media on the rate and degree of felting, relative irreversability of the felt produced, relative freedom from wrinkles and cemented folds, and desirable hand:

"Products which are fat derived to a high degree (e.g., soap, sulfonated tallow, quaternary fatty acid amide) and solid at a normal room temperature, seem to produce the most satisfactory felts when judged by freedom from cemented folds and kind hand, but the fulling rate of such materials is slow; it is uncertain whether slow fulling is an essential factor or merely a coincidental property of the more desirable media.

"No product or combination has been found ideal for both fulling and scouring and economically acceptable. The most satisfactory individual product is soap; the most satisfactory combination products are soap (for fulling) with an alkylolamide condensate (for alkaline scouring), or sulfonated tallow (for fulling) with a polyoxyethylene condensate (for saline scouring).

"While it seems quite certain that soap is not indispensable for good fulling, it is still difficult to replace satisfactorily."

Sookne, Bogaty, and Harris[361] report upon the felting properties of wools of different geographical origins, of commercial blended tops,

TABLE 131. ELASTIC AND FRICTIONAL PROPERTIES OF WOOL FIBERS AND THEIR RELATION TO THE FELTING BEHAVIOR OF WOOL TOP

(From Sookne, Bogaty and Harris[361] "Some Felting Properties of Wools of Different Geographical Origin")

Sample	Source	Grade	Felting Data				Elasticity Data				Friction Data			
			Top Shrinkage, Mild Conditions		Top Shrinkage, Severe Conditions		Mean Fiber Diameter	Load to Extend 20%	Work to Extend 20%	Work Recovered From 20% Exten.	Mean Fiber Diameter	Friction Coefficient		D.F.E.
			for 15 min. (%)	for 90 min. (%)	for 4 min. (%)	for 20 min. (%)	(μ)	(g/den.)	(ergs/cm^3)	(ergs/cm^3)	(μ)	With Scales (μ_1)	Against Scales (μ_2)	($\mu_2 - \mu_1$)
1	Texas	70's	23	43	19	50	21	0.31	0.55	0.27	21	0.24	0.45	0.21
2	Australia	64's	32	49	19	45	26	0.34	0.60	0.32	24	0.27	0.49	0.22
3	Australia	62's	28	46	22	49	24	0.36	0.65	0.34	25	0.28	0.47	0.19
4	Texas	64's	20	39	19	52	27	0.37	0.65	0.35	27	0.24	0.44	0.20
5	Montevideo	64's	22	42	19	49	30	0.37	0.62	0.33	25	0.23	0.42	0.19
6	"Domestic" Pulled	62's	15	29	16	40	26	0.35	0.61	0.32	26	0.25	0.44	0.19
7	Australia	58/60's	27	46	23	52	30	0.33	0.57	0.30	28	0.27	0.46	0.19
8	New Zealand	62's	29	46	20	47	28	0.38	0.68	0.35	28	0.24	0.43	0.19
9	Argentina (Corrientes)	60's	24	42	19	49	24	0.34	0.61	0.29	25	0.27	0.45	0.18
10	Brazil	58's	21	39	20	51	26	0.34	0.59	0.30	25	0.28	0.46	0.18
11	Buenos Aires	58's	22	40	21	52	28	0.35	0.62	0.33	27	0.27	0.48	0.21
	Mean of ten wools*		25	43	20	49.5								

* Excluding Sample 6.

of wools of different staple lengths, and of wools of different quality (diameter).

The top shrinkage test of Bogaty, Frishman, Sookne, and Harris,[357] described on page 355 was employed. Table 131 tabulates felting behavior, fiber friction properties, and fiber elastic properties.

No significant differences exist in elastic or frictional properties, and, with the exception of Sample 6, no significant differences exist in shrinkage properties. Subsequent study of staple fiber length distributions indicated that Sample 6 was of short staple, and the authors[361] present evidence to show that for their shrinkage test, longer staple promotes felting.

There appears to be no correlation between fiber diameter and top shrinkage. Since no differences in elastic properties or D.F.E.'s were found, one would not expect differences in shrinkage, if the previous discussions and conclusions concerning the factors which control felting are sound. The popular conception that "fine" wools felt more than coarse wools appears to be erroneous, Sookne, Bogaty, and Harris[361] pointing out that:

> "Felting in the top shrinkage test was apparently unaffected by fiber diameter, a result which is in agreement with the findings of other investigators, who report that the laundering shrinkage of garments is not greatly affected by wool grade."

(68) The Effect of Fabric Geometry on Wool Felting

Bogaty, Weiner, Sookne and Harris[362] discuss the "Effect of Construction on The Laundering Shrinkage of Knitted Woolens." Their approach is concerned with the prevention of felting shrinkage during laundering rather than the attainment of a milled fabric of specific characteristics.

> " . . . Work in this field was prompted by the recognition by the Army Quartermaster Corps that replacement of wool service clothing was largely due to shrinkage in washing under field and other conditions. While antifelting treatments have contributed greatly to the amelioration of this problem, it is becoming clear that specification of the use of shrink-resistant wool, in the absence of construction limits, provides only a partial solution to the problem. It was therefore, with the practical goal of providing a basis for the modification of procurement specifications with respect to construction that this investigation was undertaken, in the hope that improvement in laundering stability might be achieved and that some

insight into the quantitative factors contributing to it might be gained."

The conclusions reached by these investigators[362] are listed below:

"(1) For any given yarn, the tightness of knit or density of the fabric appears to be the most important variable of construction from the point of view of effect on felting shrinkage . . . the tighter construction resists felting to a greater extent than does the slack knit made with the identical yarn. By increasing the knitting stiffness to a fairly high level, a substantial improvement in fabric stability is attained.

"(2) . . . to a much smaller extent yarn twist contribute(s) to the felting behavior. . . . Increase in the number of wales and courses per inch and in the twist, can be used to effect appreciable improvement in laundering stability.

"(3) As the weight of the yarn used in a knitted structure is increased, the feltability decreases.

"(4) The 'cover factor' which is a measure of the amount of wool packed into a unit area of fabric, and which is proportional to the wales and courses and inversely proportional to the square root of the yarn number, correlates well with the relative shrink-resistance of a construction. (Writer's note: i.e. as cover factor increases, area shrinkage decreases.)

"(5) Plying of yarns and type of spinning (Bradford vs. French) do not appear to affect feltability, other things being equal.

"(6) Application of a shrink-resistant treatment to the wool produces a greater effect in reducing laundering shrinkage than any modification of construction here employed. Construction variables must necessarily be considered in relation to the level of treatment nonetheless, since unsatisfactory stability may be found with shrink-resistant wools if the fabric construction is sleazy.

"It is to be noted that the range of constructions considered in this experiment did not deviate too far from those considered normal in terms of conventional commercial practice. It is quite possible that combinations of variables which would give considerably better felting control than was found here, and which are not now used in industry, exist."

In a recently published article, Bogaty, Weiner, Sookne, Cozart and Harris[371] have also investigated the effect of geometry on the shrinkage of woven fabrics, using cover factor, flexural rigidity, and air permeability as criteria of measurement and evaluation. Their findings are summarized as follows:

"Effect of Fabric Texture: Three plain-woven fabrics were made from identical yarns, varying only the number of ends per inch. . . . Substantial increases in felting . . . occur as the texture is made more open. . . . Increasing the weight through the use of more picks and ends results in increased stability. This result is exactly analogous to that found for knitted constructions. . . .

"Effect of Yarn Twist: Results indicate a conspicuous improvement in stability to laundering as the singles twist increases . . . Moderately high twists are required to achieve this effect to any important degree.

"Effect of Plying Yarns: The felting of fabrics made with single-ply yarns is compared . . . with that of fabrics of similar weight and texture made with plied yarns. . . . Shrinkage is similar for (these) fabrics irrespective of the ply of the yarns.

"Effect of Twist Direction: . . . the direction of twist of the yarns used will affect the appearance, fullness and density of the fabric. . . . Strong[372] observed that fabrics made with yarns twisted in opposite directions have a fuller feel and show higher air permeability. This arises from the fact that when yarns of similar direction of twist are used for warp and filling, the fibers on the top of the yarn and those on the under surface of a crossing yarn coincide in direction, the yarns "bedding" into one another and resulting in a flatter, more compact fabric. With yarns of opposing twist direction, the warp and filling yarns maintain their integrity to a greater extent, yielding a softer, fuller, and more open cloth. One would expect therefore, that the latter would be more feltable in laundering. . . . Fabric Q (Table 132), woven from yarns of opposing twist direction is seen to shrink in laundering to a greater extent than Sample N, woven from yarns of similar twist direction, the fabrics being otherwise nearly identical. . . .

"Effect of Yarn Number: . . . The data previously given have shown that decreasing the weight through the use of fewer ends results in increased felting shrinkage. . . . (Here) a method of changing the fabric weight through the use of different yarn weights but maintaining the texture is considered. . . . Where a large difference in weight is produced by using heavier yarns, a pronounced reduction in felting results. In the comparison between fabrics A and K (Table 132), the differences in weight are smaller and the fabrics are relatively tight in texture, so that the resulting effect on felting, although in the proper direction, is very small in magnitude.

"Effect of Type of Weave: Of the various weaves tabulated, the plain-woven fabric seems to be relatively felt-resistant.

TABLE 132. EFFECT OF YARN AND FABRIC CONSTRUCTION ON THE LAUNDERING SHRINKAGE OF WOOL FABRICS

(From Bogaty, Sookne, Weiner, Cozart and Harris[371] "Effect of Construction on Laundering Shrinkage of Wool")

(a) Effect of Texture (Varying Number of Ends)

Fabric	Yarn Number	Yarn Twist Singles tpi	Ply tpi	Fabric Wt oz/yd²	Fabric Texture Warp yarns/inch	Filling	Area Laundering Shrinkage per cent	Remarks
A	2/11.1	9.2Z	5.6S	11.0	31	22	29	Plain weave. Identical
B	2/11.1	9.2Z	5.6S	9.9	31	16	39	yarns used in warp and
C	2/11.1	9.2Z	5.6S	9.2	30	14	46	filling.

(b) Effect of Yarn Twist

Fabric	Yarn Number	Filling Yarn Twist Singles	Ply	Fabric Wt	Fabric Texture Warp	Filling	Shrinkage	Remarks
I	2/11.4	5.9Z	5.2S	10.5	32	26	31	
A	2/11.1	9.2Z	5.7S	11.0	31	22	29	Plain weaves
J	2/11.4	15.0Z	5.7S	10.9	31	25	23	

(c) Effect of Yarn Ply

Fabric	Yarn Number Warp	Filling	Fabric Wt	Fabric Texture Warp	Filling	Total	Shrinkage	Fabric Flexural Rigidity (gm.cm.) Warp	Filling	Remarks
PX	1/5.5	1/5.3	10.7	27	27	54	30	0.31	0.33	
A	2/11.2	2/11.2	11.0	31	22	55	29	0.42	0.37	Plain weaves
M	1/5.3	1/5.3	9.7	24	21	45	34	0.27	0.28	
C	2/11.2	2/11.2	9.2	30	14	44	46	0.33	0.14	

(d) Effect of Twist Direction

Fabric	Yarn Number Warp	Filling	Yarn Twist Warp	Filling	Fabric Texture Warp	Filling	Shrinkage	Air Permeability ft³/min/ft²	Remarks
N	1/5.3	1/5.3	5.3S	5.3S	25	27	41	150	2/2 Twill Weaves
Q	1/5.5	1/5.3	5.4Z	5.3S	25	26	48	190	

(e) Effect of Yarn Number

Fabric	Yarn Number Warp	Filling	Fabric Wt	Fabric Texture Warp	Filling	Shrinkage	Air Permeability ft³/min/ft²	Remarks
B	2/11.2	2/11.2	9.9	31	16	39	126	
L	2/11.2	2/3.9	14.6	31	17	28	56	Plain weaves
A	2/11.2	2/11.2	11.0	31	22	29	35	
K	2/11.2	2/6.8	13.0	31	23	26	22	

(f) Effect of Type of Weave

Fabric	Weave	Fabric Wt	Fabric Texture Warp	Filling	Shrinkage	Air Permeability ft³/min/ft²
PX	Plain	10.7	27	27	30	53
Q	2/2 Broken twill	10.6	25	26	48	190
H	3/1 Unbalanced broken twill	12.5	32	34	20	41
E	2/2 Broken twill	11.8	33	28	26	41
F	2/1 Twill	12.4	32	31	27	58
D	2/2 Broken twill	11.5	30	29	32	76
A	Plain	11.0	31	22	29	35

Plain-woven sample PX shrinks much less than does Q, a twill weave, although constructionwise the two fabrics are quite similar. . . . Differences among the various twills with respect to shrinkage are not very great if the texture differences are taken into account. The air permeability measurements, however, do rate the twill fabrics in approximately the order of their laundering shrinkage."

These authors[371] suggest that

"the compactness of the fabric structure, whether due to the number or weight of the yarns, or to the nature of their inter-

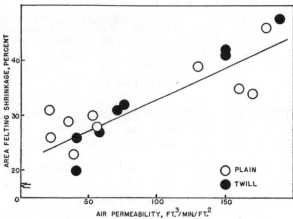

Graph 75. Relationship between felting shrinkage and air permeability. (*From Bogaty, Weiner, Sookne, Cozart and Harris,*[371] "*Effect of Construction on Laundering Shrinkage.*")

lacing, is the factor which is basic to the feltability of the fabric. It was considered desirable to determine whether a single parameter could be used to describe this tightness or compactness factor. The present study suggests the possible use for this purpose of air permeability, of the flexural rigidity of the fabric, and of the cover factor. . . . The relationships between felting shrinkage and (these parameters) are plotted in Graphs 75–77."

"Each of these parameters—cover factor, flexural rigidity and air permeability—appears to be related to the feltability of a fabric, and may be considered to be a measure of fabric tightness. Cover factor and flexural rigidity are interdependent to some extent. . . . "[371]

Additional information on the influence of fabric structure is reported by Hill and Kornreich[363] and Best-Gordon.[364]

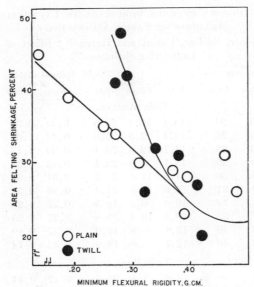

Graph 76.   Relationship between felting shrinkage and flexural rigidity.   (*From Bogaty, Weiner, Sookne, Cozart and Harris,*[371] *"Effects of Construction on Laundering Shrinkage."*)

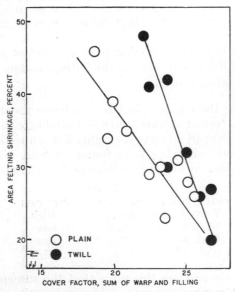

Graph 77.   Relationship between felting shrinkage in laundering and cover factor. (*From Bogaty, Weiner, Sookne, Cozart and Harris,*[371] *"Effects of Construction on Laundering Shrinkage."*)

TABLE 133. RELATIONSHIP BETWEEN SHRINKAGE IN LAUNDERING AND VARIOUS MEASURES OF FABRIC COMPACTNESS

(From Bogaty, Weiner, Sookne, Cozart and Harris[371] "Effect of Construction on Laundering Shrinkage")

Fabric	Shrinkage in Laundering (%)			Cover Factor			Flexural Rigidity (g cm.)		Air Permeability (ft³/min/ft²)
	Warp	Filling	Area	Warp	Filling	Sum	Warp	Filling	
				Plain Weaves					
J	10	15	23	13.1	10.4	23.5	0.49	0.39	39
K	12	16	26	13.1	12.5	25.6	0.48	1.05	22
L	10	20	28	13.1	12.0	25.1	0.39	1.17	56
A	12	19	29	13.1	9.3	22.4	0.42	0.37	35
PX	16	16	30	11.6	11.6	23.2	0.31	0.33	53
I	15	19	31	13.6	10.8	24.4	0.46	0.51	21
M	17	21	34	10.4	9.1	19.5	0.27	0.28	170
P	18	21	35	10.4	10.4	20.8	0.27	0.25	160
B	19	25	39	13.1	6.8	19.9	0.37	0.19	130
C	24	29	46	12.7	5.9	18.6	0.33	0.14	180
				Twill Weaves					
H	9	12	20	13.6	13.1	26.7	0.42	0.44	41
E	15	13	26	14.0	11.9	25.9	0.44	0.32	41
F	14	15	27	13.6	13.1	26.7	0.43	0.41	58
G	18	16	31	10.6	13.1	23.7	0.52	0.38	71
D	17	18	32	12.7	12.3	25.0	0.41	0.34	76
N	23	23	41	10.8	11.6	22.4	0.27	0.30	150
O	25	23	42	10.8	12.9	23.7	0.29	0.31	150
Q	26	30	48	10.8	11.2	22.0	0.28	0.29	190

The former authors have investigated the effect of yarn twist direction and fabric twill line direction on the felting tendencies of laundered wool, rayon and cotton articles.

"If we use the letters S and Z to indicate the direction of twist in the accepted manner, and also to indicate the direction of the line of twill (S down to the right, Z down to the left) the following relationship has been found to exist between the twist of yarn and the line of twill in respect to the susceptibility to felting:

Twist of Yarn	"S" Twill	"Z" Twill
Warp S	Low	High
Warp Z	High	Low
Weft S	High	Low
Weft Z	Low	High

"It can be seen from this table that the susceptibility to felting is greater when the twill and twist directions cross than when they do not. If large letters are used for the direction of twill and small letters (vertical for warp; horizontal for weft) for the yarn twist, the relationship can be represented pictorially:"[363]

Best-Gordon[364] confirms the above observations:

"With severe mechanical abrasion the surface of a rayon can be so broken up as to produce a distinct "barbed" effect, this effect is accelerated when the fibres are in a swollen state. Therefore, when a "barbed" character has been developed on a damaged fibre, it is likely that a fabric would commence to felt, provided there is also fibre and yarn movement at the same time, but in spite of fibre/yarn movement, felting cannot commence until some barbs are developed.

FILLING

WARP

Figure 19. The relationship between yarn twist, twill direction and tendency to felt. (*From Hill and Kornreich,*[363] *"Influence of Fabric Structure on Felting."*)

" . . . A partially felted rayon tablecloth was examined . . . its design and construction gave a variation in twist/twill relationship. It was a border dobby satin-faced cloth, woven on a continuous filament viscose rayon warp with a spun viscose rayon weft. In two portions in which the twill ran downwards to the right, felting occurred, in the other two portions with the twill in the opposite direction, felting had not occurred. . . . The yarn was **Z** twist. . . .

" . . . the continuous filament warp was barbed to a small degree, whilst the spun rayon weft showed a more pronounced barb.

"That[364] the continuous filament yarns were not felted may be regarded as evidence that without fibre/yarn movement, felting cannot take place, even with fibre surface damage. The spun rayon had felted in certain areas because there was more fibre/yarn movement in one area than another, although there was fibre surface damage all the way across the weft. Thus the only apparent difference in the pairs of areas being a difference in the direction of twill, it was concluded that when the twist lay across the twill greater freedom of fibre/yarn takes place when the cloth is subjected to severe laundering conditions."

(69) The Effect of Fiber Blending on Wool Felting

The blending of other fibers, natural and synthetic, with wool is currently commanding considerable attention. We have stated that wool is the only fiber which will felt in the accepted practical sense. The dilution of wool with any non-felting fiber produces blends which for the most part have less tendency to felt. Again depending upon the end-use requirement, this may be advantageous or disadvantageous. By introducing certain percentages of non-felting fiber, milling may be reduced to the point where a fabric of required felt-like characteristics may be unobtainable. Similarly, blended fabric structures can be made which will be resistant to felting shrinkage during wet laundering.

Whewell[231] makes "Some Observations on The Finishing of Fabrics Containing Wool and Other Fibres":

"The attractiveness of . . . blended fabrics arises not only from the comparatively low cost of many of the non-wool components but also from the fact that in blended fabrics, advantage may be taken of the outstanding properties of all the components. Fibres other than wool are not regarded merely as diluents but as raw materials which make their own contribution towards the final character of the fabric. For example, fabrics containing wool and nylon may be so designed as to yield a cloth with a woolly handle and exceptional wearing qualities. Again, Fibro or acetate staple fibre when blended with wool and piece dyed yields attractive mixture cloths; tone in tone effects are readily produced by piece dyeing cloths containing wool and Rayolanda, whilst soft handling materials may be obtained by the use of mixtures of wool and protein rayons. With such possibilities available to the designer it is evident that blended fabrics will become more and more important."

Table 134 shows data on the effect of blending fibers on the shrinkage of union fabrics after scouring and milling.

"The dimensional changes which take place during scouring are clearly determined by the type of scour employed and arise from the release of strains in the material and from the felting of the wool. The changes in width accompanying a typical washing procedure are summarised in Table 134, together with other relevant data, and it is evident that the shrinking produced during the scouring decreases as the

TABLE 134. THE INFLUENCE OF BLENDING WOOL WITH OTHER FIBERS UPON THE CHANGES IN DIMENSIONS OF UNION FABRICS AFTER SCOURING AND MILLING (From Whewell[231] "Some Observations on Finishing of Fabrics Containing Wool and Other Fibres")

Fabric Number	% Wool	% "Fibro"	% "Rayolanda"	% Shrinkage Reed to Greige Cloth	% Shrinkage on Scouring (% of reed width)	% Width Shrinkage after Milling for 15 min.	46 min.
A	100.0	.....	.....	7.9	17.4	21.2	30.5
B	62.5	37.5	.....	6.3	14.3	21.8	31.3
C	50.0	50.0	.....	6.3	13.5	19.8	31.7
D	25.0	75.0	.....	5.6	12.7	19.9	31.7
E	12.5	87.5	.....	6.3	12.7	18.6	25.2
F	.....	100.0	.....	6.0	9.5	....	....
G	.....	.....	100.0	6.3	14.3	....	....
H	62.5	.....	37.5	7.1	13.5	23.2	38.8
I	50.0	.....	50.0	6.0	12.7	23.9	38.1
J	25.0	.....	75.0	5.6	13.5	23.9	38.1
K	12.5	.....	87.5	6.3	12.7	22.9	34.8
L	100.0	.....	.....	11.9	19.0	35.2	53.4
M	62.5	37.5	.....	9.5	19.0	33.2	49.2
N	50.0	50.0	.....	8.7	17.4	31.1	47.4
O	25.0	75.0	.....	7.1	16.7	27.8	43.1
P	12.5	87.5	.....	6.3	17.4	24.9	....
Q	.....	100.0	.....	6.3	16.7	....	....
R	.....	.....	100.0	7.5	15.1	....	....
S	62.5	.....	37.5	8.7	17.4	33.3	50.8
T	50.0	.....	50.0	8.7	17.4	33.2	51.7
U	25.0	.....	75.0	7.9	15.9	31.7	51.0
V	12.5	.....	87.5	7.9	15.1	25.2	43.3

Description of fabric in loom:

Series I: A–K worsted fabrics

Warp, 1/16's worsted counts, 8 t.p.i., 58 ends/inch, reed width 63 inches.

Weft, 2/32's worsted counts, 63 picks/inch.

Warp and Weft yarns were made from the same blend.

Weave 2/2 twill.

Series II: L–V woolen fabrics

Warp, 21's Y.S. woolen spun, 30 ends/inch, reed width 63 inches.

Weft, 18's Y.S. woolen spun, 29 picks/inch.

Warp and Weft yarns were made from the same blend.

Weight, 7.0 ounces.

amount of synthetic fibre in the cloth increases. Both Fibro and Rayolanda behave similarly. It is interesting to note that the greater the percentage of wool in the cloth, the greater is the difference between the reed width and that of the grey cloth.

"Milling

"Since wool only is capable of felting, it is to be expected that admixture with other fibres will affect this characteristic to an extent which will be reflected in the rate and the amount of shrinkage. . . . It is clear that in the case of the woollen spun materials (fabrics L-M) the incorporation of 'Fibro' or 'Rayolanda' in wool fabrics results in a reduction in shrinking power. The effect of the 'Rayolanda' is, however, much less than that of 'Fibro,' for in all the fabrics examined, those containing 'Rayolanda' shrink more than corresponding ones containing 'Fibro.' As much as 75 per cent of 'Rayolanda' may be introduced without greatly reducing the shrinking power. The figures obtained on the worsted fabrics also show differences between 'Fibro' and 'Rayolanda,' for fabrics made from wool and 'Rayolanda' shrink more quickly than corresponding fabrics made from wool and 'Fibro.' It is surprising that the 50/50 wool-'Rayolanda' cloth shrinks more than the 100 per cent wool material and even the 50/50 'Fibro'-wool union shrinks slightly more. These figures illustrate the importance of cloth structure in the case of determining the shrinking powers of blended fabrics, for in the case of woollen spun cloths, the 'Fibro'-wool blended material always shrinks less than the 100 per cent wool cloth, but in the worsted structure the 50/50 blend has a slightly greater shrinking power than the wool cloth. The superiority of the 50/50 wool-'Rayolanda' blend is much more marked with the solid worsted fabrics than with woolens."[231]

TABLE 135. EFFECT OF STAPLE LENGTH ON MILLING PROPERTIES

(From Whewell[231] "Some Observations on Finishing of Fabrics Containing Wool and Other Fibres")

	% Shrinkage after One Hour Woven Fabric Containing (In Weft):			
% Wool in Fabric	2-inch "Fibro"	6-inch "Fibro"	2-inch "Rayolanda"	6-inch "Rayolanda"
100	3	33	32	33
75	29	32	33	37
50	26	29	33	37
25	21	22	30	33
12.5	17	16	25	28

"It is evident that whilst the fabrics containing the longer staple fibres show slightly higher shrinkage than those of cloths containing two-inch fibres, the differences between the two sets of data are small. This has an interesting commercial consequence, for yarns containing the longer staple rayon are considerably stronger than those containing the shorter material, and hence if a strong milled cloth is required it is advisable to use the longest staple fibre possible, and this will apparently have no serious effect on the milling shrinkage."[231]

Whewell continues,

"The effect of other non-felting fibres on the shrinkage of mixture fabrics has also been examined and the results obtained are summarised as follows:

"*Acetate Rayon*

"In general, blended fabrics containing wool and acetate staple fibre shrink much less readily than corresponding all-wool materials.

"This reduced rate and extent of shrinkage is occasionally a disadvantage, e.g., when fabrics are to be finished in heavy milled styles, but it may be partly overcome by the addition to the milling liquor of reagents which are capable of plasticising the acetate rayon . . . Alternatively the rayon may be softened by first soaking the cloth in a softening agent and then milled in the presence of the reagent . . . Suitable mixtures for use in this way include formic or acetic acid solution containing an organic solvent like acetone.

"*Protein rayons*

"In general, blended fabrics containing as much as 75 per cent of rayon, mill as well as, or in some cases better than, all-wool materials of the same structure.

"*Nylon*

"The incorporation of nylon in fabrics generally reduces their shrinking power. This is illustrated in Table 136, Part C . . . in which are summarised the shrinkage of cotton warp cloths with wefts containing various percentages of nylon waste. The yarns (27 Yorkshire skeins, 7 t.p.i.) were spun on the woolen system, the waste having previously been cut so that the maximum fibre length was two inches. To provide comparative data, results are also included relating to cloths of similar structures having wefts made from blends of wool and Peruvian cotton. It is evident that fabrics containing nylon shrink less readily during milling than all-wool cloths, but in the fabrics used in the present investigation a considerable amount of non-felting fibre must be introduced before the shrinkage is seriously affected. The nylon is more effective than cotton in reducing the shrinkage. Similar results have also been obtained in a recent investigation . . . on the properties of blended fabrics containing wool and nylon staple. It was demonstrated that the blended fabrics shrink less readily and to a smaller extent than corresponding all-wool materials.

"It appears from the results given below, and those obtained in other investigations, that the fibres which have been examined may be placed in the following order of effectiveness in reducing milling shrinkage: acetate > nylon > cotton > 'Fibro' > 'Rayolanda' > protein rayons.''[231]

TABLE 136. MILLING SHRINKAGE OF BLENDED FABRICS

(Adapted from Whewell[231] "Some Observations on the Finishing of Fabrics Containing Wool and Other Fibres")

(a) Acetate Rayon-Wool Blends

| | % Area Shrinkage | | | |
| | After Soap Milling | | After Acid Milling | |
Composition	20 min.	68 min.	15 min.	69 min.
100% wool	14.3	53.9	12.5	51.1
50% acetate, 50% wool	4.5	29.6	3.4	27.0

(b) Protein Rayons-Wool Blends

| | % Area Shrinkage | |
| | After Acid (?) Milling | |
Composition	20 min.	50 min.
100% wool	27.0	46.7
69% wool, 31% casein	30.6	52.4
50% wool, 50% casein	32.8	52.1
21% wool, 79% casein	26.0	46.1
100% wool	5.8	16.5
75% wool, 25% "Ardil"	6.9	20.4
51% wool, 49% "Ardil"	7.0	23.8

Description of fabrics: Warp, 2/40's American Cotton, 56 ends per inch
Weft, see above compositions, 44 picks per inch
Weave, 2/2 twill

(c) Nylon- or Cotton-Wool Blends

| Compositions of Weft (The Warp is 100% Cotton) | % Shrinkage after Milling | |
	30 min.	90 min.
100% wool	15.6	33.0
75% wool, 25% nylon	14.4	31.8
46% wool, 54% nylon	11.4	24.3
27% wool, 73% nylon	9.5	14.6
100% wool	15.6	33.0
73% wool, 27% cotton	17.6	35.0
52% wool, 48% cotton	15.4	37.5
24% wool, 76% cotton	13.2	36.0

A private communication from Dr. Whewell states that a paper entitled "The Finishing of Fabrics Containing Wool and Man Made Fibres" by Whewell, Barrett, and Senior[402] is to be published in The Journal of The Textile Institute in the near future. This paper lists additional information on the milling properties of blended fabrics, and the reader is referred to it.

Referring to the same series of navy meltons cited in Table 112, composed of blends of wool and other fibers, Table 137 lists shrinkage values after laundering.

TABLE 137. EFFECT OF FIBER BLENDS ON LAUNDERING SHRINKAGE*
(From Fabric Research Laboratories, Inc.[248] "Development of Navy Meltons From Wool Blends"; Report to The United States Naval Clothing Depot)

Fabric Number	% Wool	% Viscose	% Cotton	% Nylon	1st Wash W.	1st Wash F.	2nd Wash W.	2nd Wash F.	3rd Wash W.	3rd Wash F.
0 melton	100	..	..	..	7.9	2.1	9.5	3.3	11.4	5.0
1 melton	63	22	..	15	5.7	0.9	5.8	1.3	6.3	1.4
2 melton	72	28	..	..	9.8	0.8	11.4	3.2	12.4	3.3
3 melton	73	..	27	..	7.8	0.0	9.1	0.4	10.6	1.3
4 melton	74	..	..	26	7.8	0.4	8.7	1.4	10.1	1.7
2A covert	72	28	..	..	13.1	1.7	14.8	3.1	16.4	4.2
2B venetian	72	28	..	..	11.2	4.1	12.8	4.9	14.5	6.2

% Shrinkage after

* *Note:* The A.A.T.C.C. procedure for the determination of shrinkage in laundering was employed. A 20 × 20" sample was washed for one complete cycle in an automatic wheel-type washer using a neutral soap and warm water.

The replacement of approximately ⅓ of the wool (in Fabric 1) with viscose and nylon cuts the shrinkage to approximately half in the warp and one fourth in the filling. As might be expected, nylon is somewhat more effective in reducing shrinkage than are cotton and rayon. This is probably because of the greater hydrophobicity of nylon; Table 52 shows its diameter to increase 5 per cent when wet out, while cotton swells 14 per cent and viscose 26 per cent. However, even in the case of nylon, and for the construction involved, 25 per cent replacement is apparently insufficient properly to stabilize dimensionally these fabrics in wet laundering.

To develop "washable woolens" has been a long-sought objective of the textile industry. In recent years the major approach has been the development of chemical treatments to render wool unshrinkable. To a lesser degree, the blending of wool and other fibers has been given consideration. In very recent months, blending has had extensive publicity but with a sparsity of quantitative information. It does not appear unreasonable to predict that blends of wool and other non-felting fibers will, when properly constructed, produce fabrics of excellent shrink resisting qualities. Here the hydrophobic fibers will be of advantage over the hydrophillics because of their dimensional stability. Certainly additional work on the blending approach to shrink resistance appears to be in order.

(70) Chemical Methods for Preparing Shrink Resistant Wool

When we talk about shrink-resistant wool, we mean wool which will resist "felting shrinkage" as defined on page 292 rather than "relaxation shrinkage."

Methods for producing shrink-resistant wool may be classified into the following categories:

(1) Oxidation Processes, e.g., wet or dry chlorine and derivatives, bromination, permanganates, peroxides.

(2) Hydrolysis Processes, e.g., alkalies, alcoholic alkalies, proteolytic enzymes.

(3) Resin Applications, e.g., melamine formaldehyde, vinyls, acrylates, chloroprene-methacrylate copolymers.

The first two types produce a permanent modification to the wool fiber structure—altering the scale structure and D.F.E., or the elastic properties. The third method accomplishes the same effect but via the deposition of resinous material upon the fiber.

The number of processes for shrinkproofing wool are probably in the hundreds. A literature survey by Horigan and Sage[365] for the U.S. Army Quartermaster lists 427 references and some 80 patents on the subject of shrinkage and shrinkage control of textiles (wool and other fibers). Of the four main methods listed above, three are currently in use: wet chlorination, dry chlorination, and resin application. Gould[249] summarizes the current chemical treatment status as follows:

"To the best of our knowledge, all commercial chemical methods now in use for producing shrink-resistant wool are in (the) category (of) halogenation processes. In fact, we may restrict this to those involving chlorine.

"Most prominent in Britain is the Wool Industries Research Association process referred to previously, which uses dry gaseous chlorine. Simple in concept, the method essentially involves evacuating the carefully conditioned top, yarn, piece goods or garments, in a large air tight chamber. Following evacuation, chlorine gas is admitted, and the stock remains in contact with this for twenty minutes. The vessel is again evacuated to remove chlorine, then flushed with air and opened for removal of the treated material. This was the first successful commercial process, and now has had ten or twelve years of operation.

"All other processes involve wet chlorination, variously conducted, under acid or alkaline conditions with or without inhibitors or assistants. These include permanganate, formaldehyde, Chloramine T and others.

". . . We would expect . . . that the rate of reaction of chlorine on wool at low pH would be very rapid. . . . The effect usually is uneven treatment, and severe damage to the wool as measured in weight loss and increased alkali solubility. . . . Mechanical properties are often degraded by acid chlorination, shown by such yardsticks as the so-called 30% index. . . .

"Evidence indicates that minimum fiber damage, greatest ease of control, and maximum resistance to felting are achieved on the alkaline side."

Harris and Frishman[366] show that wet chlorination at pH 8 to 9 produces "nonshrinkable" wool of optimum physical properties. (This essentially is the Harriset process.) Table 138 shows the effect of chlorination on physical properties.

TABLE 138. EFFECT OF CHLORINE CONCENTRATION AND pH UPON AREA SHRINKAGE, FRICTION COEFFICIENTS, 30% INDEX, COMPRESSIONAL RESILIENCE AND ALKALI SOLUBILITY

(From Harris and Frishman[366] "Some Aspects of The Chlorination of Wool to Produce Shrink Resistance")

(a)

Treatment % Chlorine	Area Shrinkage %	Friction Coefficients Against Scales (μ_1)	Friction Coefficients With Scales (μ_2)	D.F.E. ($\mu_1 - \mu_2$)
0 (untreated)	69	0.39	0.19	0.20
5	28	0.39	0.22	0.17
7	12	0.44	0.36	0.08
10	6	0.47	0.44	0.03

(Writer's note: The pH for the above data is not listed.)

(b)

pH of Treatment	30% Index*	Compressional Resilience
Untreated	99	57
1.1	84	51
3.1	85	50
5.2	88	53
7.4	93	52
9.2	97	55
10.7	96	57

* Energy required to stretch a wet fiber to 30% elongation after treatment, divided by the energy requirement prior to the treatment.

(Writer's note: The per cent chlorine for the above data is not listed.)

(c)

pH of Treatment	Area Shrinkage %	Alkali Solubility %
Untreated	27	6.5
10	2	7.4
9	0	9.4
8	2	9.4
6.5	3	12.1
4.2	5	15.3
1.0	6	9.2†

† "The low alkali-solubility obtained on the sample treated at pH 1 is due to the fact that the fiber has already lost considerable weight during chlorination at this pH."[366]

(Writer's note: The per cent chlorine for the above data is not listed.)

Graph 78 shows plots of (1) loss in weight of wool fiber during chlorination, and (2) alkali solubility vs. pH of chlorinating treatment. It again shows pH 8–9 to be the optimum.

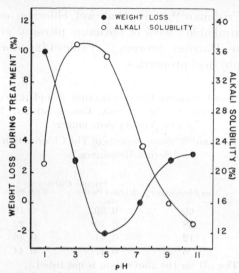

Graph 78. Loss in weight during chlorination, and the alkali solubility as a function of the pH of the hypochlorite-treating solution. (*From Harris and Frishman,*[366] *"Some Aspects of the Chlorination of Wool to Produce Shrink Resistance."*)

Gould[249] discusses the practical requirements of shrink-resistant wool with specific reference to the Harriset Process:

"Among questions most frequently asked about shrink-resistant wool are those relating to washability, bleaching and dyeing properties.

"As regards washability, let us discuss two methods, hand washing and machine laundering.

"First, with respect to hand laundering, no wool item is entitled to the label 'shrink-resistant' unless it will withstand hand washing under usual conditions of temperature, soap and ordinary care, without shrinking out of size, matting, or becoming boardy or felted in the life of the garment.

"What about machine laundering? When made of truly shrink-resistant top, most woven goods and some knitted goods can be safely and repeatedly laundered in automatic home washers or sent out for commercial laundering. It should be remembered that there are few more effective fulling mills than automatic washers which fill and empty without interruption of the mechanical cycle. Some wool garments will stand it; other more delicately constructed garments will not. This is equally true when fibers other than wool are involved. The careful housewife does not submit light cotton jersey or nylon hose to such treatment. Many wool articles, particularly knitted garments of loose knit or novelty construction, are not by nature built to take this kind of abuse. More firmly constructed garments, such as most wool socks, can be handled like the rest of the family wash.

"Harriset-treated garments may be hand washed without qualification. The answer to machine laundering must be qualified. It depends upon the grade of wool, the type of yarn, and above all the construction. The shrink resistant label is not a license to abuse.

"The term 'washable,' applied to shrink-resistant wools, includes also fastness of dyestuffs employed. Certainly no acid dyes customarily employed for the bright blues and pinks of baby shades are fast enough to laundering to warrant the designation 'washable' in the consumer's mind.

"This situation is not hopeless however. New techniques for applying vat dyes to wool make available shades of good brilliance and greatly enhanced durability.

"Originally we thought the greatest use of Harriset-treated top would be in knitwear. It has been most agreeable to discover the increased utility imparted by its reduced felting characteristics to many woven fabrics, such as washable flannels and shirtings. More recently imaginative designers have created new and exciting fabrics such as cool, porous, tropical worsteds and gabardines, made possible by wool of controlled susceptibility to felting."

The Dyeing Characteristics of Chlorinated Wool. Barritt and Elsworth[367] summarize the dyeing properties of chlorinated wool:

"Modification of the surface structure of wool fibres which occurs on chlorination, renders the fibre more accessible to penetration by dye molecules and dye aggregates, and this in turn results in the different behavior of chlorinated wool in dyeing. When applied under the conditions normally used for their application to unchlorinated wool, most dyes are taken up more rapidly by chlorinated wool; secondly, chlorinated wool absorbs dyes under conditions which would not be suitable for their application to unchlorinated wool. Thus, chlorinated wool takes up under neutral conditions metalliferous dyes, many direct cotton dyes not absorbed by unchlorinated wool, and certain chrome dyes which cannot normally be applied by the metachrome method. The colloidal acid dyes are taken up much more readily at lower temperatures. Determination of the total combining capacity of wool and chlorinated wool for acid and acid dyes indicates that chlorination does not increase the basic properties of the wool.

"With metachrome dyes it is shown that there is a definite correlation between dyeing properties and chemical constitution. Thus, sulphonated metachrome dyes are taken up by chlorinated wool more rapidly than they are by unchlorinated wool, whereas non-sulphonated metachrome dyes are taken up very rapidly and at the same rate by both types of wool.

"When dyed on chlorinated wool, the fastness to wet treatments of most wool dyes tends to be lower than when they are dyed on unchlorinated wool. With acid dyes of the level dyeing type the loss in fastness is appreciable, but with the faster types, e.g., chrome dyes and metalliferous dyes, the change in fastness properties is negligible. No significant change has been observed in the fastness to light."

The Mechanics of Anti-Shrink Treatments. The specific properties enjoyed by the wool fiber which enable it to felt may now be analyzed with respect to the application of anti-felting treatments. It appears reasonable to hypothesize that any treatment or environment which diminishes the D.F.E., reduces the requisite elastic properties, or prevents swelling will prevent felting shrinkage. With the exception of resin application which masks the scale structure, all of the chemical methods modify, or more bluntly, degrade the fiber structure to accomplish these ends. Table 138 (Part a) shows that progressively increasing chlorine concentrations diminish the D.F.E. from a value of 0.20 to 0.03. It is significant that both the "against scale" and "with scale" coefficients increase, the latter at a much more rapid rate, and this is the reason that the D.F.E. is reduced.

Morphologically, the reduction is explained as an alteration in the scale structure. Harris and Frishman show photomicrographs of fiber impressions (casts) which demonstrate the progressive diminution of clarity of scale structure produced by chlorination at pH 7 upwards to pH 11 and downwards to pH 1. Below pH 3 the scale structure substantially disappears. Alexander[368] correlates the effect of anti-shrink treatments with microscopic examination of fiber structure:

"The behaviour of wool treated with the various reagents runs parallel to the amount of fibre damage assessed by microscopic examination. . . . Thus treatments rendering wool unshrinkable on both acid and alkali milling remove the scales bodily, whereas the other treatments appear to leave the scales in position. . . .

" . . . Wool treated with potassium permanganate and fluorine is completely unshrinkable on alkaline milling but on acid milling shows little shrink-resistance. Treatments with alkaline hypochlorite solution, aqueous bromine in carbon tetrachloride, produce complete resistance to alkali but only partial resistance to acid milling. Chlorine, applied in aqueous acid, in carbon tetrachloride, or as the gas, as well as sulphuryl chloride in carbon tetrachloride, and alcoholic potassium hydroxide, produce complete resistance to both acid and alkali milling. . . . The scaliness of untreated and potassium permanganate-treated wool fibres was measured by the violin bow method (see page 69) . . . the directional friction effect of fibres treated with potassium permanganate is very much less when examined in alkali, but is equal to, or perhaps very slightly greater than, that of untreated fibres when measured in acid solution. Moreover, treated fibres showing no directional friction effect in alkali, recovered their full directional friction effect when transferred to acid."[368]

Lipson and Howard[369] concur that the reduction in D.F.E. is correlative with the degree of shrinkproofing. But they state that

" . . . it is not necessary to alter the physical structure of the fiber scales in order to reduce their D.F.E. on a smooth keratin surface. Treatment of the keratin surface alone with certain of the reagents used for reducing shrinkability will bring about the necessary reduction. These findings therefore support the views of Martin[348] in indicating that the D.F.E. is not simply the physical result of scaliness. . . . With both surfaces (i.e., the smooth keratin and the fiber) treated, it has been found that all the reagents used for reducing shrinkability (sulfuryl chloride, aqueous bromine, aqueous chlorine, chlorine in carbon tetrachloride), except alcoholic caustic potash, markedly reduce the with-scale and anti-scale coefficients. Alcoholic caustic potash . . . increases the value of each."

Sookne, Bogaty, and Harris[370] discuss both the D.F.E. and elastic properties of shrink-resistant treated fibers and arrive at the following conclusions, based on the data presented in Table 139.

"When top is subjected to felting in various solutions, if the level of treatment is low, the resilience of the fiber controls the extent of shrinkage. The shrinkage is low in solutions in which fiber resilience is low, and high in solutions in which the fibers exhibit good recoverability. When the wool has been subjected to an adequate shrink-resistance treatment, the

TABLE 139. SHRINKAGE AND ELASTIC AND FRICTIONAL PROPERTIES IN VARIOUS MEDIA, OF WOOL TOP TREATED FOR SHRINK RESISTANCE TO VARYING DEGREES (From Sookne, Bogaty and Harris[370] "The Felting of Shrink-Resistant Wool As Related to Some Properties of the Single Fiber")

Treatment	% Available Chlorine	Medium	Top Shrinkage % 4 Min.	10 Min.	Fiber Resilience*	μ_1	μ_2	$(\mu_1 - \mu_2)$
Control	0	H_2O	23	38	0.48	0.52	0.28	0.24
A	0.3	H_2O	9	30	0.43	0.49	0.32	0.17
B	0.6	H_2O	8	22	0.47	0.49	0.35	0.14
C	1.0	H_2O	2	7	0.45	0.50	0.42	0.08
D	1.2	H_2O	1	3	0.47	0.65	0.60	0.05
					Mean 0.46			
Control	0	$0.1M$ HCl	34	54	0.64	0.54	0.27	0.27
A	0.3	$0.1M$ HCl	20	40	0.63	0.48	0.29	0.19
B	0.6	$0.1M$ HCl	12	32	0.64	0.52	0.35	0.17
C	1.0	$0.1M$ HCl	3	5	0.61	0.49	0.39	0.10
D	1.2	$0.1M$ HCl	1	5	0.61	0.70	0.61	0.09
					Mean 0.63			
Control	0	9% HCOOH	38	56	0.66	0.55	0.28	0.27
A	0.3	9% HCOOH	29	48	0.69	0.56	0.33	0.23
B	0.6	9% HCOOH	20	41	0.65	0.51	0.36	0.15
C	1.0	9% HCOOH	5	14	0.69	0.54	0.48	0.06
D	1.2	9% HCOOH	1	5	0.64	....	....	....
					Mean 0.67			
Control	0	$4M$ KCl	15	28	0.37	0.49	0.27	0.22
A	0.3	$4M$ KCl	3	10	0.37	0.42	0.26	0.16
B	0.6	$4M$ KCl	5	13	0.37	0.44	0.32	0.12
C	1.0	$4M$ KCl	0	3	0.34	0.44	0.33	0.11
D	1.2	$4M$ KCl	0	3	0.35	0.66	0.56	0.10
					Mean 0.35			
Control	0	$4M$ KCl + $.01M$ HCl	11	22	0.36	0.52	0.28	0.24
A	0.3	$4M$ KCl + $.01M$ HCl	2	9	0.33	0.50	0.33	0.17
B	0.6	$4M$ KCl + $.01M$ HCl	4	11	0.35	0.55	0.40	0.15
C	1.0	$4M$ KCl + $.01M$ HCl	2	6	0.34	0.51	0.39	0.10
D	1.2	$4M$ KCl + $.01M$ HCl	2	4	0.32	0.63	0.60	0.03
					Mean 0.34			

* Ratio of the work recovered from 20% extension to the work required for extension.

difference in with-scale and anti-scale friction coefficients begins to vanish. In these cases, the nature of the solution or the elastic behavior of the fibers is unimportant, the residual directional frictional effect limiting the felting to a low value.

"Since the shrinkage is a function of resilience (at constant level of treatment) and a function of friction difference (in a given medium), one should be able to relate the shrinkage in any medium to measurements of single-fiber friction and stress-strain properties. Such a very general relationship is shown in Graph 79, in which top shrinkage is shown as essentially a linear function of the product of friction difference and fiber resilience. . . . This is a remarkably simple function relationship for such a complex phenomenon as felting."

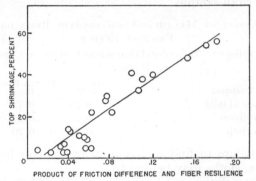

Graph 79. The relationship between felting of wool top treated with solutions of NaOCl, and the product of friction difference and fiber resilience. (*From Sookne, Bogaty and Harris,*[370] "*The Felting of Shrink-Resistant Wool as Related to Some Properties of the Single Fiber.*")

For an explanation as to the chemical reactions involved in the treating of wool with the above discussed reagents, the reader is referred to the quoted remarks of Speakman[95] given on pages 127–135.

The Shrink Resistance of Wool via Resin Application. Of the many resin formulations suggested for the attainment of wool shrinkage control, the melamine-formaldehyde type has, so far as is known, been the only one to be of commercial significance.

While it is possible to modify the mechanical properties of fibers by introducing a monomer within the fiber and polymerizing it in situ, this is not the manner in which melamine functions. Maresh and Royer,[373] and Stock and Salley[374] show that the melamine resin is anchored under the edges of the scales, but nevertheless the reaction is a fiber surface deposition. The former authors state:

"One explanation for the mechanism . . . is that (the resin) alters the scale characteristics and/or the physical relationship between the scale and the cortex portions of the fiber. . . . The membrane covering is most likely to be opened up at the scale interstices, and it is at these points that mechanical or chemical action first becomes evident when the specimen is stained."

This is not the sole, and possibly not even the primary reason why melamine works, however.

Stock and Salley[374] show that the tensional elastic properties of melamine-treated wool fibers are not significantly different from untreated fibers, but that the D.F.E. is reduced. Table 140 shows this reduction on individual fibers, but it is substantially eliminated in fibers removed from a treated cloth sample.

TABLE 140. EFFECT OF MELAMINE-FORMALDEHYDE RESIN ON DIRECTIONAL FRICTION EFFECT

(From Stock and Salley[374] "Melamine-Formaldehyde Resin in Controlling Shrinkage of Woolens")

Treatment	Directional Friction Effect	
	No Resin	Resin
individually	0.28	0.13
in sliver	0.25	0.21
in cloth	0.22	0.20

"The failure to find a change in friction for fibers withdrawn from cloths may be due to
(1) resin solution not being deposited on fibers in mass as effectively as on single fibers, or
(2) removal of fibers from the mass, causing much of the resin to be broken loose."[374]

From the foregoing, it would appear advantageous to melamine-treat wool fibers in stock rather than woven fabric form. This is not so, for Stock[345] in a private communication, states that even the largest reduction in D.F.E. shown in Table 140 (individual treatment) is insufficient to produce shrink-resistant woolens, and that the D.F.E. must be reduced to at least .05 before improvement is accomplished. Hence we must search further for additional contributory mechanisms. One of the most important of these is the local "spot-welding" of adjacent fibers by the resin to form a stable network wherein adjacent fibers are immovable relative to each other.[345] Maresh and Royer[373] state:

"It has been observed microscopically that the resin does not flow out evenly over the entire fiber surface during the drying and curing period. The resin tends to collect at the scale interstices and at points of contact between fibers. It must be assumed that local spot-welding of one fiber to another does play some part in the shrinkage control of wool."

Finally, McCleary and Royer[375] confirm the conclusion of Stock and Salley that melamine does not alter the repeated stress tensional characteristics of the wool fiber but does produce a marked increase in its torsional rigidity.

"Successive extensions of a treated fiber cause gradual decreases in the rigidity, which approaches that of the untreated fiber. These results are interpreted to mean that resin treatment affects only the surface portion of the wool fibers; this modified surface structure must, therefore, be chiefly responsible for the shrinkage resistance of wool fabrics."

Powers[376] cites some practical test results on the shrinkage of various wool, rayon, and cotton fabrics.

TABLE 141. SHRINKAGE OF FABRICS BEFORE AND AFTER RESIN TREATMENT
(From Powers[376] "Effect of Synthetic Resins on Cellulose and Protein Fibers")

Fabric*	Original Shrinkage (%)	Resin (%)	Shrinkage after Resin Impregnation (%)	Shrinkage Removed (%)
light cotton sheeting	6.74	5.2	1.09	84
heavy cotton sheeting	5.58	4.8	1.17	79
cotton flannel	12.6	5.5	2.1	84
cotton lawn	3.4	4.3	0.8	77
all spun rayon	12.1	6.1	2.9	76
cotton-rayon-wool blanket	19.4	10.6	3.2	84
cotton-rayon blanket	20.2	5.8	6.8	66
filament rayon	11.4	5.9	4.3	62
all-wool challis	23.2	6.2	5.7	75
all-wool flannel	30.1	10.8	4.1	86
all-wool shirting	20.7	5.7	6.1	71
wool-rayon shirting	24.2	12.8	4.8	80
all-wool suiting	11.5	7.2	3.2	72
cotton-rayon suiting	11.4	8.9	1.7	85

* "In each case the fabrics were washed according to the standard A.A.T.C.C. procedure for shrinkage determination. . . . The "cotton" procedure was used on all cotton fabrics; otherwise the procedure for "fabrics other than cotton" was used."[376]

Summarizing this review on the chemical methods for rendering wool shrink resistant to wet laundering, it may be concluded that processes are available which are effective in overcoming an inherent disadvantage of the wool fiber. By proper control of such processes, the desired elimination of felting shrinkage may to a large extent be accomplished without impairment to other desirable properties of wool.

(71) The Laundering Shrinkage Properties of Fabrics Composed of Fibers Other than Wool

The shrinkage values for the cotton and rayon fabrics listed in Table 140 indicate that fabrics composed of hydrophilic fibers other than wool also shrink when laundered. Here the mechanism is "relaxation" rather than felting. Reference to Tables 52–54 demonstrates that fabric shrinkage is not the result of linear fiber shrinkage, Meredith[30] showing that nylon, cotton, wool, silk and viscose fibers all increase in length when wet out. However, there is an appreciable increase in fiber diameter for the hydrophillic fibers, and the mechanism whereby this produces fabric shrinkage will be discussed below.

Collins[377] in a paper entitled "Fundamental Principles that Govern the Shrinkage of Cotton Goods by Washing" presents an excellent review of the concepts involved:

> "At the outset, there are two essentials that need to be emphasized since they constitute a continuous background to all aspects of the problem. The first is that shrinkage does not occur unless water gains access to the material by one means or another. The second is that the shrinkage can then be ascribed to two causes: swelling and release of strains. The release of strains that have previously been imposed occurs when the material is wetted; the swelling that also occurs when water is absorbed produces an internal rearrangement that can result in external shortening."

Collins' first point demonstrates that since the new synthetic hydrophobic fibers have substantially zero moisture regain they are not going to shrink when laundered. The same situation obtains as was pointed out on page 278 with respect to crease resistance and page 297 for dimentional stability, viz: If the textile structure exhibits acceptable "dry" characteristics and its fibers are incapable of absorbing water and changing dimension either in length or diameter, then the "wet" properties (resulting from mechanically held water within the fabric) should also remain acceptable (excluding surface effects due to the presence of adsorbed water). Upon subsequent drying, the original properties and dimensions will continue to prevail. In such cases the advantage of the hydrophobic fibers, "Orlon," "Dacron," "Dynel," etc., over hydrophilic wool, cotton, rayon and silk, are apparent.

Continuing now with Collin's[377] analysis, he confirms the point that fabric shrinkage is not due to fiber shrinkage. He analyzes the shrinkage of cotton yarns as follows:

"The important features of the yarn structure are the twist factor and the compactness and, in cloths, the degree of flattening. In all practical problems there is little or no loss of twist from the yarn when it is swollen by wetting, nor is there usually any lengthwise slippage of the fibres over one another. The fibre can be considered as lying around the yarn and running at an angle to the axis of the yarn, an angle that increases with twist. The question then is "What will be the effect on the yarn length and diameter when the fibres swell?" In the first place, it has already been noted that the length changes

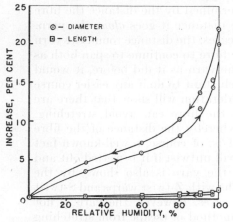

Graph 80. The increase in diameter and length of cotton fibers with increasing relative humidity. (*From Collins,*[377] *"Principles that Govern the Shrinkage of Cotton Goods."*)

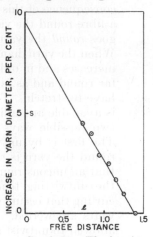

Graph 81. The increase in diameter of a cotton yarn with decreasing 'free distance' within the yarn. (*From Collins,*[377] *"Principles that Govern the Shrinkage of Cotton Goods."*)

of the fibres are likely to be small and any yarn extension on this account will also be small. The fibre diameter increases, say by 14% and unless the yarn is of a very open construction so that each separate fibre can swell without hindering its neighbours, the yarn must also increase in diameter. The effect of yarn density upon the degree of swelling is shown clearly in some results obtained at the Shirley Institute which are illustrated in Graph 80. Samples of a singles 24's Tanguis yarn were taken from air at 65% R.H. and immersed in water and the swelling measured with a microscope. Graph 81 shows how the swelling increases as the free distance* in the

* Calculated from the specific volume by the formula:

$$\text{Free distance} = (\text{sp. vol.} - 1.05)^{1/3}$$

original yarn decreases. An extension of the line in Graph 81 to "no free distance," that is, a very compact yarn, suggests that the swelling is then about 10%, a value nearly equal to that observed with the fibres themselves (about 13% from Graph 80). It may be observed that three factors that give compactness of yarn structure are tension, twist and lateral compression. Yarns are compressed in cloths of good cover and the swelling of the yarn in the cloth will be greater than when it is held out of the cloth freed from lateral constraints.

"It is necessary, however, to examine more closely the consequence of this increase in yarn diameter. The length of a fibre round the yarn is determined by the distance the fibre goes *round* the yarn and the distance it goes *along* the yarn. When the yarn diameter increases, the distance round the yarn increases and in order for the fibre to continue to span both as far round and as far along the yarn as it did before, it would have to stretch. This it is reluctant to do if any easier course is available and a little consideration will show that there are two possible ways whereby the fibre can avoid stretching. The first is by untwisting, whereby the distance of the fibre round the yarn is reduced; it is, of course, a well-known fact that an unconstrained yarn will untwist if it is wetted out and the untwisting tendency in the yarn is also shown by the curling that occurs when cloths with Z-twist warps and S-twist wefts are wetted. In most cases, however, the yarn is not allowed to untwist and this method of escape from stretching for the fibre is not possible.

"If, then, the turns are not altered, the fibre has to span as far round the yarn as before and the only means of shortening its path is for it to span a shorter distance *along* the yarn, i.e. the yarn must shrink. . . . How much does this shrinkage depend upon the amount of twist in the yarn? It is clear that in the case of no twist when the fibres run parallel to the yarn axis, there would be no tendency to stretch the fibres and a calculation shows that as the twist is increased the yarn shrinkage will increase from purely geometrical considerations. At the same time, however, increase of twist increases the compactness of the yarn and for this reason the swelling will be greater. The yarn shrinkage that results from swelling in water is increased therefore by high twist in the yarn by a twofold mechanism. But how much shrinkage of the yarn is to be expected as a result of the swelling? Calculation indicates that for a 14% increase of diameter of a hard yarn of 3.7 twist factor, the shrinkage is not likely to be much over 2 per cent. This is a small amount and when the small stretch due to fibre lengthening and the effects of lengthwise tension that may also develop are also considered, it is clear that no large shrinkage effects comparable with those in fabrics are to be expected. It should be observed that this conclusion applies to yarns of ordinary twist factors only (not exceeding a twist factor of about 5); with very highly twisted yarns, such as crepe yarns, theory indicates and practice confirms that when these are swollen in water they·manifest large untwisting and shrinkage tendencies. Shrinkage of this sort is not a fault, it is a virtue and as such is outside the scope of this account.

"Before leaving the shrinkage of yarns we may inquire whether there is not the possibility of some shrinkage occurring simply as a result of recovery from stretches previously applied. We have already seen that the shrinkage of the fibres themselves after being stretched is not often likely to exceed 1% and it can be shown that for yarns of ordinary twist factor the corresponding yarn shrinkage is only slightly greater. Any large yarn shrinkage cannot, therefore, be traced to fibre shrinkage and the only possibility that remains is whether some change in the yarn structure could occur that would cause serious shrinkage. A possible case would appear to be that of a yarn that is rather bulky, say, on account of the coarseness and stiffness of the fibres and of a moderate twist factor. It would be possible to "set" an extension into such a yarn by stretching it damp and drying under load so as to tighten the yarn into a compact structure. When wetted free from constraint the yarn would swell and largely regain its original dimensions. The mechanism of the process, is, however, essentially that already considered in some detail and from these considerations the shrinkage is unlikely to exceed a few per cent at most.

"On[377] all accounts, therefore, the shrinkage of cotton yarns of moderate twist factors is likely to be small and it may be observed that in the many routine measurements of shrinkage of cotton fabrics that have been carried out at the Shirley Institute, the shrinkage of the yarn itself has rarely exceeded 2% or at the most 3% and has usually been from 1% to 2%."

Collins points out that serious shrinkages in rayon (and other hydrophillic) synthetic filaments can result from over-stretching the filaments in previous processing operations.

He[377] continues on the shrinkage of cotton cloth:

" . . . it is evident that the large shrinkages that can occur with cotton fabrics must be due to some feature or features peculiar to the fabrics themselves. The explanation of the shrinkage of a fabric does, in fact, lie in the structure and an extended account of the several aspects of the mechanism of shrinkage in relation to the structure is given in the Memoir issued from the Shirley Institute, entitled "The Geometry of Cloth Structure."[167] This should be consulted for detail but a short explanation and account of the way cloth shrinkage occurs is possible. As before, the shrinkage can be allocated to two causes, swelling and release of strain in the fabric.

"To consider first the shrinkage due to swelling, the way this occurs is seen most readily from a picture of cloth struc-

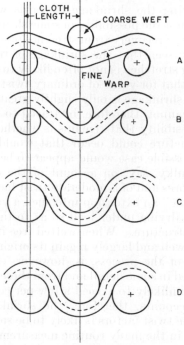

Figure 20. A geometric explanation of cloth shrinkage. (*From Collins,*[377] *"Principles that Govern the Shrinkage of Cotton Goods."*)

ture. Figure 20-B represents a warp thread in a cloth; it is shown as being finer than the weft threads that it crosses and has to bend round these threads more than they bend round it. The difference between the thread length and the cloth length, reckoned as a percentage of the cloth length is the crimp of the thread. Let us suppose that the cloth is now wetted. We have already seen that the yarns will increase in diameter and if the crossing weft threads were to remain the same distance apart from one another, as in Figure 20-C, the path of the warp thread would evidently be longer, i.e., it would be stretched. But just as with the fibre in the swollen yarn, force is necessary to effect such a stretch, and if there is any easier way out of the situation this will be taken. There is indeed available a simple "line of least resistance"; if the weft threads move nearer together as in Figure 20-D, then the path of the warp yarn is shortened so that it can span the distance without stretching or with much less stretching. If the cloth is not constrained at the ends of its length there is, of course, nothing to stop weft threads from moving nearer together. In other words, the cloth shrinks warp-way. . . . Calculations from the geometry of cloth structure show that the shrinkage that can result in this way increases as the weft thread spacing is reduced, becoming considerably larger than the shrinkages that are possible with yarn. When the weft threads are very close, however, some limit to the shrinkage is set by jamming; it is not possible to pull the weft threads any closer together since the warp threads are pressed tightly between them.

"It is evident that the shrinkage of the cloth warp-way in this manner consists essentially of an increase in the crimp of the warp threads. It may be inquired, however, why both the warp-way shrinkage of the cloth and also the stretching of the warp threads could not be avoided by straightening the warp threads. This is obviously geometrically possible as in Figure 20-A but it should be observed that in so straightening the warp threads, it has been necessary to increase the degree to which the weft crossing threads bend round the warp threads, that is to say, the weft crimp is increased and if, as is usual, the weft threads also resist extension, the cloth contracts weft-way. It is clear, therefore, that the cloth must contract one way or the other or both and some further principle is necessary to be able to forecast the most probable final state of the cloth. We are now actually involved in the mechanism whereby shrinkage of the cloth occurs as a result of a reversion to a more stable shape from a stretch that has previously been imposed. When a cloth like a poplin is subjected to a large warp-way tension while wet, the warp crimp is largely removed and if the cloth is dried under tension the stretch is effectively permanent for a considerable period. The structure is like Figure 20-A but it must be observed that it is not a natural conformation of the threads for two reasons. In the first place, when two threads are bent as a result of crossing another it is clear that the fine thread will bend more easily than the coarse thread. Secondly, it is more difficult to bend a thread if the places at which it is gripped for bending are near together. In the case of a cloth with finer warp threads, these are usually closely spaced for good cover and are therefore less able to bend the weft threads. For two reasons, therefore, the more stable balanced structure is one in which the warp threads are bent more than the weft threads, that is, the warp crimp is high and the weft crimp is low. The stretched structure having a low warp crimp is unstable and when it is wetted the cloth reverts to a more stable balance of crimp. Crimp interchange of this kind can account for quite large shrinkages of 10% or more in cotton fabrics."

Collins summarizes the factors affecting cotton cloth shrinkage as follows:

"The largest amount of the shrinkage is that represented by increase of crimp, yarn shrinkage takes a second place, being generally much less than the increase of crimp, whilst fiber shrinkage is usually negligible."[377]

It should be kept in mind, however, that all of these effects are the direct result of the ability of the fiber to swell radially.

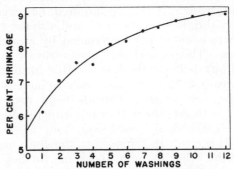

Graph 82.　Effect of the number of washings on the shrinkage of grey poplin. (*From Collins,*[377] *"Principles that Govern the Shrinkage of Cotton Goods."*)

While Collins uses cotton to demonstrate the geometric concepts, it should be evident that the principles of the analysis are valid for all other fibers, holding even in the case of hydrophobic fibers. Here the mechanism would be the same, but the effect would be small, since filament, yarn diameter, and crimp changes, on wetting would either be zero or closely approach zero.

Graph 82 is a plot of per cent shrinkage vs. number of washes for grey poplin, and demonstrates that the major portion of the shrinkage is not accomplished in the first one or two cycles. This is explained in the following manner:

"It[377] is supposed that in the first washing treatment although the forces of swelling produce relatively large changes

in the shapes of the threads, there are local strains in the structure, and that these disappear by further readjustments in the
subsequent dryings and washings.   These strains can be pictured as places in the yarn where 'sticking' has occurred; when
the yarn dries, free space develops, and this allows of accommo-
dation between fibers with a less 'strained' and more shrunk
structure when the cloth is wet out again.   Agitation during
the washing treatment helps to overcome these local strains
and therefore promotes shrinkage."

(72) Shrinkproof Treatments for Cottons and Rayons

Mechanical Methods. Because cotton cloth, as normally manufactured, cannot be shrunk to fixed dimensions in one wetting and drying
operation, considerable attention has been given to methods for "pre-
shrinking" by mechanical means (called "compressive shrinkage" by
Marsh[378]) or by the application of chemical treatments.

Typical of the compressive shrinkage methods are the American
Sanforizing and the British Rigmel processes.   Marsh[378] states

"In the Sanforizing process shrinkage is achieved by
passing the cotton fabric onto a movable elastic felt blanket
which is in a state of tension; when the tension . . . is released,
it assumes a shortened condition and the cotton fabric is
forced to conform to this compression as it is held firmly in
contact with the blanket by a drum . . . .   Before passing
the cloth through the Sanforizing range it must be tested . . .
to determine the warp and weft shrinkage it will undergo on
washing, for which the Sanforizing range is adjusted to cope
with the potential shrinkage of the material."

Prior to entering the Sanforizing area, the fabric is moistened to accomplish the compression more easily and completely.   The Rigmel Process
works in substantially the same fashion, certain engineering differences
being described by Marsh (pages 252–253 of his book).

Chemical Methods. Fabric shrinkage is primarily caused by radial
swelling of hydrophilic fibers, and it follows that those treatments which
inhibit swelling in water will prevent fabric shrinkage.   Reference has
already been made to the work of Gagliardi and Nuessle[237] who show
(Table 109 and Graph 55) the correlation between rayon fiber swelling
and fabric warp shrinkage.   Formaldehyde, glyoxal, urea-formaldehyde
and melamine formaldehyde all have the ability of reducing the absorption of free water by cellulose, thus tending to maintain the "dry"
physical properties of the *modified* cellulosic structure.   Marsh[378] shows
that a formaldehyde type resin-treated fabric exhibits advantages over

an untreated control with respect to wet strength, crease resistance, and laundering shrinkage because of the reduction in imbibed water.

" . . . due to the mechanical constraint exercised by the internal resin, there is no evidence of the formation of a compound between the resin and the cellulose, either with urea-formaldehyde or phenol-formaldehyde, nor is there any evidence of the chemical blocking of hydroxyl groups by these resins."

With formaldehyde or glyoxal, either or both of these latter mechanisms must prevail since there is no formation of resin per se to render the fiber more hydrophobic via mechanical constraint.

Since the wool fiber is hydrophillic, wool fabrics are capable of undergoing relaxation shrinkage in the same fashion as cotton or rayon. Were it not for the fact that felting shrinkage is a far more serious effect, relaxation shrinkage in wool would probably receive more attention. Chemical treatments such as hypochlorite which render wool resistant to felting shrinkage do not inhibit, but probably increase the tendency of the wool fiber to swell, thereby enhancing the relaxation shrinkage effect. Resin treatments such as melamine on the other hand, being mostly hydrophobic, inhibit the tendency of the fiber to swell and thus reduce relaxation as well as felting shrinkage.

TABLE 142. LAUNDRY SHRINKAGE OF SPUN RAYONS
(From Marsh[378] "An Introduction to Textile Finishing")

		Per cent Shrinkage		
	Fabric A		Fabric B	
% Resin	Pin Stenter		Clip Stenter	Pin Stenter
20%	. . . .		1.7%	0.5%
10	4%		2.4	0.7
7.5	5		2.4	0.7
5	5		4.8	0.6
2.5	6		7.0	1.4
0	12		10.0	6.0

Chapter 19

FABRIC SOILING, SOIL REMOVAL, LAUNDERING, AND DRY CLEANING

Soiling, laundering and dry cleaning involve two topics worthy of consideration:

(1) The objective quantitative measurement of the tendency of fabrics to become soiled, and the ease of soil removal.

(2) The more complex subjective and objective evaluation of a textile's general appearance; its ability to maintain a clean and fresh appearance, and the ease and degree to which it can be restored to such a condition, via laundering or dry cleaning, and pressing. Such factors as crease resistance, dimensional stability, drape, hand, wear resistance, luster, and shrinkage all have a bearing on a garment's appearance and its ability to maintain that appearance. The fastness of dyestuffs to laundering, dry cleaning, bleaching, perspiration, ironing, and pressing cannot be overlooked.

The two topics will be taken up in the order listed above, the first portion involving soiling and soil removal, the second involving the problems of laundering, cleaning, and "rejuvenation."

(73) The Mechanics of Fabric Soiling

Considerable information is found in the literature on the subject of detergency. Standard soil-test cloths and soiling mixtures have been proposed, usually the end objective being the evaluation of detergents or methods for laundering or dry cleaning. Little information has been found of the tendency of fabrics to become soiled and the degree of difficulty in removing the soil. The exception is a report[379] which the New York Section of the American Association of Textile Chemists and Colorists has recently presented. Cited at length below, it discusses certain laboratory and service soiling tests:

> "Looking into the technical literature as a whole, the earliest reference located on textile soiling goes back to 1929, when Åstrom[380] wrote a review of the literature on particle

size of smokes and fogs, and their adsorption by cotton and wool fibers.

"In 1936, Krüger[381] made a microscopic study on soiling of textile goods with usage. He showed with photomicrographs the contamination of cotton fibers in garments by secretions from sweat glands and hair. It was concluded from experiments with cotton fabrics of various constructions that degree of soilage and resistance to removal depends on solubility of the skin excretions and the nature of the fabric construction. Open weaves permit dirt to penetrate which hinders cleaning, while surfaces which are close and even, with a tight layer of starch, are resistant to contamination.

"Masland[382] analyzed causes of soil retention on various fibers and reported the following conclusions in 1939:

"(1) Fiber diameter and cross-sectional outline are factors of prime importance in soil retention.

"(2) These factors are interdependent. Only when a fiber has large diameter (above 27 microns) and smooth circular cross-section essentially free from indentations and channels, can low soil retention be attained.

"(3) The origin of the fiber is of no moment, whether synthetic or natural, animal or vegetable, except as origin influences morphology. . . .

"Masland's work was slanted toward evaluation suitability of fibers for use in pile fabrics, particularly carpets. Carpets are exposed to more severe soiling conditions in service than any other textile, and carpet people have long been aware of soiling as an important factor in color changes during service. They have learned that the presence of wool grease, spinning oils, or soaps on carpet fibers, even in small percentages, promotes the adhesion of foot-borne soil.

"Leonard[383] reported in 1949 on the phenomenon of "resoiling," a condition of frequent occurrence wherein a washed carpet soils rapidly to a severe degree shortly after replacement in service. It was determined that if the detergent used in cleaning leaves an oily or liquid residue on the fibers, dirt particles will stick tenaciously, accumulating soil rapidly. . . .

"One other reference has been located in the carpet field: in July 1949, a manufacturer put on the market a cotton rug advertised[384] as "soil-resistant." It was claimed that the fabric is treated to shed dirt and dust and need be washed once a season as compared with four or six times for untreated cotton rugs. Further information has not been made available. . . .

"Snell et al.[385] reported a conclusion that dirt is retained on fabrics by mechanical and electrostatic forces, and oil bonding.

This is the only reference to mention electrostatic forces, while mechanical retention and oil bonding are repeatedly brought out in the literature.

"In view of this point, the Committee searched carefully for reliable data on the electrostatic properties of soil and dust particles.

"Sachese[386] reported in 1932 on the electrical properties of dust, measuring the charges on clouds of particles. He found that magnitude and sign of charge on a cloud as a whole depends on the method of preparation, and particularly on the influence of friction therein, which could produce charges of either sign and high magnitude. No relation could be established between the sign of the charge and the chemical or physical condition of a cloud.

"Thomas[387] states that only a fraction of particles are charged . . .

"From a practical standpoint, Northrup[388] reported that the electostatic properties of nylon are of great importance with regard to its soiling. Special precautions are required in beaming and weaving to keep dirt away from nylon yarns.

"This group of references is not sufficient to give a well-rounded picture of the part which electrostatic forces play in textile soiling. The best conclusions which could be made are probably the following:

"(1) Most soil particles are uncharged and are not drawn to fabrics by virtue of *their own* electrostatic conditions.

"(2) Frictional forces and other naturally-occurring conditions can probably induce static charges of short duration on many soil particles. If these particles come close to a textile before the charges are dissipated, they may be drawn into direct contact, where mechanical forces and oil bonding can come into play.

"(3) Uncharged soil particles may be strongly attracted to fabrics which have become charged, e.g. nylon in processing.

"On soiling in general, one other area of knowledge has been found to contain pertinent data, and that is the subject of air filtration. "The Handbook On Aerosols"[389] gives an excellent survey of the properties of suspended particles, the mechanism whereby adhesion to fibers occurs, the effect of fabric structure on filter efficiency, and a brief discussion on electrostatic effects. Suspended particles are defined as those having a diameter less than 50 microns, with the majority of particles suspended in air under average conditions being in the range 0.1 to 10 microns. In this reference it is first postulated that small particles adhere by natural forces to any surface with which they come in contact. From that point mechanisms are described whereby particles suspended in air impinge on fibrous structures:

"(1) *Direct interception* of a particle in an airstream by a fiber.

"(2) *Inertial effect*, based on the assumption of streamline air flow through the structure, wherein large particles (over 1–2 microns) have sufficient inertia to leave the stream lines bending around a fiber and make contact with it. Increase of velocity favors this mechanism of filtration.

"(3) *Kinetic diffusion*, which is very effective for particles under 0.1 micron. Such particles exhibit Brownian motion which greatly increases the probability of impingement on fibers. For particles in this size range, filtration is favored by low velocity. . . .

"A common observation is reported that filters show lowered effectiveness at high humidity. It is concluded that electrostatic charges are built up in a filter under dry conditions, which polarize uncharged particles and attract them from the airstream. An electrostatic filter is made in Canada by curing resin-treated wool, which generates high field intensities by the friction of air passage. This filter removes large particles with extreme effectiveness and is very effective for particles in the range of 0.2–0.5 microns.

"It is obvious that all the principles of particle adhesion to fibrous structures must apply whether they be filters or woven textiles. . . . . However, most textiles are not designed to have high "air permeability," while air filters must have it. The fact immediately increases the importance of direct interception as a factor in impingement of particles on textile fibers and might be expected to show greater retention of small particles. Masland[382] corroborates this by estimating retained particles to be in the range 0.2–4 microns. Compton and Hart[390] worked with soils of particle size 10–100 microns. They found the 10-micron soil to have the greatest darkening power and to be the most difficult to remove by detergency.

"This short history of researches on soiling has brought out the following published conclusions:

"(1) That dirt particles may be brought in contact with fibers by diffusion or deposition from quiet or slowly moving air, by interception or inertial effects from more rapidly moving air, by direct transfer from another surface, or by electrostatic attraction.

"(2) That having been brought in contact, the particles may adhere to the fibers by mechanical forces or occlusion in pits and crevices on the fiber surfaces, by "oil" bonding, and possibly by electrical forces.

"(3) That fine fibers retain soil more readily than coarse fibers.

"(4) That fibers having uneven cross-sectional contours retain soil more readily than those which have smooth circular contours.

"(5) That soil particles commonly encountered range in size from 50 microns down, and may be subclassified into (the following) overlapping size groups which correspond to the different mechanisms by which they are brought into contact with fiber structures."

TABLE 143. SOIL PARTICLE CLASSIFICATION
(From A.A.T.C.C.[379] "Measurement of Fabric Soiling")

Size	Contact Mechanism (from airstream)
<0.1 μ	diffusion
0.1 to 1 μ	direct interception
>0.3 μ	Stoke's Law deposition
>1 μ	inertial effect

The above discussed mechanisms of soil deposition are limited for the most part to airborne particles or direct contact. Other methods of staining or spotting entail the direct application of a liquid or a liquid-borne soil particle. In such cases, the degree of mutual compatability of the particle, the "vehicle," and the fiber will govern the extent of soiling. The hydrophilic fibers are more susceptible to water systems than are the hydrophobic fibers. However, soil can be deposited on the hydrophobic fiber surface via liquid adsorption followed by evaporation, leaving the soil particles behind. Where the vehicle is an oil and where the soil particles are easily wetted or dispersed by oil, penetration into the hydrophobic fibers may be enhanced, particularly if the oil has any swelling effect upon the fiber. The application of resins to fibers, or other chemical treatments which inhibit the swelling characteristics of the fibers will depress the tendency of the fiber to pick up soil.

The state of aggregation of the fibers in the textile structure has a bearing on soilability. Niven[391] comments

"The manner in which the fibers are spun and woven into the fabric should be of much significance. Thus, fabrics loosely woven from coarse threads should be more readily penetrated by solid soil than finely woven fabrics. Fabrics such as towelling which are designed for ready penetration by and high absorption of liquids may be readily and extensively penetrated by soil."

Staple fabrics which have rough surfaces and are porous and thick usually make good carriers of dry soil, especially dust. However, such dirt is often not readily seen because of entrapment rather than surface deposition. Also, staple fabrics, because they are not as lustrous as continuous filament fabrics, are less prone to appear soiled. This is because a less sharp contrast in luster may exist between the unsoiled and soiled areas. On the other hand Whewell, Messiha and Selim[392] state that the shorter the staple length, the greater the tendency to soil. This is probably because short staple produces rougher fabrics and a greater number of fiber ends through which soil can enter—the latter being particularly pertinent for hydrophylic fibers.

In conjunction with the development of standard procedures for soiling fabrics and test methods for measuring the degree of soiling or soil removal, the A.A.T.C.C. group[379] tabulated the "Most Probable Soiling Mechanisms for Various Textiles," (Table 144). They state:

"Service conditions form an inescapable part of the consideration in estimating the soiling properties of fabrics. It is thus an incomplete question to ask, "What are the soiling properties of Fabric A?"; and the question must be made complete by asking, "What are the soiling properties of Fabric A when exposed [for example] to direct transfer . . . ?"

"The mechanisms of impingement and of retention are separate factors in soiling. They are independent of one another, with the possible exception of electrostatic forces, which can both attract and hold particles to fibers. Generally speaking however, retention is a function of the fabric, while impingement is a function of the service or test condition. The degree of soiling . . . is a result of both functions.

"It is more than likely that no single test method can properly balance all the mechanisms of impingement so as reliably to reproduce service conditions for all kinds of textiles. It is clear . . . that gloves and floor coverings contact soil principally by direct transfer, while curtains and flags contact soil by all other mechanisms except transfer. We can conceive . . . the evaluation of floor covering soilage by controlled service tests in which people walk over rugs in a conditioned atmosphere with traffic counters, etc.; and of soiling curtains and flags by blowing dust into a chamber containing strips of test cloth. . . . The . . . objection to using one test for all items in a group (is that) it will not resemble service conditions for at least some of the items."

TABLE 144. MOST PROBABLE SOILING MECHANISMS FOR VARIOUS TEXTILES
(From A.A.T.C.C.[379] "Measurement of Fabric Soiling")

Fabric and Conditions	Mechanism of Impingement	Mechanism of Retention	Normal Service Time for Soiling
1. light curtains at open window	interception and inertial effect	occlusion, "oil" bonding by finishing agents	few weeks—few months
2. light curtains at closed window	diffusion and deposition	occlusion, "oil" bonding by finishing agents	few weeks—few months
3. suitings	(a) sleeves, seat and cuffs—direct transfer	occlusion	(a) few days
	(b) top of shoulders—deposition		(b) few weeks
	(c) body—interception and diffusion		(c) few weeks
4. women's stockings	interception, direct transfer	occlusion, "oil" bonding by skin secretions	few hours—few days
5. men's shirts	(a) sleeves, collar and cuffs—direct transfer	(a) occlusion, "oil" bonding by skin secretions	(a) few hours
	(b) top of shoulders—deposition	(b) occlusion	(b) few days
	(c) body—interception or diffusion	(c) occlusion	(c) few days
6. carpets and rugs	direct transfer, deposition	occlusion, "oil" bonding	few months
7. working clothes	direct transfer, interception	occlusion, and "oil" bonding	few hours—few days
8. flags	interception, diffusion, inertial effects	occlusion	few weeks—few months
9. tents	deposition, direct transfer, interception	occlusion, "oil" bonding by fireproof finish if any	few weeks
10. gloves	direct transfer	occlusion	few hours—few days

(74) Laboratory Methods for Applying and Removing Soil

Preparation of Standard Soil Cloths. Many investigators have suggested standard soil formulations and the preparation of standard soil cloths. Representative are those of Utermohlen and Wallace[393] who used combinations of carbon black, black iron oxide, vegetable shortening, mineral oil, etc. Standard procedures with respect to formulation, application to a standard fabric, and ageing are rigorously followed.

Laboratory Methods for Soiling Fabrics. The A.A.T.C.C. Committee[379] lists the following methods:

"(1) Blower Test . . . This test evaluates the comparative soiling rates of air-permeable fabrics when exposed to impingement of suspended particles, chiefly by direct interception and inertial effect. Air containing naturally-suspended particles is drawn through the test fabrics until they soil to a degree which permits observation of soiling visually or by instruments.

"(2) Tumbler Test . . . This test may be used to compare soiling properties of a wide range of fabrics when soil impingement occurs principally by deposition and direct transfer. Test specimens are tumbled in a Launderometer jar with dry pigment soil and steel balls. After removal of excess soil, the results are evaluated optically and by chemical analysis of soil retained on the specimens.

"(3) Floor Soiling . . . This test may be used to compare the soiling properties of fabrics normally exposed to direct transfer and deposition. It is especially suitable for floor coverings. Test specimens are inserted into a small rug and exposed to foot traffic until they soil to a degree which permits observation of soiling visually or by instruments."

Laboratory Methods for Studying the Efficiency of Soil Removal. Many references have been found concerning apparatus and test methods for ascertaining the effectiveness of soil removal.[394,395,396,397] The best known equipment includes the A.A.T.C.C.-approved Launder-o-meter[398] wherein test-fabric specimens of the order of 6 x 6 inches or smaller are tumbled in jars of test solutions at constant temperature; the Detergency Comparator,[399] a scaled-down dolly washer developed by the Wool Detergency Committee of The A.A.T.C.C., which compares detergents under the conditions of high concentration and low bath ratio; the Tergo-tometer[395] which is said to provide mechanical conditions of washing more closely related to actual conditions than does the Launder-o-meter. Household washing machines have also been used for test purposes.

Methods for Measuring Degree of Soiling or Soil Removal. Two basic methods are employed to measure degree of soiling or soil removal:

(1) Quantitative reflectance measurements of the surface of the specimen by any one of a number of optical techniques, e.g., the spectrophotometer, reflectometer. There is justification for employing such measurements in that they are normally correlative with the subjective evaluation of appearance. If a garment or carpet looks dirty to the average person, the reflectance will probably show it. On the other hand, a garment may have considerable soil buried within the structure and yet appear "clean" on the surface. This leads to the second method of measurement:

(2) Quantitative chemical analysis of the soil present. For artificially soiled fabrics such a procedure is relatively straightforward. Knowing the type of soil applied, analytical methods can be designed to ascertain the amount present.

Unfortunately, visual observations and surface measurements do not always agree with quantitative measurements, nor should they for obvious reasons. One's philosophy and requirements will govern whether a garment may be considered clean if it looks clean, whether it must be quantitatively free from soil, or whether it must be scrupulously clean and sterile.

(75) Evaluation of the Soiling Characteristics of Fibers

The A.A.T.C.C. Committee[379] conducted many experiments on the effect of fiber type and fabric construction on soilability, using the Blower Test, the Tumble Test, and Floor Soiling Tests. Their conclusions are given below:

> "(1) Blower Test: Results are very sensitive to fabric construction. For this reason the blower test probably cannot be used to evaluate soiling tendencies of fiber types. . . . Tests made with constant volume and varying velocity (of air passing through the fabric, show) that impingement increases with air velocity. . . . A tighter fabric resists the passage of air and produces less soiling.
>
> "(2) Tumble Test: The tumble test is less sensitive to differences in fabric construction than the blower test . . . and may be useful for evaluating soiling tendencies of fiber types. . . . It is sensitive to the effects of treatments and finishing. . . . (For example) treatments of an oily nature produced increased soil retention. . . . "

Table 145 shows the change in reflectance and soil pickup of a series of miscellaneous fabrics composed of different fibers.

TABLE 145. THE EFFECT OF FIBER TYPE AND FABRIC CONSTRUCTION ON SOIL RETENTION BY MEANS OF THE TUMBLE TEST

(From A.A.T.C.C.[379] "Measurement of Fabric Soiling")

Fabric	Frazier Air Permeability ft³	Weave	Weight oz/yd²	Thread Count W	F	% Change in Reflectance R	% Soil Pick up P
wool gabardine	82.4	twill	5.5	61	51	28.8	1.25
wool flannel	126.0	twill	6.1	53	46	29.3	1.60
wool challis	191.0	plain	3.2	61	57	21.7	0.85
nylon	39.3	plain	2.8	113	76	27.0	0.86
acetate	109.0	plain	5.6	60	38	33.9	1.04
viscose	210.0	plain	3.7	76	69	37.2	1.36
cotton	171.0	plain	3.9	66	60	34.8	0.96

On a reflectance basis, the wool and nylon soil less than the viscose, acetate, and cotton. However, on a soil-pickup basis results are inconclusive, the wool challis having the lowest value and the wool flannel the highest. The Committee[379] again states that since the fabrics are of different constructions and since construction is obviously a prime factor in controlling soiling, the effect of fiber type cannot be isolated from the above data. Hence, a test was made on five pile fabrics of essentially constant construction, but different fiber types.

TABLE 146. THE EFFECT OF FIBER TYPE ON SOIL RETENTION FOR CARPET FABRICS OF ESSENTIALLY CONSTANT CONSTRUCTION (TUMBLE METHOD)

(From A.A.T.C.C.[379] "Measurement of Fabric Soiling")

Carpet Type	Reflectance Change ΔR	% Soil Pickup P
wool axminster	17.5	3.5
nylon axminster	32.1	3.64
cotton needled	31.6	1.95
acetate axminster	37.9	2.34
viscose axminster	46.7	3.08

On an appearance basis, the wool resisted soiling most but it was next highest on soil pickup. This would make it appear that wool has the greatest ability of retaining soil without actually looking soiled. No mention is made, in this A.A.T.C.C. paper, of the color of the original samples under consideration. However, a "black and white" photograph shows the wool carpet *originally* to be appreciably darker than any of the others. Since Utermohlen and Wallace[393] show a logarithmic relationship to exist between reflectance change and soil pickup, it would be expected that the change in a darker sample upon exposure would be less obvious to the eye than would a light-colored one. Thus in the opinion of the writer, no conclusive proof of the advantage of wool is given by Table 146.

(3) Floor Soiling Test: The same five carpets were subjected to a controlled floor-soiling service test (see page 404), the reflectance changes being listed below:

TABLE 147. THE EFFECT OF FIBER TYPE ON SOIL RETENTION OF FLOOR-TESTED CARPETS OF ESSENTIALLY CONSTANT CONSTRUCTION

(From A.A.T.C.C.[379] "Measurement of Fabric Soiling")

Carpet	Reflectance Change (ΔR) After Exposure		
	5 Days	10 Days	20 Days
wool	22.9%	23.4%	24.8%
nylon	31.5	32.1	34.5
acetate	39.4	40.5	43.8
viscose	52.6	55.1	56.2
cotton	32.8	32.9	40.4

"the[379] wool fabric showed the least tendency to soil, with nylon, cotton, acetate, and viscose soiling increasingly in that order . . . these results are close to those of the tumbler experiment. . . . "

Again, a photograph (Figure 21) is furnished showing the original carpets and their appearance at the end of 5, 10 and 20 days of service.

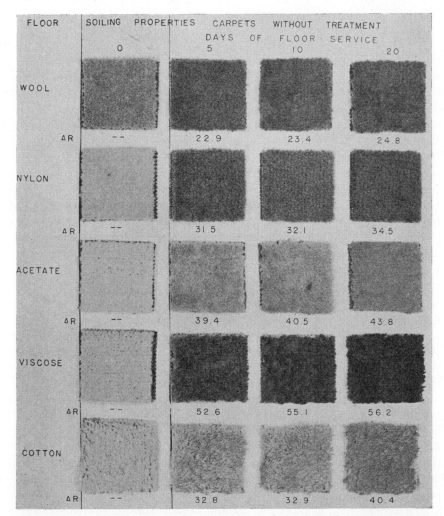

Figure 21. The soiling properties of carpets of substantially identical construction, but of different fiber types. (*From A.A.T.C.C.,*[379] "*Measurement of Fabric Soiling.*") (*Photograph furnished through the courtesy of Alexander Smith Carpet Co., Research and Development Department.*)

This appears to bear out the point that the only reason why the wool carpet showed a smaller reflection change is that it was darker to begin with.

Examination of the photograph (and it is appreciated that this may be hazardous) shows the following rankings of reflectance, originally, and after 20 days:

Lightest ————————————————→ Darkest

original:	acetate	viscose	cotton	nylon	wool
20 days:	acetate	cotton	wool	nylon	viscose

There appears to be a general opinion among both textile people and the public-at-large that wool is particularly good in its resistance to soiling. No quantitative data beyond those discussed above have been found in the literature which confirm or refute this feeling. In a private discussion with a representative of one of the major carpet companies, one of the authors of the A.A.T.C.C. report,[379] the opinion was voiced that while wool is undoubtedly one of the better fibers insofar as soil resistance is concerned, it does not exhibit as much advantage as most people believe. Basing his remarks on his subjective reaction to the test carpet samples, he was of the opinion that cellulose acetate was better than expected, cotton was far better than most people expected or believed, viscose was very poor, and nylon was fair.

One does not attempt to use white or pastel shades of wool to the extent that cotton, rayon, or nylon is so employed. Furthermore, much wool goes into dark men's wear. Thus, it is not called upon to meet the soil-resistant requirements of the other fibers. This of itself is an advantage, and in all probability is one of the reasons why wool is accepted as having such outstanding soil resistance.

Additional subjective research is needed in order to ascertain the importance of "change in appearance" vs. absolute condition after exposure. Undoubtedly these criteria will vary in their relative importance depending upon original color and type of fabric.

No information has been found in the literature of the soiling characteristics of "Vinyon," "Acrilan," "Orlon," "Dacron," or glass. The fact that all are hydrophobic, do not swell in water, and do not readily dye would indicate that any soil which is deposited must remain on the fiber surface. Since an important criterion for soil evaluation is visual appearance as measured by surface reflection, it appears logical to suppose that such surface soiling would be more obvious to the eye than would be the case if an equal amount of soil were deposited so that a portion of it could actually penetrate the fiber. On the other hand, the hydrophobic fibers probably resist soiling so that under equivalent exposure conditions, the total amount of soil accumulated would be less.

Which effect predominates and whether the synthetic hydrophobics actually soil more or less than the hydrophilics is a subject on which more factual information is required.

(76) The Electrostatic Properties of Fibers as They Pertain to Soil and Lint Attraction

Mention has been made of the fact that one of the mechanisms of soil deposition is via the build up of an electrostatic charge on the fiber or fabric, which then attracts an uncharged or oppositely charged particle. In addition to the collection of dirt particles of micron size, lint or dust of a larger dimension may also be attracted. This has caused some problems with the hydrophobic synthetics. Lehmicke[400] reviews the general problem of static as follows:

"This phenomenon of the generation of electrostatic charges is quite general. It probably occurs whenever two dissimilar materials come in contact or, more especially, are rubbed together. However, only very rarely and under certain conditions are there any observable effects.

"In the first place, the charges must be retained and accumulated so that a potential of sufficient magnitude is obtained to produce a physical effect. Usually the offending substance is a dielectric, on which the charges remain at the point of generation. In the case of a conducting material, the charges distribute themselves over the entire surface of the body and if the body happens to be grounded, the charges are completely removed. However, an isolated metallic body can accumulate a large charge . . .

" . . . With any two materials it is found, on rubbing them together, that one has become positively charged and the other negatively charged. Let us call the positively charged material "P" and the other "N." If we now test a third material against both of these we may find that "A" becomes positive to both "N" and "P," that "B" becomes negative to both "N" and "P," or that "C" becomes positive to "N" and negative to "P." What will not occur is that "D" will be positive to "P" and negative to "N." In testing more materials, it is found they may be arranged in a vertical series so that any material rubbed against another lower on the list will acquire a positive charge. Conversely, if they are rubbed against a material higher on the list, they will acquire a negative charge.

"This electrostatic series is determined by testing various substances against one another in pairs and finding in each test which of the pair is charged positively and which negatively. " . . . The electrostatic series is shown in Table 148 . . . "

TABLE 148.   ELECTROSTATIC SERIES FOR POLYMERIC MATERIALS
(From Lehmicke[400] "Static in Textile Processing")

positive end
glass
human hair
nylon yarn
nylon polymer
wool
silk
viscose rayon
cotton
paper
ramie
steel
hard rubber
acetate rayon
"Dacron"
synthetic rubber
"Orlon"
saran
polyethene
negative end

"What does this series tell us about the electrostatic behavior of various fibers? Our first thought is that when rubbed against a given material, each fiber will be given a charge of a magnitude related to its separation from that material in the electrostatic series.

"For example, against rubber, which is near the negative end of the series, we should predict that 'Orlon' acrylic fiber would not generate much static, that nylon would be worse than cotton, and wool nearly as bad as nylon. These predictions are not borne out by experiment. A series of tests was run on a number of fibers to determine the electrostatic voltage generated against a single material. Ten-gram skeins of the fibers were rubbed against a rubber glove by manipulating the skein while wearing the glove, and then the voltage generated was measured by dropping the skein into an aluminum beaker attached to the 'high' terminal of the voltmeter. All skeins were boiled off and thoroughly conditioned before testing with all tests performed by the same person. The results are shown in (the first column of) Table 149. It is seen that wool generates little static compared with the rest, and that 'Orlon' acrylic fiber is very bad where static is concerned.

"Clearly, then, other factors must be taken into consideration to explain the relative susceptibility of the different fibers to static. One factor which comes readily to mind is moisture. On any fiber, static is less troublesome at higher humidity. This is partly a result of the quicker dissipation of the charges in more humid air, but it is also true that dry fibers generate much more static than conditioned fibers in the same atmosphere. It is therefore plausible that wool owes its low static susceptibility to its high moisture regain. The second column (Table 149) lists the same fibers in order of moisture regain, with highest regain at the top of the list. The third column shows the separation of the fibers from rubber in the electrostatic series. We see from Column Two that wool has the highest moisture regain of all the fibers, which may account for the fact that its static propensity is lower than that predicted; and that acrylic fibers have extremely low moisture regain, which may cause greater static propensity than that predicted from the electrostatic series. . . . "

We have thus at least two criteria which govern the relative electrostatic ranking of various fibers (1) the inherent characteristics of the substance, and (2) its moisture regain. Ambient conditions will govern the contribution of each and the resulting ranking in an electrostatic series. Lehmicke[400] points out however, that these two factors do not explain completely all the electrostatic phenomena observed.

TABLE 149. ORDER OF ELECTROSTATIC SUSCEPTIBILITY AGAINST SYNTHETIC RUBBERS
(From Lehmicke[400] "Static In Textile Processing")

	Experimental Rank Determined by Electrostatic Voltage	Predicted Rank from Moisture Regain	Predicted Rank from Electrostatic Series
cotton	50v	wool	"Orlon"
viscose rayon	100	silk	"Dacron"
wool	350	viscose	acetate
acetate rayon	550	cotton	cotton
"Vinyon" N	800	acetate	viscose
silk	850	nylon	silk
"Orlon"	900	"Orlon"	wool
"Dacron"	1025	"Dacron"	nylon
nylon	1050	"Vinyon" N	

The hydrophobic fibers, because of their inherent characteristics, one of which is their hydrophobicity, can build up and hold a larger electrostatic charge than the hydrophilic fibers. It would therefore be predicted, but no data are available to confirm, that for equivalent fabric surfaces "Orlon," "Vinyon," "Dacron" and nylon would pick up and hold lint more than viscose, wool or cotton. It also follows that were electrostatic charge one of the prime factors which influence soiling, the hydrophobic synthetics would soil much more easily than the hydro-philcis. This is not so, at least when viscose and nylon are compared. Hence other soiling mechanisms must be more important than the electro-static contribution. It would appear plausible to opine that since "Dacron," "Orlon," "Vinyon" and nylon do not swell and do not dye, they would resist soiling via water absorption.

Another property not pertinent to soiling but apropos of this discus-sion is that of the static electrical discharge experienced by a person when he scuffs his feet across a rug and touches a metal object, or rides in an auto with "plastic" seat covers and then touches a door handle. The higher the charge capable of being built up, the greater the "shock" to the person. Since the hydrophobic fibers are capable of building up and holding such charges, they are particularly obnoxious in this respect. However, the hydrophilic fibers can be just as bad at low relative humidities.

In the same vein, Lehmicke[400] comments

> "Static may cause observable effects in finished garments,
> as well. Either outer or under garments will occasionally cling
> to the wearer. It depends upon whether one is the wearer or
> observer as to whether this is an undesirable effect."

Lehmicke also mentions that static accumulation on garments can cause sparks. No information has been seen which indicates that this is a potential fire hazard in clothing per se. Of course numerous fires and explosions have resulted from a spark discharge in the presence of an inflammable gas or dust. Hospitals, chemical plants, and the like are cognizant of such hazards, and the disadvantages of the hydrophobic fibers in such applications are apparent.

(77) The Soil Removal Characteristics of Fibers and Fabrics

The factors which influence the rate and extent to which fibers and fabrics will soil undoubtedly play an equally important part in soil removal. Both inherent and geometric form properties must be considered.

The literature is not profuse with data showing the relative ease of cleaning the various fibers. To a large extent attempts at comparisons of ease of soil removal (as well as ease of soiling) are analogous to attempt-ing to compare the proverbial apples and oranges. This is because the tasks which textiles are called upon to perform are diverse, and com-parisons of the soiling and soil-removal properties of two fabrics of differ-ent fibers is in many cases illogical and in other cases impossible. The very nature of the fiber—its soil resistance and ease of cleaning, as well as a host of other controlling properties—has caused to be developed, by trial and error if in no other way, the fiber's end usages which are to be avoided and those which are to be exploited.   Wool is not called upon to perform those tasks where it may become badly soiled, not because soil per se cannot probably be relatively easily removed by wet washing, but because of the accompanying milling shrinkage and felting problem. Hence, in evaluating the ability of fibers to be washed or dry-cleaned, consideration of the physical and chemical properties of the fiber and textile structure relative to the proposed cleaning method must be kept in mind.   The setting up of controlled evaluation experiments wherein all fibers are cleaned under identical conditions of formula and process are precluded.   We must compare each fiber and fabric when washed or dry-cleaned under conditions which are optimum for it.

With respect to the hydrophilics, those which soil easily appear to clean easily.   Snell[395] states that the nature of soiling on cotton is one in which the soiling effect is relatively permanent until the material is washed.   That is, once cotton is dirty it must be laundered to restore its clean appearance, whereas the apparent cleanliness of some materials can be restored by brushing or shaking.   For example, a great deal of dry dirt and dust can be removed from woolen materials by brushing. However, considerable amounts may still remain so that the wool fabric may not actually be as clean as it appears.

No information has been found which compares the relative ease of cleaning the new hydrophobic synthetics.   The fact that water is absorbed by them to a minor degree or not at all probably means that dirt deposited by any mechanism will stay on the fiber's surface, and should therefore be reasonably easy to remove, providing that the cleaning operation is tailored to fit the fiber.

Bacon and Smith[401] have investigated the quantitative relationship between the concentration of a surface active detergent in water and the mechanical work required in removing soil in a detergent process, the variables involved being the detergent, mechanical force, time, temperature, ease of soil removal, soil suspension and deposition.   Their conclusions are:

> "The concentration of detergent required is inversely proportional to the mechanical force applied when the degree of soil removal, time and temperature are kept constant.
>
> "The time of scouring and the detergent concentration required are inversely proportional when the degree of soil removal, force and temperature are kept constant.
>
> "The time of scouring and the force are inversely proportional when concentration, temperature and degree of soil removal are kept constant."

Clark and Holland[394] compare the efficiency of soil removal, under constant conditions, for fabrics composed of various combinations of cotton, viscose, wool and nylon.

TABLE 150. EFFICIENCY OF SOIL REMOVAL FROM VARIOUS FABRICS
(From Clark and Holland[394] "Studies in Soiling and Detergency")

No.	Fabric Composition warp	filling	Sodium Oleate (%) → % Soil Removed 0.25	0.5	% Brightness Increase 0.25	0.5	% Oil Remaining 0.25	0.5
1	100% C	50% C-50% V	49	48.5	20.5	20.5	5.0	4.8
2	100% C	100% V	41	42	18	18	4.4	4.2
3	100% C	50% N-50% C	50	48	21.5	20.5	4.0	4.2
4	100% C	50% N-50% V	55.5	54	19.5	19.5	3.4	3.6
5	100% C	75% N-25% V	53	53	18	18	3.4	3.4
6	w:25% W-25% N-50% V f: 20% W-20% N-60% V		38.5	38	9	9	4.8	4.6

C = cotton, V = viscose, N = nylon, W = wool.

Since the first five fabrics all have the same warp, the filling yarns may be used to compare soil removal. Differences do not appear to be great but the probability exists that nylon is as good as cotton, with viscose somewhat inferior to both. Clark and Holland point out that the yarns in Fabric 6 were heavier and imply that for this reason it would be more difficult to launder this fabric, i.e., the geometric effect is more important than the inherent fiber properties. They also state that the nature of the wool fiber does not lend itself to reflectivity as well as do the other fibers.

Castonguay, Leekley, and Edgar[403] in a paper containing voluminous data, compare the light absorption of cotton, viscose, acetate, silk, and wool fabrics laundered up to 50 times with a silicated soap, neutral soap, and sulfated alcohol detergent. Unfortunately for our purposes, the fabrics were not originally soiled. However, the data do indicate the tendency of the fabrics to become darker upon laundering and also compare the efficiencies of the selected detergents.

The original light absorption is easily maintained with the silicate soap and the neutral soap. The sulfated alcohol detergent is unsatisfactory for silk and wool. It should be remembered that criteria other than light reflectance must be given consideration in selecting a soap formulation and laundering procedure. These will be discussed below.

Furry and McLendon[404] also report on the effectiveness of soil removal from a cotton and a chlorinated-wool cloth using various soaps and detergents. Light reflectance was the selected criterion; the washing was done in a Launder-o-meter at 40°C. Results show that with soap, the soil removal effectiveness was about the same for cotton and wool. For the synthetic detergents, the effectiveness on the wool was greater.

TABLE 151. ABSORPTION OF LIGHT BY WASHED FABRICS

(From Castonguay, Leekley, and Edgar[403] "The Washing of (Fabrics) With Soap, Etc.")

Fabric	Washing Number	% Light Absorption		
		Silicate Soap	Soap	Sulfated Alcohol
cotton	0	20	20	20
	30	16	18	21
	50	16	18	22
viscose rayon	0	20	20	20
	30	16	19	20
	50	16	24	20*
acetate rayon	0	16	16	16
	30	..	12	13
	50	12	13	12
silk	0	26	26	26
	30	23	25	35
	50	26	27	40
wool	0	30	30	30
	30	29	31	37
	50	32	31	45

* 40 washes.

In distilled water without a detergent, more soil was removed from the wool than from cotton. "Unbuilt" non-ionic detergents were the least effective with wool, but were fairly effective with cotton, while non-ionics were the most efficient of the detergents tested with wool.

Direct comparison of wool vs. cotton is actually impossible because while wool might be laundered at 40°C (104°F), cotton would most certainly not be; again, we are not comparing soil removal at the optimum condition for each fiber.

Two additional miscellaneous references are given below:

Snell[405] states that it is easier to remove soil from a loosely-woven fabric than from a tightly-woven one. Clark and Holland[394] found that an acetate tricot

"gave exceptionally high soil removal values, probably because of its extreme limpness. Obviously the weave and not the fiber is the cause of this since the acetate voile taffeta (tested) gave very average results."

(78) General Considerations of Laundering and Dry Cleaning as They Pertain to Problems Other than Soil Removal

It hardly appears necessary to point out that the design of a procedure for the cleansing and conversion of a soiled garment into a fresh and attractive article must take cognizance of the many inherent chemical and physical properties of fibers, and the influences of fabric geometry. On the basis of convenience and expense, water washing is preferred to other methods, and is used wherever possible. We have discussed at length the various criteria which are involved in the performance of textile fibers and structures under wet conditions, and so we can proceed immediately to a discussion of the relative merit of the various fibers, calling upon this background of knowledge.

Cotton. Cotton fabrics soil and wrinkle easily; but they can be equally easily laundered even to a sterile condition, because they are little affected by alkaline soaps, temperatures to the boil, and alkaline bleaches. The Sanforizing and other shrinkage-control processes have substantially eliminated this problem. The fact that cotton is stronger when wet than dry is of obvious advantage in resisting mechanical stresses encountered in laundering.

Honnegger and Schnyder[406] show that for a cotton-linen union fabric, alkaline bleaches have a destructive influence as indicated by reduction in the degree of polymerization of the cellulose. They state that upon repeated laundering with bleach, the total chemical damage is greater than mechanical damage, but in the absence of bleach, the damage is primarily mechanical. It is obvious that the chemical damage resulting from bleaching will ultimately lead to more rapid mechanical failure.

Linen and Ramie. The comments made for cotton generally hold. However, Honnegger and Schnyder[406] state that linen is somewhat more susceptible to chemical and mechanical damage than is cotton.

Viscose Rayon. Since viscose loses approximately half of its strength when wet, more care must be taken with it than with cotton. Furthermore, graph 25-f (page 105) shows that upon wetting, viscose's average tensional modulus is reduced to about 40 per cent of its 65 per cent R.H. value, while for cotton, the average modulus changes but slightly. Viscose is thus more susceptible to deformations resulting from mechanical agitation during laundering. Since such deformations are composed, to a considerable extent, of secondary creep, permanent distortions are more prone to develop in viscose rayon garments during laundering, than for cotton.

With respect to shrinkage, Tables 52–54 show viscose to swell two to four times more than cotton; concomitant shrinkage resulting from yarn take-up and crimp interchange (page 392) will be greater than for cotton. However, the application of wrinkle-resisting finishes such as melamine-formaldehyde, insofar as they inhibit fiber swelling, should reduce fabric shrinkage.

We may conclude that viscose fabrics may be wet-laundered, but more precautions must be taken than with cotton.

Acetate. Because of the substitution of hydroxyl groups with acetyl groups in the cellulose structure, cellulose acetate exhibits a larger degree of hydrophobicity. It has a lower moisture regain, swells less, loses less strength when wet, and probably has better wet elastic recovery than does viscose. We should expect that wet laundering would be somewhat of a lesser problem than for viscose. Because fabrics made from acetate usually are of a more delicate nature, probably they are not called upon to withstand the rigorous washing procedures of cotton.

The thermoplasticity of acetate at temperatures of about 300–325°F requires caution in ironing and pressing. In addition to the danger of actually melting fibers, permanent creases or distortions can easily be pressed in. Also, unattractive glossy areas may be produced at seams, cuffs, etc., wherever edges or double thicknesses of the fabric can produce a high compressional stress.

Silk. Care must be taken to avoid high pH and temperature in wet washing. When wet, its tensional modulus is reduced to about 25 per cent of its dry value and thus the fiber may be subject to permanent distortions during wet washing. The fact that silk is usually used in continuous-filament luxury fabrics means that such fragile fabrics are more prone to have their geometric status altered via mechanical agitation. Satins, for example, might have their luster altered via crimp changes, float movement, or filament breakage.

Wool. Because of the shrinkage and felting problem, with certain exceptions, wool cannot be wet laundered. Most of the wool socks currently manufactured have had their fibers treated for shrink resistance. Wool sweaters and blankets can be hand washed if extreme care is taken not to induce the mechanical action necessary for milling. The larger portion of wool apparel fabrics must be dry cleaned, and a dry-cleaning industry has thus come into being to satisfy this demand. The consumer has become accustomed to the need of sending worsted and woolen suits, dresses, and coats to the dry cleaner. This does not mean that he would not welcome equivalent or better garments which he could wet launder—preferably at home—provided that they required a minimum of ironing or pressing.

It appears apropos at this point to present some information on dry cleaning methods. Crockatt,[407] in an article entitled "Cleanable Outerwear," makes the following remarks:

> "We must now inquire what the dry cleaner does with the goods collected. What happens to your suit or dress or cur-

tains between your surrender of them to the cleaner's shop and the time you call for it, ready for a further period of service?

"The central process in dry cleaning is cleaning with the help of an organic solvent instead of water. Most dirt is held on by grease. Some dirt is loose; it can be got rid of by beating or tumbling, but mere beating would not make the goods clean. Grease, however, is not soluble in water, and the laundryman has to emulsify it in order to clean the goods, but once that is done the solid dirt comes away and can be rinsed out.

"The dry cleaner puts his goods in a solvent which dissolves the fat. This in itself is not a cleaning action, since the particles of solid dirt will come away from the fabric and can be rinsed out by more solvent. This cleaning action has to be assisted by mechanical means, and we use washing machines built on very similar lines to those used by the laundry.

"There are two principal solvents very different in nature and origin which are used in the industry. . . . White spirit is a petroleum distillate having a boiling range of 150–210°C, with a flash point of 90°F. It is inflammable and will burn readily, but its vapor will not form an explosive mixture with air at ordinary temperatures. . . .

"The arrival of the synthetic solvents, the chlorhydrocarbons, which are non-inflammable, permitted the creation of a new sort of cleaning organization. It became possible to install a small, self-contained plant in a shop and to perform all the operations on many sorts of goods on the premises. The solvent used is trichlorethylene. Its action is similar to that of white spirit in most ways and differences between them need not concern us here. It has, however, the disadvantage of being narcotic, and careful design of plant is necessary and most efficient ventilation is essential.

"The dried goods have now to be examined. We have dry cleaned them, but not all are clean. They are dust-free and grease-free but the solvent does not take out things like food stains, tea and coffee, gravy and a host of other stains which people get on their clothes. The goods, therefore, are sorted— most will be fit for finishing, but some will need further treatment. Those which are generally clean but are stained will go to the spotters. Others are so generally dirty that they need wet cleaning and go to be treated with soap and water.

"The dry cleaner's motto is 'Do not wet anything unless you have to,' but the necessity does arise, and some classes of goods have to be washed—some can be washed in machines such as the laundries use and many have to be treated most carefully by hand, one at once.

"Once the goods are clean and dry, they must be finished. They must be smoothed out and made smart. There are many ways of finishing goods, but they all use steam. Steam softens the fabric, and whilst soft, it can be smoothed and set.

"The principal tool is the steam press, familiar to all in the clothing trade. We use a general utility model and it serves its purpose well. Many clothes do not need to be pressed but need steaming only, and perhaps brushed down to give a perfectly good finish. There are other machines and devices designed for this purpose only. The other mainstay is the iron—a tool giving a dry heat in itself, but invariably used with a damp cloth or on a fabric which has been dampened by steaming."

If the objective of dry cleaning with respect to wool is the avoidance of water, and water is mandatory to remove certain types of stains on wool and other fabrics, it becomes obvious that wool and the other hydrophilics are at a disadvantage relative to the hydrophobics. On the other hand, the hydrophobic fibers present other problems to the dry cleaner.

The Synthetic Hydrophobic Fibers. Since nylon, "Dacron," "Orlon," "Dynel," "Vinyon," "Acrilan," and "X-51" all exhibit substantially the same wet and dry properties, it can generally be stated that they can be wet laundered with a minimum of concern with respect to damage, distortion, or shrinkage.

The hydrophobic-fiber manufacturers love to point out the ease and rapidity with which garments made from their particular fiber can be wet washed and dried without ironing or pressing; and for blouses, shirts, socks, etc., probably few problems present themselves. However, it will be a long time before the conventional man's-suit, made of hydrophobic fiber, will be tossed into the washing machine, tumbled dried or air dried, and be ready to wear. For this to be accomplished, *all* components of the garment must be equally hydrophobic: lining, shoulder pads, sewing thread, lapel stiffening, pockets, zipper fabric, etc.

If the assembled garment is not so constructed and wet washing is employed, the swelling shrinkage developed in any of these auxiliary yarns or fabrics will cause puckering and distortion, which even subsequent pressing might not alleviate. Until the entire garment is made water insensitive, it is unlikely that wearing apparel presently dry cleaned will be handled exclusively by wet-washing methods. The dry cleaner, of course, will have an easier time with garments made up substantially of hydrophobic fibers because he can use water for spot removal with less concern over possible damage.

The pressers and tailors must become acquainted and educated in order that they may properly handle hydrophobic fibers. The steam press which Crockatt[407] discusses will be of less value. The hot iron will be more useful but will have to be handled with greater care. An improperly placed crease in a "Dacron" or other thermoplastic fiber fabric may be difficult or impossible to remove. The writer has already seen men's suitcoats where pressing at a button has fused a permanent impression into the fabric. One manufacturer, for example, has already made the following suggestions with respect to the manufacture of "Dacron" suits:

(1) Sew with "Dacron" thread.
(2) Cut slightly oversize.
(3) Use light tensions to avoid puckering.
(4) Keep needles cool to avoid holes.
(5) Iron at low temperature (below 275°F), as for silk or rayon.
(6) Press at less than 30 psi.
(7) Keep the iron away from direct contact with the cloth.

The writer does not mean that such problems are going to preclude the development of synthetic hydrophobic apparel fabrics. But he is confident that more conventional, presently-used dry cleaning and pressing techniques will continue to be employed. As such, wool will not be relegated to the scrap heap.

Latest trends in fabric manufacture are calling for blends of hydrophilic and hydrophobic fibers to enhance the advantages and compensate for the disadvantages of each. If this trend is followed with respect to men's and ladies' suitings and coatings, there is further assurance that conventional cleaning and pressing methods will be followed.

An additional topic of concern to the dry cleaner is one encountered because of garment accessories. Crockatt[407] and Davies[408] list such problems as: Poorly dyed buttons which "mark-off" onto the fabric during pressing; polystyrene buttons, buckles, or zippers which either distort in pressing or dissolve in trichlorethylene, subsequently acting as a stiffening agent in adjacent fabric areas; solvent-soluble or water-soluble sequins; rubber shoulder pads which become sticky or brittle subsequent to the solvent cleaning; rubber shoulder-pads out of which anti-oxidents or inhibitors are leached, causing fabric discoloration and subsequent oxidation of the rubber; poorly dyed fabric inter-liners which crock or bleed; polyvinyl chloride films as interliners in raincoats from which the plasticizer is leached during dry cleaning, leaving the residual film brittle so that it cracks.

Chapter 20

FABRIC HAND

(79) Objective and Subjective Properties of Textiles

The inherent and geometric form properties so far discussed all may be considered to be *objective* performance characteristics. They are capable of being measured and evaluated in quantitative terms on the basis of scientific knowledge, independent of personal preferences and psychological experiences.

There are certain equally important *subjective* performance characteristics which are evaluated at least in part by personal reaction. These can be expressed only in relative qualitative terms, although quantitative physical parameters in part govern the subjective rankings. The remaining chapters of this book discuss three of the more important subjective criteria: fabric "hand" or "handle," "drape," and "luster." All are important factors in the traditional concept of fabric performance, particularly in the apparel and household markets. Despite their vague and at times illusory nature, when these terms are examined closely it becomes quite evident they are symbolic of an extremely complex interaction between basic, quantitative, physical properties of fiber, yarn, and fabric, and the whole gamut of cultural and psychological influences to which any consumer is subject and to which all consumers react differently.

Textile science is thus faced with a quandry which has not been completely recognized in the past. On the one hand, the rapid advances in physical instrumentation have afforded the means of making careful and precise measurements of this or that physical property of textile fibers and fabrics. It has become possible logically to deduce from the apparent factors involved in handle or drape or luster that some physical property *must be* associated with these phenomena and then proceed to make accurate and precise determinations of the property so defined. The many physical data reported in the literature purporting to represent these parameters attest to the growth of this approach.

On the other hand, our widening knowledge of human behavior clearly points to the fact that in matters reflecting psychological conditioning or aesthetic urges, the logic on which behavior "should" depend, more often than not yields at the moment of action to illogic or non-logic.

Here we have the crux of a fundamental issue in textile research: in certain areas of performance such as those in which handle, drape, and luster are involved, the usefulness of any instrument is limited more by its ability to correlate with some average, qualitative consumer viewpoint than by the precision with which it can measure and reproduce some physical constant. Once this is recognized and more effort in such research is devoted to making the necessary correlations, the more quickly and efficiently will we learn which of the many physical constants which have been or might be measured are pertinent to progress in the design of improved subjective properties.

Further complications arise because qualitative subjective reactions vary from person to person; secondly tactile and visual properties, as has been stated, are an interaction of several quantitative properties; and thirdly, requisite tactile and visual properties are ever changing, depending upon the end-use to which the textile will be put.

(80) Hand and Drape Nomenclature

The long list of terms used to describe different types of hand is indicative of the inability of the human mind to separate the many interacting effects involved.

Schwarz[253] lists the following terms employed by a group of judges in evaluating a series of worsted fabrics:

> "*Visual:* smart, level, clear, well-covered, even, smooth, bright, homogeneous, compact, well-rounded, balanced, rawky, rough, irregular, streaky, "grins," knoppy, crepey, rubbed up, clumsy, cockly, thin, flannelly, solid, sharp, stripy, evenly-balanced, lustrous.
>
> "*Tactile:* silky, soft, full, kind, firm, pliable, tight, solid, well-bedded, mellow, velvety, rich, elastic, sticky, loose, springy, lofty, boardy, weighty, foody, warm, tapery, drapes well, cottony, lumpy, dead, leathery."

He defines handle, flexibility, rigidity, and drape as follows:[253]

> "*Handle* describes the feel of the material and qualitatively includes such terms as stiff, limp, hard, soft, rough, and smooth.
>
> "*Flexibility* is the ease with which a specimen may be bent. In certain cases the weight of the material acts to bend it about an axis.
>
> "*Rigidity* is the measure of resistance offered by the specimen to bending. This is a measure of stiffness.

"*Drape* differs from rigidity in that the weight of the material influences a deformation at some angle to the line of action."

Peirce[254] states that

"In judging the feel or handle of a material, use is made of such sensations as stiffness or limpness, hardness or softness, and roughness or smoothness."

Hoffman and Beste[255] define hand as the impressions which arise when fabrics are touched, squeezed, rubbed or otherwise handled. They list such words as soft, crisp, firm, hard, harsh, boardy, dead, lively, wiry, cold, warm, waxy, dry, muss resistant, limp, compliant, stiff, rubbery, leathery, mushy, smooth, drapeable. They also include visual impressions, e.g. covering power and luster.

Reference has already been made to the A.S.T.M. table of "Terms Relating to the Hand of Fabrics" (Table 78, Page 180) and Smith's[13] comments thereon.

The four authors referred to above, attempt to break down the various descriptive qualitative terms which they cite into precise categories of quantitative physical measurement. Before proceeding to such parameters, it is interesting to cite a few references on the correlation between quantitative physical measurement and qualitative subjective reaction.

Hamburger, Platt and Chu,[256] in an unpublished paper entitled "Sensation Psychology and Science Applied to The Evaluation of Complex Properties," discuss the problem of agreement among a group of people employed in various aspects of the textile industry (technologists, salesmen, fashion stylists, merchandising people, etc.), in their evaluation of the stiffness and draping properties of a series of fabrics. Their findings will be discussed in the next chapter. The points to be raised here are: (1) Whether people statistically agree among themselves in their ability to rank a property which is dependent upon their own reaction to what they see or feel. (2) If there is good agreement, can the property which they psychologically evaluate, and which, no doubt, is an integrated effect, be broken down into precise physical measurements such that the property can be defined in quantitative terms?

von Bergen and Kraus[257] discuss this problem as it involves the grading of wool for fineness:

"In present commercial practice, the routine grading of wool is done by men of long experience in the industry, who by merely handling and observing the material assign it intuitively to its proper grade. Such an estimate has many sources of error, principally based upon mental and physical qualities of the sorter. At the same time other factors, for example, light or color and luster of the hairs, considerably influence the result. Through experience we found that by a weak light, the estimate is too fine, and by direct sun, it is too coarse. Because of all these disadvantages, for more than one and a half centuries the replacing of the system of manual sorting by a system of measurements in a scientific manner has been felt necessary.

"In July, 1926, the U.S. Department of Agriculture promulgated the Official Standards of the United States for Wool and Top. After the adoption of this standard, the scientist had a foundation upon which to build an accurate method of measurement.

"The most astonishing results were found by Winson as he carried out a painstaking research on the measurement of the standard top. He found that for a range of selected British tops (the same tops were used in making up the U.S. master set), the progressive scale of fineness ascending from 48's to 80's quality is in geometric progression. A similar relationship was found for the French, German and Italian standard tops and it proved that the fundamental basis underlying wool sorting was the same in all countries.

"In 1860, Fechner in his "Elemente der Psycho-Physik" put forward the law now known as the Fechner-Weber law, which states: "In order that the intensity of a sensation may increase in arithmetical progression, the stimulus must increase in geometrical progression." This law, holding good between certain limits only, is expressed in his general formula $I = C \log S$, where I represents the sensation, S the stimulus, and C is a constant. If we regard the wool sorter's judgment as indicative of I, then it must immediately follow that any attempt on his part to form a gradation of fineness will result in a scale in which successive finenesses increase in geometrical progression. This is exactly the case in practice and in all countries.

"It can be said that for the normal operation of the wool sorter the Fechner psycho-physical law is the fundamental basis of this work; therefore, for wool sorting the eye in the visual sense is the paramount factor."

Binns[258] reports on the "Psychological Investigations of The Influence of The Various Methods of Manufacturing Worsted Yarns On Single and Two-Fold Twist Warp Cloths." He discusses the ability of groups of people to evaluate fabrics prepared in different ways. The subjects were asked to grade the various ranges of cloth:

" (1) By *sight* alone, for 'smartness of appearance' the experimenter placing the cloth in rank order, as desired by the subject.

" (2) By *touch* alone for 'softness of handle' great care being taken to avoid even a casual glance at the cloths. Blind-folding was found to be unsuitable, being unnatural and likely to disturb the normal judgment.

" (3) By *full* judgment on a commercial basis of unfettered judgment, the instruction being to 'place the cloths in the order in which you would buy them if all were offered at the same price'—any deliberate or subconscious preference might thus be biased towards smartness of appearance, softness of handle or other characteristic, according to the fancy of each person."

Reserving the term "hand" for tactile evaluation only, let us now attempt to analyze some of the factors which contribute to fabric hand.

Using Peirce's[254] nomenclature of (1) "stiffness or limpness," (2) "hardness or softness," and (3) "roughness or smoothness," the first mentioned will be thoroughly discussed here. The second has already been discussed in Chapter 11 on Compressional Resilience, and the third will be discussed in Section 83, this chapter, on "Fabric Friction."

(81) Methods for Measuring Fabric Stiffness

In a paper of classical significance entitled "The Handle of Cloth as a Measurable Quantity," Peirce[254] discusses methods for measuring fabric stiffness and hardness. Excerpts are quoted at length as follows:

"(1) The Bending Length, c.

" The way in which a fabric drapes or hangs depends largely on its stiffness, i.e., its resistance to bending, and on its weight. The most important measurement described in this paper is the determination of the ratio of these two quantities expressed in suitable units, and this ratio, or for convenience its cube root, may therefore be regarded as a quantitative measure of the property on which the "hang" of the fabric depends. The cube root of the ratio is conveniently termed the 'bending length,' for it measures the length of fabric that will bend under its own weight to a definite extent. The stiffer the fabric, the greater is the length necessary to ensure sufficient bending, so that a high value of c corresponds to a stiff fabric, and vice versa."

"Rectangular Cantilever

The simplest method for measuring bending length is to cut a 6 × 1-inch strip and extend it over a horizontal edge until either the tip of the specimen subtends a pre-selected

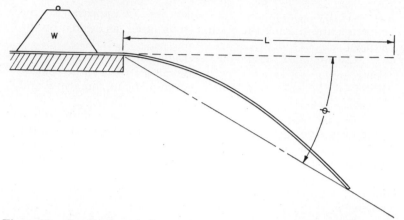

Figure 22.   Bending length diagram.   *(From Peirce,*[254] *"The Handle of Cloth As a Measurable Quantity.")*

angle, or a fixed length subtends an angle which is then ascertained.   In either case obviously, for a rectangular cantilever

$$c = lf_1(\theta) \quad \text{where } f_1(\theta) = (\cos 0.5\theta/8 \tan \theta)^{\frac{1}{3}}.\text{"}$$

Table 152 plots values of $f_1(\theta)$ for angles of zero to 69 degrees.

TABLE 152.   VALUES OF $f_1(\theta) = (\cos 0.5\theta/8 \tan \theta)^{\frac{1}{3}}$ TO BE USED IN CALCULATING RECTANGULAR AND CIRCULAR STRIP BENDING LENGTHS

(From Peirce[254] "The Handle of Cloth as A Measurable Quantity")

Values of $f_1(\theta)$

θ = 0	1	2	3	4	5	6	7	8	9
0	~	1.928	1.530	1.336	1.213	1.126	1.059	1.005	0.961	0.923
10	0.891	0.862	0.836	0.813	0.792	0.773	0.756	0.739	0.724	0.710
20	0.697	0.684	0.672	0.661	0.650	0.640	0.630	0.620	0.611	0.602
30	0.594	0.585	0.577	0.569	0.562	0.554	0.547	0.540	0.533	0.526
40	0.519	0.513	0.506	0.500	0.493	0.487	0.481	0.475	0.468	0.462
50	0.456	0.450	0.444	0.438	0.433	0.427	0.421	0.415	0.409	0.403
60	0.397	0.391	0.385	0.379	0.373	0.366	0.360	0.354	0.347	0.341

"Weighted Rectangle.

"For fabrics too stiff for the standard method, a weight W is fixed to the end of a strip of width b and weight w per unit area:

$$c = l \left(\frac{W}{3wbl} + 0.13 \right)^{\frac{1}{3}} \cdot \left(\frac{\cos 0.93\theta}{\tan \theta} \right)^{\frac{1}{3}}$$

The ratio of $\cos 0.93\theta$ to $\cos \theta$ varies so little over the range used in this method that the value at 20° may be assumed in order to use the table of $f_2(\theta)$ given below, when

$$c = lf_2(\theta) \cdot (0.336W/wbl + 0.131)^{\frac{1}{3}}.\text{"}$$

TABLE 153. VALUES OF $f_2(\theta)$ TO BE USED IN CALCULATING WEIGHTED RECTANGULAR STRIP AND HANGING HEART BENDING LENGTHS

(From Peirce[254] "The Handle of Cloth as A Measurable Quantity")

Values of $f_2(\theta)$

$\theta = $	0	1	2	3	4	5	6	7	8	9
0	~	3.855	3.059	2.671	2.425	2.250	2.115	2.007	1.917	1.841
10	1.774	1.716	1.663	1.616	1.573	1.533	1.496	1.462	1.430	1.400
20	1.372	1.345	1.319	1.294	1.271	1.248	1.226	1.205	1.186	1.164
30	1.144	1.126	1.107	1.089	1.071	1.054	1.037	1.020	1.003	0.986
40	0.970	0.954	0.938	0.922	0.906	0.891	0.875	0.860	0.845	0.829
50	0.813	0.799	0.784	0.768	0.753	0.738	0.722	0.707	0.692	0.676
60	0.661	0.645	0.630	0.614	0.598	0.582	0.566	0.549	0.533	0.516
70	0.499	0.482	0.465	0.447	0.429	0.411	0.392	0.373	0.354	0.333
80	0.313	0.291	0.269	0.246	0.222	0.197	0.170	0.140	0.107	0.067

"*Circular Cantilever.*

"This[254] method . . . avoids the difficulty of curling, goes rather lower in range of stiffness than the standard (rectangular) method, and allows measurement of stiffness in any direction on one specimen. If r is the radius of the circular specimen, then

$$c = l \cdot f_1(\theta) \cdot f(l/r)."$$

TABLE 154. VALUES OF $f(l/r)$ TO BE USED IN CALCULATING CIRCULAR CANTILEVER BENDING LENGTHS

(From Peirce[254] "The Handle of Cloth As A Measurable Quantity")

Values of $f(l/r)$

$l/r = $	0.0	0.1	0.2	0.3	0.4	0.5	0.6	0.7	0.8	0.9
$f(l/r) = $	0.811	0.814	0.817	0.825	0.825	0.829	0.834	0.839	0.844	0.850
$l/r = $	1.0	1.1	1.2	1.3	1.4	1.5	1.6	1.7	1.8	1.9
$f(l/r) = $	0.857	0.864	0.872	0.881	0.892	0.905	0.921	0.940	0.967	1.007

"*Hanging Heart.*

"Very[254] limp fabrics beyond the range of the cantilever method may thus be tested. The two ends of a strip are clamped together to form a length L into a heart-shaped loop. From the grip to the lowest or mid-point, the undistorted length of such a loop l_0 is $0.1337L$. The actual length l of the loop hanging under its own weight is measured with a cathetometer or otherwise, and the stiffness calculated from the difference $d = l - l_0$.

$$c = l_0 f_2(\theta)$$

where $\theta = 32.85° \cdot d/l_0$, and $f_2(\theta) = (\cos\theta/\tan\theta)^{1/3}$.

"As this method is used only for very soft fabrics, it is practicable to fix on a suitable value of L, say, 15 cms., and to construct a table giving the value of c direct from the measured value of l. This will save labour of calculation when the method is used in a routine way."

"These[254] four methods are recommended as best for the types of fabric referred to, which include all types amenable to test.   The following methods have also been worked out and occasionally applied; they extend the resources of the test when applied to materials other than fabrics."

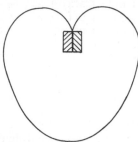

Figure 23.   Heart loop diagram.   *(From Peirce,*[254] *"The Handle of Cloth As a Measurable Quantity.")*

"*Triangular Cantilever.*
"In this form, the range of the cantilever method is extended a little below that covered by the standard method."

$$c = l \cdot 0.6933 f_1(\theta)$$

"*Weighted Triangle.*
"Material that is both stiff and curly may be tested."

$$c = l \cdot f_2(\theta) \cdot \left(\frac{W}{2wbl} + 0.044 \right)^{\frac{1}{3}}$$

"*Pear-loop Cantilever.*
"This method may be used for soft, curly material. . . .

$$c = l \cdot 0.212 / \tan^{\frac{1}{3}} \theta."$$

"*Hanging Loops.*
"Various forms of loop may be used to measure the stiffness of very soft materials, and they have the further advantage of minimising the effect of curl or twist, by the positive grip on both ends.   While the heart shape seems the most useful, others may have special applications.   The ring shape gives most promise of a practicable method for yarns.   Using the same symbols as for the heart shape, l_0 is $0.3183L$, θ is $157.0° \cdot d/l_0$ and

$$c = L \cdot 0.133 f_2(\theta)$$

The last expression holds also for the heart-shaped loop, though the value of the coefficient is a best-fit, not determinable within 1%.

"In the hanging pear loop, l_0 is $0.4243L$, θ is $504.5° \cdot d/l_0$ and the bending length is given approximately by

$$c = L \cdot 0.133 f_2(\theta)/\cos 0.87\theta."$$

"*Stiffness in Any Direction*
"After measuring the value of c in the warp and weft directions, c_1 and c_2, the value in any other direction at an angle α to the warp is given by

$$c = c_1(\cos^2 \alpha + k^2 \sin^2 \alpha)^{-\frac{2}{3}}$$

where
$$k = (c_1/c_2)^{\frac{3}{4}}$$

and the mean value
$$\bar{c} = \sqrt{c_1 \cdot c_2} \cdot \tfrac{1}{2}k + I/k$$
$$= \sqrt{c_1 \cdot c_2} \text{ approximately."}$$

"(2) The Flexural Rigidity, G.

"While[254] the bending length is the measure of stiffness that determines the draping qualities of the fabric, the flexural rigidity is a measure of the stiffness as appreciated by the fingers. It is, in fact, the resistance to bending mentioned in (1) above—the couple on either end of a strip of unit width bent into unit curvature, that is, the pair of forces acting in opposite directions that would be appreciated as a pressure on the skin if such a bent strip were held between the finger and thumb.

"The evaluation of flexural rigidity is extremely simple when the bending length has been measured. It was pointed out above that the bending length is the cube root of the ratio, resistance to bending divided by the weight per unit area, hence the only additional measurements required are the weight and area of the specimen.

"The flexural rigidity measures the actual forces produced in bending the material; thus two fabrics may bend to the same extent under their own weight, but the heavier of the two will exert more resistance to bending, say, by the fingers, and so feel stiffer. The only additional measurement required is the weight of the fabric, whence the flexural rigidity can be calculated from the equation $G = wc^3$, where G is the flexural rigidity, w is the weight of the fabric in grams per square centimeters, and c is the bending length. The weighing of specimens is therefore recommended as a regular routine in the stiffness test."

"(3) The Thickness, d.

"All[254] the succeeding quantities depend on the measurement of the thickness of the fabric, and this property is also of interest on its own account, since it is appreciated in handling the material."

"(4) The Hardness, or Resistance to Compression, H.

"The thickness of a fabric depends on the pressure applied to it, and the relation between these quantities is a measure of the hardness of the material. In order to obtain a numerical value, the thickness is measured under two definite pressures, and the ratio of the difference of pressure to the difference of thickness is used as a measure of the hardness."

"(5) The Bending Modulus, q.

"The[254] flexural rigidity described in (2) above is highly dependent on the thickness of the specimen, for it takes more force to bend a thick strip than a thin one; in fact, doubling the thickness increases the flexural rigidity eightfold. When the thickness of the fabric is known, however, it is possible to calculate a quantity that is independent of the dimensions of the strip. For a strip of metal or other uniform (homogeneous and isotropic) material, this quantity expresses the specific resistance of the material to bending and is definitely related to the resistance to extension. For a structured material like a fabric, however, the modulus so calculated has not quite the same meaning, but it may still be used to compare the stiffness of the material or weave in fabrics of different thickness.

Bending modulus or 'the intrinsic stiffness of the material' can then be expressed by the modulus

$$q = 12G/d^3.$$

"(6) The Compression Modulus, h.

"The bending modulus q may be obtained as above for the two directions parallel to the fabric. From the hardness H may be evaluated the compression modulus h, which is a similar quantity for the direction normal to the fabric surface. This quantity is also a measure of the compactness of the material."

"(7) The Density, ϱ.

"The density of the fabric is obtained by dividing the weight in grams per square centimetre by the thickness in centimetres. It represents a third measure of compactness, but is more influenced by the proportion of space left between the hairs."

"(8) The Extensibility, q′.

"The resistance to extension of a cloth is a property that affects the personal judgement of handle. The extensibility is expressed by Young's modulus, obtained from an autographic strip test. . . . This test yields a curve between load and extension that is usually far from straight, the strip being more extensible at the beginning of tension, and to compare with handle and the bending test, the extensibility should be judged from the initial slope. In a rod of uniform material, Young's modulus and the bending modulus are identical. In a fabric, the internal structure differentiates resistance to tension from resistance to bending, but a general relation is found between them, stiff cloths being less extensible. Thus Young's modulus was calculated from the load at 1% extension of a series of fents of white satin schreinered at various pressures.

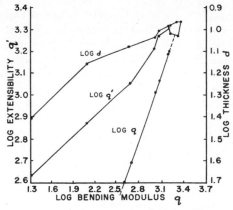

Graph 83. Relationships among fabric bending modulus q, extensibility q' and thickness d. (*From Peirce,* [254] "*The Handle of Cloth As a Measurable Quantity.*")

A high correlation was found between the tensile and bending moduli, and between both and thickness as shown in Graph 83. The resistance to tension is greatly increased by compression of the fabric in a calender, but the resistance to bending is increased very much more.

"The close agreement of the two moduli for a structureless sheet has already been demonstrated for starch film. A relation almost as close may be expected in heavily doped fabrics for aircraft or electrical insulation. Flexibility is an important quality of the latter when the fabric is wrapped round moving parts of an accurately machined instrument. It must bed into variations of curved surfaces, the capacity for which involves both extensibility and softness to bending. The stiffness test should be sufficient indication of both qualities.

"Flexibility, in the ordinary use of the word, involves not only ease of bending but also the capacity to bend to a large degree without cracking or breaking. There is the same duality of meaning in extensibility. Again, the two quantities are fundamentally the same, the limiting amount of bending being determined by the local extension in the material of the outer surface at the greatest curvature."

In addition to the above-mentioned methods for measuring flexibility, stiffness, hardness, and related subjects, Winn and Schwarz[259] describe the following instruments for measuring stiffness properties.

The Gurley Stiffness Tester.

"The Gurley stiffness tester supports a strip in a vertical position and measures the force in milligrams needed to bend the strip through a sufficient angle to cause slippage of the specimen over a vane. The force is produced by the deflection of a weighted pendulum-type vane which slides over the surface of the specimen as the supporting arm is rotated alternately to each side. The thickness of the material is not considered. The influence of the weight of the material is not wholly eliminated because the specimen is bent out of its vertical position. The reading obtained in the test is multiplied by a factor to give the stiffness in milligrams for a standard size sample $1'' \times 3''$. The size of the specimen, the number of thicknesses of material used at the same time, and the weight of the vane may change the final result. The angle to which the specimen is bent varies a few degrees. A very soft fabric has been found to be too near the lower limit of the machine to be tested exactly. A thicker heavier material shows relatively stiffer in the Gurley stiffness tester than by the hanging heart loop. When the samples are approximately the same weight and thickness the two methods give the same results."

The Schiefer Flexometer.

"The[259] Schiefer flexometer measures the force which is necessary to bend two specimens $1\frac{3}{4}'' \times 4''$ mounted in opposition on plates to an angle β by means of the deflection of a steel spring. Angle β is calculated from the thickness of the sample so as to give comparable results. Since both ends of the specimen are supported, the weight factor is eliminated. The Schiefer flexometer shows results similar to those of the hanging heart loop and the Gurley stiffness tester. Close agreement is lacking because the compactness of the sample is more important in the flexometer which bends the specimen to a much smaller angle. The difference is not due to the calculation of β because materials of the same thickness also show this difference in agreement. A hard finish, such as that on tracing cloth and friction calendered tag cloth shows stiffer in the Schiefer flexometer. The measurement is more variable and harder to control because so much force is necessary to bend two specimens to such a small angle."

Two additional testers which must be mentioned are the Clark and the Olsen Stiffness Testers. The former measures the length of test specimen which causes itself to bend through a 90° angle, the specimen being fed through a pair of rolls until the required angle is attained. The Olsen Tester measures the force necessary to bend a rectangular specimen through a selected angle, thus measuring flexural rigidity as defined by Peirce. Plots of force vs. angular deflection may be made.

It is deemed advisable at this point to describe the M.I.T. Drape-o-meter and the Fabric Research Laboratories Drapemeter. Both have been proposed as instruments which measure drape, although their principles of operation are entirely different. While drape will be discussed in the next section, the mechanics of test in using either of these instruments are based upon the measurement of stiffness; hence they are included here.

The M.I.T. Drape-o-meter.

Schwarz[253] describes the Drape-o-meter as follows:

"A test for bending deformation about a vertical axis is a drape tester designed by Bellinson at the M.I.T. Textile Research Laboratory. In this device a fabric specimen of desired length and width is suspended vertically with its upper edge secured closely in contact with the periphery of a horizontal disk of semi-circumference equal to the width of the specimen. The disk is adjustable as to height of support so that the bottom edge of the specimen just grazes the surface of a base on which is drawn a circle of diameter equal to the diameter of the disk and concentric with it. Tangent to the circle is drawn a straight line and two perpendiculars are erected to this line which are also tangent to the circle. If the fabric is entirely flexible and uniformly so, the bottom edge of the specimen will form a semicircle matching one-half of the base circle. The stiffer the fabric, the more nearly the bottom edge will approach a straight line. When the fabric falls between these two forms, the intercept of the edge with the vertical tangents is noted. The distance from the base line to the intercept is divided by the length of the respective tangent measured from the base line to the point of tangency with the circle. Another method of using the device in the case of a stiff fabric, is to shorten the length of the specimen progressively until the lower edge shows a definite degree of departure from a straight line. The length of sample is then an inverse measure of the stiffness.''

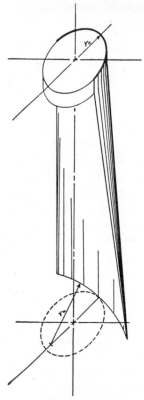

Figure 24 shows a diagrammatic sketch of the Drape-o-meter. It may be noted from the sketch that

> ''a pliable specimen cannot resist the shape to which it has been bent by the drape disc, and hangs in that shape below the disc and flares very little at the bottom. A stiff specimen resists the bending and returns to a nearly flat surface at some point along its length. Samples of intermediate stiffness assume a shape between these two, indicating their relative stiffness by the closeness to which they return to a flat surface.''[259]

It will be recognized that (for samples not tested on the bias) the Drape-o-meter causes only one set of yarns to be distorted out of its plane, the bend being "two dimensional." The perpendicular set of yarns remain substantially undeformed. This may be a disadvantage in measuring the draping characteristics of fabrics wherein three dimensional deformations are required, e.g., at the shoulder

Figure 24. Sketch of the principle of the M.I.T. Drape-o-meter.

of a suit; here the interaction of warp and filling flexibility must be considered. On the other hand, for curtains and drapes, the Drape-o-meter reproduces, in essence, the deformations which are likely to occur in actual use.

Quantitative measurements with the Drape-o-meter consist in determining the rate of change of radius of curvature or chord length with distance from the starting disc. Winn and Schwarz[260] define "drape length" as

> ''the length of sample as supported on the drape tester measured from the top of the material to a point such that the length of the chord is a given constant value. The greater

the drape length, the more flexible the material will be. In order to correct for the effect of weight or determine what the drape length would be for a material of different weight, assuming that they have the same stiffness, we can relate the length as measured to the length desired by means of the weight per unit area of the sample which was measured and the weight per unit area of the sample whose drape length it is desired to determine. The formula takes the form

$$H_c = L - \frac{W_m}{W_c} (L - H_m)$$

where H_c = the corrected drape length
L = the length of the specimen
H_m = the measured drape length
and W_m and W_c represent the weight per unit area of the sample measured and of the sample whose properties are desired respectively."

Rate of change of radius of curvature from the top to the bottom of the specimen (r_0 to r_n in Figure 24) may be used as a measure of drape. Winn and Schwarz[260] prefer to measure the rate of change of chord length, the limits being the diameter of the top disc to which the sample is attached, and the semi-circumference of this same disc.

The F.R.L. Drapemeter. Most of the bending tests described above allow a fabric to be distorted into two dimensions. The F.R.L. Drapemeter was designed to allow a fabric to deform three dimensionally. The idea stemmed from the observation that the drapeability of yard goods is usually demonstrated in store windows by draping them over circular or hemispherical pedestals. Such a technique allows for the *interaction* of warp and filling fabric stiffnesses. It is here that the technique essentially differs from Peirce's cantilever bending tests.

Figure 25 shows a diagram of the Drapemeter. The test consists of placing a circular specimen (say 10 inches in diameter) on a circular support of appreciably smaller diameter (say 5 inches) and measuring its projected image on a plane surface. For a material of complete rigidity with zero deflection under gravity, the projected area would equal the original area of the test specimen (line C in Figure 25). If, on the other hand, the sample were completely flexible such that it hung entirely vertically, then the projected area would equal exactly the supporting disc area (line A in Figure 25). Of course in actual practice neither condition can exist for fabrics, since in any distortion due to gravity, the fabric must assume some sort of clover-leaf pattern which will give a projected area smaller than the original specimen, but larger than that of the supporting disc.   This is the essence of drape as measured by the Drapemeter.

Representative diagrams of a cotton sateen and cellulose acetate plain weave fabric are shown in Figure 26.

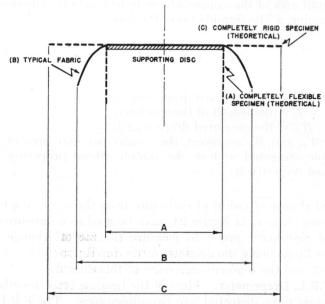

Figure 25.   Drapemeter diagram.

(A) Theoretical condition of complete flexibility wherein projected area equals supporting disc area.

(B) Typical fabric condition.

(C) Theoretical condition of complete rigidity wherein projected area equals sample area.

Three drape criteria are calculated from the Drapemeter.[262]

(1) Drape Coefficient, F.

Referring to Figure 26-B, the following projected areas are apparent

$$A_D = \text{area of specimen}$$
$$A_d = \text{area of supporting disc}$$
$$A_s = \text{actual projected area of specimen}$$

The drape coefficient F is defined as the ratio of the projected area of the draped sample to its theoretical maximum.   In the above diagram,

A_D and A_S must be corrected by subtracting from each the constant area of the supporting disc A_d. Thus

$$F = \frac{A_S - A_d}{A_D - A_d} = \frac{\bar{r}^2 - r_d^2}{r_D^2 - r_d^2}$$

(2) Number of Nodes, N.

Figure 26-A shows a fabric which drapes into five pleats or nodes; 26-B drapes into six nodes. The significance of the number of nodes has not been ascertained. It would appear logical that it is related to some aesthetic criterion which may be deduced by correlation with subjective evaluation. A discussion of the applied mechanics of the drapemeter pattern by Hamburger, Platt, and Chu[262] leads them to conclude that the number of nodes is a function of the buckling length and for textile fabrics this is virtually a constant.

(3) The Shape Factor of The Nodes, $\frac{h}{\lambda}$.

Hamburger, Platt and Chu[262] discuss the shape of the nodes as follows:

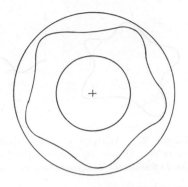

(A) TYPICAL DRAPE DIAGRAM FOR COTTON SATEEN

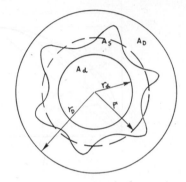

(B) TYPICAL DRAPE DIAGRAM FOR
CELLULOSE ACETATE PLAIN WEAVE FABRIC

Figure 26. Typical drape diagrams. *(From Chu, Cummings, and Teixeira,[261] "Mechanics of Elastic Performance of Textile Materials, Part V: A Study of the Factors Affecting the Drape of Fabrics— the Development of a Drapemeter.")*

"The discussion that follows is based on the assumption that the nodes in a Drape Diagram are uniform. Hence the Drape Diagram becomes a cyclic function in polar coordinates. The task of analysis can be made very much simpler by means of transferring the polar coordinates to rectangular coordinates. (Figure 27.)

"Consider a single node, the shape of which may be approximated by a variety of known functions, such as: (Figure 28.)

The triangle	The complete cycloid
The sine	The semi-ellipse
The parabola	The rectangle
The circular arc	etc."
The semi-circle	

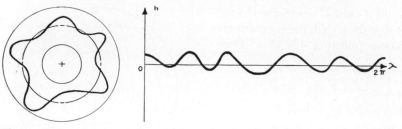

Figure 27. Analysis of drape diagram: Conversion of polar to rectangular coordinates. (*From Hamburger, Platt and Chu,*[262] "*Determination of the Factors Which Influence the Draping Properties of Cotton Fabrics.*")

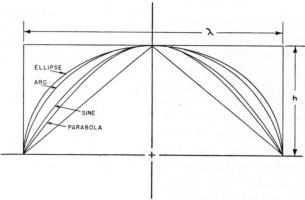

Figure 28. Functions which may approximate the shape of a node in the drape diagram. (*From Hamburger, Platt and Chu,*[262] "*Determination of the Factors Which Influence the Draping Properties of Cotton Fabrics.*")

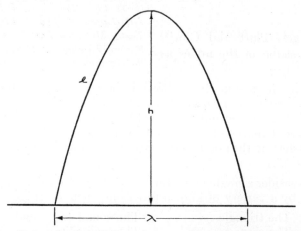

Figure 29. Determination of shape factor. (*From Hamburger, Platt and Chu,*[262] "*Determination of the Factors Which Influence the Draping Properties of Cotton Fabrics.*")

"The[262] sum of the perimeters of all the nodes in a Drape Diagram is equal to the circumference of the sample, and the ratio of λ/h depends on the Drape Coefficient, i.e., if the number of nodes, n, were fixed then λ/h varies inversely with the Drape Coefficient."

h/λ thus varies directly with the drape coefficient F and is called the "shape factor."

In using the Drapemeter, the specimen diameter and/or the supporting disc diameter may vary in order to attain maximum sensitivity. Since F will be dependent upon the ratio of supporting disc to specimen diameter, a convenient term to use is $r_D/\bar{r}$ because

$$\frac{A_D}{A_S} = \frac{r_D{}^2}{\bar{r}^2}$$

The shape factors for the various functions are tabulated in terms of this ratio as follows:

Triangle: $\dfrac{h}{\lambda} = \dfrac{1}{2}\sqrt{\left(\dfrac{r_D}{\bar{r}}\right)^2 - 1}$

Rectangle: $\dfrac{h}{\lambda} = \dfrac{1}{2}\left(\dfrac{r_D}{\bar{r}} - 1\right)$

Sine Function: $\dfrac{r_D}{\bar{r}} = \dfrac{2}{\pi}\left[1 + \pi^2\left(\dfrac{h}{\lambda}\right)^2\right]^{1/2} E$

where E = an elliptical integral

Parabola: $\dfrac{r_D}{\bar{r}} = \dfrac{1}{2}\sqrt{1 + 16\left(\dfrac{h}{\lambda}\right)^2} + \dfrac{1}{8\left(\dfrac{h}{\lambda}\right)} \ln\left[4\dfrac{h}{\lambda} + \sqrt{1 + 16\left(\dfrac{h}{\lambda}\right)^2}\right]$

Circular Arc: $\dfrac{r_D}{\bar{r}} = \left[\dfrac{1}{4}\left(\dfrac{\lambda}{h}\right) + \dfrac{h}{\lambda}\right]\sin^{-1}\left[\dfrac{1}{\dfrac{1}{4}\left(\dfrac{\lambda}{h}\right) + \dfrac{h}{\lambda}}\right]$

Semi-Ellipse: $\dfrac{r_D}{\bar{r}} = \dfrac{\pi}{4}\left(1 + 2\dfrac{h}{\lambda}\right)\left(1 + \dfrac{R^2}{4} + \dfrac{R^4}{64} + \dfrac{R^6}{256}\right)$

where

$$R = \left(\frac{1 - 2\dfrac{h}{\lambda}}{1 + 2\dfrac{h}{\lambda}}\right)$$

(82) Evaluation of Fabric Properties with Respect to Hand

Data in the literature which compare physical properties as they may pertain to fabric hand are sparse. Data which compare qualitative subjective reaction with quantitative physical measurement are nil.

In addition to the terminology suggested by A.S.T.M. in Table 78, Hoffman and Beste[255] also attempt to relate physical measurement with human sensation. Their paper to a large extent is philosophical in nature. They propose terminology which, possibly, with continued research on the subject, might lead to the relationships required. It must be pointed out, and Hoffman and Beste so state, that the concepts which are included in their paper are largely speculative and have been proposed "with the hope that they may be helpful or suggestive of further work." The reader, therefore, should exercise caution to insure that the proposed terms do not become accepted as standard terminology without further investigation and consideration, whereby the textile technology profession will have the opportunity to confirm, refute or modify the proposed nomenclature.

Peirce lists the weight, thickness, density, bending length, flexural rigidity, bending modulus, hardness, and compression modulus of a series of fabrics. Most of them are cottons of various constructions, with some information on type of finishing process.

Peirce[254] comments on Table 155 as follows:

"A range of stiffness from 1.81 to 6.35 cms (mean value of c) is here recorded. Fabrics approaching the lower limit were too soft to be measured by the standard method, so were tested by the pear cantilever and triangle methods. . . . Later, the "hanging heart" method was developed, and is now used for material with a lower value than 2 cms (which gives 43° deflection with a 4 cm rectangular cantilever), especially if it tends to curl. The softest fabric that could be found was a knitted viscose, with a bending length of 0.6 cm., measured without difficulty by this method. The highest value does not approach the upper limit that can be measured by the weighted rectangle method . . . in fact, there is no practical limit of stiffness for that method.

"The flexural rigidity, G, ranges from 21 for the lightest, a mull of 3.53 mgm per sq cm, to 26,420 for the heaviest, belting of 104 mgm per sq cm. Other things being the same, the flexural rigidity varies with the third power of the thickness, but if any one cloth is calendered or otherwise compressed, the relation is reversed owing to the rise in specific stiffness. This quantity, q, is the best to consider when it is desired to estimate the effect of the structural factor, which is chiefly the extent to which the hairs cohere. There is also a close correlation between the compression modulus, h, and the density, ρ, most of the values falling near the line $h = 10\rho/3$; the deviations can reasonably be explained by differences in openness of weave. Cotton cellulose has a density of about 1.5, but few of the materials reach one third of this. About the value 0.5 the hairs are evidently in intimate contact, for the specific stiffness increases rapidly. The greatest density attained mechan-

TABLE 155. STIFFNESS CHARACTERISTICS OF VARIOUS FABRICS
(From Peirce[254] "The Handle of Cloth As A Measurable Quantity")

The entries in the columns are:

w = weight per sq cm, in milligrams, at 70 per cent R.H.

d = thickness in μ (micron = 10^{-4} cm) measured under a foot of $\frac{1}{4}$-inch diameter; load 20.5 g

$\rho = w/d$, the density.

c = the bending length in centimetres, from flexometer reading at 70 per cent R.H.

$G = wc^3$, in mgm cm, the flexural rigidity.

$q = 12G/d^3$, in kg/cm³, the bending modulus.

H = the hardness, the ratio of changes in pressure and thickness in mgm/cm³.

h = the compression modulus = Hd, in kgm/cm².

No.	Material	w	d	ρ	c Warp	Weft	G	q	H	h	Notes
1	aircraft fabric	6.32	139	0.45	2.70	2.12	86	386	134	1.86	L
3	calico	18.8	380	0.49	3.35	3.61	790	173	33	1.25	L
5a	calico, grey	12.1	324	0.37	2.70	2.14	169	59	31	1.02	L.2
5b	calico, water-boiled	12.0	299	0.40	2.03	1.94	93	42	32	0.96	
5c	calico, scoured	10.6	272	0.38	2.17	2.06	101	60	31	0.85	
5d	calico, bleached	10.8	263	0.45	2.55	2.03	127	84	34	0.89	B
6a	mull	3.53	142	0.25	1.92	1.70	21	88	73	1.04	B
7a	satin	7.56	231	0.33	2.64	1.46	57	55	45	1.03	B
8a	taffeta	8.09	242	0.34	2.09	2.06	72	61	55	1.34	B
10	low weft sateen	8.70	395	0.22	2.23	1.38	47	9	22	0.86	B
13	harvard shirting	13.5	473	0.29	2.94	2.36	246	28	18	0.87	B
14	long cloth	13.7	228	0.60	3.15	3.24	444	450	79	1.79	B
16	twill	20.0	505	0.40	3.44	2.29	443	41	30	1.53	B
17	satin drill	22.2	470	0.47	2.99	2.17	367	42	35	1.65	B
18	mull 0.17% wax	6.62	162	0.41	3.91	2.47	199	566	76	1.23	C
19	mull 0.29% wax	6.61	189	0.35	2.99	1.85	86	152	54	1.02	C
20	poplin	10.5	225	0.47	2.69	1.73	105	111	71	1.60	C
22a	beetled shirting	11.7	142	0.82	3.53	3.17	438	1836	95	1.35	C
23a	beetled shirting	11.7	140	0.84	3.64	3.52	537	2343	94	1.32	C
22b	before beetling	13.3	395	0.34	2.47	2.45	198	39	36	1.41	B
23b	before beetling	13.3	405	0.33	2.28	2.47	177	32	42	1.69	B
24a	black satin	7.87	234	0.34	2.68	1.38	56	52	48	1.12	
25a	black sateen	20.5	486	0.42	2.22	2.15	214	22	30	1.48	
8b	mercerised taffeta	7.45	217	0.34	2.22	2.58	102	120	50	1.09	
6b	mercerised mull	3.51	132	0.27	2.20	2.21	38	194	73	0.96	
6c	organdie	3.39	100	0.34	5.45	3.89	331	3972	171	1.71	
9c	acid treated	9.33	234	0.40	2.52	2.08	112	104	72	1.68	
9d	parchmentised	13.3	154	0.86	8.00	6.78	5308	17350	123	1.90	
28	printed lawn	5.52	132	0.42	3.10	1.86	774	404	98	1.29	F
29	gingham (print)	9.80	284	0.35	6.15	2.71	667	350	55	1.56	F
30	cretonne (print)	12.9	350	0.37	2.76	4.37	537	151	57	1.99	F
31	flannelette (dyed)	15.9	420	0.38	4.81	2.04	487	79	21	0.87	F
32	ticking	25.4	437	0.58	3.57	5.11	1985	285	52	2.28	F
33	velveteen (dyed)	29.9	1450	0.21	2.69	1.85	331	1.3	5	0.69	F
34	conveyor belting	104	2200	0.47	6.32	6.35	26420	30	8	1.72	F
35	crepe rayon	6.13	179	0.34	1.55	2.82	56	118	65	1.16	F
36	crepe print	10.2	270	0.38	1.67	1.92	59	36	69	1.87	F
38	worsted weft, twill	24.9	623	0.40	2.18	2.09	242	12	26	1.65	F
39	American cloth	32.5	331	0.98	3.23	2.47	733	242	49	1.63	F
40	graph paper	4.83	75	0.64		6.03	1059	30110	211	1.58	F
41	feeler steel	30.2	381	7.93		6.76	9354	2.03×10^6			

Notes: L, loom state; B, bleached; C, calendered; F, normal commercial finish.

ically is in the beetled and calendered shirting (0.84), where
the finish has almost closed the spaces laterally.

"The density and stiffness are influenced at many of the
early stages of production; the raw cotton, the counts and
twist of yarns, the amount and composition of the size, the
number of picks and ends, and the warp tension. Thus the
difference between poplins 20 and 21 was associated with lower
extensibility and crimp, i.e., greater warp tension, in the
stiffer cloth.

"The[254] presence of lubricating or cementing matter on
the hairs has evidently a big effect. Thus the removal of wax
in bleaching increases the stiffness (compare the figures for
the water-boiled and bleached calico, Nos. 5b and 5d). The
absence of wax is also responsible for the excessive harshness
caused by mercerising after a scour. The effect of wax in
impeding the development of stiffness in mechanical finishes
is shown by the figures for the mulls, Nos. 18 and 19, and the
beetled shirting, Nos. 22a and 23a. In the grey state, fats in
the size do not appear to have any effect on the stiffness.
Starch, as size or filling, has a great stiffening effect, more by
cementing the hairs than by virtue of its own rigidity. Dyeing
seems to have the opposite effect, the diminution of stiffness
being particularly noticeable in the schreinered satins; heavy
printing has an appreciable stiffening effect. The swelling in
mercerisation brings the hairs into intimate contact, so that the
specific stiffness is doubled in the example given. Sulphuric
acid, in the organdie and parchmentising treatments, multi-
plies the modulus 50 or 100 times, virtually welding the hairs
together.

"The stiffness of cloth is ultimately dependent on the
elastic properties of the hairs, that is, on the sum of the forces
necessary to bend and to stretch them. If it is assumed that
half the hairs lie in the direction of the strip, then the force
necessary for bending alone is $G/2$, where G is the flexural
rigidity of single hairs, and the corresponding value of c will be
$\sqrt[3]{G/2m}$, where m is the hair weight per centimetre of single
hairs. From data formerly obtained, the value of $G/2m$ for
Texas hairs at 70% R.H. is about 6 cm^3 or $c = 1.82$. This
agrees with the value for the very flimsiest cloth, the low-weft
sateen, in which the fibres are apparently so loosely held that
they do not take any tension. At the other limit of a compact
continuous sheet with elastic properties the same as those of the
hair wall material, the value of q would be about 60,000
kgm/cm^2. It is, of course, impossible to realise such a value,

and a nearer approach could hardly be made than that made by the parchmentised sheet with a modulus, $q = 17,350$. There is no relative movement of the fibres in this, and the lower modulus is sufficiently explained by the degradation of the cellulose, the two orientations of the hairs, and the imperfect uniformity of the sheet. In all other fabrics more or less air space is included, and the hairs take some tension but also yield by relative movement.

"The[254] graph paper is also mainly cellulose and is of high quality, thin, tough, and uniform, and gives a value of q half that of the Young's modulus of cotton hairs. It may be noted that the value for feeler steel agrees with the Young's modulus given in tables of physical constants.

"The figures of the table yield on perusal many more interesting relations. They express facts that could be appreciated in handling the cloths, but in definite numbers and an impersonal, unified scheme of comparison."

Peirce neither includes nor discusses the relations between stiffness and hardness, and the psychological sensation of hand. With the exception of the drape data which will be presented in the next chapter, no other literature reference has been found which discusses such relations.

Winn and Schwarz[260] show the relative ranking of stiffness as measured by several of the test methods described above (Table 156).

TABLE 156. RELATIVE RANKING OF STIFFNESS PROPERTIES OF VARIOUS FABRICS (From Winn and Schwarz[260] "Flexibility and Drape As Measurable Properties of Fabric")

					Stiffness Rank				
								Drape-o-meter	
				Flex-	Bend-			Radius	
		Thick-	Bend-	ural	ing	Schieffer		of	
	Wt	ness	ing	Ri-	Modu-	Flex-	Chord	Curva-	
	oz/yd²	.001 in.	Length	gidity	lus	ometer	Length	ture	Gurley
treated thick cotton	12.60	31.7	1	1	3	1	1	1	1
plain thick cotton	13.25	17.1	5	3	8	3	2	2	2
tracing cloth	3.19	3.25	2	2	1	2	10	10	4
unlaundered organdie	1.46	6.0	3	4	2	6	4	3	9
laundered organdie	1.55	6.9	4	5	4	9	3	6	10
treated thin cotton	3.23	8.4	6	9	6	4	8	7	8
plain thin cotton	3.34	6.3	7	8	5	7	9	9	7
A.C. Congo	7.70	14.5	8	6	7	5	7	5	3
plain Congo	6.89	14.7	9	7	9	8	6	4	5
"Velvet"	4.73	21.1	10	10	10	10	5	8	6

The authors use Spearman correlation coefficients to ascertain rank correlation among the various tests:

TABLE 157. SPEARMAN RATINGS (PER CENT) OF RANK CORRELATION BETWEEN
STIFFNESS DETERMINATION METHODS

(From Winn and Schwarz[260] "Flexibility and Drape As Measurable Properties
of Fabric")

	Gurley Tester	Radius of Curvature	Chord Length	Schiefer Flexometer	Bending Modulus	Rigidity
bending length	+12%	+27%	+29%	+69%	+88%	+86%
rigidity	+48%	+48%	+42%	+71%	+65%	......
bending modulus	−15%	− 6%	− 9%	+48%	......	......
Schiefer Flexometer	+64%	+30%	+ 4%	......	......	......
chord length	+20%	+83%	......	......	......	......
radius of curvature	+38%	......	......	......	......	......

Spearman ratings are calculated such that a value of +100 per cent shows perfect direct correlation, 0 per cent shows no correlation, minus 100 per cent shows perfect inverse correlation.

It will be noted that with a few exceptions, correlations between test methods are not high.

(83) Frictional Properties of Fabrics as They Pertain to Hand

Referring to Peirce's[254] definition of fabric hand as given on page 423, we note that roughness or smoothness is one of the parameters listed. Two references cited below indicate that poor correlation exists between coefficient of friction and the subjective sense of fabric smoothness.

Hoffman and Beste[255] state:

"There is considerable doubt that the entire 'feel' of stroking the fingers over a fabric can be described by a coefficient of friction. A velvet and a satin may have equal coefficients . . . and yet feel different because of the brushiness of the former.

"In measuring fabric friction, a piece of soft cowhide was used to approximate the human skin; this material was designated the 'standard hand.' The fabric sample, mounted on a Lucite panel . . . was laid on the leather, face down, and loaded with a 180-g. weight. The force parallel to the fabric face was measured by means of a strain gage upon which the fabric block pulled.

"A series of five twill fabrics was selected and ten observers were asked to rate these from low to high in smoothness, assigning the numbers 1 to 5, respectively. These subjective ratings agree fairly well with the static coefficients of friction."

TABLE 158. COEFFICIENTS OF FRICTION (FABRIC VS. LEATHER)

(From Hoffman and Beste[255] "Some Relations of Fiber Properties to Fabric Hand")

Material	Subjective Rating of Smoothness	Static Coefficient of Friction, μ
66 nylon	2.1 ± 0.8	0.62 ± 0.03
viscose rayon	1.8 ± 0.7	0.60
acetate rayon	2.2 ± 1.0	0.59
experimental fiber	3.7 ± 0.4	0.46
polyethylene	5.0 ± 0	0.35

"In another experiment, two pieces were cut from a tropical worsted and a nap was raised on one piece by means of a hand card. Everyone who examined these fabrics described the piece with the nap as being softer than the other. The coefficients of friction were measured under a 10-gram load (0.95 g/cm²) with the result that the napped piece gave a higher value than the other (0.67 and 0.63 respectively). Finally, a μ value of 1.31 was obtained on a piece of velvet under the 10-gram load. Most people would describe the surface feel of velvet as being very soft or smooth. We believe that softness of this type and smoothness and waxiness are three separate and distinct properties."[255]

Morrow[332] also found it difficult to relate coefficient of friction with "smoothness" since most people would not evaluate smoothness alone, but combined it with "softness":

"The figures obtained seem to bear little relation to personal judgment of the feel of various fabrics and their state of finish, and the general conclusion from many and varied experiments is that resistance to sliding is not readily appreciated, or is overborne in personal judgments by other features. As there was little prospect of utilising the measurement for technical purposes, systematic experiments were discontinued, and are briefly described here mainly to support the above not unimportant conclusion and to save unnecessary repetition by other workers.

"No difficulty was experienced in accurately measuring the force of friction between a cloth specimen and any desired surface, over a range of pressure and speed, except the difficulty due to variations in that force itself. Many experiments were made to find conditions, and particularly a test surface that would give results for different surfaces bearing some relation to technical or aesthetic value. To avoid the confusion of a mass of figures of little individual significance, the experience so gained is summarised in descriptive form below.

"A similar piece of cloth being used as test surface, it was found that fabrics with irregular surfaces bind on each other and will not slide smoothly. This is especially true of ridgy surfaces, a very common feature, as in repps. The friction immediately alters the state of the surface, making successive readings very erratic, and the result is unduly affected by adventitious previous treatment, such as folding or rubbing.

"Chrome[332] leather was tried for the test surface as an approximation to skin. The same jerky motion was observed to a less extent, also the disturbance of the surface by the test. Among fabrics which allowed smooth motion, the results were often insensitive to appreciable differences of feel. Significant differences could be observed on the same cloth with markedly different finish. For instance, the following values of μ were obtained. Plain weave grey 0.31; bleached 0.30; schreinered 0.26; twill (2/2), bleached 0.31; cold calender finish 0.30; five-shaft weft sateen, grey 0.45; bleached and mercerised 0.31; dyed, glazed and schreinered 0.26.

"Against a polished steel surface the motion was smooth and accurate reading was easy, without disturbance of the surface. All fabrics showed very much the same coefficient of friction (0.22). This is evidently the true molecular friction of cotton against steel and has little bearing on feel.

"On the view that the fine surface irregularities predominate over true surface friction in subjective judgment, a test surface was sought which would be sensitive to these irregularities. Card clothing—with the wire pointing backwards—is such a surface which is constant and reproducible in character, and causes little disturbance of the surface of the cloth. Friction against this test surface proved reproducible, and distinguished sensitively between different fabrics. Thus a satin in the grey gave a figure 0.35; after a schreiner finish 0.20. A finished satin with rayon warp gave 0.29 weft-way, 0.19 warp-way. It would be generally agreed that in both cases the lower figure corresponded to the smoother surface. On the other hand, a soft mercerised finish gave a higher value than a hard finish that felt harsher whilst flannelettes gave values about 0.5; but velveteens 0.7 or more. Generally the test is more sensitive to hairiness than to the thready irregularities that determine the sensation "smooth" or "rough" which it is desired to measure.

"To[332] sum up, the measurement with a card clothing test surface may give interpretable figures in special cases within a limited range of similar fabrics. The figures obtained on diverse fabrics, however, cannot be related to any one feature of technical import.

"It was, moreover, found that whilst such descriptions as "smooth," "harsh," etc., may be applied as a result of handling a fabric, observers were very uncertain and divergent in judgment based on softly stroking a fabric laid flat on a table, that is, when nothing but sliding friction could be appreciated. When that feature is in question, reasonably good means of measuring it are available, if the result is interpreted according to the qualitative character of the surface—whether hairy or hard; but there seems little ground for supposing, even in the latter case, that sliding friction is of importance in deciding aesthetic value. Cases may occur, however, where it is of direct importance for a particular technical purpose."

(84) The Influence of Fiber Properties upon Fabric Hand

To attempt to evaluate and rank the various fibers for fabric hand is probably an impossibility because different end-usages entail different demands on those properties required of a fabric. The softness of a blanket is a requisite for good hand—in a blanket; the stiffness of an organdie is a requisite for good hand—in an organdie. A fiber property which is an asset in one instance can be a liability in another. So many subjective factors are involved, that in order to compare the relative ability of fibers to produce specific fabrics, the cataloging of fabric properties would be required, after which notation could be made as to the ability of the various fibers to meet the necessary demands.

Returning to Peirce's statement that handle encompasses stiffness, hardness, and smoothness (and their antonyms) some consideration may be made of the ability of the various fibers to produce requisite hands for specific usages.

The low tensional and bending moduli, high elastic recovery, and excellent compressional resilience properties of wool accounts for the soft, lofty, flexible characteristics of such woolen goods as sweaters, blankets, and flannels. Nylon and "Dacron" fit the same category, except that these fibers according to Cassie[61] (pages 183–185) are more prone to pack down to give "lean, cold yarns." Various types of wool will, of course, have different bending moduli depending upon fiber diameter and denier (page 51). The fact that synthetic filaments can be made in a range of diameters gives the synthetic filament-maker opportunity to produce, within limits, desirable bending moduli. This, coupled with proper yarn and fabric engineering, enables the attainment of a range of fabric flexibilities.

Similarly, it is illogical to attempt to rank the frictional characteristics of fibers as they might influence hand. The wool fiber, as pointed out by Gralen and Olofsson,[341] (page 79) is a smooth fiber, but so many fabric geometry effects can become of greater import and significance that friction coefficient, as it affects fabric property, may become of secondary consideration. Subjective evaluation criteria also depress its importance because people cannot, or at least are not willing to separate it from, flexibility, compressional resilience, warmth, etc.

The next chapter will discuss "drape," and here some progress has been made in ascertaining the relationship between physical measurement and subjective reaction.

Chapter 21

FABRIC DRAPE

With the exception of Section (89), this chapter consists of selected portions of a series of Fabric Research Laboratories, Inc. reports[262] entitled the "Determination of The Factors Which Influence The Draping Properties of Cotton Fabrics." The research is being conducted at Fabric Research Laboratories, Inc., under the sponsorship of the Research and Marketing Act, United States Department of Agriculture.

Three objectives were investigated in studying the factors which influence draping characteristics:

(1) What defines drape, and what are the qualities requisite for good drape?

(2) Do fabric "experts" who evaluate fabrics visually and tactilely, agree among themselves in their ability to rank fabrics for drapability?

(3) What correlation, if any, exists among the F.R.L. Drapemeter, other stiffness measurements, and the subjective rankings obtained in (2) above?

(85) The Definition of Drape

Interviews were held with groups of people from the fabric trade selected because of their close relationship with the designing, styling, and merchandising of fabrics. They were asked questions such as:

"What properties in a fabric are looked for in judging draping quality?"

"Can an assortment of fabrics be ranked according to their drapabilities independent of their end-use?"

"What are your general opinions regarding drape?"

The following are typical miscellaneous statements concerning their response:[262]

> "Drape should be classified by end-usages such as draperies, curtains, women's wear, men's wear, etc.
> "Emphasis is on the distinction of end-uses; this may mean the draping quality of any material may be good for curtains, but poor for a woman's skirt.

449

"Distinction should be made between the 'drape' of apparel and drapery materials.

"The criteria for drapability for different end-uses are not the same.

"Even within the same end-use classification (i.e., whether draperies or apparel) different types of materials cannot be evaluated together, viz., knitted jersey vs. chambray.

"Consumers have fixed conceptions regarding the properties and the end usages of various fibers.

"Certain poor draping characteristics are desirable for the sake of fashion or for novelty effects, such as the "crispness" of taffeta and the coarse texture of burlap cloth.

"'Hand' is equally important as visual evaluation in judging drapability.

"Drape and hand go together.

"'Hand' cannot be separated from 'drape.'

"Drape and handle should not be divorced.

"It is commonly agreed that 'handle' goes together with 'drape.'

"Crease resistance may be related in some way to drape.

"Resin treatments on synthetic fibers to improve drape are not as satisfactory as the use of natural fibers.

"Drape is dictated by fashion.

"The weight of the fabric, the length of fabric hanging and the ratio of the two will affect drape.

"Linings which add weight to apparel or drapery fabrics will usually improve drape.

"Addition of weight can improve drape.

"Drape is not defined by graceful form alone, but rather by the material's ability to form such shapes by itself.

"The problem of drape is not serious in men's wear.

"Drape is important in men's apparel.

"Cut and tailoring can improve drape more than the draping qualities of the material.

"'Liveliness' which is that property of a fabric enabling it to form into graceful and pleasing folds without being deliberately set, is good for drape.

"'Resilience' and 'liveliness' are good for drape, while 'limpness' is poor.

"Synthetic fibers drape poorly because of their lack of 'liveliness.'

"The importance of fabric construction and its effect on drape is recognized.

"Cotton fabrics, with the proper construction, can be just as drapable as other fabrics."

The gamut of answers is indicative of the inability of people to define their feelings and reactions to both drape and hand.

(86) Correlation among People in Their Ability to Evaluate Drape

This portion of the research[262] is not yet completed, but sufficiently promising results are being obtained to warrant the inclusion of the following preliminary results at this time.

"Forty-eight[262] fabrics of miscellaneous constructions, weights, fiber contents, and end-usages were selected at random. Included were curtain and drapery materials, men's and women's worsted and woolen suitings, dress goods, and upholstery fabrics.

The Bending Length (c_s) and Drape Coefficient (% F.) were determined for each fabric (Table 159). The general range of % F values is 26% to 78%; and of c_s (Peirce's[254] weighted average of warp and filling bending lengths) is 0.48 to 1.37 inches. Ten fabrics were selected from the forty-eight listed in Table 159 such that their c_s values were spaced throughout the range.* In other words, bending length values obtained in the laboratory showed a gamut of stiffnesses for the selected series.

TABLE 159. DRAPE COEFFICIENTS AND BENDING LENGTHS OF MISCELLANEOUS FABRICS

(From Hamburger, Platt and Chu[262] "Factors Which Influence The Draping Properties of Cotton Fabrics")

No.	Type	Drape Coefficient (% F.)	Bending Length (inches) Warp Filling
1	100% women's worsted suiting	44.3	0.53 × 0.63
2	100% women's worsted suiting	42.0	0.57 × 0.53
3	100% women's worsted suiting	42.6	0.58 × 0.55
4	100% women's worsted suiting	42.0	0.59 × 0.55
5	100% women's worsted suiting	41.8	0.53 × 0.61
6	100% women's worsted suiting	41.7	0.51 × 0.61
7	100% women's worsted suiting	44.7	0.51 × 0.67
8	100% women's worsted suiting	45.2	0.67 × 0.53
9	100% women's worsted suiting	49.8	0.67 × 0.58
10	86% rayon-14% mohair women's suiting	45.3	0.71 × 0.59
11	86% rayon-14% mohair women's suiting	46.6	0.63 × 0.66
12	46% cotton-54% rayon damask drapery fabric	73.1	1.29 × 1.10

* At the time of selection of fabrics for the subjective evaluation tests, only c values rather than %F values were available. Subsequent results, shown in Table 160, confirm the excellent rank correlation between these two parameters, the effect being that selection via drape coefficients would have produced the same ten fabrics.

TABLE 159. DRAPE COEFFICIENTS AND BENDING LENGTHS OF MISCELLANEOUS FABRICS.—(*Continued*)

No.	Type	Drape Coefficient (% F.)	Bending Length (inches) Warp	Filling
13	100% cotton damask drapery fabric	74.1	1.04 × 1.23	
14	100% cotton brocade drapery fabric	78.0	1.17 × 1.57	
15	100% cotton damask drapery fabric	72.1	1.08 × 1.16	
16	100% silk damask drapery fabric	42.7	0.50 × 1.17	
17	100% silk damask drapery fabric	58.6	1.04 × 1.54	
18	100% nylon marquisette netting	*	1.18 × 0.96	
19	100% rayon brocade drapery fabric	88.9	1.17 × 1.86	
20	44% cotton-56% rayon damask drapery fabric	86.2	1.25 × 1.48	
21	100% nylon ripstop parachute cloth	39.4	0.72 × 0.60	
22	67% cotton-33% rayon upholstery fabric	63.8	0.82 × 0.92	
23	100% cotton velveteen pile fabric	42.5	0.64 × 0.62	
24	33% cotton-67% rayon drapery fabric	47.0	0.63 × 0.82	
25	17% cotton-83% rayon upholstery fabric	41.2	0.65 × 0.83	
26	72% mohair-28% rayon "Springweave" worsted suiting	51.5	0.71 × 0.71	
27	75% mohair-25% rayon worsted suiting	48.1	0.72 × 0.73	
28	42% mohair-58% rayon "Sunfrost" worsted suiting	46.6	0.69 × 0.65	
29	34% flax-33% rayon-33% mohair drapery fabric	*	1.00 × 1.19	
30	31% rayon-43% cotton-11% mohair-15% metal drapery fabric	76.4	1.04 × 1.06	
31	71% cotton-29% mohair drapery fabric	62.4	0.78 × 0.86	
32	38% rayon-49% cotton-13% mohair drapery fabric	60.7	0.66 × 0.92	
33	69% cotton-31% mohair curtain fabric	46.8	0.46 × 1.04	
34	12% rayon-50% cotton-38% mohair drapery fabric	57.9	0.66 × 0.92	
35	continuous filament blouse fabric	26.6	0.46 × 1.04	
36	spun dress goods	31.5	0.69 × 0.98	
37	spun dress goods	29.1	0.50 × 0.59	
38	spun dress goods	34.7	0.60 × 0.64	
39	continuous filament blouse fabric	33.3	0.64 × 0.48	
40	rayon satin blouse fabric	66.9	1.49 × 0.85	
41	gabardine suiting	56.8	0.74 × 0.60	
42	worsted suiting	46.0	0.76 × 0.56	
43	worsted suiting	38.3	0.69 × 0.65	
44	worsted suiting	37.3	0.60 × 0.54	
45	continuous filament dress goods	48.6	0.74 × 0.59	
46	dress goods	31.6	0.58 × 0.57	
47	crepe dress goods	24.9	0.49 × 0.47	
48	crepe dress goods	25.6	0.56 × 0.49	

* The nature of these fabrics is such that they do not give accurate readings on the Drapemeter. This happens only when there are visible openings in the structure; such as marquisette, netting, burlap, etc.

"The ten fabrics were submitted to seven individuals for subjective evaluation. (It is recognized that seven is not a large sample, and many more people are being sampled as the research progresses.)

"The[262] subjects involved . . . were located mostly around Boston, . . . and consisted of the following people:

    2 quality control men
    1 retail drapery salesman
    1 factory representative of a drapery manufacturer
    1 woolen-goods buyer
    1 dress-goods buyer
    1 assistant dress-merchandising manager

"The subjects, upon receiving the samples were requested to do the following:

"(1) By visual and tactile examination rank the fabrics in order of increasing stiffness.

"(2) By visual observation of hanging samples, rank the fabrics in decreasing order of gracefulness of folds or pleats.

"These requests, rather than a request for a ranking of drapability were the result of a considerable amount of study. Since most of the people contacted . . . would refuse to rank drapability for different end-usages, the two separate rankings, i.e., one for stiffness and the other for gracefulness, were designed to by-pass this mental block."

TABLE 160. RANK CORRELATION ON THE SUBJECTIVE EVALUATION OF STIFFNESS: AGREEMENT AMONG SEVEN SUBJECTS

(From Hamburger, Platt and Chu[262] "Factors Which Influence The Draping Properties of Cotton Fabrics")

					Fabric Number					
Subjects	47	23	21	24	33	31	30	15	12	14
A	2	1	3	5	4	9	10	6	7	8
B	2	4	1	5	3	9	10	7	6	8
C	3	1	2	5	4	8	10	7	6	9
D	1	4	3	5	2	8	10	6	7	9
E	2	4	1	7	3	5	9	8	6	10
F	2	1	4	5	6	7	10	3	8	9
G	3	1	2	7	4	9	10	6	5	8

Analysis for concordance shows that at the 99 per cent significance level, the seven subjects rank the ten fabrics in a similar manner, the concordance coefficient being 0.87. For perfect concordance the coefficient is +1.00; for no concordance the coefficient is zero.

TABLE 161. RANK CORRELATION ON THE SUBJECTIVE EVALUATION
OF "GRACEFULNESS": AGREEMENT AMONG SEVEN SUBJECTS

(From Hamburger, Platt and Chu[262] "Factors Which Influence The Draping
Properties of Cotton Fabrics")

Subjects	47	23	21	24	Fabric Number 33	31	30	15	12	14
A	1	2	5	3	4	6	10	8	7	9
B	1	3	6	5	2	4	7	9	8	10
C	10	9	4	1	2	3	5	7	6	8
D	1	3	2	5	4	8	10	6	7	9
E	2	1	4	3	6	5	10	7	8	9
F	4	3	5	6	1	7	8	9	2	10
G	2	1	5	4	8	3	9	6	7	10

Analysis for concordance shows that at the 99 per cent significance level, the seven subjects rank the ten fabrics in a similar manner, the concordance coefficient being 0.56.

It will be noted that the people's ability to rank "stiffness" (tactile and visual) is better than their ability to rank "gracefulness" (visual; drape?). However, it should be pointed out that one individual, in ranking gracefulness relegated that fabric which most others placed first, at the bottom of the list.

"He explained that according to his opinion, the first place fabric was too limp for proper draping. If he is removed from consideration, the concordance coefficient for the remaining six rises from 0.56 to 0.75."[262]

In any event, it can be stated that for both stiffness and "gracefulness" (drape?) it appears (but is not proved) that most people are able to rank a series of fabrics and agree on such a rank. How they correlate with quantitative physical measurements will now be discussed.

(87) Correlation among Subjective Rankings, and Stiffness and Drape Measurements

Tables 162 and 163 show the relationship between strip bending length ranking and subjective stiffness ranking, and Drapemeter ranking and subjective gracefulness ranking, respectively.

"The agreement between the seven subjects and the laboratory measure of stiffness is significant with a concordance coefficient of 0.84."[262]

TABLE 162. CORRELATION BETWEEN STRIP BENDING LENGTH RANK AND SUBJECTIVE STIFFNESS RANKING (IN ORDER OF INCREASING STIFFNESS)

(From Hamburger, Platt and Chu[262] "Factors Which Influence The Draping Properties of Cotton Fabrics")

Fabric Number	Strip Bending Ranking	Subjective Rankings (in order of increasing stiffness)						
47	1	2	2	3	1	2	2	3
23	2	1	4	1	4	4	1	1
21	3	3	1	2	3	1	4	2
24	4	5	5	5	5	7	5	7
33	5	4	3	4	2	3	6	4
31	6	9	9	8	8	5	7	9
30	7	10	10	10	10	9	10	10
15	8	6	7	7	6	8	3	6
12	9	7	6	6	7	6	8	5
14	10	8	8	9	9	10	9	8

The subjects evaluated stiffness by tactile evaluation of resistance to bending, the request being made that all aesthetic considerations be omitted.

Concerning gracefulness:

" . . . it would not be anticipated that the seven subjects would agree upon a matter of personal taste as closely as they did on stiffness. . . . (However) the agreement amongst the subjects' opinions of gracefulness, and the Drapemeter, is indicated as being significant with concordance coefficients of 0.59 and 0.76 for seven and six subjects, respectively."[262]

TABLE 163. CORRELATION BETWEEN DRAPEMETER RANKING AND SUBJECTIVE GRACEFULNESS RANKING (IN ORDER OF DECREASING GRACEFULNESS)

(From Hamburger, Platt and Chu[262] "Factors Which Influence the Draping Properties of Cotton Fabrics")

Fabric Number	Drapemeter Ranking	Subjective Rankings (in order of decreasing gracefulness)						
47	1	1	1	10	1	2	4	2
21	2	5	6	4	2	4	5	5
33	3	4	2	2	4	6	1	8
23	4	2	3	9	3	1	3	1
24	5	3	5	1	5	3	6	4
31	6	6	4	3	8	5	7	3
15	7	8	9	7	6	7	9	6
12	8	7	8	6	7	8	2	7
30	9	10	7	5	10	10	8	9
14	10	9	10	8	9	9	10	10

Stiffness rankings as given in Table 162 were compared with Drapemeter rankings as given in Table 163 and were shown to be significantly alike, viz:

TABLE 164. CORRELATION BETWEEN STIFFNESS AND DRAPE RANK
(From Hamburger, Platt and Chu[262] "Factors Which Influence The Draping Properties of Cotton Fabrics")

Fabric Number	Strip Bending Rank	Drapemeter Rank
47	1	1
23	2	4
21	3	2
24	4	5
33	5	3
31	6	6
30	7	9
15	8	7
12	9	8
14	10	10

$T = +0.778$, where $+1.00$ = perfect direct correlation
0.00 = no correlation
-1.00 = perfect inverse correlation

Excellent correlation existing between these two test methods,

"one may then ask, if this is the case, why use the Drapemeter, since the strip bending test is so much simpler to use? The answer is (that) . . . the strip bending test is . . . capable of measuring the bending properties of materials in any one direction. However, it falls down when performance under two directions is desired. An example is given by the comparison of *papers* and *fabrics* with the same strip bending stiffness.[262] Typical results are given in Table 165."

TABLE 165. EFFECT OF PAPERINESS AS DETECTED BY THE DRAPEMETER
(From Hamburger, Platt and Chu[262] "Factors Which Influence The Draping Properties of Cotton Fabrics")

	Bending Length c_s inches		Drape Coefficient % F at $\beta^* = 0.5$
	Warp	Filling	
tissue paper	0.96	1.35	92.8%
thin wax paper	1.21	1.21	90.5%
fabric 13	1.04	1.23	74.1%
fabric 12	1.29	1.10	73.1%

* β = ratio of supporting disc diameter to specimen diameter.

Although the bending lengths of the papers and the fabrics are similar, their draping qualities as measured by per cent F are not, nor are they subjectively classed as being alike.

Similar discrepancies may be observed with the M.I.T. Drape-o-meter.[263] Drape-o-meter results on the above paper and fabric samples show that the papers drape better than the fabrics, while common knowledge indicates that this is not the case.

(88) Comparison of the Draping Characteristics of Fabrics Composed of Various Fibers

The fabrics listed in Table 159 are a heterogeneous collection and no interpretation concerning relative draping qualities of the various fibers (in fabric form) is feasible.

A pedigreed series of fabrics were submitted for drape evaluation by the U.S. Department of Agriculture, Textile and Clothing Division, Bureau of Human Nutrition and Home Economics.[264]   Table 166 shows fiber content and drape coefficients.

TABLE 166.   FIBER CONTENT AND DRAPE COEFFICIENTS OF U.S.D.A. EXPERIMENTAL
FABRICS

(From Fabric Research Laboratories Report 966-2; To the U.S. Department of
Agriculture, Textile and Clothing Division, Bureau of Human Nutrition
and Home Economics[264])

Group	Fabric Number	64's	Wools 56–58's	48–50's	Mohair	Rayon	Nylon	Drape Coeff. (%)
I	HE-1		100%					71.0
	HE-2	100%						67.5
II	HE-3			50%	50%			74.5
	HE-4			75%	25%			77.2
	HE-5		50%		50%			76.1
	HE-6		75%		25%			74.9
III	HE-7			50%*		50%		66.5
	HE-8			75%		25%		69.9
	HE-9		50%*			50%		64.1
	HE-10		75%			25%		68.4
IV	HE-11				50%	50%		73.4
	HE-12				25%	75%		63.7
	HE-13				75%	25%		68.0
V	HE-14			50%			50%	79.3
	HE-15			75%			25%	75.5
	HE-16		50%				50%	76.0
	HE-17		75%				25%	72.9
VI	HE-18			50%	25%	25%		70.7
	HE-19			33%	33%	33%		70.8
	HE-20		50%		25%	25%		68.5
	HE-21		33%		33%	33%		71.2
VII	HE-22			50%	25%		25%	77.7
	HE-23			33%	33%		33%	79.8
	HE-24		50%*		25%		25%	75.2
	HE-25		33%		33%		33%	76.3

* These fibers are actually mohair of the designated quality.   They are included under the wool heading for quality identification only.

All of these fabrics were of identical construction and substantially the same weight.   Thus the effect of fiber content on physical properties could be determined.

> "The weave of these experimental fabrics was rather tight; hence the low drapability (high Drape Coefficient).   Experience . . . (has shown) . . . that the range of values for good drapability lies somewhere between 40 and 60%.   The effect of the tight weave may (thus) have overshadowed any effects due to fiber blending . . . since all values lie in the 63–79% range."[264]

However, some trends concerning the effect of blending may be proposed.

(1) 100% 64's vs. 56's–58's wool (2 vs. 1)   no significant difference
(2) 100% wool vs. 50% wool-50% mohair (1 vs. 5)   no significant difference
(3) 100% wool vs. 50% wool-50% rayon (1 vs. 9)   significant difference; rayon makes fabric less stiff

(4) 100% wool vs. 50% wool-50% nylon (1 vs. 16)   no significant difference
(5) 50% wool-50% mohair vs. 50% wool-50% rayon (3 vs. 7)   significant difference; rayon decreases stiffness; mohair increases stiffness

(6) 50% wool-50% mohair vs. 50% wool-50% nylon (3 vs. 14)   no significant difference
(7) 33% wool-33% mohair-34% rayon vs. 33% wool 33% mohair-34% nylon (19 vs. 23)   significant difference; nylon increases stiffness over rayon

(8) 33% wool-33% mohair-34% rayon vs. 33% wool-33% mohair-34% nylon (21 vs. 25)   no significant difference

It would be expected that 64's wool would be less stiff than 56–58's, but the difference is not significant.   The other comparisons must be considered in terms of the stiffness of the particular fibers going into the blends, in turn related to inherent stiffness and fiber diameter (see Tables 26 and 27, pages 52 and 54).

For the particular sizes of fibers used in these fabrics, and considering the statistical significance of the data, we can conclude that the blending of 48–50's or 56–58's wool with rayon produces a more flexible, more drapable (on the F.R.L. Drapemeter) fabric.   Mohair and nylon possibly have a tendency to produce stiffer fabrics.

These remarks should not be construed to mean that nylon and mohair, when blended with wool always produce stiffer fabrics, while rayon produces more flexible fabrics.   It is a function of fiber diameter as well as inherent property.

Additional data on the draping characteristics of blended wool navy melton fabrics are listed in the following table.[248]

TABLE 167. STIFFNESS AND DRAPE PROPERTIES OF BLENDED MELTON FABRICS
(From Fabric Research Laboratories, Inc.[248] "Development of Navy Meltons from Wool Blends"; Report to the United States Naval Clothing Depot)
(See Table 112 for fabric composition and other physical properties.)

Fabric Number	Bending Length* (inches)		Drape (% F)	
	Warp	Filling	Face	Back
0 all wool	0.89	0.75	61.1	62.3
1 wool-viscose-nylon	0.83	0.70	58.0	59.4
2 wool-viscose	0.73	0.66	53.2	51.8
3 wool-cotton	0.74	0.66	62.2	58.2
4 wool-nylon	0.78	0.65	58.8	57.7

* Average bending length for face and back sides of fabrics.

It is clear that there are no large differences in stiffness or drape coefficients among the various blends. The wool-rayon fabric appears to be somewhat less stiff than the others.

(89) Supplementary Information on the Subjective Evaluation of Fabric Stiffness

Subsequent to the preparation of the previous chapter on "Fabric Hand" and this chapter on "Fabric Drape," Abbott[265] has reported on "The Measurement of Stiffness in Textile Fabrics." He compares nineteen fabrics for stiffness by means of subjective evaluation as well as by five physical measurements, viz: (1) cantilever bending length, (2) heart loop, (3) Schiefer Flexometer, (4) Dreby[266] Planoflex,† (5) M.I.T. Drape-o-meter.

Table 168 shows the list of fabrics and the resulting subjective evaluation for stiffness wherein the nineteen fabrics were ranked by seventeen people

> " . . . . not all of whom were equally used to handling fabrics. Accordingly, a weight varying from one to four depending upon the individual's familiarity with fabrics, was assigned to each ranking and a weighted average rank obtained for each fabric. . . . It will be seen that except in a few instances remarkably good agreement was obtained, even though in many cases there was very little apparent difference

† "In[266] this instrument a 3-inch wide strip of fabric is mounted in a frame which permits lateral displacement of one end of the fabric, in the plane of the fabric. This movement distorts the fabric, and is carried on until diagonal wrinkles appear. The angle through which the frame has been moved at the appearance of the wrinkles is read off a scale. . . . This angle is determined on each side of the center and the sum of the two angles so obtained is taken as a measure of the stiffness of the material."

TABLE 168. SUBJECTIVE EVALUATION OF STIFFNESS

(From Abbott[265] "The Measurement of Stiffness in Textile Fabrics")

Fabric	Weight (oz/yd²)	Code Letter	1	2	3	4	5	6	7	8	9	10	11	12	13	14	15	16	17	Weighted Ave.
										Subjective Evaluation Person Number										
acetate taffeta	3.1	A	17	19	17	18	19	18	15	17	15	19	19	15	16	16	17	19	17	17.5
viscose rayon, taffeta	3.2	B	16	16	15	15	13	15	12	14	19	16	16	12	12	17	14	8	15	14.4
acetate-viscose satin	3.1	C	13	10	9	10	14	11	16	7	13	16	12	16	13	14	15	11	12	12.3
viscose rayon crepe	3.0	D	1	1	1	1	2	3	3	1	2	1	4	4	1	1	2	3	1	1.73
spun viscose rayon, plain weave	3.2	E	12	3	3	3	4	5	8	3	8	3	3	13	4	4	4	4	3	4.3
cotton broadcloth	4.3	F	18	15	16	13	16	18	18	17	16	10	10	17	19	18	18	17	18	16.0
cotton broadcloth	2.0	G	14	5	5	7	5	4	7	5	3	4	2	6	5	5	5	5	5	5.0
cotton broadcloth	5.1	H	19	17	19	19	18	17	18	19	18	14	17	18	18	19	19	18	19	18.0
nylon plain weave	1.7	I	5	13	14	17	15	12	10	16	10	13	14	11	15	11	11	9	10	12.4
nylon twill	2.0	J	6	7	6	8	8	8	4	11	7	7	6	5	7	9	7	7	8	7.2
nylon broken twill	2.0	K	2	8	7	9	6	7	9	6	4	8	13	7	10	8	8	12	8	8.1
nylon matte	1.8	L	3	4	8	6	7	6	6	8	6	6	7	3	6	6	6	6	6	6.1
nylon plain weave	2.2	M	9	14	18	16	17	16	14	13	11	15	18	10	17	15	16	15	16	15.4
nylon satin	2.3	N	8	9	11	11	9	9	5	9	9	11	9	8	8	11	10	13	9	9.9
nylon matte	3.2	O	10	11	12	14	12	10	13	12	14	9	8	14	11	13	12	10	13	11.6
nylon matte	2.5	P	11	12	13	12	10	14	11	10	12	12	15	9	14	12	10	14	11	12.2
nylon-cotton broken twill	1.9	Q	7	6	4	4	3	1	2	4	5	5	5	2	3	3	3	2	4	3.6
silk fabric	1.6	R	4	2	2	2	1	2	1	2	1	2	1	1	2	2	1	1	2	1.68
wool flannel	10.0	S	15	18	10	5	11	13	17	15	16	17	11	19	9	7	13	16	14	12.6

Weights

		1	2	3	4	5	6	7	8	9	10	11	12	13	14	15	16	17	18	19
average rating (soft to stiff)		R	D	Q	Ẹ	G	L	J	K	N	O	P	C	I	S	B	M	F	A	H
standard rank No.		1	2	3	4	5	6	7	8	9	10	11	12	13	14	15	16	17	18	19

in stiffness between a fabric and its neighbor. Thus the weighted average can be considered to be a reasonably reliable estimate of the rank of the fabric, and a standard rank number can then be assigned to each fabric. This is indicated at the bottom of Table 168."[265]

The subjective stiffness rank having been established, Abbott then shows its correlation with laboratory stiffness tests (Table 169). Table 170 shows the resulting Kendall correlation coefficients.

TABLE 169. SUBJECTIVE RANKING AND LABORATORY RANKING OF STIFFNESS
(From Abbott[265] "The Measurement of Stiffness in Textile Fabrics")

subjective rating:	1	2	3	4	5	6	7	8	9	10	11	12	13	14	15	16	17	18	19
cantilever, c:	2	7	3	4	8	1	5	19	6	9	13	17	12	16	10	11	14	18	15
G:	2	1	3	8	5	6	7	13	9	4	16	11	12	10	18	19	17	15	14
heart loop, c:	2	1	13	3	4	5	10	16	9	6	7	11	14	8	12	18	17	19	15
G:	1	13	2	3	6	5	7	16	9	8	4	10	11	12	18	17	15	19	14
Schiefer Flexometer:	2	5	6	7	3	4	1	8	9	11	13	16	17	10	12	19	14	15	18
Planoflex:	3	6	7	8	12	1	4	10	9	11	14	15	2	5	13	16	18	17	19
Drape-o-meter:	16	6	11	5	7	10	13	8	9	17	3	2	18	1	19	4	12	15	14

TABLE 170. RANK CORRELATION OF LABORATORY MEASUREMENTS WITH SUBJECTIVE MEASUREMENT
(From Abbott[265] "The Measurement of Stiffness in Textile Fabrics")

Method	Kendall coefficient (τ)
cantilever, c	0.56
cantilever, G	0.78
heart loop, c	0.63
Heart loop, G	0.62
Schiefer Flexometer	0.70
Planoflex	0.58
Drape-o-meter	0.09

Abbott[265] points out that

"none of the coefficients is sufficiently higher than the others to suggest that one test is decidedly the best. This may not, however, be the result of a lack of correlation, but may only reflect inaccuracies in establishing the subjective ranking. The range of fabrics used perhaps was not selected in the best way, for . . . there was not complete agreement upon the rank of any fabric in the group. Therefore another test was carried out in which the fabrics were ranked subjectively at the start, and only those were selected for laboratory measurement which were ranked without difficulty."

Results of this test give Kendall correlation coefficients as follows:

cantilever, c	0.60
cantilever, G	0.89
heart loop, c	0.60
heart loop, G	0.71
Schiefer Flexometer	0.67

Abbott concludes that

"the most promising correlations were obtained from the flexural rigidity as determined by Peirce's cantilever test, and from Schiefer's Flexometer."

Chapter 22

LUSTER

Buck and McCord[245] have made a thorough study of luster with particular emphasis on the problems of cotton. Their report is of such broad scope that, as is the case with so many other portions of this book wherein complete reviews of certain topics are available, it would serve no purpose to re-investigate, re-abstract, and rephrase the papers of other authors, but rather to use Buck and McCord's text with a minimum of alteration.

(90) The Subjective Aspects of Luster

To an extent, luster is a subjective criterion dependent upon the personal reaction of the viewer. Hence the remarks already put forth concerning hand and drape obviously apply. Buck and McCord[245] comment,

> "In many textile applications, particularly in household and apparel uses, more or less intangible fabric characteristics such as hand, texture, luster, and style play as significant roles as such functional qualities as launderability, soil resistance, durability, or warmth.
>
> "Luster is one of the major, non-functional appeal characteristics of textiles. It is a quality that defies complete measurement, yet one for which there is a strong demand. It is a quality that is regarded with various degrees of favor by the consumer, depending on its brightness, the fiber with which it is associated, and the specific use of each textile article. Always implying the highest quality in silk and the finest wools and cottons, luster in the early artificial fibers carried a suggestion of inferiority in most functional properties. Today, demand for luster is based largely on its attractive appearance in fabrics, the brighter colors of lustrous textiles, and the contrast with duller fabrics or yarns which permits greater freedom in styling.
>
> "Cotton yarns and fabrics provide the only important outlet for a textile luster finish because cotton accounts for more than 73% of the total consumption of apparel-type fibers in the United States and because the synthetic fibers and silk have

463

inherent qualities of luster.   Usually, a high degree of luster is not desirable in uses where wool is consumed.   In addition to offering the largest market for a luster finish, the demand for luster in cotton is stronger than in other fibers because luster in cotton has always implied quality . . .

" . . . Tradition is an important influence in men's apparel uses, where changes in buying habits occur slowly.   In women's apparel markets, well-developed preferences for the dressy appearance of lustrous textiles are already apparent. Style trends can quickly develop the latent desire for luster in other women's apparel uses . . . "

The survey of Buck and McCord[245] centers attention on cotton, and most comparisons are made between it and other fibers.   In discussing marketing aspects, they state that increased luster in cotton would enable this fiber to make inroads into the rayon and synthetic-fiber field wherever lustrous fabrics are in demand.   Wool is not considered as being a competitive fiber for such end-use requirement and one would conclude that with the exception of rather isolated cases, the lack of luster in wool is an attribute.   Certainly the shine on a worn worsted fabric, for example the seat of the blue serge suit, is not considered advantageous.

"Luster in textiles is a form of light reflection originating in the fibers that make up the yarn or fabric.   Its appeal is essentially sensory and may very well give a somewhat different impression to each observer, although at least certain of its components can be measured objectively.   It is a quality as difficult to define as it is to measure. . . .

" . . . 'Luster' is one of several terms used to describe the characteristic light reflection of certain materials.   'Glitter,' 'sparkle,' 'gloss,' and 'sheen' are among the other terms used, and although each has no doubt a special connotation to different individuals, they are used interchangeably to some extent, and none of the five completely describes the nature of the light sensation.   'Glitter' may be used to describe the intense highlights of a diamond, while 'sparkle' seems to imply a larger number of lesser reflections.   'Gloss' finds most frequent application in the description of polished surfaces, or more particularly with reference to varnishes, paints, and lacquers. 'Sheen' carries some impression of texture, and has been defined as the characteristic light reflection from a nearly matt surface viewed at almost grazing angles.

"'Luster' is perhaps somewhat broader in scope than the other four terms.   It has been used to describe the light-reflecting properties of gems, glassware, china, and metals, as well as of textiles. As far as textiles are concerned, however, 'luster' is the principal term used to describe light-reflecting properties. In textiles, luster is essentially a phenomenon of contrasts between bright or highly reflective areas and duller backgrounds. Movement of the reflective surface, as well as undulations, curves, and folds, accentuates the contrasts between lustrous and matt areas, with shifts in the locality of the lustrous highlights occurring as the position of either the observer, the fabric, or the light source changes. When a fabric is examined for luster, it is customary to hold it so that light falling on it is reflected to the eye from several different angles; if the contrast between brightness and dullness is pleasing, the fabric is said to have desirable luster.

"Many factors cause the perception of luster in textiles to be a very complex sensation, involving not only physical, but physiological and psychological considerations as well. However, the following technical discussion will be concerned principally with the physical phenomena of luster, with only necessary reference to physiological and psychological effects. Fortunately, for most purposes an adequate comprehension of the subject can be obtained through the application of the simpler rules of optics in which light is treated as a beam or bundle of essentially parallel rays. The application of a few of the simpler principles of light explain much of the origin of textile luster."[245]

(91) The Physics of Light Reflection and Luster

"When a beam of light falls on the surface of a material, it may be reflected, it may pass through the material, or it may be absorbed and converted into heat energy. (Figure 30.) Note that in B, the direction of the light is changed in passing from one medium (the air) into the second medium. Some combination of these three effects can, and does, take place in many instances.

"Since luster is a form of light reflection, case A would appear to have the greatest importance, and will therefore be discussed before the complicating factors of B and C are considered. In A (also illustrated in Figure 31) all of the light falling on the surface may be reflected, as from a mirror. This is known as regular or specular reflection. In this case, the angle of incidence i of the original ray is equal to the angle of reflection r, and both the original and the reflected rays lie in the same plane perpendicular to the reflective surface. This type of reflection reproduces a distinct image of the light source.

"The great majority of surfaces, however, lack the polished uniformity of a mirror, and minute irregularities tend to scatter the incident light in all directions. The extreme case of scattered, or diffuse, reflection is shown in B (Figure 31), in which

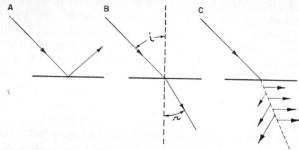

Figure 30. Reflection, refraction, and absorption of light, illustrated in A, B, and C, respectively, contribute to the phenomenon of luster. (*Adapted from Buck and McCord,*[245] *"Luster and Cotton."*)

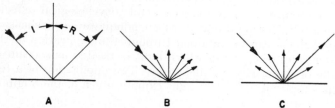

Figure 31. A—Specular reflection. B—Diffuse reflection. C—Diffuse reflection with a mirror or luster peak. (*From Buck and McCord,*[245] *"Luster and Cotton."*)

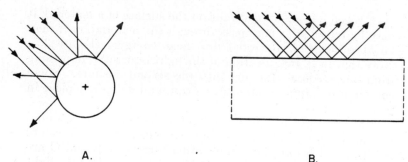

Figure 32. Luster is always more apparent along the fiber axis, as in B, than across the fiber, as in A. (*From Buck and McCord,*[245] *"Luster and Cotton."*)

the surface appears to be equally well illuminated when viewed from any angle. Such surfaces are called "matt."

"The third type of reflection, illustrated in C (Figure 31), is a combination of A and B. Part of the incident light is reflected diffusely, but at the angle of specular reflection the intensity of the reflected light is greatest, and this maximum reflection is known as the "mirror peak." Surfaces such as that illustrated in C, which show a mirror peak, represent one type of luster.

"The irregularities that cause this deviation from mirror reflection may be very small, such as would occur on a highly polished surface that had been rubbed lightly with an abrasive material. In other cases, the surfaces may be much more irregular, with areas of fairly high reflection occurring as islands of brightness on a matt background. The distinct image that is observed in the case of A blurs and disappears as more light is diffusely reflected; in the case of surfaces as irregular as those of textiles, images are never visible.

"Textile fibers differ in shape from the flat surfaces discussed above, but the same rules of geometrical optics can be applied to them. A fiber may be considered to be an extremely attenuated cylinder, the simplest case being a cylinder of circular cross section. Figure 32 illustrates light falling on a section of such a cylinder or fiber—across the fiber in A and in the direction of the fiber in B. It will be noted that in A the same intensity of reflection is observed from almost any angle, and that, due to the divergence of the rays, the reflection tends to be weaker than the source, even assuming perfect reflectance. In B, however, reflection of all the rays is at the same angle, and a definite mirror peak will be observed at the angle of specular reflection.

"The fact that mirror peaks occur predominantly when fibers are viewed in the direction of their axes, thus providing the important contrast between matt appearance and bright reflectance, is one of the primary rules of textile luster. The design of every textile product in which lustrous effects are desired utilizes this principle. The phenomenon can be observed nicely by winding a lustrous yarn around a flat card so that a flat pad of fibers or filaments is obtained. Rotation of this card between the observer and a light source, first around the fiber axes and then across the axes, will show the pronounced contrasts of reflection in the fiber direction.

"Since lustrous effects in textiles depend on reflection along the length of a cylinder as illustrated in B of Figure 32, it is readily apparent that irregularities in the shape of the fiber cylinder will diffuse or otherwise interrupt the continuity of light reflection. This was found to be true in some of the earliest studies of textile luster. Several workers concluded that the cross-sectional shape of the fiber exerts the most important influence on textile luster, and that surface reflection has more significance than any other type of light reflection."[245]

Buck and McCord discuss the importance of cross-sectional shape and surface uniformity. Photomicrographs of fiber cross-sections aid in demonstrating that the rounder the section and smoother the surface, the greater the luster. However, they point out that these are not the only criteria.

"The conclusion that surface reflection is primarily responsible for luster emphasizes the importance of shape and shape continuity as the principal fiber properties contributing to luster. Experimental work backed by mathematical calculations has been presented to show that the ideal cross-sectional shape is that of an ellipse the ratio of major to minor axes of which approaches unity. Thus, flatter, ribbon-like cottons would have less luster than those with rounded shapes. Considerable support was lent to this conclusion by the rounding-out of the shape of cotton fibers during mercerization. . . . Besides making the cotton fiber more nearly round, mercerization removes its convolutions to a considerable extent and thus improves the continuity of shape along the fiber.

"While the cross sections of the rayon fibers (Writer's note: viscose and acetate sections are shown in photomicrographs) are far from circular, the shape of an individual filament is fairly constant throughout its length, and thus each fiber could be conceived to act as a bundle of smaller cylindrical fibers. Very high luster is a natural property of both of the rayons shown.

"The silk fiber cross sections shown . . . differ from the majority of textile fibers in that they are triangular in shape rather than curved. The luster of silk is much softer than that of normal rayons, yet greater than that of any other natural fiber.

"The origin of textile luster is evidently more complex than simple specular reflection from fiber surfaces, however, and although the influences of fiber surface and fiber shape cannot be disregarded, other and perhaps equally important fiber properties must be considered. The fact that cotton fibers mercerized without tension improve in shape with little or no improvement in luster throws some doubt on the conclusion that shape is all-important. The degree of shape improvement between unmercerized and mercerized-unstretched cotton is much greater than the shape improvement from mercerized-unstretched to mercerized-stretched cotton, yet the development of luster is far more pronounced in the latter case than in the former. Some further question of shape-factor importance, with respect to surface reflection is raised by the fact that textile fibers are relatively transparent, so that only a fraction of the incident light is reflected from the surface, the major part passing into or through the fiber. According to Fresnel's law, only about 4% of the light normally incident on a cotton fiber will be reflected, and even at 60° incidence not over 10% of the incident light is reflected. It is logical, therefore, that example B in Figure 30 be studied to determine what happens to the light passing into the fiber.

"In B of Figure 30 the light ray is shown to be bent or refracted upon entering the second medium. This condition is reproduced in Figure 33, where light is shown falling on a layer of transparent fibers. At each air-fiber surface, a part

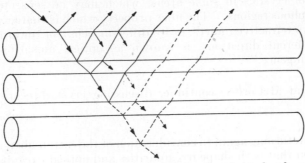

Figure 33. At each air-fiber boundary light is partly refracted and partly reflected. (*From Buck and McCord,*[245] *"Luster and Cotton."*)

of the light is reflected and part refracted. It will be noted that much of the light passing through one or more fibers can find its way out again on the top of the layer of fibers, reinforcing the light reflected from the first surface.

"Figure 33 is intended to represent the longitudinal sections of perfectly uniform circular cylinders. Naturally, the circular cross section will cause light reflected from the inside of the fiber to emerge fanwise, but the effect will be about as shown in the diagram. Glass fibers are probably the only textile fibers that may nearly duplicate the conditions represented. Glass fibers have a smooth, uniform shape of circular cross section, and the interior is homogeneous or optically isotropic. Even in the case of glass fibers, however, only a portion of the incident light will finally re-emerge to reinforce the light specularly reflected from the surface. Some of the incident light is lost within the fibers by total internal reflection, and some will pass through the entire layer of fibers to be absorbed by surfaces beneath.

"The proportion of the original refracted beam that can re-emerge to add to the intensity of specular reflection will be affected by irregularities in the shape of the fiber, by irregularities in the fiber arrangements, and by materials within the fiber that absorb, diffuse, or disperse the transmitted light. . . . Most textile fibers, the exception being glass, are not optically isotropic. In other words, their composition is not entirely homogeneous to light; thus, they commonly show two indices of refraction. Light is refracted differently in the longitudinal and transverse directions by these fibers because the long thread-like molecules which make up the fiber are preferentially oriented in the direction of the fiber axis and because the degree of packing of the fiber molecules results in the formation of crystals in some areas, which may be separated by amorphous regions. The fiber property which is characterized by two refractive indices, or by different behavior toward light in different directions, is known as optical anisotropy, or birefringence."[245]

Buck and McCord[245] continue, discussing crystallite orientation in cotton:

"Returning again to consideration of the cotton fiber, it can be seen that both shape irregularities and optical irregularities in composition will add to the scattering of light from within the fiber, and thus to the masking of the specular or lustrous reflection. Mercerization without tension will improve the shape without improving luster significantly, as noted above, and therefore some importance must be attached to other light-scattering influences within the fiber . . . It can be seen that both the spiraling arrangement of the crystallites and the lumen or hollow center of the fiber can act to scatter light. Not only do the crystallites in cotton spiral around the fiber axis, but they change direction frequently, and the direction of the spiral in some layers opposes that in others.

"At this time evidence seems to point to the crystallite orientation or spiral angle as affecting luster more significantly than the lumen. Cottons with the highest natural luster, such as Sea Islands, have the best alignment of crystallites with the fiber axis, and the dullest cottons, such as Indias, have wide-angle orientation.

"Perhaps the influence of light which is refracted into the fiber can best be illustrated by the mechanism of delustering synthetic fibers. A normally bright synthetic fiber can be

rendered dull or lusterless if during manufacture small particles
of an opaque material are incorporated into the fiber. The
result of this treatment is illustrated in Figure 34. In the
bright fiber A, the reflected component plus the reinforcement
from refracted and internally reflected light results in the
necessary specular reflection for high luster. In B, the small
particles on the interior of the fiber have caused the refracted
light to be scattered in all directions, re-emerging from the
fiber so as to completely mask the reflected component of the

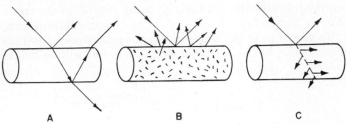

Figure 34.   Effect of delustering and dyeing on the reflectance properties of
fibers.   (*From Buck and McCord,*[245] "*Luster and Cotton.*")

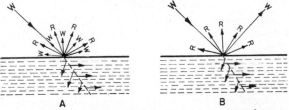

Figure 35.   The color of the red material A is made brighter by concentrating the
white surface reflection specularly as in B.   (*From Buck and McCord,*[245] "*Luster and
Cotton.*")

original beam. The reflected component is still present, however, and the fiber can be delustered if the masking effect of
randomly scattered light is removed. This can be done by
dyeing the fiber black, causing nearly all of the light passing
into the fiber to be absorbed, so that the specular component of
surface reflection is again observed without interference. This
is illustrated in C of Figure 34."

With respect to the effect of color on luster, Buck and McCord[245] state:

"In actual materials or surfaces, absorption is never
perfect. In the case of (a) red material . . . part of the

incident white light will be reflected from the surfaces, and a part of the red light will be absorbed with the other wave lengths. Graph 84 shows reflectance (%) plotted against wave lengths of light (Å), and here it can be seen that the effective color of the material is a combination of the reflected red light and some surface-reflected white light. Reflection of the white light therefore dilutes the intensity of the red light, causing the shade to be somewhat paler than it might otherwise be, as illustrated in A of Figure 35. If the surface reflection can be concentrated in one direction and prevented from mixing with the red light at most angles, as shown in B of Figure 35, the full intensity of the red color will be observed. At the mirror peak the white light is at a maximum, and little red is visible, but at all other angles the red will be brighter

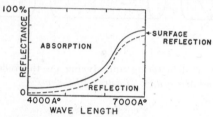

Graph 84. The apparent color of a red material is a combination of reflected red light and surface-reflected light of all wave lengths. (*From Buck and McCord*,[245] "*Luster and Cotton.*")

than in the matt surface shown in A. The pronounced contrast between white light at the mirror peak and bright color at other angles accentuates the lustrous character of the surface. Dye shades are brighter in lustrous textiles for this reason, and at the same time luster is more apparent because of the added contrasting effect of white light against colored light.

"In summary, the influence on luster of the three types of light phenomena illustrated in Figure 30 has been suggested, but no conclusions have been presented as to the relative importance of cases A, B, and C. Considering case C, first, it is obvious that the contrasting effects of color are effective only in colored goods. Furthermore, the dyes used on textiles sometimes roughen the fiber surfaces, so that although contrast tends to be improved, specular reflection may be reduced. Therefore, color may or may not significantly increase the luster effects in textiles, depending on the circumstances involved. It seems reasonable to consider color as an added effect which may enhance luster rather than a primary contributor to luster."[245]

(92) The Measurement of Luster

Still quoting Buck and McCord[245]

"Harrison,[329] in his monograph 'Definition and Measurement of Gloss,' outlines six general types of luster measurement. Only four of these methods seem applicable to textiles, and since two of the four are the same in principle, the methods outlined here will be: (1) objective luster measurements; (2) subjective luster measurements; and (3) goniophotometric measurements.

"(1) 'Objective' luster measurements involve a determination of the amount of light that a surface can reflect specularly. In instruments which measure objective luster, light falls on the test sample from some chosen angle, usually between 45° and 80° to the normal, and the intensity of the reflected light is measured from the corresponding specular angle. The proportion of incident light reflected specularly by the test specimen is compared with that reflected from some glossy surface chosen as a standard. No measurement is made of light reflected at any but the specular angle.

"The objective luster method provides a rating of one of the parameters of textile luster—the ability of a surface to reflect light specularly. None of the important effects of surface texture and depth are recorded by this method, however, and the primary considerations of contrast and color contrast are not taken into account. Objective luster measurements are probably most useful for comparisons of the effectiveness of various luster finishes on similar materials and for adaptation to the continuous measurement of luster during the manufacturing or finishing of textiles.

"(2) 'Subjective' luster methods attempt to measure the contrasts between specular and diffuse reflection that perhaps contribute most to visual impressions of luster in textiles. In these methods reflected light is measured in two directions, one of which is always that of specular reflection. The other direction of measurement may be any angle decided upon, although most frequently the normal to the test surface is used for the diffuse reflectance measurement. The ratio of specular intensity to diffuse intensity is used as an index of luster.

"Like the objective measurements, values of subjective luster include none of the effects of surface texture, color, or binocularism. Subjective luster measurements generally give a better rank correlation with visual estimates of the luster of different types of surfaces than do the objective methods. In both the objective and subjective methods, the angle chosen for specular measurements may give reflection and intensities appreciably lower than those at some other angle where reflection may be especially influenced by surface texture. The contrast, or subjective method, tells nothing about the change from specular intensity to diffuse intensity. This change may be quite abrupt in some fabrics, while in others a more gradual change causes luster to be less noticeable.

"(3) Goniophotometric methods are the fundamental physical methods for studying the lustrous or light-reflecting properties of surfaces. The intensity of reflected light is observed at all angles in the plane containing the angle of incidence. A curve or a family of curves is obtained which rather completely describes the light-reflecting properties of the material. Goniophotometric methods have limited value for routine measurements because of the time and effort involved in obtaining the numerous readings, and because full interpretation of the resulting curves demands mathematical analysis, but they are a valuable research tool where detailed information on the reflecting characteristics of a surface is desired.

"Each of the three general methods listed above will give some interpretation of the effect of color if color filters are used. There is no assurance, however, that the instruments thus modified will be affected by color in the same manner as are the eyes. Moreover, none of the methods adequately interpret the texture and binocular effects of which the eyes are so conscious. Therefore, it seems likely that visual observations will continue to be necessary for the final appraisal of textile luster."[245]

(93) Refractive Index and Birefringence as They Pertain to Luster

The refractive index of a substance is defined as the ratio of the velocity of light in a vacuum to the velocity of light in the substance. Snell's law states:

$$\text{Refractive index} = \frac{\sin i}{\sin r}$$

where i = angle of incidence
and $\quad r$ = angle of refraction, (see Figure 30-B, p. 466)

Preston[63] states

"With all fiber substances the velocity of light is always less than the velocity in a vacuum, so that the refractive index is always greater than unity. The velocity of light in a vacuum is independent of the wave-length of the light, but with all material substances the velocity is greater with longer than with shorter wave-length light. Therefore, the refractive index is greater for shorter than for longer wave-length light. Consequently, refractive index measurements must be made with light of a given wave length."

It is common practice to report refractive indices at a wave length of 5890 Angstrom Units (Sodium D_2 line).

Bunn[326] discusses the directional refractive indices as follows:

"It is a fundamental characteristic of textile fibers, whether they are obtained from natural sources or are made by man, that they all consist of long-chain molecules, and that these molecules lie along the fibre axis; in some fibres they are almost exactly parallel, in other fibres they are only roughly parallel, but in all fibres there is this tendency for the molecules to lie along the fibre axis. Owing to the orientation of the chain molecules, the optical properties, like other physical properties, vary with direction in the fibre, the maximum difference being between the properties along the fibre axis and those perpendicular to the fibre axis. Treatment of the optical properties of fibres in terms of the properties of the molecules themselves and of the relation of these properties to directions in individual molecules is particularly direct; since there is little interaction between neighboring molecules; the refractive index of the assemblage of molecules in a fibre, for any particular direction in the fibre, is approximately the sum of the properties of the individual molecules for that direction."

The difference in refractive indices parallel with and transverse to the fiber axis is called birefringence and is a quantitative measure of the degree of anisotropy of the fiber. Table 171 lists values of the various fibers.

Consider now the relationship between luster and birefringence. One may draw an analogy between the molecular units making up a fiber, and the filamentous units making up a yarn. For the same reasons that uniform, low twist, properly aligned, continuous filaments uniformly reflect light to give a lustrous appearance, properly aligned molecular units will also reflect light within a fiber to cause it to appear lustrous. It follows that, all other factors being equal, the higher the birefringence, the higher should be the luster. Of course all other factors are not equal, and many other effects (some already cited) so far outweigh the birefringence contribution that it becomes of relatively minor importance. A glass fiber is an excellent example since it has no birefringence and yet is considered to be particularly lustrous.

TABLE 171. REFRACTIVE INDICES AND BIREFRINGENCES OF TEXTILE FIBERS

I

(Source: Preston[63] "Modern Textile Microscopy")

Fiber	Refractive Indices Parallel (n_γ)	Perpendicular (n_α)	Birefringence (Double Refraction)
silk	1.595	1.538	+0.057
spun silk	1.581	1.542	+0.039
wool	1.553 / 1.555	1.542 / 1.546	+0.010
ramie	1.590 to 1.597	1.533 to 1.540	+0.058
linen	1.576 to 1.595	1.536 to 1.528	+0.056
hemp	1.585 to 1.591	1.530 to 1.526	+0.060
jute	1.577	1.536	+0.041
cotton	1.577 to 1.580	1.534 to 1.533	+0.045
viscose rayon:			
fine filament	1.550	1.514	+0.036
coarse filament	1.539 to 1.532	1.519 to 1.523	+0.018
cuprammonium rayon:			
fine filament	1.552	1.520	+0.032
coarse filament	1.548	1.527	+0.021
acetate rayon	1.476	1.470	+0.006

II

(Source: "Modern Plastics Encyclopedia"[7])

	Parallel (epsilon)	Perpendicular (omega)	Birefringence
acetate rayon, regular	1.478	1.473	+0.005
acetate rayon, high elongation	1.478	1.473	+0.005
saponified acetate rayon, ("Fortisan")	1.547	1.513	+0.034
cuprammonium rayon	1.548	1.527	+0.021
viscose rayon, regular tenacity	1.547	1.521	+0.026
viscose rayon, medium tenacity	1.547	1.521	+0.026
viscose rayon, high tenacity	1.547	1.521	+0.026
nylon, regular	1.580	1.520	+0.060
nylon, high tenacity	1.580	1.520	+0.060
glass	1.55 ± 0.01	1.55 ± 0.01	0.000
vinyl resin, regular	1.536	1.536	0.000
vinyl resin, high tenacity	1.536	1.536	0.000
vinyl resin, staple	1.536	1.536	0.000
vinylidene chloride resin, (saran)	1.60 to 1.63	1.60 to 1.63	0.000
acrylonitrile-vinyl chloride, ("Vinyon" N): NOZZ	1.530	1.530	0.000
NORU	1.530	1.530	0.000
NORT	1.530	1.530	0.000
cotton	1.580	1.533	+0.047
silk	1.591	1.538	+0.053
wool	1.556	1.547	+0.009

TABLE 171. REFRACTIVE INDICES AND BIREFRINGENCES OF TEXTILE FIBERS.—(*Continued*)

III

(Source: Bunn[326] in Preston's "Fiber Science")

	Parallel (epsilon)	Perpendicular (omega)	Birefringence
native ramie	1.596	1.528	+0.068
silk	1.591	1.538	+0.053
nylon	1.580	1.520	+0.060
polythene	1.556	1.512	+0.044
wool	1.553 to 1.555	1.542 to 1.546	+0.010 to 0.011

IV

(Source: Ray[327] "Private Communication)

	Parallel	Perpendicular	Birefringence
"Dacron" type 5400			0.179
"Dacron" type 5600	1.72 (approx.)	1.53 (approx.)	0.198 (approx.)
"Orlon"			<0.01

V

(Source: Preston[418] "Identification of Textile Fibers")

Fiber	Birefringence
"Terylene"	0.25
native cellulose, ramie, or linen	0.06
nylon	0.06
regenerated cellulose, e.g., "Fortisan," "Durafil"	0.04
cellulose acetate, highly stretched	<0.01
regenerated cellulose (normal viscose or cuprammonium rayon)	0.02–0.03
keratin, wool	0.01

(94) Relative Reflectance Values of Textile Fibers

Little information on inherent reflectance values is available. Attention is called to Table 110 from Buck and McCord[245] on page 290 which cites some data.

von Bergen[328] comments on the luster of wools as follows:

"Wools vary in luster considerably. It is natural of certain wools to be lustrous. This luster cannot be noted in a single hair, but in locks and accumulated quantities. Luster varies with origin and breed of animal and with climate. The trade differentiates between silver luster, silk luster, and glass luster. The silver luster is especially prominent in the finest and strongly-crimped Merino wools where it is often characterized as a mild luster. The silk luster is present in the long-staple and long-waved wools, represented by the English wools, and designated as 'luster wools.' The Lincoln and Leicester wools are especially valued for this reason.

"The highest, the glass luster, always points to the straight smooth hairs which are especially apparent in goat hair such as mohair. The glassy hairs on sheep are found on the head, neck, tail root, and lower part of the legs. This variation in luster of different wools is of great value in the manufacture of certain types of materials, because it influences the beauty and vividness of color and appearance of goods. The luster of wools can be altered through changes in the physical structure. Epidermis cells may have lost their smoothness, and the rough surface makes an unfavorable reflection surface. Such wools are known as dull wools. The rough surface is caused by atmospheric influences or mildew, whereby the scales are partly destroyed or dissolved."

von Bergen implies that a certain amount of luster in wool fabrics is desirable; yet the amount and type must be proper to insure an appearance of "quality." Such descriptive terms as "silver," "silk," and "glass" luster demonstrate subjective reaction.

(95) The Effect of Fabric Construction upon Luster

"A[245] few simple rules for constructing fabrics of good luster can be developed from the basic principle that a pad of parallel fibers produces maximum values in reflectance. In a pad of parallel fibers, brightest luster (maximum specular reflection) occurs when the plane of incident and reflected light parallels the direction of the fibers in the pad, and luster is least discernible when the plane of incident and reflected light is perpendicular to the fibers' axes. This preferential reflection causes the changes in luster values from different angles of viewing a fabric and thus effects the contrasts that contribute so much to luster.

"In general, constructions in which the fiber arrangement most nearly approaches a pad of parallel fibers exhibit the greatest luster. Departures from this ideal, such as twist, yarn crimps, fiber kinks, and loose fiber ends which cause fuzziness, tend to reduce luster. The appeal of luster is not directly related to the intensity of specular reflection, however, and in many cases attractive luster in fabrics is dependent on a pleasing contrast of moderately reflective regions against a duller background. The choice of colors can further accentuate lustrous effects, both by contrast in colors and by the use of colors to which the eye is especially sensitive. Therefore, fabric design for luster must be based on a recognition of both the importance of specular reflection and the significance of contrast.

"Considering first only specular reflection, it is immediately apparent that continuous-filament yarns have a twofold advan-

tage over all spun yarns; freedom from fuzzy, light-scattering
fiber ends, and a lower required twist. Nevertheless, manufacturing processes for the spun yarns have partially overcome
the superiority of continuous-filament yarns in these respects.
The practice of doubling spun singles in an opposing direction
returns the twisted fibers to a position parallel with the fiber
axis, and gassing or burning off the fuzz fibers improves surface
smoothness. . . .

" . . . Twist in yarns reduces the effective length of fibers
lying on the upper surface of a yarn in a fabric, and as this
effective length decreases, luster also decreases. Twist also
rotates the direction of maximum specular reflectance from

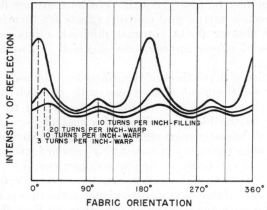

Graph 85. The effect of twist on the orientation and intensity of luster peaks.
(*From Buck and McCord,*[245] *"Luster and Cotton."*)

that of the yarn axis in the case of no fiber twist to a new point
which corresponds to the inclination of the fibers in the yarn.
Both the effect of twist on intensity of reflectance and its
directional effect on reflectance can be observed nicely by
measuring the specular reflectance from fabrics rotated in their
own plane from 0 to 360°. If, for example, warp sateens are
chosen, in which the warp twist differs from sample to sample
and the filling twist is kept constant, the observations of specular intensity will be as shown in Graph 85. Note the decrease
in warpwise reflectance and its shifting as twist increases.

"The curves in Graph 85 indicate contrasts in intensity of
specular reflection at different angles of viewing. Contrast is
greater, however, between the angle of specular reflectance
and some other angle, such as perpendicular viewing for 45°
illumination. Constructions which provide parallel fibers,

and parallel surface yarns as in sateen floats, concentrate the greatest possible amount of light in specular reflection and thus produce, in the float direction alone, the maximum contrasts which result in highest luster effect. The greater contrasts in the float direction can easily be seen in damasks, in which yarn floats form patterns on the fabric surface. At specular angles, the float-depicted patterns stand out brightly from a duller background of filling yarns. However, at other angles the filling yarns appear brighter than the warp patterns.

"In referring to textile luster, it is perhaps best to consider angles of specular reflectance rather than one particular or control angle. In almost all cases the surface fibers or yarns are sufficiently curved so that within a range of angles the specular intensities may be nearly equal. For long surface floats this range becomes narrow and contrast effects are therefore highest. For shorter floats contrast diminishes but sometimes other special effects appear, one of which is double-peaked reflectance.

"Fabrics with relatively flat surfaces lend themselves better to luster development than those with a rough or nobby texture. Here again, the reason can be traced to a better approach to the ideal condition of a pad of parallel fibers. Oxford and basket-weave shirtings, in which two warp yarns may be woven together over one filling yarn or four warp yarns over two fillings, or some similar arrangement, are noted for good luster even though singles yarns are used. Certain other constructions utilize heavy-soft-twisted yarns in one direction interwoven with finer yarns in the other, so that the heavy yarns produce a surface suitable for pressing or calendering and especially for embossing or Schreinering. . . .

"Uniformity is one of the keys to good luster in textiles— its importance traces all the way from uniformity in fiber cross section to yarn evenness and to uniformity of construction in the fabric. Luster arises from the uniform reflection of light, and all irregularities and uneven places in yarns and fabrics break up in some manner the desired uniform reflection. Photometric measurements show that even irregularities in the singles twist and the doubling twist of yarns reduce luster.

"Kinkiness or crimp in fibers might be considered a non-uniformity, and this irregularity, whether natural or artificially introduced, reduces luster markedly. For example, a yarn of crimped viscose staple has a decidedly dull and delustered appearance normally, but when the yarn is wet and rewound under tension to remove the crimp, the yarn takes on a lustrous appearance. Kinks in cotton fibers which prevent their assuming a smooth, parallel arrangement diminish the luster of cotton products. It seems likely that at least one of the functions of tension during the mercerization of cotton is removal or reduction of fiber kinkiness.[245]"

The wool fiber is normally crimpy, and it follows that woolens, and to a large extent worsteds, are not highly lustrous. Luster is not one of wool's outstanding attributes, nor by custom, is high luster normally demanded in wool.

BIBLIOGRAPHY

The following abbreviations are used below:

    A.D.R.—American Dyestuff Reporter
    A.S.T.M.—American Society for Testing Materials
    J.A.C.S.—Journal of the American Chemical Society
    J.S.D.C.—Journal of the Society of Dyers and Colourists
    J.T.I.—Journal of the Textile Institute
    R.T.M.—Rayon Textile Monthly
    T.F.S.—Transactions of the Faraday Society
    T.R.J.—Textile Research Journal

1. Hamburger, W. J., and Schwarz, E. R., "Inherent and Form Properties," Massachusetts Institute of Technology Textile Research Seminar (1940).
2. Loasby, G., "The Development of The Synthetic Fibres," *J.T.I.*, **42**, P411 (1951).
3. Newell, W. A., "Synthetic Fiber Table," *Textile World* (Sept. 1951).
4. Cassie, A. B. D., "Natural Fibres vs. Man Made Fibres," *J.T.I.*, **37**, 556 (1946).
5. Sherman, J. V., and Sherman, S. L., "The New Fibers," New York, D. Van Nostrand Co., Inc. (1946).
6. White, A. H., "Engineering Materials," New York, McGraw-Hill Book Company (1939).
7. "Modern Plastics Encyclopedia," New York, Plastics Catalogue Corp. (1949).
8. Meredith, R., "Tensile Behaviour of Raw Cotton and Other Textile Fibres," *J.T.I.*, **36**, T107 (1945).
9. Hamburger, W. J., "Mechanics of Abrasion of Textile Materials," *T.R.J.*, **15**, 169 (1945).
10. Kaswell, E. R., "Low Temperature Properties of Textile Materials," *A.D.R.*, **38**, P127 (1949).
11. Meredith, R., "The Elastic Properties of Textile Fibres," *J.T.I.*, **37**, 469 (1946).
12. Schwarz, E. R., "Certain Aspects of Yarn Structure," *T.R.J.*, **21**, 125 (1951).
13. Smith, H. DeW., "Textile Fibers: An Engineering Approach to Their Properties and Utilization (Nineteenth Edgar Marburg Lecture). *A.S.T.M. Proc.*, **44**, 543 (1944).
14. Hamburger, W. J., "Mechanics of Elastic Performance of Textile Materials: I. Development of an Elastic Performance Coefficient in Tension," *T.R.J.*, **18**, 102 (1948).
15. Leaderman, H., "Elastic and Creep Properties of Filamentous Materials and Other High Polymers," Washington, The Textile Foundation (1943).
16. Fabric Research Laboratories Reports: Nos. 635, 693, 1025.
17. Meredith, R., "A Comparison of the Tensile Elasticity of Some Textile Fibres," *J.T.I.*, **36**, T147 (1945).

18. Gagliardi, D. D., and Grunfest, I. J., "Creasing and Creaseproofing of Textiles," *T.R.J.*, **20**, 180 (1950).
19. Hamburger, W. J., "Mechanics of Elastic Performance of Textile Materials: II. The Application of Sonic Techniques to the Investigation of the Effects of Visco-Elastic Behavior Upon Stress-Strain Relationships in Certain High Polymers," *T.R.J.*, **18**, 705 (1948).
20. Ballou, J. W., and Silverman, S., "Sound Velocity Measurements," *T.R.J.*, **14**, 282 (1944).
21. Hamburger, W. J., Platt, M. M., and Morgan, H. M., "Mechanics of Elastic Performance of Textile Materials: X. Elastic Behavior at Low Strains," *T.R.J.*, **22**, 695 (1952).
22. Frank, N. H., "Introduction to Mechanics and Heat," p. 226. New York, McGraw-Hill Book Company (1934).
23. Finlayson, D., "Effect of Filament Size on Yarn Properties," *J.T.I.*, **37**, 168 (1946).
24. Finlayson, D., private communication.
25. Carlene, P. W., "Bending Modulus of Monofils," *J.T.I.*, **38**, T38 (1947).
26. Thomson, R. H. K., and Traill, D., "The Bending Fracture of Fibers," *J.T.I.*, **38**, T43 (1947).
27. Finlayson, D., "The Shear Strength of Filaments and Fibers," *J.T.I.*, **38**, T50-53 (1947).
28. Platt, M. M., "Mechanics of Elastic Performance of Textile Materials: III. Some Aspects of Stress Analysis of Textile Structures," *T.R.J.*, **20**, 1 (1950).
29. Morton, W. E., and Permanyer, F., "Torsional Relaxation in Textile Fibers," *J.T.I.*, **38**, T54 (1947).
30. Meredith, R., "Properties Depending on the Amorphous Regions of Fibres," Chapter XII, "Fiber Science," edited by Preston, Manchester, The Textile Institute (1949).
31. Steinberger, R. L., "Torque Relaxation and Torsional Energy in Crêpe Yarn," *T.R.J.*, **7**, 83 (1936).
32. Peirce, F. T., "Rigidity of Cotton Hairs," *J.T.I.*, **14**, T1 (1923); "Plasticity of Cotton and Other Materials," *J.T.I.*, **14**, T390 (1923).
33. Lochner, J. P. A., "Measurement of Modulus and Damping Capacity in Torsion and Bending for Wool and Other Textile Fibers," *J.T.I.*, **40**, T220 (1949).
34. Foppl, O., *J. Iron Steel Inst.*, **11**, 393 (1936).
35. Maillard, F., "Properties and Uses of Nylon Fabrics," *J.T.I.*, **40**, 379 (1949).
36. Schiefer, H., Fourt, L., and Kropf, R., "Textile Testing in Germany," *T.R.J.*, **18**, 18 (1948).
37. Bohringer, H., and Schieber, W., "Testing the Serviceability of Textile Fibers," translated from Milliand Textilberichte and published as a volume entitled "Developments in the Wear Resistance of Textiles and Related Papers Published in Germany During World War II" (U.S. Department of Commerce) p. 245.
38. Carlene, P. W., "Moisture Relations of Textiles—A Survey of the Literature," *J.S.D.C.*, **60**, 232 (1944).
39. Urquhart, A. R., and Williams, A. M., "Taking Up of Water By Raw and Soda-Boiled Cotton at 20°C," *J.T.I.*, **15**, T138 (1924).
40. Schloesing, *Compt. Rend.*, **116**, 808 (1893).
41. Hartshorne, W. D., "The Moisture Content of Textiles and Some of Its Effects," *Trans. Am. Soc. Mech. Engs.*, **39**, 1073 (1917).

42. Rakovski, *J. Russ. Phys. Chem. Soc.*, **37**, 18 (1915).
43. Urquhart, A. R., and Williams, A. M., "Absorption and Desorption of Water by Soda-Boiled Cotton at 25°C," *J.T.I.*, **15**, T433 (1924).
44. Urquhart, A. R., and Eckersall, N., "The Moisture Relations of Cotton: VII. A Study of Hysteresis," *J.T.I.*, **21**, T499 (1930).
45. Peirce, F. T., "A Two-Phase Theory of The Absorption of Water Vapour By Cotton Cellulose," *J.T.I.*, **20**, T133 (1929).
46. Urquhart, A. R., and Eckersall, N., "The Adsorption of Water By Rayon," *J.T.I.*, **23**, T163 (1932).
47. Speakman, J. B., "The Adsorption of Water By Wool," *J. Soc. Chem. Ind.*, **49**, T209 (1930).
48. Speakman, J. B., and Stott, E., "The Adsorption of Water By Wool: II. The Influence of Drying Conditions on The Affinity of Wool for Water," *J.T.I.*, **27**, T186 (1936).
49. Cassie, A. B. D., "Regain of Textiles and Humid Atmosphere Changes," *J.T.I.*, **31**, T17 (1940).
50. Anon., *Silk and Rayon*, **17**, 88 (1943).
51. Hailwood and Horrobin, S., "Absorption of Water By Polymers," *T.F.S.*, **42-B**, 84 (1946).
52. Speakman, J. B., "The Rigidity of Wool and Its Change With Adsorption of Water Vapour," *T.F.S.*, **26**, 92 (1929).
53. Chamberlain, N. H., and Speakman, J. B., "Hysteresis Phenomena In The Absorption of Water By Human Hair," *Z. Elektrochem.*, **37**, 374 (1931).
54. Goodings, A. C., and Turl, L. H., "The Density and Swelling of Silk Filaments In Relation to Moisture Content," *J.T.I.*, **31**, T69 (1940).
55. Bull, H. B., "Adsorption of Water Vapor By Proteins," *J.A.C.S.*, **66**, 1499 (1944).
56. Cassie, A. B. D., Atkins and King, "Thermostatic Action of Textile Fibres," *Nature*, **143**, 163 (1939).
57. Rees, W. H., *Shirley Institute Memoirs*, **21**, 333 (1947).
58. Hermans, P. H., "Contribution to The Physics of Cellulose Fibers," p. 37, New York, Elsevier Publishing Co., Inc. (1946).
59. Shorter, S. A., "Thermodynamics of Water Absorption By Textile Materials," *J.T.I.*, **15**, T328 (1924).
60. Hedges, J. J., "The Absorption of Water By Colloidal Fibres," *T.F.S.*, **22**, 178 (1926).
61. Cassie, A. B. D., "Characteristics for Warmth in Underwear Fabrics," *J.T.I.* **40**, P444 (1949).
62. Hermans, P. H., "Density and Refractivity of Cellulose Fibres in Relation to Structure," *J.T.I.*, **38**, 63 (1947).
63. Preston, J. M., "Modern Textile Microscopy," p. 40, London, Emmott & Co., Ltd. (1933).
64. Collins, G. E., "The Swelling of Cotton Hairs in Water and in Air at Various Relative Humidities," *J.T.I.*, **21**, T311 (1930).
65. Lawrie, L. G., "The Microscopical Investigation of Artificial Silk Fibres," *J.S.D.C.*, **44**, 73 (1928).
66. Hindman, H., and Fox, K. R., "Effect of Relative Humidity on the Load-Elongation Properties of Certain Fibers," *R.T.M.*, **24**, 235 (1943).
67. Speakman, J. B., "The Intra-Cellular Structure of The Wool Fibre," *J.T.I.*, **18**, T431 (1927).

68. Mann, "Influence of Humidity on The Elastic Properties of Cotton: On the Breaking Load at 20°C," *J.T.I.*, **18**, T253 (1927).
69. Denham, W. S., and Lonsdale, T., "The Tensile Properties of Silk Filaments," *T.F.S.*, **29**, 305 (1933).
70. Schenke, E. M., and Shearer, H. E., "Strength and Elongation of Silk Yarns As Affected By Humidity," *J. Research Nat'l. Bur. Standards*, **25**, 783 (1940).
71. Harris, M., and Brown, A. E., "Natural and Synthetic Protein Fibers," *T.R.J.*, **17**, 323 (1947).
72. Sookne, A. M., and Harris, M., "Stress-Strain Characteristics of Wool As Related to Its Chemical Composition," *J. Research. Nat'l. Bur. Standards*, **19**, 535 (1937).
73. Speakman, J. B., "The Reactivity of the Sulfur Linkage in Animal Fibres," *J.T.I.*, **27**, P231 (1936).
74. Clayton, F. H., and Peirce, F. T., "The Influence of Humidity on The Elastic Properties of Cotton," *J.T.I.*, **20**, T315 (1929).
75. Speakman, J. B., "An Analysis of The Water Adsorption Isotherm of Wool," *T.F.S.*, **40**, 6 (1944).
76. Baxter, S., "The Thermal Conductivity of Textiles," *Proc. Phys. Soc.*, **58**, 105 (1946).
77. Matthews, J. M., "The Textile Fibers," Fourth Ed., New York, John Wiley & Sons, Inc. (1923).
78. Dietz, "Specific Heat Capacity of Fibers," in Matthews' "Textile Fibers," Fourth Ed., page 9, New York, John Wiley & Sons, Inc. (1923).
79. Matthews, J. M., "Textile Fibers," Fifth Ed., edited by Mauersberger, New York, John Wiley & Sons, Inc. (1947).
80. American Society For Testing Materials, "Tentative Methods of Test For Resistance of Textiles to Water," Designation D583-40T, *A.S.T.M. Standards* 148 (1949).
81. Brown, R. H. *et al.*, "Properties and Applications of Chemical Engineering Materials," *Ind. Eng. Chem.*, **40**, 1773 (1948).
82. Church, J. M., "Flameproofing Textile Fabrics," edited by Little, R. W., New York, Reinhold Publishing Corp. (1947).
83. Little, R. W., "Flameproofing Textile Fabrics," New York, Reinhold Publishing Corp. (1947).
84. Casey, R. S., and Grove, C. S., Jr., "Properties and Applications of Chemical Engineering Materials of Construction," *Ind. Eng. Chem.*, **40**, 1773 (1948).
85. Hager, H. E., "Flammability of Wearing Apparel," *A.D.R.*, **36**, 141 (1947).
86. Anon., *Wool Record and Textile World*, **76**, 410 (1949).
87. Johnson, A., "The Development of Flame-Resisting Fabrics Containing Wool," *J.T.I.*, **39**, 561 (1948).
88. Fletcher, H. M., "Fabrics for Glass Curtains and Draperies," *A.D.R.*, **38**, 603 (1949).
89. du Pont de Nemours, E. I., "Protection of Nylon Yarns and Fabric Against Light Tendering," British Patent #572,136.
90. LaFleur, K. S., "Wetting of Wool As A Function of The Duration of Fadeometer Exposure," *T.R.J.*, **18**, 39 (1948).
91. Cody, W. H., "The Tendering Action of Light on Textile Fibers," *A.D.R.*, **27**, 325 (1938).
92. Fletcher, H. M., and Houston, M. H., "Effect of Light and Heat on the Deterioration of Fabrics," *T.R.J.*, **11**, 4 (1940).

93. Khandheria, K. S., and Vaidya, B. K., "Action of Light on Direct and Vat Dyes, Dyed on Nylon." *J. Sci. Ind. Research (India)* 6B, 24 (1947), abstracted in *J.T.I.*, **38**, A416 (1947).

94. Appleby, D. K., "Action of Light on Textile Materials: A Review of the Literature," *A.D.R.*, **38**, 149 (1949).

95. Speakman, J. B., "Survey of the Chemistry of Keratin Fibres," Chapter XVI in Preston's "Fibre Science," Manchester, The Textile Institute (1949).

96. Race, E., Row, F. M., Speakman, J. B., and Vickerstaff, T., "The Unlevel Dyeing of Wool With Acid and Chrome Dyes," *J.S.D.C.*, **54**, 141 (1938).

97. Speakman, J. B., and Stott, E., "The Titration Curve of Wool Keratin," *T.F.S.*, **30**, 539 (1934).

98. Harris, M., Mease, R., and Rutherford, H. A., "Reaction of Wool With Strong Solutions of Sulfuric Acid," *J. Research Natl. Bur. Standards*, **18**, 343 (1937).

99. Speakman, J. B., "The Chemistry of Wool and Related Fibres," *J.T.I.*, **32**, T83 (1941).

100. Lustig and Kondritzer, *Arch. Biochem.*, **8**, 51 (1945).

101. Schoberl, A., *Ann.*, **507**, 111 (1933).

102. Cuthbertson, W. R., and Phillips, H., "Action of Alkalies on Wool: I. The Subdivision of The Combined Cystine Into Two Fractions," *J. Biochem.*, **39**, 7 (1945).

103. Smith, A. L., and Harris, M., "Oxidation of Wool: Effect of Hydrogen Peroxide on Wool," *J. Research Natl. Bur. Standards*, **16**, 301 (1936).

104. Rutherford, H. A., and Harris, M., "Reaction of Wool With Hydrogen Peroxide," *J. Research Natl. Bur. Standards*, **20**, 559 (1938).

105. Goddard, D. R., and Michaelis, L., "A Study on Keratin," *J. Biolog. Chem.* **106**, 605 (1934).

106. Elsworth, F. F., and Phillips, H., "The Action of Sulfites on The Cystine Disulfide Linkages in Wool: I. The Influence of pH Value On The Reaction; II. The Influence of Temperature, Time and Concentration on The Reaction." *J. Biochem.*, **32**, 837 (1938); **35**, 135 (1941).

107. Middlebrook, W. R., and Phillips, H., "The Action of Formaldehyde on The Cystine Disulfide Linkages on Wool: I. The Subdivision of The Combined Cystine Into Two Fractions Differing In Their Reactivity Toward Formaldehyde," *J. Biochem.*, **36**, 294 (1942).

108. Blackburn, S., Consden, R., and Phillips, H., "Action of Sulfites on Cystine Disulfide Linkages of Wool: IV. Methylation of Thiol Groups of Bisulfited Wools," *J. Biochem.*, **38**, 25 (1944).

109. Neish, W. J. P., and Speakman, J. B., "Reactivity of The Sulphur Linkage In Wool," *Nature*, **155**, 45 (1945).

110. Douglass, F. B., and Johnson, T. B., "The Interaction of Chlorine With Different Types of Organic Sulfur Compounds," *J.A.C.S.*, **60**, 1486 (1938).

111. Hudson, R. F., and Alexander, P., "Symposium on Fibrous Proteins," *Soc. Dyers Colourists*, **193** (1946).

112. Blackburn, S., and Phillips, H., "The Action of Iodine on Wool," *J.S.D.C.*, **61**, 100 (1945).

113. Mezincesco, M. D., "Composition of Human Sweat," *Bull. Soc. Chem. Biol.*, **20**, 39 (1938) abstracted in *Chemical Abstracts*, **32**, 3801 (1938).

114. Marchionini, A., and Hausknecht, W., 'The 'Acid Coat of the Skin and Resistance to Bacteria," *Klin. Wochschr.*, **17**, 663 (1938), abstracted in *Chemical Abstracts*, **32**, 6709 (1938).

115. Bergeini, O., and Cornbleet, T., "Antibacterial Action of the Lactic Acid and Volatile Fatty Acids of Sweat," *Am. J. Med. Sci.*, **205**, 785 (1934), abstracted in *Chemical Abstracts*, **37**, 4757 (1943).

116. Barail, L. C., "Perspiration, What Do Textile Men Know About It?" *R.T.M.*, **27**, 663 (1946); **28**, 93 and 496 (1947).

117. Nopitsch, M., "The Influence of Perspiration on the Bacterial Damage of Fibers, and Its Prevention," *Melliand Textilber.*, **28**, 161 (1947).

118. Bien, R. R., "The Action of Anti-Perspiration Creams on Fabrics," *A.D.R.*, **35**, 269 (1946).

119. Way, S. C., and Memmescheimer, "The Sudariporous Glands: Sweat," *Arch. Dermatol. and Syphilol.*, **41**, 1086 (1940). (72 references.)

120. Emerson, F. W., "Basic Botany," Philadelphia, The Blakiston Co. (1947).

121. Hylander, C. J., "The World of Plant Life," New York, The Macmillan Company (1944).

122. Topley, W. W. C., and Wilson, G. S., "The Principles of Bacteriology and Immunity," Second Ed., Baltimore, William Wood and Company (1937).

123. Foster, J. W., "Chemical Activities of Fungi," New York, Academic Press, Inc. (1949).

124. Prescott, S. C., and Dunn, C. G., "Industrial Microbiology," Second Ed., New York, McGraw-Hill Book Company, Inc. (1949).

125. Hylander, C. J., and Stanley, O. B., "Plants and Man," Philadelphia, The Blakiston Co. (1947).

126. Anon., "The Mildewing of Wool," *Wool Science Review, No.* 6, **31** (1950).

127. Prindle, B., "Microbiology of Textile Fibers," *T.R.J.*, **3**, 475 (1933); **4**, 413 (1934); **5**, 11 (1934); **5**, 542 (1935); **6**, 23 (1935); **6**, 481 (1936); **7**, 413 (1937).

128. Smith, G., "An Introduction to Industrial Mycology," Third Ed., London, Edward Arnold & Co., Ltd. (1946).

129. Weston, W. H., "Tropical Deterioration Preparation and Preservation of Fungus Cultures of Military Importance." (Report on Q. M. C. Project #60), Research report from the Quartermaster General Laboratories, Microbiology Series No. 15 (1949).

130. Borlaug, N. E., "Resistance of Various Textile Fibers to Mildew," *R.T.M.*, **24**, 8 (1943); **24**, 9 (1943).

131. Siu, R. G. H., and White, W. L., "Microbiological Degradation of Cotton Fabrics," U.S. Office of Quartermaster General, Military Planning Division, Research and Development Branch, Microbiological Series Report No. 1. Released for public information by the Office of Publication Board, U.S. Department of Commerce (1945).

132. Matthews, J. M., "Textile Fibers," pp. 91, 297, Fifth Ed., edited by Mauersberger, New York, John Wiley & Sons, Inc. (1947).

133. American Wool Handbook, p. 206, Second Ed., New York, Textile Book Publishers, Inc. (1948).

134. Marsh, P. B., "Mildew and Rot-Resistance of Textiles," *T.R.J.*, **17**, 597 (1947).

135. Burgess, R., "A Contribution to the Study of the Microbiology of Wool," *J.T.I.*, **19**, 315 (1928); **20**, 333 (1929); **21**, 441 (1930); **25**, 391 (1934).

136. Geiger, W. B., Patterson, W. I., Mizell, L. R., and Harris, M., "Nature of the Resistance of Wool to Digestion by Enzymes," *J. Research Nat. Bur. Standards*, **27**, 459–468, R.P. 1433 (Nov. 1941).

137. Heyes, T. F., and Holden, H. S., "The Action of Micro-organisms on Silk," *J. Soc. Chem. Ind.*, **45**, T262 (1926).

138. Virginia-Carolina Chemical Corporation, "Vicara" (Bulletin). (1950).

139. du Pont de Nemours & Co., Inc., E. I. Nylon Technical Service (Bulletin). (1946).

140. Carbide and Carbon Chemicals Division, "Dynel Technical Information" (Pamphlet). (Feb. 1950).

141. du Pont de Nemours & Co., E. I. Inc., "Fiber V Continuous Filament Yarn" (Bulletin). (1948).

142. Matthews, J. M., "Textile Fibers," pp. 606, 786, 851, 866, and 892; Fifth Ed., edited by Mauersberger, New York, John Wiley & Sons, Inc. (1947).

143. Proceedings of the American Association of Textile Chemists and Colorists, "Tentative Method for the Evaluation of Fabric Pest Deterrents," *A.D.R.*, **34**, 400 (1945).

144. Barghoorn, E. S., "Field Studies of the Deterioration of Textiles Under Tropical Conditions," Office of the Quartermaster General, Military Planning Division, Research and Development Branch, Textile Series Report No. 24, Microbiological Series Report No. 4, pp. 8–11.

145. Zinkernagel, R., "Modern Protection Against Moths," *Textil-Rundschau*, **4**, 169 (1949), abstracted in *T.R.J.*, **19**, 853 (1949).

146. St. George, R. A., and Furry, M. S., "The Resistance of Treated Cotton Fabrics to Attack by Termites and Micro-organisms," *A.D.R.*, **35**, 207 (1946).

147. Shah, N. H., "Finished Cotton Fabrics: Attack by Termites and Micro-organisms," *Indian Textile J.*, **57**, 241 (1946).

148. Lailbach, E., "Affinity of Silverfish for Rayon Fabrics," *Textilber.*, **29**, 397 (1948), abstracted in *J.T.I.*, **40**, A328 (1949).

149. Micksch, K., and Herfs, A., "Rayon Fabric: Attack by Moths," *Zellwolle Kunstseide*, **45**, 222, 370 (1940), abstracted in *J.T.I.*, **39**, A143 (1948).

150. Patton, R. L., "Insect Damage to Nylon Fabric," *J. Econ. Entomol.*, **38**, 522 (1945).

151. Lewis, W. K., Squires, L., and Broughton, G., "Industrial Chemistry of Colloidal and Amorphous Materials," New York, The Macmillan Company (1942).

152. Whittaker, C. M., and Wilcock, C. C., "Dyeing with Coal-Trar Dyestuffs," Fifth Ed., New York, D. Van Nostrand Co., Inc. (1950).

153. McMyn, J. W., and Bardsley, J. W., "Bleaching, Dyeing, Printing and Finishing for the Manchester Trade," Second Ed., London, Sir Isaac Pitman and Sons, Ltd. (1932).

154. Matthews, J. M., "Application of Dyestuffs," New York, John Wiley and Sons, Inc. (1920).

155. Hauser, E. A., "Colloidal Phenomena," New York, McGraw-Hill Book Company, Inc. (1939).

156. Carlene, P. W., Rowe, F. M., and Speakman, J. B., "The Dyeing of Wool With Chrome Dyes, Part II. The Chroming of Wool," *J.S.D.C.*, **62**, 329 (1946).

157. Luttringhaus, H., "Merits of the Metallized Dyestuffs," *A.D.R.*, **39**, 152 (1950).

158. Silverman, M., "Pigmented Resin Emulsions for Printing and Pad Dyeing," *A.D.R.*, **37**, 44 (1948).

159. Belding, H. S., in Newburgh's "Physiology of Heat Regulation and The Science of Clothing," Philadelphia, W. B. Saunders Company (1949).

160. Evans, J. G., "The Fine Structure of Fibres in Relation to Dyeing and Finishing," Chapter XV, "Fibre Science" edited by Preston, Manchester, The Textile Institute (1949).

161. du Pont de Nemours & Co., Inc. E. I., "The Dyeing of Orlon," *du Pont Technical Bull.*, **6**, #3, 155 (1950).

162. Carbide and Carbon Chemical Company, "Dyeing and Wet Finishing Techniques for Dynel," (July 1950).

163. du Pont de Nemours & Co., Inc., E. I. "The Aqueous Dyeing of Fiber V," (Bulletin). (1950).

164. Schwarz, E. R., "Certain Aspects of Yarn Structure," Paper presented at Textile Research Institute Meeting, New York City, November 1950.

165. Hamburger, W. J., Platt, M. M., and Ross, M. W., "A Study of the Effects of Form Factors on the Translation of the Inherent Physical Properties of Textile Fibers into Textile Structures." (Literature Survey.) Office of the Quartermaster General, Textile Series Report No. 59.   Released by Office of Technical Service, U.S. Department of Commerce.

166. Schwarz, E. R., "Textiles and the Microscope," New York, McGraw-Hill Book Company, Inc. (1934).

167. Peirce, F. T., "The Geometry of Cloth Structure," *J.T.I.*, **28**, T45 (1937).

168. Painter, E. V., "Mechanics of Elastic Performance of Textile Materials: VIII. Graphical Analysis of Fabric Geometry," *T.R.J.*, **22**, 153 (1952).

169. Backer, S., "The Relationship Between the Structural Geometry of A Textile Fabric and Its Physical Properties: II. The Mechanics of Fabric Abrasion," *T.R.J.*, **21**, 453 (1951).

170. Platt, M. M., "Mechanics of Elastic Performance of Textile Materials: III. and IV. Some Aspects of Stress Analysis of Textile Structure," *T.R.J.*, **20**, 1 (1950); **20**, 519 (1950).

171. Platt, M. M., and Hamburger, W. J., "A Study of the Effect of Form Factors on the Translation of Inherent Physical Properties of Textile Fibers into Textile Structures," Fabric Research Laboratories, Inc. Report No. 635 to the Office of the United States Quartermaster General.

172. Hamburger, W. J., "Effect of Yarn Elongations on Parachute Fabric Strength," *R.T.M.*, **23**, 51 and 85 (1942).

173. Kaswell, E. R., "Wear Resistance of Apparel Textiles," *T.R.J.*, **16**, 413 and 502 (1946).

174. Dillon, J. H., "Resilience of Fibers and Fabrics," *T.R.J.*, **17**, 207 (1947).

175. Mark, H., "Some Remarks About Resilience of Textile Materials," *T.R.J.*, **16**, 361 (1946).

176. American Society for Testing Materials, Committee D13, "Terms Relating to Hand." Supplement III, *A.S.T.M. Standards for Textile Materials*, 370 (1943).

177. Fox, K. R., and Schwarz, E. R., "An Instrument for the Study of Compressional Creep and Creep Recovery of Yarns and Fabrics," *T.R.J.*, **11**, 227 (1941).

178. Schiefer, H. F., "The Compressometer, An Instrument for Evaluating the Thickness, Compressibility and Compressional Resilience of Textiles and Similar Materials," *T.R.J.*, **3**, 505 (1933).

179. van Wyk, C. C., "Notes on the Compressibility of Wool." *J.T.I.*, **37**, T285 (1946).

180. Rees, W. H., "The Over-all Specific Volume, Compressibility, and Resilience of Fibrous Materials," *J.T.I.*, **39**, T131 (1948).

181. Schiefer, H. F., Stevens, H. T., Mack, P. B., and Boyland, P. M., "A Study of the Properties of Household Blankets," *J. Research Natl. Bur. Standards* **32**, 261 (1944).

182. Schiefer, H. F., "Factors Relating to the Thermal Insulation of Fabrics," Symposium on the Functional Properties of Clothing Fabrics; New York, Textile Research Institute, November 1943.

183. Gilmore, P. A., and Hess, K. P., "Effect of Fibre Content and Care on Resilience, Thickness, and Thermal Conductivity of Blankets," *R.T.M.*, **27**, 252 (1946).

184. Mutschler, H., "Changes in Bulk Elasticity in Processing Fibers," *Textil-Praxis*, **4**, 106 (1949), abstracted in *J.T.I.*, **40**, A376 (1949).

185. Hardy, J. D., "Heat Transfer," p. 78, Chapter 3, in L. H. Newburgh's "Physiology of Heat Regulation and the Science of Clothing," Philadelphia, W. B. Saunders Company (1949).

186. Rees, W. H., "The Transmission of Heat Through Textile Fabrics," *J.T.I.*, **32**, T149 (1941).

187. Peirce, F. T., and Rees, W. H., "The Transmission of Heat Through Textile Fabrics, Part II," *J.T.I.*, **37**, T181 (1946).

188. Marsh, M. C., "The Thermal Insulating Properties of Fabrics," *J.T.I.*, **22**, T245 (1931).

189. Baxter, S., and Cassie, A. B. D., "Thermal Insulating Properties of Clothing," *J.T.I.*, **34**, T41 (1943).

190. Hodgman, C. D., "Handbook of Chemistry and Physics," p. 1878, 23rd Ed., Cleveland, Chemical Rubber Publishing Co. (1939).

191. Rees, W. H., "The Protective Value of Clothing," *J.T.I.*, **37**, P132 (1946).

192. Gagge, A. P., Burton, A. C., and Bazett, H. C., "A Practical System of Units for The Description of the Heat Exchange of Man with His Environment," *Science*, **94**, 428 (1941).

193. Newburgh, L. H., "The Physiology of Heat Regulation and The Science of Clothing," Philadelphia, W. B. Saunders Company (1949).

194. Speakman, J. B., and Chamberlain, N. H., "The Thermal Conductivity of Textile Materials and Fabrics," *J.T.I.*, **21**, T29 (1930).

195. Cassie, A. B. D., "Physical Properties of Fibres and Textile Performances," *J.T.I.*, **37**, P154 (1946).

196. Hock, C. W., Sookne, A. M., and Harris, M., "Thermal Properties of Moist Fabrics," *J. Research Nat'l. Bur. Standards*, **32**, 229 (1944).

197. Carlene, P. W., "Thermal Properties of Textiles," Technical Report, Imperial Chemical Industries, Ltd. DLR 20, January 29, 1945.

198. Marsh, M. C., "Some Notes on the Permeability of Fabrics to Air," *J.T.I.*, **22**, T56 (1931).

199. Landsberg, M. I., and Winston, G., "Relationship Between Measurements of Air Permeability by Two Machines," *T.R.J.*, **17**, 214 (1947).

200. Clayton, F. H., "The Measurement of the Air Permeability of Fabrics," *J.T.I.*, **26**, T171 (1935).

201. Robertson, A. F., "Air Porosity of Open-Weave Fabrics," *T.R.J.*, **20**, 838 and 844 (1950).

202. Robinson, S., "Tropics," p. 348, Chapter 11, in L. H. Newburgh's "Physiology of Heat Regulation and the Science of Clothing," Philadelphia, W. B. Saunders Company (1949).

203. Fourt, L., and Harris, M., "Physical Properties of Clothing Fabrics," p. 308, Chapter 10, in L. H. Newburgh's "Physiology of Heat Regulation and the Science of Clothing," Philadelphia, W. B. Saunders Company (1949).

204. Gregory, J., "The Transfer of Moisture Through Fabrics," *J.T.I.*, **21**, T66 (1930).

205. Fourt, L., and Harris, M., "Diffusion of Water Vapor Through Textiles," *T.R.J.*, **17**, 256 (1947).

206. Peirce, F. T., Rees, W. H., and Ogden, L. W., "Measurement of the Water Vapour Permeability of Textile Fabrics," *J.T.I.*, **36**, T169 (1945).

207. Rouget de Lisle, "Science of Ventilation and Open Air Treatment," p. 235, Part II, by Hill.

208. Roaf in "Science of Ventilation and Open Air Treatment," Parts I and II, by Hill (1919–1920).

209. Fisher, E. A., "Some Moisture Relations of Colloids: I. A Comparative Study of the Rates of Evaporation of Water From Wool, Sand, and Clay." *Proc. Royal Soc.*, **103**, 139 and 664 (1923).

210. King, G., and Cassie, A. B. D., "Rate of Absorption of Water Vapour by Wool Fibres," *T.F.S.*, **36**, 445 (1940).

211. Cassie, A. B. D., "Regain of Textiles and Humid Atmosphere Changes," *J.T.I.*, **31**, T17 (1940).

212. American Association of Textile Chemists and Colorists, Year Book, **19**, 255 (1942).

213. American Association of Textile Chemists and Colorists, Year Book, **26**, 131 (1950).

214. Mandikos, G. J., "Comprehensive Comparison of the More Common Water-Resistance Test Methods Existing Today," *A.D.R.*, **37**, P587 (1948).

215. Rowen, J. W., and Gagliardi, D., "Properties of Water-Repellent Fabrics," *J. Research Nat'l. Bur. Standards*, (Jan. 1947), reprinted in *A.D.R.*, **36**, 533 (1947).

216. Baxter, S., and Cassie, A. B. D., "The Water Repellency of Fabrics and A New Water-Repellency Test," *J.T.I.*, **36**, T67 (1945).

217. Wakeham, H., Strickland, W. B., and Skau, E. L., "The Water Repellency of Textile Fabrics," *A.D.R.*, **34**, 178 (1945).

218. Wengraf, P., and Schwarz, E. W. K., "Waterproof and Water-Repellent Finishes," *A.D.R.*, **31**, 551 (1942).

219. Scott, W. M., "The Testing of Textiles for Water Proofness," *A.D.R.*, **27**, 479 (1938).

220. Slowinske, G. A., "The Evaluation of Water-Resistant Textile Finishes," *A.D.R.*, **30**, 6 (1941).

221. Caryl, C. R., and Ericks, W. P., "Esters of Sodium Sulfosuccinic Acid," *Ind. Eng. Chem.*, **31**, 44 (1939).

222. Kennedy, S. J., "Problems for Future Quartermaster Textile Research," *A.D.R.*, **34**, 511 (1945).

223. Sookne, A. M., "The Problem of Water-Repellent Fabrics." Symposium on the Functional Properties of Clothing Fabrics, Textile Research Institute Special Report, November 18, 1943.

224. Simpson, J. E., "The Army's Water Repellent Clothing," *A.D.R.*, **35**, 243 (1946).

225. Karrholm, M., and Karrholm, G., "The Impact of Raindrops on Fabrics," *T.R.J.*, **20**, 215 (1950).

226. Slowinske, G. A., and Pope, A. G., "A Correlation of Water-Repellent Garment Performance and Laboratory Penetration Tests on Fabrics," *A.D.R.*, **36**, P108 (1947).

227. Armour, R., "How To Tell A Crease From A Wrinkle." *Saturday Evening Post*, **223**, 40 (1950).

228. Buck, G. S., Jr., and McCord, F. A., "Crease Resistance and Cotton," *T.R.J.*, **19**, 216 (1949).

229. Jaumann, A., "The Resistance to Deformation of Fibers and Fabrics," *Kunstseide u Zellwolle*, **22**, 17 (1940), abstracted in *J.T.I.*, **31**, A269 (1940).

230. Hebeler, H. H., and Kolb, H. J., "The Measurement of Fabric Wrinkling," *T.R.J.*, **20**, 650 (1950).

231. Whewell, C. S., "Some Observations on the Finishing of Fabrics Containing Wool and Other Fibres," *J.T.I.*, **41**, P219 (1950).

232. Grunfest, J. J., and Gagliardi, D. D., "Wrinkle Resistance of Fabrics," *Ind. Eng. Chem.*, **41**, 760 (1949).

233. Susich, G., and Backer, S., "Tensile Recovery Behavior of Textile Fibers," *T.R.J.*, **21**, 482 (1951).

234. DeWaard, R. D., Hvizdak, A., and Stock, C. R., "Improved Evaluation of the Wrinkle Resistance of Resin-Treated Fabrics," *A.D.R.*, **37**, 513 (1948).

235. Fabric Research Laboratories, Inc., "Investigation of Methods for Evaluating Crease Resistance," Report No. 932.

236. Beste, L. F., and Hoffman, R. M., "A Quantitative Study of Resilience," *T.R.J.*, **20**, 441 (1950).

237. Gagliardi, D. D., and Nuessle, A. C., "Modification of Fiber and Fabric Properties by Wrinkleproofing and Stabilizing Agents," *A.D.R.*, **39**, P12 (1950).

238. Fluck, L. A., Keppler, G. J., Cooke, T. F., and Zimmermann, C. L., "Odor Prevention in Resin-Treated Fabrics," *A.D.R.*, **40**, 154 (1951).

239. Powers, D. H., "New Resinous Materials and Their Effects on Various Fibers and Fabrics," *A.D.R.*, **34**, 77 (1945).

240. Thompson, L. S., "Changing Aspects in Dyeing and Finishing," *A.D.R.*, **38**, 276 (1949).

241. Gantz, G. M., "Textile Fibers From Synthetic Textiles," *A.D.R.*, **41**, P100 (1952).

242. Coplan, M. J., "A Study of Wrinkle Resistance at High Relative Humidities," Fabric Research Laboratories, Inc. Report No. 1183.

243. Staudt, A. W., "The Element "X" in Nylon," *A.D.R.*, **38**, 339 (1949).

244. Helmus, W. G., "Latest Developments in the Dyeing and Finishing of Synthetic Fibers," *A.D.R.*, **38**, 62 (1949).

245. Buck, G. S., Jr., and McCord, F. A., "Luster and Cotton," *T.R.J.*, **19**, 715 (1949).

246. Powers, D. H., "Modification of Textile Fiber Properties Through Finishing Operations," *A.S.T.M. Bull.*, **149**, 35 (1947).

247. Das, D. B., and Speakman, J. B., "The Action of Chlorine Dioxide on Wool," *J.S.D.C.*, **66**, 583 (1950).

248. Fabric Research Laboratories, Inc., "Development of Navy Melton From Wool Blends," Report No. 968.

249. Gould, J. M., "Some Aspects of the Chemical Control of Wool Shrinkage" *A.D.R.*, **38**, 407 (1949).

250. von Bergen, W., and Clutz, C. S., "Dimensional Stability of Woolen and Worsted Fabrics," *T.R.J.*, **20**, 580 (1950).

251. Anon., "Cloth Shrinkage in Garment Production," *Wool Science Review*, **4**, 25 (1949).

252. King, G., "The Swelling of Textile Materials," *J.S.D.C.*, **66**, 27 (1950).

253. Schwarz, E. R., "Technical Evaluation of Textile Finishing Treatments," *T.R.J.*, **9**, 216 (1939).

254. Peirce, F. T., "The Handle of Cloth As A Measurable Quantity," *J.T.I.*, **21**, T377 (1930).

255. Hoffman, R. M., and Beste, L. F., "Some Relations of Fiber Properties to Fabric Hand," *T.R.J.*, **21**, 66 (1951).

256. Hamburger, W. J., Chu, C. C., and Platt, M. M., "Sensation, Psychology and Science Applied to the Evaluation of Complex Properties." An unpublished paper presented before the Textile Section, American Association for the Advancement of Science, Gordon Research Conference, Colby Junior College, New London, New Hampshire, July 18, 1950.

257. von Bergen, W., and Kraus, W., "Textile Fiber Atlas," p. 9, New York, American Wool Handbook Company (1942).

258. Binns, H., "Psychological Investigations of the Influence of the Various Methods of Manufacturing Worsted Yarns on Single and Two-Fold Twist Warp Cloths," *J.T.I.*, **25**, T89 (1934).

259. Winn, L. J., and Schwarz, E. R., "Technical Evaluation of Textile Finishing Treatments: IV. A Comparison of Certain Methods of Measuring Stiffness in Fabrics," *A.D.R.*, **29**, P469 (1940).

260. Winn, L. J., and Schwarz, E. R., "Technical Evaluation of Textile Finishing Treatments: III. Flexibility and Drape as Measurable Properties of Fabric," *T.R.J.*, **10**, 5 (1939).

261. Chu, C. C., Cummings, C. L., and Teixeira, N. A., "Mechanics of Elastic Performance of Textile Materials: V. A Study of the Factors Affecting the Drape of Fabrics—The Development of a Drapemeter," *T.R.J.*, **20**, 539 (1950).

262. Hamburger, W. J., Platt, M. M., and Chu, C. C., "Determination of the Factors Which Influence the Draping Properties of Cotton Fabrics," Fabric Research Laboratories, Inc. Report 966.

263. Winn, L. J., and Schwarz, E. R., "Technical Evaluation of Textile Finishing Treatments: VI. The Effect of Relative Humidity on Flexibility; Test Methods for the Drape-o-meter," *A.D.R.*, **30**, P226 (1941).

264. Fabric Research Laboratories, Inc. Report 966-2 to the Textile and Clothing Division, Bureau of Human Nutrition and Home Economics, United States Department of Agriculture.

265. Abbott, N. J., "The Measurement of Stiffness in Textile Fabrics," *T.R.J.*, **21**, 435 (1951).

266. Dreby, E. C., "The Planoflex," *A.D.R.*, **30**, 651 (1941).

267. Whittaker, C. M., "The Serviceability of Fabrics," *J.T.I.*, **28**, P173 (1937).

268. Peirce, F. T., "The Serviceability of Fabrics in Regard to Wear: Testing Fabrics to Foretell Serviceability," *J.T.I.*, **28**, P181 (1937).

269. Binns, H., "The Judgement of Fabrics," *J.T.I.*, **28**, P193 (1937).

270. Harwood, F. C., "The Wearability of Fabrics: A Comment From the Point of View of the Launderer," *J.T.I.*, **28**, P200 (1937).

271. Bradley, H. B., "The Wearability of Fabrics: A Comment From the Point of View of the Linen Dyer," *J.T.I.*, **28**, P202 (1937).

272. Cunliffe, P. W., "The Wearability of Fabrics: Fastness to Light and Laundering," *J.T.I.*, **28**, P203 (1937).

273. Petrie, T. C., "The Serviceability of Fabrics in Regard to Wear," *J.T.I.*, **28**, P206 (1937).

274. Lester, J. H., "Abrasives for Wear Testing," *J.T.I.*, **28**, P209 (1937).

275. Gibson, W. H., "The Serviceability of Fabrics in Regard to Wear," *J.T.I.*, **28**, P212 (1937).

276. Davis, W., "The Wear Testing of Knitted Fabrics," *J.T.I.*, **28**, P215 (1937).
277. Lomax, J., "The Serviceability of Fabrics in Regard to Wear: Testing Fabrics to Foretell Serviceability," *J.T.I.*, **28**, P218 (1937).
278. Mann, J. C., "The Testing of Fabrics for Resistance to Abrasion," *J.T.I.*, **28**, P220 (1937).
279. Hall, W. J., "The Serviceability of Fabrics," *J.T.I.*, **28**, P223 (1937).
280. Williams, J. G., "Testing and the Serviceability of Fabrics," *J.T.I.*, **28**, P225 (1937).
281. Pritchard, W., "The Wearability of Fabrics: Testing from the Point of View of the Large Consumer," *J.T.I.*, **28**, P233 (1937).
282. Ball, H. J., "Problems Which Abrasion and Wear Testing Present," *T.R.J.*, **8**, 134 (1938).
283. Zook, M. H., "Historical Background of Abrasion Testing," *A.D.R.*, **39**, 625 (1950).
284. Smith, H. DeW., "Wear and Wear Testing," U. S. Institute of Textile Research Conference, *Textile World*, **84**, 852 (1934).
285. Skinkle, J. H., "Textile Testing," p. 97, New York, Howes Publishing Company (1940).
286. Stoll, R. G., "An Improved Multipurpose Abrasion Tester and Its Application for the Evaluation of the Wear Resistance of Textiles," *T.R.J.*, **19**, 394 (1949).
287. Dawson, T. R., "Abrasion and Wear Testing of Textile Fabrics," *J. Rubber Research*, **15**, 65 (1946).
288. Dean, R. F., "Recent Advances in Abrasion Testing of Textiles," *J.T.I.*, **37**, 380 (1946).
289. Schiefer, H. F., Crean, L. E., and Krasny, J. F., "Improved Single-Unit Schiefer Abrasion Testing Machine," *J. Research Natl. Bur. Standards*, **42**, 481 (1949).
290. Tanenhaus, S. J., and Winston, G., "First Report of The A.S.T.M. Task Group Studying the Wyzenbeek Precision Wear Test Meter." Textile Series Report No. 45, Philadelphia Quartermaster Depot, Research and Development Division.
291. American Society of Testing Materials, "Tentative Methods of Test for Resistance to Abrasion of Textile Fabrics," A.S.T.M. Designation D-51T (1951).
292. Tait, J. H., private communication via reference 305.
293. Gagliardi, D. D., and Nuessle, A. C., "The Relation Between Fiber Properties and Apparent Abrasion Resistance," *A.D.R.*, **40**, P409 (1951).
294. Backer, S., "The Relationship Between the Structural Geometry of a Textile Fabric and Its Physical Properties: II. The Mechanism of Fabric Abrasion," *T.R.J.*, **21**, 453 (1951).
295. Hamburger, W. J., and Lee, H. N., "A Study of Lining Fabric Abrasion," *R.T.M.*, **26**, 61 (1945).
296. Vogt, W. W., "Analysis of a Typical Angle Abrasion Machine," *Ind. Eng. Chem.*, **20**, 302 (1928).
297. Clegg, G. G., "A Microscopic Examination of Worn Textile Articles," *J.T.I.*, **40**, T449 (1949).
298. Williams, J. G., "The Strength of Textile Fabrics and Their Satisfaction-Giving Qualities in Conditions of Normal Use," *J.T.I.*, **23**, P161 (1932).
299. Williams, J. G., "The Wearing Qualities of Fabrics," *J.T.I.*, **39**, P164 (1948).
300. Hicks, E. M., and Scroggie, A. G., "Taber Yarn Sheet Abrasion Test," *T.R.J.*, **18**, 416 (1948).
301. Stout, E. E., and Moseman, M. B., "The Effect of Abrasion on Breaking Strength and Elongation of Fifty-Eight Clothing Fabrics," *A.D.R.*, **38**, 417 (1949).

302. Rosenzweig, A., "Relative Durability of Textile Fabrics," *Textile Mfr.*, **58**, 212 (1932).

303. Simon, C. L., "Abrasive Wear Tests on Garment Lining Fabrics," Report to Textile Materials Engineering Laboratory, Philadelphia Quartermaster Depot, January 5, 1949. Unpublished.

304. Simon, C. L., "Weaving Qualities and Methods Used in Testing Synthetic Yarns," *Textile World*, **83**, 576 (1933).

305. Backer, S., and Tanenhaus, S. J., "The Relationship Between the Structural Geometry of a Textile Fabric and Its Physical Properties: III. Textile Geometry and Abrasion Resistance," *T.R.J.*, **21**, 635 (1951).

306. Burwell, J. T., "Lubrication and Friction," Course Notes, Massachusetts Institute of Technology, Cambridge, Massachusetts (1950).

307. Finch, R. B., "Inter-Fiber Stress and Its Transmission," *T.R.J.*, **21**, 375 (1951).

308. Germans, I. F. H., "The Abrasion Test as a Criterion to Determine the Wear of Textiles," *J.T.I.*, **42**, T185 (1951).

309. Matthew, J. A., "Comparison of Some Fabric Test Methods," *J.T.I.*, **22**, T497 (1931).

310. Walker, A. C., and Olmstead, P. S., "Textile Yarn Abrasion Test," *T.R.J.*, **15**, 201 (1945).

311. Peirce, F. T., "Geometrical Principles Applicable to the Design of Functional Fabrics," *T.R.J.*, **17**, 123 (1947).

312. Leites, L. G., "New Structure Fabrics for Bed Linen and Underclothes," *Textilnaya Promyshlennost (Textile Industry)*, **9**, 21, September (1948).

313. Morton, W. E., "The Designing of Fabrics to Meet Consumer Requirements," *J.T.I.*, **39**, P187 (1948).

314. Federoff, N. S., "Russian Study of the Wearing Qualities of Fabrics," *Textilnaya Promyshlennost (Textile Industry)*, **7**, 41 (1948).

315. Cranshaw, H., Morton, W. E., and Brown, K. C., "Experiments on Fabric Wear Testing," *J.T.I.*, **22**, T64 (1931).

316. Koch, P. A., Satlow, G., and Bobeth, W., "Examination of the Wear Resistance of Cotton and Staple-Fiber Fabrics With Apparatus," "Developments in the Wear Resistance of Textiles and Related Papers Published in Germany During World War II," p. 9, Heidelberg, *Melliand Textilberichte* (1949).

317. Matthew, J. A., "A Cloth Wear Testing Machine," *J.T.I.*, **21**, T546 (1930).

318. Collins, G. E., "Construction of Fabrics for Specified Purposes," *J.T.I.*, **37**, P392 (1946).

319. Sommer, H., "Testing Abrasion Resistance of Textiles," "Developments in the Wear Resistance of Textiles and Related Papers Published in Germany During World War II," p. 59, Heidelberg, *Melliand Textilberichte* (1949).

320. Williams, J. G., "Textiles on Test," London, Chapman and Hall, Ltd. (1931).

321. U.S. Army Quartermaster Board Letter Report, "Wear Resistance of Fabric, Effect of Weave." Camp Lee, Virginia, 20 Nov. 1947. Unpublished.

322. Winston, G., "Analysis of the Effect of Weave Upon the Abrasion Resistance of Five Fabrics as Evaluated on the Combat Course." Camp Lee, Virginia; Memorandum to Quartermaster Textile Materials Engineering Laboratory, Philadelphia Quartermaster Depot, 12 Dec. 1947. Unpublished.

323. Feild, T. A., and Fremon, G. H., "The Copper Technique for Dyeing Acrylonitrile Fibers," *T.R.J.*, **21**, 531 (1951).

324. Menkart, J., and Speakman, J. B., "The Felting of Animal Fibres," *Nature*, **159**, 640 (1947).

325. Susich, G., "Shear Tenacity of Some Textile Fibers," private communication.
326. Bunn, C. C., "The Optical Properties of Fibres," Chapter X, "Fibre Science," edited by Preston, Manchester, The Textile Institute (1949).
327. Ray, L. G., private communication from the duPont Company.
328. von Bergen, W., "Microscopical and Physical Properties of Wool," in Matthews' "Textile Fibers," edited by Mauersberger, New York, John Wiley and Sons, Inc. (1947).
329. Harrison, "Definition and Measurement of Gloss," Printing and Allied Trades Research Association (1945).
330. Fuller, C. E., and Johnson, W. A., "Applied Mechanics: I. Statics and Kinetics," New York, John Wiley and Sons, Inc. (1913).
331. Speakman, J. B., and Stott, E., "A Contribution to the Theory of Milling: I. A Method for Measuring the Scaliness of Wool Fibres," *J.T.I.*, **22**, T339 (1931).
332. Morrow, J. A., "The Frictional Properties of Cotton Materials," *J.T.I.*, **22**, T425 (1931).
333. Speakman, J. B., Chamberlain, N. H., and Menkart, J., "The Lepidometer— An Instrument for Measuring the Scaliness of Animal Fibres," *J.T.I.*, **36**, T91 (1945).
334. Martin, A. J. P., and Mittelmann, R., "Some Measurements of the Friction of Wool and Mohair," *J.T.I.*, **37**, T269 (1946).
335. Buckle, H., and Pollitt, J., "An Instrument for Measuring the Coefficient of Friction of Yarns Against Other Materials," *J.T.I.*, **39**, T199 (1948).
336. Lipson, M., and Howard, P., "Friction Between Keratin Surfaces As Affected by Some Shrinkproofing Treatments," *J.S.D.C.*, **62**, 29 (1946).
337. Lindberg, J., and Gralen, N., "Measurement of Friction Between Single Fibres: II. The Frictional Properties of Wool Fibres Measured by the Fibre Twist Method," *T.R.J.*, **18**, 287 (1948).
338. Mercer, E. H., and Makinson, K. R., "The Frictional Properties of Wool and Other Textile Fibers," *J.T.I.*, **38**, T227 (1947).
339. Bowden, F. P., and Leben, L., "The Nature of Sliding and The Analysis of Friction," *Proc. Royal Soc.*, **169**, 371 (1939).
340. Breazeale, F., "Apparatus for Determining the Coefficient of Friction of Running Yarn," *T.R.J.*, **17**, 27 (1947).
341. Gralen, N., and Olofsson, B., "Measurement of Friction Between Single Fibres," *T.R.J.*, **17**, 488 (1947).
342. Lindberg, J., "Measurement of Friction Between Single Fibres: III. Influence of Different Treatments on the Frictional Properties of Wool Fibres," *T.R.J.*, **18**, 470 (1948).
343. Lindberg, J., and Gralen, N., "Measurement of Friction Between Single Fibres: IV. Influence of Various Oxidizing and Reducing Agents on the Frictional Properties of Wool Fibres," *T.R.J.*, **19**, 183 (1949).
344. Olofsson, B., and Gralen, N., "Measurement of Friction Between Single Fibres: V. Frictional Properties of Viscose Rayon Staple Fibres," *T.R.J.*, **20**, 467 (1950).
345. Stock, C. R., private communication.
346. Platt, M. M., Klein, W. G., and Hamburger, W. J., "Factors Influencing the Efficiency of Cordage," Fabric Research Laboratories, Inc. Report 736.
347. King, G., "Some Frictional Properties of Wool and Nylon Fibres," *J.T.I.*, **41**, T135 (1950).
348. Martin, A. J. P., "Observations on the Theory of Felting," *J.S.D.C.*, **60**, 325 (1944).

349. Alexander, P., "The Chemical Reactivity of Wool in Relation to Anti-shrink Processes," *A.D.R.*, **39**, P420 (1950).
350. Bohm, L., "Frictional Properties of Wool Fibers in Relation to Felting," *J.S.-D.C.*, **61**, 278 (1945).
351. Bogaty, H., Sookne, A., and Harris, M., "The Felting of Wool as Related to the Elastic and Swelling Behavior of the Fiber," *T.R.J.*, **21**, 822 (1951).
352. Shorter, S. A., "The Moisture Content of Wool—Its Relation to Scientific Theory and Commercial Practice," *J.S.D.C.*, **39**, 270 (1923).
353. Speakman, J. B., and Goodings, A. C., "The Chlorination of Wool," *J.T.I.*, **17**, T607 (1926).
354. Menkart, J., and Speakman, J. B., "The Felting of Animal Fibres," *J.S.D.C.*, **64**, 14 (1948).
355. Arnold, *Leipzig. Monatschr. Textil-Ind.*, **44**, 463, 507, 540 (1929).
356. Speakman, J. B., Menkart, J., and Liu, W. T., "On the Existence of a Critical Temperature for Milling," *J.T.I.*, **35**, T41 (1944).
357. Bogaty, H., Frishman, D., Sookne, A. M., and Harris, M., "A Simple Quantitative Test for the Felting of Wool Top," *T.R.J.*, **20**, 270 (1950).
358. Peryman, R. U., and Speakman, J. B., "The Influence of Lubrication on the Felting of Wool," *J.T.I.*, **41**, T241 (1950).
359. Whewell, C. S., Charlesworth, A., and Kitchin, R. L., "Some Recent Experiments in Cloth Finishing," *J.T.I.*, **40**, P769 (1949).
360. LaFleur, K. S., "Fulling Characteristics of a Light-Weight Woolen Fabric," *A.D.R.*, **40**, 145 (1951).
361. Sookne, A. M., Bogaty, H., and Harris, M., "Some Felting Properties of Wools of Different Geographical Origins," *T.R.J.*, **20**, 637 (1950).
362. Bogaty, H., Weiner, L. I., Sookne, A. M., and Harris, M., "Effect of Construction on the Laundering Shrinkage of Knitted Woolens," *T.R.J.*, **21**, 102 (1951).
363. Hill, F. R., and Kornreich, E., "Some Observations on the Influence of Fabric Structure on Felting," *J.T.I.*, **40**, T733 (1949).
364. Best-Gordon, H. W., "Some Observations on the Influence of Fabric Structure on Felting," *J.T.I.*, **40**, T770 (1949).
365. Horigan, F. D., and Sage, C. R., "A Patent and Literature Survey on Shrinkage and Shrinkage Control of Textiles," Supplement Number 1, Bibliographic Series Number 9, Technical Library, Quartermaster Research and Development Laboratories, Philadelphia.
366. Harris, M., and Frishman, D., "Some Aspects of the Chlorination of Wool to Produce Shrink Resistance," *A.D.R.*, **37**, P52 (1948).
367. Barritt, J., and Elsworth, F. F., "The Dyeing Properties of Chlorinated Wool," *J.S.D.C.*, **64**, 19 (1948).
368. Alexander, P., "Effectiveness of Oxidation Anti-shrink Treatments to Acid and Alkali Milling," *J.S.D.C.*, **62**, 199 (1946).
369. Lipson, M., and Howard, P., "Friction between Keratin Surfaces as Affected by Some Shrinkproofing Treatments," *A.D.R.*, **36**, 470 (1947).
370. Sookne, A. M., Bogaty, H., and Harris, M., "The Felting of Shrink Resistant Wool as Related to Some Properties of the Single Fiber," *T.R.J.*, **21**, 827 (1951).
371. Bogaty, H., Weiner, L. I., Sookne, A. M., Cozart, M. L., and Harris, M., "Some Effects of Construction on the Laundering Shrinkage of Wool Fabrics," *T.R.J.*, **21**, 895 (1951).
372. Strong, J. H., "Fabric Structure," Brooklyn, Chemical Publishing Company (1947).

373. Maresh, C., and Royer, G. L., "Shrinkage Control of Wool by Melamine Resins: I. Microscopical Observations," *T.R.J.*, **19**, 449 (1949).

374. Stock, C. R., and Salley, D. J., "Function of Methylated Melamine-Formaldehyde Resin in Controlling Shrinkage of Woolens," *T.R.J.*, **19**, 41 (1949).

375. McCleary, H. R., and Royer, G. L., "Shrinkage Control of Wool by Melamine Resins: II. Torsional Rigidity and Elastic Properties of Single Fibers," *T.R.J.*, **19**, 457 (1949).

376. Powers, D. H., "Effect of Synthetic Resins on Cellulose and Protein Fibers," *Ind. Eng. Chem.*, **37**, 188 (1945).

377. Collins, G. E., "Fundamental Principles That Govern the Shrinkage of Cotton Goods by Washing," *J.T.I.*, **30**, P46 (1939).

378. Marsh, J. T., "An Introduction to Textile Finishing," New York, John Wiley & Sons, Inc. (1951).

379. American Association of Textile Chemists and Colorists, New York Section, "Measurement of Fabric Soiling," *A.D.R.*, **41**, P322 (1952).

380. Åstrom, A., "Adsorption of Aerosols," *Svensk. Kem. Tid.*, **41**, P190 (1929), abstracted in *Chemical Abstracts*, **24**, 1780 (1930).

381. Kruger, P., "Soiling of Textile Goods with Usage," *Seitung ges. Textile Ind.*, **39**, P221 (1936), abstracted in *Chemical Abstracts*, **30**, 4327 (1936).

382. Masland, C. H., "Soil Retention of Various Fibers," *R.T.M.*, **19**, #10 and #11 (1939).

383. Leonard, E. A., "Combined Research about Location Cleaning Defines Important Factors," *National Rug Cleaner*, **22**, #4 16 (1949).

384. Anon. *Retailing Daily*, **21**, #130 38 (1949).

385. Snell, F. D., Snell, C., and Reich, I., "Nature of Dirt and Methods of Retention At the Surface," *J. Am. Oil Chemists Soc.*, **27**, 62 (1950).

386. Sachese, H., "Electrical Properties of Dusts and Fogs," *Ann. Physik.*, **14**, 396 (1932), abstracted in *Chemical Abstracts*, **26**, 5473 (1932).

387. Thomas, A. W., "Colloid Chemistry," p. 20, New York, McGraw-Hill Book Company (1934).

388. Northrup, A., private communication to the New York Section, A.A.T.C.C. Intersectional Contest Committee (1951).

389. Atomic Energy Commission, "Handbook on Aerosols," pp. 62, 117 (1950).

390. Compton J., and Hart, W. J., "Soiling and Soil Retention in Textile Fibers," *Ind. Eng. Chem.*, **43**, 1564 (1951).

391. Niven, W. W., Jr., "Fundamentals of Detergency," New York, Reinhold Publishing Corp. (1950).

392. Whewell, C. S., Messiha, K. H., and Selim, A., "Soiling of Union Fabrics," *J.T.I.*, **36**, P6 (1945).

393. Utermohlen, W. P., Jr., and Wallace, E. L., "Detergency Studies," *T.R.J.*, **17**, 670 (1947).

394. Clark, J. R., and Holland, V. B., "Studies in Soiling and Detergency," *A.D.R.*, **36**, P734 (1947).

395. Snell, C., "Methods of Evaluating Detergents," *A.D.R.*, **39**, 485 (1950).

396. Lambert, J., and Sanders, H. L., "Some Physical-Chemical Aspects of Cotton Detergency," *Ind. Eng. Chem.*, **42**, 1388 (1950).

397. Cunliffe, P. W., "A Method of Producing Standard Artificially-Soiled Wool Fabric," *J.T.I.*, **28**, T341 (1937).

398. American Association of Textile Chemists and Colorists, "The Launderometer," *A.A.T.C.C. Technical Manual and Year Book*, **27**, 85 (1951).

399. *Ibid.*, p. 158.
400. Lehmicke, D. J., "Static in Textile Processing," *A.D.R.*, **38**, P853 (1949).
401. Bacon, O. C., and Smith, J. E., "Mechanical Work as a Measure of Efficiency of Surface Active Agents in Removing Soil," *Ind. Eng. Chem.*, **40**, 2361 (1948).
402. Whewell, C. S., Barrett, P., and Senior, J., "The Finishing of Fabrics Containing Wool and Man-Made Fibres," *J.T.I.*, **43**, P648 (1952).
403. Castonguay, F. B., Leekley, D. O., and Edgar, R., "The Washing of Cotton, (Viscose) Rayon, Acetate Rayon, Silk, Wild Silk and Wool with Soap, Etc.," *A.D.R.*, **31**, 421 (1942).
404. Furry, M. S., and McLendon, V. I., "Effectiveness of Detergents in Removing Soil from Cotton and Wool," *A.D.R.*, **39**, 209 (1950).
405. Snell, F. D., "Soap and Detergents As Affecting Textiles," *A.D.R.*, **39**, 481 (1950).
406. Honegger, E., and Schnyder, A., "The Effect of Laundering and Laundry-Bleaching Processes on Cotton, Linen, and Viscose Fabrics," *J.T.I.*, **34**, T29 (1943).
407. Crockatt, A. J., "Cleanable Outerwear," *J.T.I.*, **40**, P1000 (1949).
408. Davies, E. J., "The Reactions of Garment Fabrics, Accessories, and Methods of Garment Manufacture to Dry Cleaning," *J.T.I.*, **42**, P821 (1951).
409. Pollitt, J., "The Geometry of Cloth Structure," *J.T.I.*, **40**, P11 (1949).
410. Linduska, J. P., and Morton, F. A., "Tests of the Permeability of Fabrics to Biting by Mosquitoes," *J. Econ. Entomol.*, **41**, 788 (1948).
411. Herrington, L. P., "Clothing from a Biophysical Point of View." *Papers of the American Association of Textile Technologists*, P30, (Dec. 1951).
412. duPont de Nemours & Co., E. I., "Orlon Technical Bulletin."
413. American Cyanamid Company, "A Summary of Facts about X-51 Acrylic Fiber," March 5, 1952.
414. Ray, L. G., Jr., "The Role of Synthetic Fibers in The Textile Industry of the Future," *T.R.J.*, **22**, 144 (1952).
415. Carbide and Carbon Chemicals Company, private communication.
416. Kaswell, E. R., and Platt, M. M., "Mechanics of Elastic Performance of Textile Materials: VII. Mechanical Properties of Hard Fibers with Reference to Their Use in Cordage Structures," *T.R.J.*, **21**, 263 (1951).
417. Sieminski, M. A., "Relation of Tensile Strength Units," *R.T.M.*, **24**, 585(1943).
418. Preston, J. M., "Identification of Textile Fibres," *J.T.I.*, **41**, P679 (1950).
419. British Textile Institute, General Technical Committee "C," "Identification of Textile Materials," *J.T.I.*, **42**, S25 (1951).
420. Virginia-Carolina Chemicals Company, "Vicara Textile Fiber." (Bulletin 1950).
421. Sprague, B. S., private communication from the Celanese Corporation of America.
422. Hamburger, W. J., and Kaswell, E. R., "Use of Effective Gage Length in Elongation Measurement," *R.T.M.*, **23**, #11 (1943).
423. Coplan, M. J., private communication.
424. Coplan, M. J., "The Effect of Temperature on Textile Materials," Fabric Research Laboratories, Inc. report to the U.S. Army Air Force No. 1134, Part III, March (1952).
425. Carlene, P. W., "The Relation between Fibre and Yarn Flexural Rigidity in Continuous Filament Viscose Yarns," *J.T.I.*, **41**, T159 (1950).
426. duPont de Nemours & Co., E. I., "This Is Orlon." (Pamphlet), (Nov. 1948).

427. Platt, M. M., private communication.
428. Hotte, G., private communication.
429. Karrholm, M., private communication.
430. Preston, J. M., and Nimkar, M. V., "Measuring the Swelling of Fibres in Water," *J.T.I.*, **40**, P674 (1949).
431. Ott, E., "Cellulose and Cellulose Derivations," New York, Interscience Publishers (1943).
432. Fourt, L., Sookne, A. M., Frishman, D., and Harris, M., "The Rate of Drying of Fabrics," *T.R.J.*, **21**, 26 (1951).
433. Dillon, J., "The Textile Rainbow," *A.D.R.*, **41**, 65 (1952).
434. Preston, J. M., "The Temperature of Contraction of Fibres as an Aid to Identification," *J.T.I.*, **40**, T767 (1949).
435. Goodings, A. C., private communication.
436. Traill, D., "Clothing An Expanding Population," *J.T.I.*, **42**, P221 (1951).

AUTHOR INDEX

SUBJECT INDEX

A

α-amino acrylic acid, 133
"A-3" fiber, 5
A.A.T.C.C. spray test, specifications for, 239, 246
A.S.T.M. abrasion test methods, 301
A.S.T.M. elasticity definition, 39
abaca fiber, 117
  burning behavior, 117
  denier, 52
  fiber slippage in cordage, 82
  load-elongation diagram, 22
  properties of, 8, 13, 26, 34
abrasion, definition of, 298, 299
abrasion resistance (*see also* wear resistance), 298
  abradant characteristics, 310, 311, 326, 328
  acetate and viscose fabrics, 314–316
  backing material influence, 339, 340
  basic causes of failure, 305
  bending, 300
  bulk modulus, 330
  compressive compliance, 329, 339, 340
  contact area, 329, 330
  cover factor, 329, 340, 341
  creaseproofing finishes, 327, 328
  creep rate, 305, 306
  crimp balance and interchange, 336
  criteria of, 303, 304
  crown height effect, 329, 331–333
  damping capacity, 66
  destruction rate, 307, 315
  direction, 329, 342, 343
  durability coefficient, 307, 309
  elastic properties, 29, 305, 306
  end point criterion, 319
  energy absorption, 22, 281, 305–307, 318, 345, 346
  energy coefficient, 309
  evaluation of, 177, 304
  of fabrics, 51, 63, 318–322, 329, 333, 340, 341
  factors affecting, 325
  fibers, 312–314, 322, 344

abrasion resistance (*Cont'd*)
  fiber blending, 305, 311, 312, 372–374
  fiber plucking, 339, 340
  fiber properties influencing, 345, 346
  flexing, 300
  float length, 329, 336–339
  friction effects, 307, 310–311
  load-elongation diagram, 307
  low strain relations, 310, 326
  mechanical conditioning, 310
  mechanics of, 303, 305, 310–312
  prediction, danger of, 326, 327
  pressure, effect on, 327, 328
  repeated stress, 22, 24, 305, 306, 308–310
  resin treatment, reduction of, 280–281
  reversals in rank, 328
  Schiefer abrader, 327
  stabilizing finishes, 327, 328
  Stoll abrader, 301
  strength loss criterion, 307, 315
  stress concentration, 312, 329, 330
  stress-strain diagram, 16
  surface cutting, 311, 312
  Taber abrader, 306, 307
  T.B.L. abrader, 327
  tension magnitude and direction, 329, 343
  testers, 301, 302
  texture, 329, 330
  threshold strength value, 316, 317
  torsional rigidity, 340
  toughness, 281
  warp protection, 337
  wear resistance relation, 301, 313, 325, 326
  weave and float length, 331, 336–338
  weighted indices of evaluation, 345
  yarns, 307, 313–315, 318, 319
  yarn properties affecting, 311, 329, 333–336, 339, 340, 343
absorption-desorption properties of fibers, 84
absorption-desorption curve for wool, 83
absorption of water by fabric, 100
"Acele" fiber, 6

511